THE "TOP SECRET"

REGISTRY OF U.S. GOVERNMENT RADIO FREQUENCIES

8th Edition

BY TOM KNEITEL, K2AES

CRB Research Books, Inc.

P.O. Box 56, Commack, New York 11725

The federal agency emblems shown herein are used solely for identification, design, and recognition purposes. Their use in this registry neither indicates nor implies any official status nor sanction to the information herein, nor of this registry, nor of any official participation in the preparation of this registry by those agencies.

Dedicated to Robin

**Cover Design by Robin Smith.
Realistic PRO-43 scanner courtesy Radio Shack,
a Division of Tandy Corporation.
Scantenna Mark II and Special Agent badge
courtesy CRB Research Books, Inc.**

Book layout & design by CRB Research Graphics Department.

ISBN: 0-939780-20-8

Printed in The United States of America

Table of Contents

Introduction

Here we are at Edition #8. Does anybody other than the author recall Edition #1, back in 1978? It was the first scanner directory devoted to federal frequencies. It spurred interest in federal monitoring at a time when there were very few clubs or national publications that would print most of the listings we went ahead and published. Before that, most fed scanner monitors operated in a couple of relatively small and close-knit cliques where frequencies were privately exchanged. Our Edition #1 proved that many scanner owners wanted to be in on this, but had no idea of how and where to monitor for the federal comms.

A lot of work went into that edition, but we now realize that it contained only a small fraction of the data that became incorporated into later editions. This continued as the series became more widely known and lots of information began pouring in from enthusiastic monitors who enjoyed being a part of the Registry project.

It continues to this day. A rather steady stream of letters and cards adds to, amplifies, clarifies, changes, and corrects the listings. This is certainly encouraged and welcomed at this end. I have enjoyed federal monitoring for many years. I like it because it's exciting and interesting, and because there's always something new to learn. You never get to be an expert. That's why I want, seek, and enjoy all the help I can get from other monitoring enthusiasts. This input is important to me, and why this Registry series has achieved such wide acceptance and success. Although the Registry started out as a guide for scanner hobbyists, it long ago became the standard reference to federal communications systems. This Registry is now relied upon by law enforcement agencies, communications techs, security personnel, the news media, and others. Even the government uses our book!

We would, therefore, at this time like to acknowledge and thank those who submitted material for inclusion in Edition #8. For whatever reasons, some contributors submitted information anonymously. Some signed the data, but requested that their names not be published. We always honor such requests.

While we can't list everybody else individually, there were several contributors whose help was particularly valuable. We would like to give them special thanks. These are Dave Torres (NY); John Klaff (CT); Ron Bruckman (MD); Steven M. Garber (AZ); Frank Yates (TN); Larry Gold (TX); Harry Caul, KIL9XL (IL); Doug Moe (IL); Ralph Gellows II, WB5FTV (CA); R. L. Van (NY); Jeanette Johnson (NY); Chuck Robertson (IL); John Bohn, KD3EI (PA); Rick Maslau, KNY2GL (NY); Todd Shideler (MD); and "The Bloodhound" (OH).

The active federal frequency monitoring enthusiast is directed to the following fine magazines, clubs, and newsletters that include the topic in their coverage:

Popular Communications Magazine, 76 North Broadway, Hicksville, NY 11801

Monitoring Times, P.O. Box 98, Brasstown, NC 28902

Radio Communications Monitoring Association Journal, P.O. Box 542, Silverado, CA 92676

Radio Monitors Newsletter of Maryland, P.O. Box 394, Hampstead, MD 21074

National Scanning Report, Box 291918, Kettering, OH 45429

Popular Electronics, 500-B Bi-County Blvd., Farmingdale, NY 11735

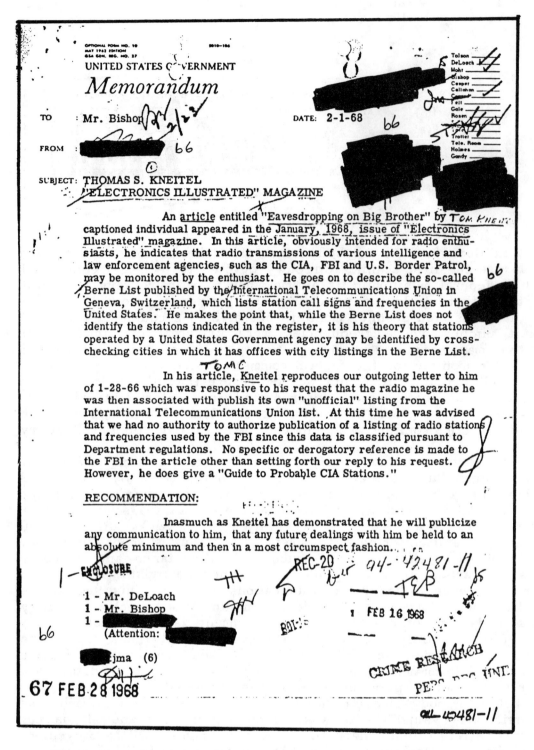

UNITED STATES GOVERNMENT

Memorandum

TO : Mr. Bishop   DATE: 2-1-68

FROM :

SUBJECT: THOMAS S. KNEITEL
"ELECTRONICS ILLUSTRATED" MAGAZINE

An article entitled "Eavesdropping on Big Brother" by captioned individual appeared in the January, 1968, issue of "Electronics Illustrated" magazine. In this article, obviously intended for radio enthusiasts, he indicates that radio transmissions of various intelligence and law enforcement agencies, such as the CIA, FBI and U.S. Border Patrol, may be monitored by the enthusiast. He goes on to describe the so-called Berne List published by the International Telecommunications Union in Geneva, Switzerland, which lists station call signs and frequencies in the United States. He makes the point that, while the Berne List does not identify the stations indicated in the register, it is his theory that stations operated by a United States Government agency may be identified by cross-checking cities in which it has offices with city listings in the Berne List.

In his article, Kneitel reproduces our outgoing letter to him of 1-28-66 which was responsive to his request that the radio magazine he was then associated with publish its own "unofficial" listing from the International Telecommunications Union list. At this time he was advised that we had no authority to authorize publication of a listing of radio stations and frequencies used by the FBI since this data is classified pursuant to Department regulations. No specific or derogatory reference is made to the FBI in the article other than setting forth our reply to his request. However, he does give a "Guide to Probable CIA Stations."

RECOMMENDATION:

Inasmuch as Kneitel has demonstrated that he will publicize any communication to him, that any future dealings with him be held to an absolute minimum and then in a most circumspect fashion.

1 - ENCLOSURE

1 - Mr. DeLoach
1 - Mr. Bishop
1 -
(Attention:

jma (6)

67 FEB 28 1968

REC-20   94-42481-11

1 FEB 16 1968

CRIME RESEARCH

94-42481-11

In an early (1968) try at presenting federal frequency information, it seems that my frequency information was right on target. It earned me a place in Big Brother's computer! This internal FBI memo seems to fear their personnel letting me get any of their data and publishing it.

North-East Scanning News, P.O. Box 62, Gibbstown, NJ 08027
Ontario DX Association, P.O. Box 161 Sta. A, Willowdale, ON, Canada M2N 5S8
Bay Area Scanner Enthusiasts Club, 4718, 4718 Meridian Ave. #265, San Jose, CA 95118
Intercepts Newsletter, 6303 Cornell, Amarillo, TX 79109

Each of the above should be contacted directly regarding their current rates. Clubs, associations, and newsletters will probably appreciate return postage or a stamped self-addressed long envelope (SASE) in order to send you the information you are requesting. This includes North-East Scanner News.

A most interesting and useful low-band (30 to 76 MHz) "skip" newsletter is published by Brian Webb for the benefit of his fellow low band DX fans. This

REWARD

$ 500.00

Will be paid to anyone providing information leading to the
identity of a person who interfered in a criminal investigation.
The subject is described as follows:

A Customs Service reward poster for a scanner owner who heard something and then blabbed to the suspect. Not at all a good idea.

> WHITE/MALE, 65-75, 5'10, 180-190 lbs., light
> skinned. He drives a: 1980ish green or blue
> STATION WAGON, possibly a Chevrolet with a
> Maryland HANDICAPPED Tag (Registration unknown).

The elderly man interfered with the investigation of a heroin
smuggling conspiracy by Pakistani crewmen who attempted to
deliver 2 kilograms of heroin on April 21, 1988 on Fort Avenue
and Key Highway, Locust Point, Baltimore. The elderly man
apparently had a police radio scanner in his station wagon and
notified the suspects of police surveillance.

If you have any information, call:

Special Agent Robert Trader

or any Customs agent at

(301) 962-2620.

U.S. CUSTOMS SERVICE

sometimes includes federal station loggings. As of this writing, I don't think Brian is charging for this newsletter. I believe that he is sending it only to those who are actively and regularly contributing their loggings. With printing and postage rates being what they are, even active contributors should be willing to voluntarily send along a couple of bucks per year to help Brian keep his excellent newsletter going. For starters, your best bet is to send him an SASE to ask how to get on his mailing list. Write to him at: Brian Webb, 3329 Silver Spur Court, Thousand Oaks, CA 91360-1041.

Let's Monitor Federal

Scanner monitoring is great. It provides a spectacular view at the inner operations of your area police, sheriff, fire, EMS, air and ground transportation, and other activities. You can hear business, private security services, and all sorts of other things from forest rangers to florist delivery trucks.

Many scanner monitors will tell you that, unless you're scanning federal stations, then you are only getting a partial view of your community in action. In fact, in the USA, federal agencies have frequency space reserved for their exclusive operation that equals hundreds of MHz worth of communications spectrum, and on scanner frequencies! These frequencies are where agencies such as the Secret Service, FBI, DEA, U.S. Customs, Bureau of Alcohol Tobacco and Firearms, IRS, Border Patrol, Immigration Service, Department of State, Department of Agriculture, Department of Labor, FCC, ICC, FAA, all military services, and other agencies operate.

The government doesn't-- won't-- give out information on the frequencies used by these stations. At one time such information was available from the government for all but a few agencies, but no more. During the Reagan years, the government slammed down the lid on federal frequency and station information, and now the government releases virtually nothing except that information considered necessary for the safety of life and property. Washington simply considers everything else "secret," and that's the end of that!

But you should encounter **no** problems just listening. The law (Communications Act, Section 705) dictates that anything you might overhear should be kept to yourself. Basically, you shouldn't record it, act upon it, profit from it, or report the contents of what you heard to anybody else. More than the law, it's just good sense. You are advised to obtain a copy of the Communications Act of 1934, USCA Section 705, and familiarize yourself with what it says. It deals with Secrecy of Communications. There are penalties for violations. You are solely responsible for your own activities, and there have been problems when people overhear things, but decide to reveal what they heard to others.

As has been previously reported, the US Customs service in Baltimore offered a $500 reward for information leading to the identy of a particular scanner owner. This fellow overheard some communications and then apparently tipped off the suspect, who was a foreign national working as a crew member aboard a vessel. The suspect was being investigated because the feds thought he was smuggling 2 kilograms of heroin. The investigation was destroyed by the information being given to the suspect.

There have been other stories similar to this. Those who gave out the information have felt the wrath of the law when caught. Still, sometimes the story has a wry and offbeat twist that works out differently than the usual pattern of events.

In 1992, a Philadelphia scanner owner was tuned to a frequency used by a federal agency. In fact, for some reason he happened to be taping what he heard. Within days, his activities were the topic of a half page story in **The Philadelphia Inquirer** ("U.S. Agents Assailed For Radio Gab," by Jeffrey Fleishman and Karl Stark, April 4, 1992).

The scanner owner, who was not named in the paper, taped conversations by the agents kidding around while discussing a suspect. One agent was asking another if he was going to beat the subject during the interrogation. The other agent replied that it would be only a "light questioning," which meant that the suspect would require no more than ten stitches.

The agents then turned their comments to the suspect's "scantily clad" wife. After that, they discussed taking over the suspect's pizza parlor and changing its name to that of one of the supervisor in charge of the surveillance. Also, the agents were kidding one another about which of them was going to win a $50 employee award, although one hoped that it wouldn't put him into a higher tax bracket.

All of the taped conversations took place during a surveillance that led to the confiscation of 4,000 lbs. of illegal fireworks. In fact, one agent even joked about hoarding cases of the confiscated fireworks in "our garage." Another agent responded to this with the comment, "Talk himself right into the grave, won't he?"

And he practically did. Next thing you know, the tapes with their small talk, chit chat, and kidding around turned up in all the wrong places. Like the federal agency that employs the agents. Like the news media. Even though it was obvious that the agents were doing nothing more than passing the time during their surveillance by exchanging the type of jocular wisecracks cops always make, their agency saw no humor in the entire matter.

Their agency felt it all sounded unprofessional. Also, the jokes about brutality coming right at the time of the Rodney King incident seemed to jab at a very sensitive nerve point. The parallel to the public's video recording of the King incident and the audio recording of this incident by a member of the public didn't at all sit well. The newspaper report carried quotes from prominent members of the law enforcement community criticizing the poor image this type of thing creates for those in law enforcement.

The agents received no disciplinary action, but they were cautioned about future small talk over their radios. The agency said the agents had used poor judgment.

My own personal feeling? Once the media and the agency had been given tapes of the conversations, they had no choice to play out the ball of string to its end. These agents were obviously not serious about what they were saying. Their comments should have been listened to and forgotten. The agents had no reason to be fried. Their agency had no reason to be humiliated because of a couple of agents joking around while stuck on a boring stakeout.

It's unfortunate incidents such as this, just as much as idiots tipping off suspects, that has made some federal agencies and their employees unfriendly towards people who own scanners. My own experience has been that scanner owners generally are responsible people who mean no harm. Of course, this isn't true of all scanner owners. Some are not well-intentioned, and some mean well but simply have very poor judgment. If all people with scanners would simply be content to listen and no more than that, everybody would be the better for it. Scanner owners would benefit, to say nothing of the agencies we like so much to monitor.

OK, you're saying that federal agencies have the ability to use digital voice scramblers that assures complete privacy. If they don't want to be monitored, you feel, they should use their scramblers. I would point out that not all agencies have this equipment, although those that do have the scramblers do tend to use it liberally when they they wish to talk exchange sensitive traffic. This is fine, but only means something if the agents feel the traffic is sensitive and then decide to switch into scrambled mode.

In the instance of the Philadelphia federal agents and their banter, it could very well be that they (rightfully) assumed that their small talk was not at all sensitive, and didn't need to be scrambled. Hindsight proves that they were wrong, which is why someday we may all be saddened to find that most federal comms are scrambled. And we will have only ourselves to thank for that eventuality.

However, I'd also like to point out that fed agents who use digital scramblers freely admit that they really prefer to communicate "in the clear" as much as possible. This is because scramblers often sound lousy and are garbled. Also, agents complain that they can't communicate over the same range when they are in scrambled mode. President Reagan had a digital scrambled telephone aboard Air Force 1 and almost never used it-- couldn't understand a single word that came over the thing.

9

The wisdom for the day is, just listen. Keep the contents of the messages to yourself.

Information

All information has been checked as much as possible. In some instances, the author has farmed out certain listings for double checking by monitors who specialize in certain agencies. This doesn't mean that we haven't still managed to leave out some information that would have been here if we had known it. Nor does it mean that you won't occasionally spot some conflicting or otherwise seemingly incorrect data here. In any publication containing the large amount of information supplied by many different sources, some listings turn up this way no matter how much we tried to get everything reconciled.

As usual, when it comes to federal data, there is some amount of guesswork, presumptions, and assumptions that can be made, based upon certain patterns. This has been done, but despite all efforts to keep our information as current, correct, and complete as possible there will still be those that managed to slip through the cracks.

While one of our strengths and joys has been the volume of data that arrives from well-intentioned monitoring enthusiasts, this hasn't been without its own problems. Occasionally, information arrives that contains errors that were previously published elsewhere, or even in an earlier edition of this Registry. We have tried to weed out this type of data. Data, even error-laced, never dies. It goes on forever and is passed down through the generations.

In 1972, the author compiled a frequency listing about New York City on behalf of a client. The NYC Fire Department has a number of fire boats, each having its own individual maritime radio service call letters. One fire boat didn't seem to have an assigned FCC call, so I filled in the blank spot using WH-3844. This was a long-expired marine service callsign that I had personally held in the early 1950's. That data was some how perpetuated and, to this very day, my old call letters still appear in someone's current directory showing NYC Fire Department comms.

I tried an experiment to test my theory on data being immortal. In an earlier edition of the Registry, I deliberately listed a Secret Service channel (165.375) in two places. It was shown were it belonged, with the Secret Service. But it was also added to the list of frequencies of the Bureau of Alcohol Tobacco and Firearms. Many federal frequencies are actually used by more than one agency, but I selected this one because it seemed so obvious, and was so well known as being used by only one agency, the Secret Service.

The response to this has been interesting. Some of this Registry's regular reporters picked up on it immediately and wrote that they got a chuckle when it showed up. Three years later, though, one newsletter columnist was still grumbling about our "infamous error." Ho boy, that sure taught us never to try to sneak one past someone who is obviously an expert. No sir!

Eventually, however, the swallows came back to Capistrano. I spotted the bizarre new (or "infamous," if you prefer) ATF frequency starting to show up elsewhere. People just didn't realize how infamous it was. It appeared in several publications. It has also shown up in some of the ATF information monitors have sent here for our use in future editions of this Registry. God, what kind of Frankenstein have I created? The data that wouldn't die. I think the call letters for that ATF frequency are-- ah... WH-3844.

So, everything in this directory should be regarded with all of the above factors in mind. Because of the basic nature of the listings herein, keep in mind that it's all unofficial, mostly speculatory, with quite a few guesses, and some gaps. We hope and assume that it is mostly on-target, but we offer no guarantees and we are always open to your thoughts-- and your suggestions.

By the way, we have had inquiries as to why this series is not regularly updated with a new edition every year. Frankly, our feeling is that most scanner owners don't need a directory updated every year. Well, obviously it's a good way of selling scanner owners a new book every year, but there are seldom enough changes to justify the cost to the average monitor. My inclination is to update a directory when there are a sufficient number of changes to make the previous edition become outdated enough to justify the purchase of a new one. This is a variable period with each edition of every directory. In the case of this Registry, it was a three year gap before I (and readers who started to write in on the subject) thought it was time for Edition #8 to make an appearance.

This Registry carries no advertising. Also note that we have not included many pages that contain a few scraps of data plus large areas of vacant white space. Such pages look pretty, I'll admit. There are directories with this fancy format. They run up the total number of pages and price of the book. It allows the book to be described as having almost as many pages as the Hong Kong telephone directory. But for what? I have opted to give you as much information as possible, with very little blank white space. There are no ads to pad out the pages, either. You want data. Right? Our straightforward informational format offers you several times the amount of listings available anywhere else at any price.

The Frequencies

The majority of VHF/UHF federal communications take place within certain bands. In the USA, the FCC has no authority to issue licenses for stations on those frequencies. In this Registry, these frequencies will be our primary interest. They are: 29.89 to 30.51 MHz; 32.00 to 33.00 MHz; 34.00 to 35.00 MHz; 36.00 to 37.00 MHz; 38.00 to 39.00 MHz; 40.00 to 42.00 MHz; 49.66 to 50.00 MHz; 137.00 to 144.00 MHz MHz; 148.00 to 150.80 MHz; 157.04 to 157.19 MHz; 162.02 to 173.20 MHz; 173.40 to 174.00 MHz; and 225.00 to 420.00 MHz.

Most scanners have a search/scan mode. Put your scanner in search/scan, then explore each of these frequency ranges. Concentrate your efforts on 500 kHz segments, searching at the fastest rate your scanner can operate. Search each segment for at least a few days at a time before moving along to the next one. Keep a detailed record of each active frequency you spot-- and the agency you suspect may be operating there. You should be able to discover new frequencies. The 30 to 50 MHz band has the potentials of bringing in long distance reception due to ionospheric propagation.

Not every scanner can operate in the 225 to 400 MHz range. This band is mostly used for military aeronautical comms. These comms are virtually all in **AM** mode. There are some narrowband FM (NFM) or wideband FM (WFM) satellite comms in portions of this band, too, as noted in the listings. Military transmissions between 30 and 75 MHz are most often in WFM mode, although civilian agencies on these frequencies use NFM. Between 118 and 139 MHz, comms are in AM mode, while everything above 139 MHz is usually in NFM mode. We have also listed many HF comms frequencies (those between 2000 and 30000 kHz). These are usually upper sideband (USB) mode, and require a communications receiver to be monitored.

Some repeater systems have a "talkaround" feature. At times this is the "F-2," or "direct" short-range method of operation in the system. It means that the mobile and handheld units stop transmitting on the repeater input frequency and receiving on the repeater output frequency. In this mode they go into simplex operation where they transmit and receive on the repeater output frequency. This means that their signals no longer pass through the repeater. Therefore, the radios become useful for short range surveillance work, although the field agents are still tuned to the repeater frequency in case other units want to contact them.

Some surveillance comms have also been noted in the 869 to 894 MHz cellular band, also the 49.67 to 49.99 MHz no-license low-power comms band. Sources have reported DEA surveillance in the 72 to 76 MHz band, but this remains questionable.

Note that some frequencies in the Registry are shown to 4 places after the decimal, as in 173.4875 MHz (for example). Not every scanner will accept this exact frequency. Your scanner may register 173.485 or 173.49 MHz when you attempt to program in 173.4875 MHz. That means your scanner is designed to accept programming every 5 kHz. Do not be at all concerned as either frequency possibility is a mere 2.5 kHz away from 173.4875. In FM radio, this means practically nothing at all since the FM signals are 16 kHz wide. Rest assured that you will still hear anything and everything that is taking place on 173.4875, and you'll never be able to tell the difference. This goes for all frequencies with 4 digits after the decimal that can't be programmed into your scanner exactly that way. Not to worry. Trust me.

Usage

Not all frequencies buzz away with activity day and night. Some are used only for special uses or occasions, or emergencies, and some may not be used at all in your local area. Many federal agencies are your basic 9 to 5 weekday operations, so keep this in mind as you search through for activity. It may be that a frequency may be active in your local area, but that activity could well take place within a 9 to 5 timeframe, Monday to Friday-- and the station could be used only a couple of times each day.

Budgetary constraints have cut back on a number of federal activities. There are quite a few military installations recently closed or ready to shut down as this Registry is being prepared. The USAF is in the midst of a major reorganization, which we have taken into account as much as we could with the knowledge at hand. Things are ever-changing, and some federal activities may be operating with less vigor than it would seem from the number of frequencies at their disposal. For the time being, we are still not ready to ditch all of this information, although we have zapped some that was in Edition #7. The world is still rather screwd up, and until they come in with the bulldozers and knock down empty buildings, I'd still not rush to abandon certain frequencies. Would you?

Keep your station records, files, logs, or other data on what you're hearing. Indicate the frequencies, the amount of activity, the apparent users, and other relevant information. As you go, you will find that you are constructing a wonderful base of information. In this edition, we are running a by-frequency listing of many high-interest monitoring channels. This is a feature that readers have requested be included to help them program their scanners. Use it as a starting point to custom-design the programming scheme for your own scanner. It may give you some good idea with which to work.

Keep your ears peeled for newsworthy events, such as VIP visits to your area, search and rescue missions, major pollution problems, disasters, civil unrest, and other things that can trigger activity on federal frequencies.

Please be sure to share your information with us for future editions. Your information will be appreciated and used by many. I will try to answer all who submit information, although it may take me a while to get back to you. Edition #8 is the largest yet. With your kind help, the next edition with contain even more!

Send your information to me in care of the publishers of this Registry. And good monitoring!

Military & Other Federal Installations Including Selected Major Government Contractors & Military Frequencies at Civil Airports

Unless otherwise noted, all freqs are MHz. All freqs listed after each usage abbreviation code relate to the service it describes. Double frequencies shown connected by a slash bar (as in 166.90/166.30) indicate paired frequencies, such as for duplex or repeater systems. In repeater systems, the repeater output frequency is the first of the two frequencies shown. The following abbreviations are used throughout this directory in order to allow the maximum amount of information to be presented with a minimum of wasted space:

AAF	Army Airfield
A/C	Aircraft
ACC	Air Force Air Combat Command (ex Tactical Air Command & other units)
AD	Aircraft approach and/or departure communications
AF	USAF or Air National Guard
AFS	Air Force Station
AHP	Army Heliport
ALCE	Airlift Control Element
AMC	Air Force Air Mobility Command (ex Military Airlift Command)
ANG	Air National Guard (ANGB= Air National Guard Base)
Army	Army or National Guard
ASW	Anti-Submarine Warfare
ATC	Air Traffic Control
BIA	Bureau of Indian Affairs
BP	Border Patrol
CFB	Canadian Forces Base
CG	Coast Guard
CID	Criminal Investigation Division
CP	Command Post
CTCSS	Continuous Tone Code Squelch System ("PL tone")
DEW	Distant Early Warning
DI	Pilot-to-Dispatcher Service
DIA	Defense Intelligence Agency
DoE	Department of Energy
E	Aircraft Clearance Delivery
EOD	Explosive Ordnance Disposal
FD	Fire Department
FEMA	Federal Emergency Management Agency
FSS	Flight Service Station
FWS	Fish & Wildlife Service
G	Aircraft Ground Control
HF	High Frequency (2,000 to 30,000 kHz) SSB Communications
HPT	Heliport
ICC	Interstate Commerce Commission
INS	Immigration & Naturalization Service
LRRS	Long Range Radar Station
MAC	US Air Force Air Mobility Command (ex Military Airlift Command)
Maint	Maintenance
MARS	Military Affiliate Radio System
MCAF	US Marine Corps Airfield
MIR	Russian "Mir" Orbiting Space Station
MOA	Military Operations Area

MP	Military Police
Msc	Miscellaneous
Muni	Municipal Airport
NAF	Naval Air Facility
NALF	Naval Auxiliary Landing Field
NAS	Naval Air Station
NFM	Narrow Band Frequency Modulation
NG	National Guard
NORAD	North American Aerospace Defense
NS	Naval Station
NWF	Naval Weapons Facility
NWS	Naval Weapons Station
OLF	Naval Outlying Field
OP	Operations
OSI	Air Force Office of Special Investigations
PD	Police Service
S	Aircraft Terminal Informational Service (ATIS) recording
SAC	Air Force Strategic Command (ex Strategic Air Command)
SP	Navy Shore Patrol
T	Airport or facility Control Tower
TAC	Air Force Air Mobility Command (ex Tactical Air Command & other units)
USCG	US Coast Guard
USMC	US Marine Corps
USN	US Navy or Naval Reserve
USPS	US Postal Service
USSS	US Secret Service
USSTRATCOM	US Air Force Strategic Command (ex Strategic Air Command)
WFM	Wide Band Frequency Modulation mode
WHCA	White House Communications Agency
WX	Weather reports/advisories/communications

Military/Miscellaneous Federal Installations & Military Frequencies
Used at Civil Airports

Aberdeen Proving Ground, MD- See Phillips AAF

Aberdeen Regional Apt., SD: FSS 255.4 AD 371.9

Abilene Apt, TX: AD 338.3 T 257.8 FSS 255.4

Abrams Muni Apt., Grand Ledge, MI: AD 226.4 NG 41.85 122.7 241.0

Acadiana Regn'l. Apt., New Iberia, LA: AD 278.5 338.25 T 267.2

Accomack Co. Apt., Melfa, VA: AD 372.1

Adak Naval Station, AK: DI 130.7 S 250.0 AD 134.5 263.6 T 127.2 E 132.3 336.4
WX 344.6 Terminal 130.7 305.0 G 132.3 USN 138.72 138.96 139.50 140.10 140.25
140.28 148.29 270.8 293.05 294.75 301.9 306.45 307.95 309.35 310.85 312.3 AF
165.1625 336.6

Ada Muni Apt., OK: AD 322.4 AF 413.10 413.40

Adams Field, Little Rock, AR: AD 306.2 353.6 385.6 T 257.8 AF 38.65 165.0625

Addington Field, KY: AD 327.0 388.2

Addison Apt., TX T 239.0

Adirondak Apt., NY: AD 380.3

Aero Corp., Lake City, FL: 123.2 123.4 123.45 (HF 5598 6661 8919 kHz)

Aeroflex-Andover Apt., NJ: AD 379.9

Aeronca, Inc., Middletown, OH: 462.50

Aerojet General Co.
   Chino, CA 157.74 462.25
   Nimbus, CA 151.835 153.095 462.25 462.225 462.275 462.425 464.325 464.375
   Sacramento, CA 123.1 151.775

Aerospatiale Aviation, Grand Prairie, TX: 123.05 123.25 123.5 123.325 123.45
153.185 451.575 456.275

Aerotron Inc., Raleigh, NC: 854.8125 855.3125 856.9125 858.8625 860.9125

Agana NAS/Brewer Fld., GU: AD 119.8 269.0 269.5 T 118.1 340.2 G 121.9 336.4
WX 344.6

Aiken Muni Apt., SC: AD 231.1

Airborne Airpark, Dayton, OH: AD 327.1

Air Force Academy, Colorado Springs, CO: AD ("Eagle Cntrl.") 123.5 DI 119.35
376.0 T 121.25 121.8 320.1 G 121.8 Base OP ("Eagle Cntrl.") 119.4 Bullseye
Aux. Airstrip OP 121.95 Police 163.4625 AF 139.68 148.245 148.55 149.095 149.115
149.235 149.425 149.55 150.225 150.345 163.375 165.0125 173.4375 173.5375 173.5875

Air Force Space Command Station, Cape Cod, MA (6th Missile Early Warning
System): Security ("Pave Paws") 165.0375 FD ("Pave Paws") 173.5625

Airlake Apt., MN: AD 284.7

Airpark South Apt., MO: AD 234.2 269.4

Akasaka Press Center Heliport/Hardy Barracks, Honshu, Japan: T 122.5 288.8

Akron, OH: USN 34.55

Akron-Canton Regional Apt., AD 226.4 257.8 323.0 G 348.6 T 257.8 NG 41.00
46.75 121.75

Akron/Fulton Muni Apt., OH: AD 226.4 257.8

Akron-Washington Co. Apt., CO: FSS 255.4 AD 319.2

Alabama Army Ammunition Plant, Childersburg, AL: 173.4875

Alameda NAS (Nimitz Fld.), CA: AD 120.9 124.4 134.5 135.1 135.4 257.2 268.7
307.2 313.2 317.6 323.2 338.2 350.8 351.8 354.1 S 284.2 T 127.05 340.2 360.2 384.4
G 123.95 352.4 WX 359.6 OP 376.8 CID 140.075 140.65 140.775 Weapons ("Bullfrog
Quebec") 140.125 140.925 Security 149.075 149.125 150.075 FD 149.075 Medic 142.025
149.40 USMA Air Group 139.525 140.90 Fueling 140.825 Fire/Crash 140.10 140.30
Supply 139.55 Electronics 138.60 Maintenance 141.975 142.675 143.575 143.625
USN 30.55 32.05 36.53 36.57 36.60 36.63 36.87 138.625 138.65 138.725 138.775 140.13

140.40 140.875 140.975 142.68 142.70 142.775 143.525 143.675 148.325 265.9 275.4 280.2 320.2 320.4 336.2 341.0 344.1 356.25 365.5 366.5 367.5 368.5 CG 171.3625 Army 230.5 231.5 241.5 244.5 245.5 246.5 247.5 345.5 392.5 393.5 (Listings include shipyard.)

Alamogordo-White Sands Regn'l. Apt., NM: AD 284.0 324.3

Albany Co., Apt., NY: FSS 255.4 AD 226.8 307.2 T 257.8 G 348.6 NG 41.00 122.775 242.4

Albert J. Ellis Apt., Jacksonville, NC: AD 257.6 272.75

Albert Lea Muni Apt., AD 307.3

Albert Whitted Apt., St. Petersburg, FL: AD 363.8 T 257.6

Albrook AFS, Panama: AD 119.7 121.2 263.0 317.7 Security/MP 33.25 34.85 36.30 36.50 36.85 Msc 349.4 (HF 6738 11176 15015 kHz) AF 34.34 122.1 123.1 123.1 123.3 126.9 128.8 138.70 162.985 163.05 163.30 163.475 163.60 163.80 241.0 297.5 323.9 413.025 413.10 413.15 413.20 413.39 413.40

Albuquerque Int'l. Apt./Kirtland AFB, NM (USAF Parachute School): AD 121.1 123.9 124.4 127.4 301.5 316.7 317.6 354.1 DI 372.2 S 118.0 363.8 FSS 255.4 T 118.3 120.3 126.3 351.9 G 121.9 348.6 E 119.2 385.6 CP 349.4 372.2 WX 342.5 AF 32.45 34.20 36.85 40.15 40.17 40.19 41.95 46.75 46.95 138.075 138.165 138.175 138.25 138.50 139.605 139.80 139.995 141.80 141.915 142.275 143.725 143.80 148.075 148.225 148.515 148.575 147.755 149.145 149.175 149.205 149.385 149.475 149.525 150.195 150.225 150.285 150.345 150.35 163.4625 163.4875 163.5125 163.5375 163.5875 163.90 164.025 164.70 165.0625 165.1125 165.1375 165.1625 165.1875 170.15 173.4375 173.5125 173.5375 173.5875 229.2 236.0 242.0 249.5 251.9 254.4 272.0 276.8 291.0 299.1 305.5 311.2 311.4 314.4 315.0 337.5 379.2 381.0 382.6 395.5 396.1 399.5 407.375 407.425 407.50 413.10 413.15 413.40 Army 149.80 170.575 225.5 387.5 USN 143.725

Alcoa ANG Sta., TN: ANG 46.75 271.1 322.7 396.9

Alconbury USAF, UK: DI 235.1 AD 134.05 135.275 268.2 306.85 362.3 381.9 T 122.1 257.8 361.55 G 339.25 CP 283.6 WX 259.4 Security 32.20 76.55 Msc 76.75

Alexandria Esler Regional Apt., LA: AD 289.1 381.5 T 324.3

Alexander Muni. Apt., NM: AD 299.3

Alexandria, VA: USN 140.25 143.70 CG 409.825

Aliamanu Military Reservation, HI: Army 142.905 143.235 165.0875 165.1875

Alice Int'l. Apt., TX: FSS 255.4 AD 291.6 383.6

Allaire Fld., NJ: AD 363.8

Allegheny Co. Apt., Pittsburgh, PA: FSS 255.4 AD 337.4 T 239.0

Allen AAF/Ft. Greeley, AK (Cold Regions Test Center; 172nd Inf Bde; N. Warfare Training Center; High Altitude Rescue Team): WX 114.9 FSS 255.4 AD 135.3 322.5 OP 40.80 241.0 Range 38.30 246.2 Rescue 36.85 37.00 150.475 150.55 MP's 173.4875 FD 30.85 39.50 165.0875 173.125 173.5125 Medevac 40.45 CID 172.30 Motor Pool 164.70 Army 148.80 150.705 163.5375 163.5625 173.125

Allen Co. Apt., Lima, OH: USN 148.40 150.075

Allendale Co. Apt., SC: AD 363.2

Allentown-Bethlehem-Easton Apt., PA: AD 397.9 T 397.9

Allentown Queen City Muni Apt., PA: AD 397.9

Alliance Muni Apt., NE: FSS 255.4

Almaden, CA: AF 150.20 228.9 234.6 238.4 254.2 260.8 267.0 272.0 274.4 278.4 278.7 293.8 299.0 309.4 316.3 320.6 324.0 327.9 336.6 341.8 346.2 359.4 364.2 377.0 387.8 398.0

A. L. Mangham Jr. Regn'l. Apt., TX: AD 269.6

Almira, WA: AF 227.8 240.0 252.0 257.475 257.575 262.6 266.4 272.525 287.2 292.1 300.0 315.0 324.3 341.6 343.35 394.6 361.5 363.325 363.35 367.6 397.1

Alpena Co. Regn'l. Apt., MI-- See Phelps-Collins ANGB listings.

Altoona-Blair Co. Apt., PA: FSS 255.4 AD 299.2

Altus AFB, OK (AMC, 443rd Military Airlift Wing, 340th Air Refueling Gp., 2002 Communication Sqdn.): DI 372.2   S 372.2   S 109.8 273.5   AD 125.1 290.9 348.3   T 119.65 255.6   G 119.65 275.8   E 120.65 316.5   WX 239.8   MAC CP 349.4   SAC CP 311.0 321.0   Flight Coordinator 266.5   304th Air Refueling Gp 239.8 255.6 2259.3 260.2 273.5 289.4 290.9 319.8 324.3 338.6 359.1 363.1 364.2 381.3 391.9 395.9   AF 46.75 139.60 139.65 142.25 148.035 148.065 148.175 148.545 149.30 149.565 149.135 163.4625 163.4875 163.5125 163.5875 164.50 165.1125 165.1625 173.05 173.4375 173.5375 173.5875 251.9 275.8 340.6 341.5 384.7 396.9 413.15 413.45

Alva Muni Apt., OK: AD 344.8

Amarillo Int'l. Apt., TX: FSS 255.4 S 350.3 AD 290.3 307.0 351.7 G 348.6 T 257.9 SAC 311.0 AF 413.45

Amarillo, TX: USN USN 36.85

Amedee AAF/Sierra Ordnance Depot, Herlong, CA: AD 285.5 T 126.2 241.1 FD 148.85 Security 165.0625 Heliport ("Shadow 3") 41.50 Army 148.60 148.70 148.75 148.80 148.90 166.4875 167.075

Ames Munic Apt., IA: AD 252.9

Anacostia NAS, DC: USN 142.75 143.70 276.4 DIA 139.85

Anchorage Int'l. Apt., AK: AD 134.1 259.3 290.9 363.8 T 257.8 E 323.1 ANG CP ("Camper") 134.5 292.4 (HF 4898 kHz)

Andalusia-Opp Apt., AL: AD 237.5

Andersen AFB, Guam (STRATCOM; 43rd Bombardment Wing, Heavy; 60th Bomb Sqdn.): WX 344.6 Rescue 282.8 DI 372.2 AD 119.8 T 126.2 236.6 G 121.7 275.8 MAC CP 128.0 349.4 633 ABW CP ("Cobra Cntrl.") 311.0 321.0 Guam CERAP 118.7 120.5 255.4 263.0 CP 292.1 (HF 6738 8967 11176 13201 kHz) AF 139.90 140.40 142.155 148.035 148.125 148.30 148.485 149.15 149.265 149.325 149.565 150.225 162.90 163.20 163.4625 163.5125 163.5375 163.5625 163.975 164.10 164.50 164.9625 165.0125 165.1625 165.4125 167.5875 170.65 173.4125 173.4375 173.7375 173.5625 173.5875 236.6 258.2 259.4 266.0 275.8 292.1 294.2 295.3 304.9 317.1775 413.20 413.45

Anderson Co. Apt., SC: AD 306.9 FSS 255.4

Anderson Muni Apt., IN: AD 319.8

Andrau Airpark, Houston, TX: AD 257.7

Andrews AFB, Camp Springs, MD (AMC; HQ AF Systems Command; 89th Military Airlift Wing; 1776th Air Base Wing; Home Base for Air Force One & Two): DI 122.85 372.2 WX 344.6 S 113.1 251.05 AD 125.65 128.35 269.5 294.5 T 118.4 236.6 289.6 G 121.8 275.8 E 127.55 393.1 CP 141.55 149.175 378.1 407.425 Airevac 141.375 162.925 172.95 ANG 113rd TFW 234.8 AFR 143.80 351.2 OSI 40.17 40.19 138.075 Security 413.00 413.275 413.375 FD ("Red Control") 173.5875 Aircraft Maintenance 143.425 Motor Pool 163.4625 Post Transportation 169.60 Phone Patches 413.075 Maintenance 413.20 FEMA 167.975 FBI 163.4875 USMC 140.445 AF 138.165 139.65 139.875 140.40 141.55 141.70 143.825 148.065 148.095 148.10 148.485 149.025 149.265 149.30 149.475 149.565 149.65 163.4625 163.4875 163.5125 163.5875 164.40 165.0125 165.1625 165.7375 173.5625 228.8 230.5 234.7 235.5 238.8 240.5 243.5 249.5 251.0 251.9 252.5 256.6 263.2 267.4 270.4 275.0 280.2 287.8 292.2 292.7 302.4 306.7 316.4 325.5 326.0 337.0 338.4 342.2 344.0 356.0 361.6 364.2 369.0 369.5 372.5 375.1 375.5 378.5 386.2 388.5 389.0 390.5 392.5 392.5 392.8 394.5 398.5 407.025 408.425 409.35 413.025 413.125 413.15 413.35 413.45 (HF 6738 8976 11176 17975 kHz)

Andrews AFB Naval Air Facility, DC: DI 122.85 140.60 386.8 SP 413.375 OP 138.72 Security 413.05 Motor Pool 138.725 USN 138.52 138.65 138.725 139.48 139.54 139.575 142.86 FD/Crash 140.10

Andros Town Apt., Andros I., Bahamas: USN OP 126.2 148.95 149.37 277.8 355.0

Angelina Co. Apt., Luflin, TX FSS 255.4 AD 269.6

Annapolis MD (Naval Academy; Naval Station; Ship Research & Development Center): Security 148.425 149.00   FD 148.425   Motor Pool 148.35   Maintenance 149.29   Medic 148.35   USN 32.36 140.075 140.275 140.64 140.65 140.775 148.31 148.95 149.05 149.40 150.09 150.39 285.0 304.2 315.6 361.2 364.2 385.0

Anniston Metro Apt., AL: AD 381.5

Anniston Army Depot, AL (Chemical Biological Warfare weapons storage area): Helipad 41.50 126.2 241.0 Storage OP 141.225 Security 141.075 FD 407.30 Motor Pool 141.475 Msc 139.32 142.305 142.90

Anoka Co.-Blaine (Janes Fld.), Minneapolis, MN: AD 335.5 379.3

Ansbach AHP, Katterbach Kaserne, Germany: AD 124.775 342.6 T 31.80 40.80 122.1 139.05 264.85 G 141.30 250.55 OP 67.50 WX 140.30

Antrim Co. Apt., Bellaire, MI: AD 398.9

Appalachicola Muni Apt., FL: AF 347.7

Aransas Co. Apt., Rockport, TX: AD 281.9 363.1

Arapahoe Co. Apt., Denver, CO: AD 307.3

Arcata Apt., CA: FSS 255.4   CG ("Humboldt Air") 381.7 381.8 383.9 (HF 3120 5692 8980 11198 kHz)

Archer City, TX: USN 143.50

Ardmore Muni Apt., OK: FSS 255.4   AD 322.4   T 257.7

Arkadelphia Muni Apt., AR: AD 348.7

Arlington, TX: Army 30.50 34.10 46.65 49.80 139.00 141.025 142.55 148.025 148.65 148.85 226.4 231.9 234.4 237.75 242.3 265.5 277.5 299.9 356.9 374.4 376.3 386.6

Arlington, VA: USN 138.55 138.60 138.625 138.65 138.75 138.84 139.48 139.50 140.50 140.54 142.10 143.55 148.40 148.515 149.10   Army 162.20 165.1875 173.4125 AF 139.85 140.375

Arlington Hall Station, VA: MP 164.445   Army 142.875

Arlington Muni Apt., TX: AD 227.8

Arlington Muni Apt., WA: AD 306.9

Army Warfare Training Center, DC: 150.555

Arnold AFB, Tullahoma, TN (Arnold Engineering Development Center): AD 126.75 353.5   OP 127.45 WX 128.325 AF 135.85 135.95 150.195 150.345 150.35 163.4625 163.5125 163.5875 165.0125 165.0375 173.5875

Arrowhead Assault Strip, AR: AD 120.9 228.9 Range 38.50 141.30 242.6

Artesta Muni Apt., NM: AD 239.0

Ascension Aux. AF, Ascension Isl.: T ("Wideawake") 126.2 284.1 CP (HF 6738 11176 17975 kHz)

Asheville Regional Apt., NC: AD 226.8 257.9 351.8   T 257.8

Ashland-Boyd Co. Apt., KY: 257.8

Ashtabula Co. Apt., OH: 323.2

Astor, FL: USN 142.56 142.675 148.325 149.46

Athens-Ben Epps Apt., GA: AD 306.9

Atkinson Muni Apt., Pittsburg, KS: AD 343.9

Atlantic City Int'l. Apt., NJ: AD 239.0 385.5 396.0 T 239.0 385.5 E 396.0 G 284.6 ANG (117th FIG) 163.375 163.4875 163.5125 165.0375 165.1375 228.7 234.5 234.55 251.9 255.0 261.0 263.6 279.6 288.7 364.2   SAC 311.0 (Also see FAA listings section.)

Atlantic City Muni Bader Fld., NJ: AD 263.6 385.5

Atlas Powder Co., Atlas MO: 153.125

Auburn-Lewiston Muni Apt., ME: AD 290.5   AF 143.75

Auburn-Opeleika R.G. Pitts Apt., AL: AD 388.0

Augsburg AHP, Gablingen Kaserne, Germany: T 118.225 OP 30.60 141.80 399.60 Medevac 39.95

Augusta State Apt., ME: FSS 255.4   AD 290.5 299.2 322.4

Aurora Muni Apt., IL: AD 371.9

Aurora State Apt., OR AD 284.6

Austin Muni Apt., MN: AD 307.3 396.1

Austin-Straubel Apt., Green Bay, WI: FSS 255.4   AD 307.9 338.2   T 257.8   AF 150.315

Autec Heliport, Andros Isl, Bahamas: OP ("Longfellow Base") 126.3 277.8 355.0

Avantek, Inc., New Almaden, CA: 151.625 462.4375 462.40 464.8375

Ava Test Annex, Ava, NY: AF 139.80 163.4625 257.0 259.2 284.1 291.8 319.6 349.6 379.7 383.0 384.8

Avenger Fld., TX: AD 322.3

Aviano AB, Italy: DI 382.7 AD 142.75 261.275 362.3 T122.1 142.05 257.8 284.775 G262.9 CP 297.4 Maintenance 243.6 WX 259.4

Azusa, CA: USN 358.0 362.0 385.3

Babenhausen AHP, Germany: OP 242.45

Bacon Co. Apt., Alma, GA: FSS 255.4 AD 290.4

Bad Abling AHP, Germany: OP ("Condor") 33.70

Badger Army Ammunition Depot, Baraboo, WI: Army 163.5375 165.0625 165.1875

Bad Kreuznach AAF, Germany: T 31.80 40.20 122.1 141.60 399.85

Badin ANG Sta., NC: ANG 235.5 249.5 364.5 375.5 388.5 394.5 396.5

Baker AAF, Bad Tolz, Germany: Advisories 31.80 40.20 122.1 399.85 OP 41.75

Baker Muni Apt., OR: AD 387.15

Baldwin Co. Apt., Millegeville, GA: AD 269.3 279.6

Baltimore, MD: USN 40.80 140.675 149.075 150.075 275.7 283.4 307.7 339.6 348.1 358.6   Army 58th Infantry Bde 407.235   Curtis Bay Army Tugs 139.15 141.225   CG Security 419.65   CG FD 419.85   CG Shipyard 407.125 415.775 416.635

Baltimore-Washington Int'l. Apt., MD: FSS 255.4   AD 228.4 231.6 307.9 325.8   T 257.8   Security 453.90   FD/Crash 453.80 Misc 129.375

Bamberg AAF, Germany: OP 37.40 122.5

Bangor Int'l. Apt., ME: FSS 255.4   AD 239.3 390.9   T 257.8   G 348.6   E 348.6 ANG OP 238.2   ANG 148.455 148.50 149.265 149.325 163.4875 164.50 238.8 293.2 311.0 321.0 413.45   NG 41.20 142.305 142.355 142.905

Bangor, WA: USN 36.53 36.57 36.63 36.87 138.575 138.82 138.95 138.975 139.50 139.52 140.00 140.025 140.175 140.20 140.225 140.475 140.50 140.525 140.575 140.65 140.75 140.825 140.875 140.90 140.925 140.95 141.575 141.95 141.975 142.025 142.265 143.50 143.675 258.9 265.1 291.4 350.7   Rescue 282.8

Baraboo-Wisc Dells Apt., WI: AD 380.35

Barbers Point NAS, HI (Patrol Wing 2; Fleet Composite Sqdn. 1; 147th Aviation Co. (Army)): S 326.5 AD 118.3 119.1 124.8 165.0 317.6 381.6   T132.65 340.2 380.5 G123.8 336.4   VFR Advisory 118.3 120.9 124.8 269.0 285.4 338.2   WX 344.6   OP 270.8 (HF 6723 kHz) CG 381.8 393.9 FACSFAC ("Hula Dancer") 129.0 132.4 280.7 308.1 (HF 3379 kHz)   MIL 40.10 126.2 134.1 138.525 138.55 138.975 139.50 139.525 140.075 140.225 140.775 140.92 140.975 142.775 143.50 143.725 148.375 149.025 149.35 254.0 268.7 299.6 301.2 305.2 314.8 320.4 342.6 355.3 360.2 361.2 381.8 384.2 389.8 DOE 230.4 239.4 248.6 252.4 259.7 315.1 384.8 407.00 410.00

Barking Sands PMRF, HI: Unicom 122.8 AD 126.5 269.4 T 126.2 340.2 360.2 Range ("Outrider Cntrl." 126.2 322.0 (HF 4491 kHz) USN 138.525 138.55 148.30 242.0 263.7 269.8 274.9 289.8 309.2 311.9 337.8 342.8 345.0 383.6 AF 125.1 225.4 267.5 280.5 283.8 305.4 324.5 DOE 225.7 226.7 227.7 228.2 229.0 230.4 231.4 232.4 232.9 235.0 235.5 236.2 238.3 239.4 240.2 240.8 241.3 241.5 248.6 251.5 252.4 255.1 257.3 259.1 259.7 264.5 293.0

Barkley Regn'l. Apt., Paducah, KY: FSS 255.4 AD 397.9 T 226.3 G 226.3

Barksdale AFB, Shreveport, LA (ACC, HQ 8th Air Force, 2nd Wing; HQ 2nd Bombardment Wing; 917th TFG; 7, 19, 68, 97, 380, 410, 416 & 509 Bombardment Wings; 305 & 340 Air Refueling Gps; 384 Air Refueling Wing; 351, 380, 381 Strategic Missile Wings; 11 Strategic Grp; 306 Strategic Wing; 4684 Air Base Grp; 6 & 20 Missile Warning Sqdns; 12th Missile Warning Grp): DI 372.2 S 375.8 AD 108.6 111.2 117.4 118.6 119.9 121.4 125.1 250.2 350.2 363.8 372.9 T 128.25 236.6 295.7 G 121.8 275.8 WX 373.1 OSI 40.17 40.19 SAC CP 311.0 321.0 AF 148.065 148.20 148.515 148.545 149.15 149.325 149.565 149.975 150.225 162.25 163.375 163.4625 163.4875 163.5125 164.10 164.175 164.50 164.70 164.70 164.9625 164.9875 165.1125 165.1625 168.00 173.4375 173.5375 173.5625 173.5875 252.1 272.0 294.4 300.6 373.1 383.3 413.00 413.15 413.20 413.45

Barnes Co. Muni Apt., ND: AD 270.3

Barnes Muni Apt., Westfield, MA: AD 148.455 325.8 G 289.4 T ("Westfield Tower") 149.695 251.1 FD/Crash 148.215 Emergency 148.475 ANG OP ("Viper Control") 303.0 Security 148.455 Maintenance 148.095 ANG 283.8 USN 30.45 38.75

Barnstable Muni Apt., Hyannis, MA: AD 381.7 DI 372.2 T 257.8

Barstow-Daggett Apt., CA: FSS 255.4 USN 46.70 132.3 139.025 233.8 258.9 300.3 317.4 390.6

Barter Island DEW Station, AK: T 126.2 288.4

Bartlesville Mini Apt., OK: AD 319.1

Bartow Muni Apt., FL: AD 290.3

Batesville Regn'l. Apt., AR: AD 286.6

Bath, ME: USN 233.8 300.3

Baton Rouge Metro Ryan Fld., LA: FSS 255.4 AD 278.3 323.2 338.25 T 257.8

Baudette Int'l. Apt., MN: 163.4625

Baumholder AAF, Germany: Advisory 33.20 142.90 251.2 US Liason 30.80 49.85 Range 63.20

Baxley Muni Apt., GA: AD 290.4

Baxter Co. Regn'l. Apt., AR: AD 286.6

Bay City Muni Apt., TX: AD 360.8

Baytown Apt., TX: AD 396.0

Bayview, TX: USN 141.00

Beale AFB, Marysville, CA (ACC, HQ 2nd AF, 14th Air Division; 9th Recon Wing): DI 372.2 S 273.5 AD 125.4 327.5 T 119.4 276.15 WX 239.8 G 121.6 228.4 SAC CP 149.55 311.0 321.0 Security 148.50 149.05 149.225 149.55 OSI 138.075 138.165 139.175 138.325 Disaster 150.345 Civil Engineering 150.195 Commanders Net 148.035 148.05 150.225 Flightline Maintenance 148.245 148.455 149.55 Base Transportation 150.345 Crew Alerts 413.45 Medic 148.095 Pager 138.325 413.45 Flightline Fueling 150.315 AF 148.185 149.525 150.255 164.50 163.5125 235.6 243.5 259.1 269.6 287.0 281.4 316.1 373.1 383.1 385.6 396.1 420.00

Beatrice Muni Apt., NE: AD 317.7

Beaufort MCAS/Merritt Fld., SC (2nd MAW; MAG 31): S 278.0 AD 120.85 123.7 125.6 251.7 301.2 322.5 T 119.05 340.2 360.2 G 128.15 336.4 E 128.15 336.4 OP 281.8 WX 264.5 Rescue 282.8 USMC 34.55 36.05 138.60 138.74 138.95 138.96 139.545 140.10 140.25 140.325 140.46 140.875 140.895 141.00 143.625 143.715 143.725 148.27 148.29 148.31 148.425 150.00 150.11 150.125 150.15 150.375 236.0 243.9 250.3

251.9 258.9 264.0 267.6 270.8 274.8 286.0 299.3 301.2 305.2 313.8 314.7 315.3 318.5 318.8 321.9 336.4 344.4 345.8 358.9 383.6 420.00

Beaufort-Moorehead City Apt., NC: AD 268.7

Beaumont Support Office EAMTMTS, TX: Army 139.15

Beauregard Parish Apt., LA: AD 381.5

Beaver Co. Apt., Beaver Falls, PA: AD 126.2 338.2

Beech Aircraft Co.

Wichita, KS: AD 134.1 269.1 353.5   T 38.90 126.2 126.8 314.6   G 121.7   FD 33.14   Msc 122.95 123.15 123.2 123.55 151.715 153.14 462.375   Army 226.3 382.6   AF 226.3 235.0 287.0 354.4   USN 325.1

Selma, AL: 123.25

Liberal, KS: 123.2

Mojave, CA: 123.375 123.45

Salina, KS 123.2

Beeville Muni Apt., TX: 353.6

Belfast Muni Apt., ME: AD 239.3

Bellefontaine Muni Apt., OH: AD 294.5

Bellingham Int'l. Apt., WA: FSS 255.4   AD 290.8   T 385.6   AF 235.5 240.5 369.5 375.5 388.5 396.5

Bellows AFB, HI: AF 150.315 163.5125 173.5875

Beloit Apt., WI: AD 327.0

Beltsville Agri Research Ctr., MD: 164.925 168.025 413.90

Bemidji-Beltrami Co. Apt., MN: AD 251.1

Bend Muni Apt., OR: AD 288.1

Bendix Corp.

Ft. Lauderdale, FL: 123.2 123.225 123.375 123.45

Sylmar, CA: 154.54

Vandenberg AFB, CA: 461.30

San Luis Obispo, CA: 464.275

Kennedy Space Center, FL: 461.30

Benedum Apt., Clarksburg, WV: AD 239.3 280.1   T 252.9

Bennett Apt., Salisbury, MD: NASA 123.2

Bentwaters USAF, UK: DI 315.2 AD 119.0 135.275 232.9 255.8 268.2   T 122.1 257.8 381.35   CP 282.15   G 78.80 75.575 314.35 385.15   WX 254.4   Security 32.20 78.525 78.725 78.725   Msc 75.3375

Berchtesgaden AHP, Germany: OP ("Warrior") 39.70

Bergstrom AFB, Austin, TX (ACC, HQ 12th Air Force; HQ 67th Recon Wing; 27, 35, 37, 49, 366, 388, & 474 TFW; 602 Tactical Air Control Wing; 18, 355, 405, & 479 Tactical Training Wing; Detachment 2 of 1st Military Intelligence Bn (Army)) **This facility scheduled to close 6/93).** DI 372.2   S 270.1   AD 118.8 119.0 124.9 134.1 306.2 363.8 370.85   T 133.2 255.6   G 121.7 372.8   E 121.7 335.8   CP ("Raymond 28") 381.3   WX 375.2   CP 924th TFG ("Abbreviate") 314.2   Motor Pool 148.085   Trucks 165.1375   Commanders Net 150.175   FD/Crash 173.5875   Phone Patch 149.565   Medic 173.5625 413.40   Security 162.2125   Transient Aircraft 165.1375   Civil Engineering 173.5625   Base Transportation 163.4625 163.4875 Flightline Maintenance ("Green Control") 148.525 413.875 Flightline Fueling 150.25 "Outlaw OP" 258.4   Flight Test 361.4   AF 32.45 34.60 41.45 41.95 46.85 138.075 138.165 138.175 138.20 139.65 139.70 139.825 139.925 141.80 141.155 148.065 148.095 148.20 148.45 148.475 149.205 150.135 162.25 163.00 163.5125 163.5875 173.5125 252.1 259.4 262.3 268.0 286.2 290.6 296.2 321.2 327.7 347.2 349.5 351.4 358.2 361.6 413.025 413.15 413.20 413.30 413.45   SAC 311.0 321.0

Bermuda NAS/Kindley Field, Bermuda, West Indies: AD 119.1 128.5 305.4 335.8 T 118.1 291.0   WX 344.6   G 124.5 336.4   E 126.2 395.9   DI 372.2   USN 129.9 143.65 Ramp Cntrl 121.7

Berry Fld., TN: AF 138.10 149.475 163.4625 163.4875 164.10 165.0125 165.1125
Bert Mooney Apt., Butte, MT: FSS 255.4
Bethel Apt., AK: FSS 255.4 ANG 165.1625
Bethlehem Steel & Shipyards
    Baltimore, MD: 462.45
    Richmond, CA: 462.225
    San Francisco, CA: 153.08 153.20 153.305 Pager 157.74
    Sparrows Point, MD: 153.14 154.57 156.45 158.28 158.43 451.225 451.675 462.30
462.375 462.40 462.50
    Vernon, CA: 153.14
Beverly Muni Apt., MD: AD 279.6 Aero Marine Radio Co 123.45
Bicycle Lake AAF, CA: T 41.50 126.2 241.0 Range 32.10 32.70 38.90 WX 32.40
32.45 49.05 Line Fire Control 48.45 Medevac 38.90 123.05 (See listings for Ft.
Irwin, CA)
Biggs AAF/Ft. Bliss, El Paso, TX (Air Defense School; 11th Air Defense Artillery
Bde.; 3rd Armored Cavalry Regiment; Sergeants Major Academy; Army Air Artillery
Museum; William Beaumont Army Medical Center): DI 34.50 AD 119.1 119.7 124.15
263.0 307.0 353.5 T 127.9 300.1 G 121.6 237.6 E 125.0 379.1 FBI 170.025
172.825 173.4875 Security 173.4875 Base OP 32.20 37.05 McGregor Range 32.30
Range 41.70 Red Devil Range 41.00 41.95 Rescue 282.8 Army 32.20 37.05 38.89
141.10 141.20 141.30 143.225 148.605 148.925 149.525 149.80 165.0625 165.1875
170.025 237.2 251.9 267.2 304.6 321.6 345.6 356.6 356.8 365.0 365.2 365.6 366.2
367.0 368.0 394.0 407.575 412.85 412.90 413.425 416.425 AF 38.85 139.60 142.25
Big Gun DEW Line Statin, Greenland: AF 122.2 236.6 (HF 5295 kHz)
Billings Logan Int'l. Apt., MT: AD 284.6 FSS 255.4 T 257.8
Bilo, MS: USN 34.15
Binghamton Regn'l. Apt/Link Fld., NY: AD 242.7 372.0 397.2 T 242.7
Birmingham Muni Apt., AL: FSS 255.4 AD 338.2 385.6 T 377.15 G 348.6 S
220.1 E 390.8 NG 38.70 ANG (87th Maneuver Command) CP ("Dixie Control")
287.3 (HF 12931 kHz) Security 163.4875 164.10 Ground Crews 165.1375 Msc
163.4625 165.5875 390.6 396.0
Bishop Int'l. Apt., Flint, MI: AD 257.9 335.6 T 257.8 307.8
Bismarck Muni Apt., ND: AD 281.5 346.4 T 257.8 NG 49.80 134.1
Bitburg AB, Germany: DI 377.7 S 261.4 AD 141.10 289.4 257.1 370.6 T 122.1
257.8 276.1 G 233.85 E267.05 CP 367.85 WX 259.4
Black Hills/Ice Fld., SD: AD 271.3
Black River Falls Area Apt., WI: AD 363.0
Blackstone AAF/A. C. Perkinson Muni Apt., Ft. Pickett, VA: AD 118.75 353.9 T
38.30 124.05 126.2 241.0 317.1 OP 38.30 Security 139.225 139.225 Range 38.30
41.05 139.225 Army 139.05 139.125 139.275 139.375 141.075 141.175 141.375 141.475
141.80 143.075 143.15 163.0875 165.0875 173.4875 337.3 AF 41.45 138.40 141.80
414.50 USN 267.4 313.1 326.8 380.7
Blanding City Muni Apt., UT: AF 412.825 AD 363.05
Bloodsworth Island Bombing Range, VA: USN 38.35 38.55 307.4 312.2 325.0 361.8
363.4 375.0 382.1
Bloomington-Normal Apt., AD 256.9 T 388.9
Bloomsburg Muni Apt., PA: AD 256.7
Blossom Point Proving Grounds, MD: USN 140.95 143.675 Army 38.45 141.40
142.90
Blue Grass Apt., Lexington, KY: AD 259.3 343.65 298.9 T 257.8
Blue Grass Army Depot, Richmond, KY: Army 163.6375 165.0125 165.0375 165.1875
173.4625 173.4875 354.3 Helipad 126.2 241.0 229.8
Bluffton Apt., OH: AD 228.4
Blythe Apt., CA: FSS 255.4 AD 285.6

Blytheville AFB, AR: Name changed to Eaker AFB

Bob Sikes Field, Crestview, FL: FSS 255.4 272.7 AD 322.6 393.0 T 123.2 126.2 292.1 316.9 Army 162.25 417.535 Fairchild Industries 305.4

Bobby L. Chain Muni Apt., MS: AD 281.5

Boblingen Maintenance Facility AHP, Germany: OP 31.80 141.65 248.65

Boca Chica Fld., FL: See Key West NAS

Boeing Fld./King Co. Int'l. Apt.,, WA: FSS 255.4 AD 263.1 284.7 338.2 385.2 G 257.8 T 257.8 Helicopters 123.05 AF 30.25 41.00 49.90 245.9 250.0 262.5 270.0 280.0 287.2 290.0 300.0 320.0 321.0 328.0 337.5 341.6 349.6 350.1 360.0 370.0 390.0 397.1 413.45 AF Rep to Boeing Co 123.55 291.8 Boeing Co 35.02 35.04 123.225 123.25 123.275 123.325 123.35 123.375 123.425 123.45 123.475 123.525 153.08 153.26 153.32 154.57 154.60 156.975 462.20 462.225 462.325 462.375 852.4625 (HF 2996 3281 3283 4677 6661 8919 11377 13358 17967 kHz)

Boeing Company

    Kent, WA 153.32 462.375 462.65 FD 154.25 154.34

    Auburn, WA: 153.32 852.9875 FD 154.25 154.34

    Oak Ridge, TN: 462.25

    Issaquah, WA: 462.25 462.325

    Lake Charles, LA: 153.08 462.50

    Wichita, KS: 123.2 123.25 123.325 123.35 153.20 460.20 460.35 460.65 460.75 460.85 462.275 462.45 462.50 FD 154.25 154.295

    Greenville, MS 123.275 123.375

    Vandenberg AFB, CA: 462.30

    Moses Lake, WA: 123.475 123.525

    Renton, WA 123.35 123.55 462.225 FD 154.25 154.34

    Everett, WA: 153.26 462.25 852.4625 FD 154.34

    Boardman, OR: 153.26

    Eddystone, PA: 158.43 462.25 462.30

    Ridley, PA: 32.10 40.90 49.80 123.2 123.25 123.45 267.2 321.7 366.5 (HF 5775 13922 kHz)

Boehmer AAF, Hoppstadten/Weirsbach, Germany: Advisory 32.20 142.90 251.2

Bogue MCALF, Newport, NC: AD 124.1 268.7 328.4 G 262.6 T 119.5 321.8 E 262.6 WX 344.6 OP ("Bogue 03") 48.70 Security 30.15 FD/Crash 140.25 USMC 138.85 148.275 148.35 243.9 250.3 274.8 314.7 315.3 317.8 336.4 340.2 360.2 420.00

Boire Fld., Nashua, NH: AD 305.4 338.2

Boise Air Terminal/Gowen Fld., ID: S 265.5 FSS 255.4 AD 269.4 379.8 G 348.6 T 257.8 E 323.2 NG OP 41.50 NG 34.50 38.50 143.175 ANG 138.925 164.9875 165.0125 165.1675 225.1 238.2 251.9 298.7 Security 164.50 Maintenance 163.1375 Msc 49.70

Bolling AFB, Washington, DC (110th Air Base Wing; USAF Band; USAF Presidential Honor Guard): Security 139.65 141.765 163.4875 FD 173.5875 OSI 40.17 40.19 138.075 138.165 138.175 Helipad 257.6 289.1 E 128.25 AD 118.1 119.85 124.2 126.55 269.0 322.3 343.7 396.1 AF 163.4625 407.425 410.00 413.875

Bolton Fld., Columbus, OH: 279.6

Bomar Fld., Shelbyville Muni Apt., TN: AD 353.5

Bonneville Power Administration, OR: 151.625 167.075 168.225 168.30 168.325 169.50 170.075 171.825 172.50 172.525 172.575 407.025 408.025 408.475 408.525 408.55 411.65 411.675 415.15 416.675 417.375 417.525 417.65 417.725 417.825 418.85 417.95 417.975 419.85

Boone Co. Apt., Harrison, AR: FSS 255.4 AD 286.6

Boone Muni Apt., IA: AD 252.9 NG 36.70 139.05 340.0

Borfink Helipad, Germany: AD 317.5 364.2

Boron AFS, CA: T 132.5 284.7 Rockwell Int'l. 462.925

Boscobel Apt., WI: AD 380.35

Boston, MA (94th Army Reserve Cmd.; 357th Civil Affairs Bde): 139.15

Boston Naval Base, MA: 32.05 138.525 138.575 140.075 140.65 140.675 140.775 140.75 140.775 140.82 140.825 148.35 148.95 149.025 CG Intelligence 165.3375 419.125 CG 165.2625 172.30

Bowerman Apt., Hoquaim, WA: FSS 255.4

Bowers Fld., Ellensburg, WA: FSS 255.4

Bowling Green-Warren Co. Apt., KY: FSS 255.4 AD 317.6

Bowman Fld., Louisville, KY: FSS 255.4 AD 306.2 327.0 T 248.2

Boyne Mtn. Apt., MI: AD 323.0

Brackett Fld., Laverne, CA: FSS 255.4 AD 351.1

Bradford Regn'l. Apt., PA: FSS 255.4 AD 338.3

Bradley Int'l. Apt., Windsor Locks, CT: FSS 255.4 T 351.8 E 322.3 G 348.6 AD 323.2 325.8 348.3 359.0 Security 150.125 163.4875 Flightline ("Raymond Control") 149.225 FD/Crash 173.5875 ANG (103rd TFG) CP ("Shark Operations") 349.9 NG OP ("Fury Operations") 41.90 Maintenance 148.075 149.225 Weapons 149.30 NG 40.65 49.85 150.20 150.25 150.30 150.35 ANG 34.15 34.75 40.05 40.65 46.75 49.70 49.85 60.10 148.155 148.175 149.30 149.525 150.125 150.125 163.4875 311.0 321.0 413.45

Bradshaw AAF/Camp Pohakuloa, HI: S 142.95 AD 126.0 278.3 T 41.50 126.3 236.6 Range 38.30 125.2

Brainerd-Crow Wing Co. Apt. (Wieland Fld.), MN: AD 239.0

Braintree, MA: USN 236.4 250.1 280.7 338.1

Bremerhaven AHP, Germany: T 118.5 249.5

Bremerton Nat'l. Apt., WA: AD 385.2

Bremerton Naval Center, WA: USN 30.47 32.47 34.53 36.53 36.57 36.63 36.87 38.46 41.89 138.525 138.55 138.70 138.72 138.725 138.95 139.575 140.25 140.325 140.45 140.425 140.575 140.65 140.775 140.84 140.825 141.00 142.525 142.625 142.65 142.70 142.725 142.75 142.85 143.625 148.325 148.35 148.975 149.125 149.25 149.85 150.075 150.10 150.11 150.40 226.0 233.7 266.0 277.1 304.2 305.8 314.8 347.9 350.0 350.5 353.1 360.2 374.9 386.4 396.3

Brewton, AL: USN 311.4

Brigham City Apt., UT: AD 301.5

Brimfield MA: USN 30.45 38.75

Brookings Muni Apt., SD: AD 306.2

Brookley Apt.: AL: FSS 255.4 AD 269.3 T 367.7 NG 41.05 125.525

Brooklyn, NY: USN 30.13 140.675 140.725 140.75 140.825 141.00 141.425 149.075 150.235 USN Security 148.275 148.29

Brooklyn CGAS/Floyd Bennett Fld., NY: AD 125.25 258.3 CG 164.30 381.7 381.8 383.9 409.9125 416.7125 418.4125 (HF 5692 kHz) Rescue 282.8 AD 123.2 NY City Police Aviation OP 123.3 470.6875 470.8375 470.8625

Brooks AFB, San Antonio, TX (USAF Human Systems Division; Drug Testing Lab; Occupational & Envoronmental Health Lab; 6520th Air Base Grp.; School of Aerospace Medicine; Aerospace Medical Division): Security/PD 173.4125 FD 173.5875 Medic 173.05 Pager 413.425 Civil Engineering 173.4125 AF 119.5 124.3 138.875 143.075 148.245 148.515 251.9 287.2 320.1 379.9 Helo AD 124.3 320.1 379.9

Brown Co. Apt., OH: AD 290.4

Brown Fld., CA: AD 285.2 306.7 T 288.1

Brownsville/S. Padre Isl. Int'l. Apt., TX: AD 257.6 263.1 T 239.3

Brownwood Muni Apt., TX: FSS 255.4 AD 269.4

Bruce Campbell Fld., Madison, MS: AD 259.1 317.7 319.2

Brunsum Allied Forces Central Europe Heliport, Netherlands: AD 123.975 T 120.2 362.3

Brunswick, GA: See Glynco Jetport listings.

Brunswick NAS, ME (ASW Patrol Wing 5): AD 118.15 124.25 128.2 134.1 263.6 290.5 322.4 S 115.2 250.1 T 118.15 119.6 134.10 340.2 G 126.2 140.10 352.4 E 126.2 360.2 CP 264.0 OP 257.5 WX 264.0 Security 142.50 USN 32.05 36.15 138.525 138.65 138.72 138.975 140.25 140.75 140.895 143.715 148.275 236.4 238.1 251.3 253.2 256.2 257.5 263.4 263.6 264.5 272.8 273.8 277.7 281.2 285.0 288.1 282.95 293.05 294.65 294.75 296.35 296.45 297.05 298.05 299.45 299.55 306.35 306.45 307.85 307.95 309.25 309.35 310.4 310.75 310.85 325.4 350.6 354.65 380.8 380.85 383.8 384.15 385.25 AF 142.305 311.0 321.0 413.45

Bryant AHP/Ft. Richardson, AK (HQ 6th Infantry (Light); 172nd Inf. Bde.): AD 118.6 119.4 290.9 316.7 363.8 T 125.0 241.0 G 40.80 121.65 261.3 E 119.4 323.1 WX 46.90 MP 173.4875 Motor Pool 164.70 FD 30.85 39.50 173.4125 Engineeering 165.0875 173.5125 CID 172.30 Medevac 40.45 Army 118.9 150.405 150.675 165.5375 163.8125 164.625 173.125 173.4625 173.6375

Buchanan Fld., Concord, CA: AD 371.2 T 257.8

Bucholz AAF, Kwajalein, Marshall Isls.: AD 126.2 360.2 T 118.5 126.2 360.2

Buckeye Executive Apt., Hebron, OH: AD 267.9

Buckley ANG Base, Aurora, CO: DI 372.2 AD 126.1 307.3 WX 342.5 344.6 G 121.6 275.8 T 121.0 289.6 FD 173.5875 CP 253.625 Range Control ("Airburst") 253.625 287.3 MP ("Cobra") 150.225 Medic 163.5125 Flightline Maintenance ("Blue") 148.515 Civil Engineering ("India") 148.035 Ramp Control 148.215 Dept. Defense Security ("Castle") 148.625 Base Transportation ("Tango") 149.205 Crash ("Echo") 173.075 OP 372.2 Base Commander Net 148.325 149.25 Mil OP Area Control ("Spirit") 306.3 314.2 340.8 Kit Carson Mil OP Area ("Blood Alley") 344.2 363.4 140th TFW ("Redeye") 32.45 32.65 32.85 36.45 41.45 267.8 268.1 287.4 296.7 359.1 Helicopter OP ("Outlaw") 32.75 41.75 141.10 142.40 227.3 230.8 242.4 268.1 AF 148.45 149.205 149.30 163.4875 163.5375 164.05 269.3 271.3 282.8 284.0 363.0 390.0 390.8 391.2 Msc 126.2 USN 32.65 36.66 281.2 302.6 344.2

Bucks Harbor, ME: NORAD 228.7 235.8 239.2 254.8 278.4 282.5 288.0 292.8 298.8 304.9 316.2 326.4 338.8 342.1 374.4 351.6 364.2 371.8 376.2 389.2 394.8 399.0

Budingen AHP, Germany: Advisory 37.40 138.45 364.6

Buehl Fld., PA: AD 291.7

Buffalo, NY: USN 38.30 41.90

Burbank-Glendale-Pasadena Apt., CA: AD 317.5 338.2 360.6 395.9 G 348.6 T 254.3 USN 166.25 173.05 252.4 264.1 314.6 382.6 Lockheed OP 153.20 158.295 173.205 451.425 463.825 467.425

Burke Lakefront Apt., Cleveland, OH: AD 360.6 T 319.8

Burley Muni Apt., ID: FSS 255.4 AD 398.2

Burlington Int'l. Apt., VT: FSS 255.4 G 348.6 AD 360.8 396.1 T 257.8 S 269.9 NG 41.20 165.1875 ANG CP ("Maple OP") 138.525 293.7 ANG Security 165.0125 ANG FD 165.1125 ANG 165.1625 251.9 261.8 314.4

Burlington Muni Apt., IA: AD 316.1

Burlington Muni Apt., WI: AD 307.0

Burnet Muni Apt./Craddock Fld., TX: AD 343.9

Bush Fld, Augusta, GA: FSS 255.4 AD 231.1 270.3 323.0 G 348.6 T 239.3 Medevac 32.50 Army Helicopter OP 46.70 134.1 245.65 Range 356.45 Msc 165.0625

Butler Co./Scholter Fld., PA: AD 338.2

Butler Memorial Apt., PA: AD 327.0

Butts AAF/Ft. Carson, CO (4th Inf Div/Mechanized; 43rd Support Grp): S 108.8 AD 124.0 362.3 T 125.5 229.4 241.0 WX 44.10 Medevac ("MAST Ops") 38.40 38.50 154.905 155.16 Msc 167.685 Army 40.10 40.91 41.50 49.70 141.25 141.80 148.925 149.575 149.80 150.425 150.525 163.575 164.985 165.1875 173.025 173.4125 173.4875 234.4 237.5 412.875 412.90 413.425 413.825 AF ("Skywatch") 38.35 AF 32.65 38.65 139.60 139.70 142.25 164.05 286.4 290.6 319.3 325.8 Range 263.625

Byrd Surface Camp, Antarctica: FSS (HF 8997 13252 kHz) Msc (HF 4718 5726 11255 kHz)

Cabaniss Fld. NOLF, Corpus Christi, TX: AD 120.9 125.4 132.25 319.8 363.1 385.6 T 126.2 299.6

Cable Apt., CA: AD 351.1

Cable Union Apt., WI: AD 278.5

Cairns AAF/Ft. Rucker, Ozark, AL (Army Aviation School): S 111.2 374.3 AD 109.7 111.2 125.4 125.8 133.45 133.75 232.5 234.4 237.5 356.45 T 109.7 111.2 127.0 241.0 G 121.9 248.2 E 120.325 304.45 OP 139.075 347.5 SOD 127.95 242.1 WX 128.8 344.6 Army 30.10 30.30 36.90 126.2 143.20 241.1 241.2 242.5 285.0 413.15 "Warlord OP" 41.30 (Also see listings for Guthrie AAF.)

Caldwell Industrial Apt., ID: AD 269.4

Calhoun Co. Apt., TX AD 281.9

Callaway Apt., Lagrange, GA: AD 388.0

Callaway Gardens-Harris Co. Apt., GA: AD 226.4

Calumet AFS, MI: AF 140.475 229.1 233.6 239.4 251.8 254.4 258.0 262.2 273.4 278.2 279.4 284.8 289.0 292.4 297.7 307.5 312.9 318.4 327.2 348.8 357.2 364.2 371.0 379.0 384.0 396.8

Calverton Naval Weapons Industrial Reserve Plant/Peconic Fld. NY: AD 118.0 5 367.2 T 121.3 123.25 126.2 127.15 127.55 128.65 275.2 340.2 G 121.9 Security & OP 153.35 "Tracker" 123.25 281.2 345.4 382.6 CG 381.8 Grumman Aerospace Corp 36.90 123.2 123.4 123.45 151.865 268.8 309.8 314.6 360.4 415.00 420.00 Beacon "CTO" 284.2

Cambria CA: AF 149.30

Cambridge Muni Apt., MN: AD 319.2

Cambridge Muni Apt., OH: AD 370.9 379.1

Camden Co. Apt., Berlin, NJ: AD 363.8

Cameron Station, Alexandria, VA (HQ Defense Logistics Agcy; Personal Property Shipping Office; HQ Army & Air Force Exchange Service for DC Area; Institute of Heraldry; "Soldiers" Magazine; Army Recruiting Support Center): Army 40.93 139.65 142.95 143.195 164.50 FEMA 167.975

Camp Allen, VA: Security 140.925 USN 140.36

Camp Atterbury, Taylorsville, IN: Range 38.90 118.6 Army 30.10 139.00 139.125 142.90 143.05 143.10 173.5625 266.5 AF 259.4 383.3 AD 124.95 317.8

Camp Beauregard AHP, Pineville, LA: AD 118.2 289.1 T 118.0 324.3 NG 40.90 122.9

Campbell AAF/Ft. Campbell KY/TN (HQ 101st Airborne Division (Air Assault)): S 141.05 302.2 DI 142.90 372.2 AD 118.1 139.90 255.6 363.8 T 126.2 241.0 G 121.8 275.8 E 138.80 368.3. Medevac 36.90 Range 50.00 Air/Air 30.20 32.20 34.60 36.30 WX 33.20 344.6 Flight Following ("Eagle Control") 139.30 242.4 MAC 251.2 Flight Coordination Center 46.80 139.30 141.25 242.4 E 138.80 368.3 Helicopters 30.20 32.20 Army 30.50 38.50 40.90 46.75 138.10 138.525 138.70 138.75 138.85 139.035 139.075 139.125 139.20 139.375 139.425 139.60 139.75 140.025 140.275 141.025 141.10 141.15 141.20 141.30 141.35 141.40 141.45 141.50 142.25 142.235 142.375 142.40 142.425 142.45 142.475 142.875 142.90 143.00 143.05 143.075 143.10 143.125 143.15 143.20 143.20 143.25 143.30 143.35 143.40 143.515 148.575 148.59 148.625 148.675 148.725 148.775 148.825 148.875 148.925 149.505 149.575 149.625 149.675 149.725 149.775 149.85 149.875 150.775 163.375 163.5875 164.10 164.20 165.0625 165.0875 165.1625 165.1875 165.5625 173.4875 173.5875 226.6 226.7 227.3 227.6 229.7 229.9 230.1 230.9 231.2 231.3 231.5 231.7 231.9 232.1 232.3 232.5 232.7 232.9 233.3 234.1 234.5 237.7 240.9 241.3 241.5 241.75 241.9 242.1 242.5 242.7 243.9 244.15 244.3 244.5 245.15 245.35 245.55 245.75 245.95 246.15 246.35 246.75 246.95 247.15 247.55 247.75 265.5 300.1 300.2 304.3 356.4 361.4 365.1 366.6 367.3 370.7 412.90 413.15 415.525 AF 163.5125 275.8 340.8

Camp Blanding, FL: T 241.0 Range 46.70 123.0 277.45 NG 40.50 40.90 139.30 412.8375 413.5625

26

Camp Bullis, San Antonio, TX: Range 34.20 AF 139.625 149.475 149.525 164.775 165.1875 403.725 409.05 409.90

Camp Clark, Nevada, MO: Army 139.125 143.05

Camp Crowder, MO: Army 139.125 143.05

Camp David, MD (Presidential Retreat): Helipad 375.0 Maintenance 149.45 Security 169.925 Secret Service 32.23 36.07 (Also see Secret Service & White House listings.)

Camp Dodge, IA: Army 139.00 139.125

Camp Edwards, Sandwich, MA (26th Aviation Bde Army NG; 1st Bn 25th Marines USMC Reserve): Range 30.45 38.50 38.75 (Also see listings for Otis ANGB.)

Camp Grafton, Devils Lake, ND: NG 49.80 122.8

Camp Grayling, MI: See listings for Grayling AAF.

Camp Guernsey, WY: NG Helicopters 122.7 242.4

Camp H.M. Smith Naval Reservation, HI: USN 40.90 142.625 149.075 149.43 149.425 150.075

Camp Lejeune, Jacksonville, NC (Marine Corps Base Cmd; 2nd Marine Div; 2nd Force Service Support Grp): USMC 32.05 36.15 38.85 138.55 139.55 139.575 139.575 140.075 140.125 149.46 140.475 140.55 140.975 141.95 141.975 142.025 142.50 142.52 142.525 142.55 142.575 142.675 142.775 142.84 142.85 143.50 143.55 143.60 148.275 148.29 148.35 149.45 150.07 150.125 150.775 262.6 264.2 265.8 267.4 268.2 270.6 271.4 273.8 274.6 275.4 278.3 279.4 280.2 280.6 281.2 283.4 284.4 285.0 289.9 290.0 291.4 300.2 300.3 304.2 305.8 305.9 306.7 307.4 308.2 309.0 309.8 310.6 312.2 312.4 313.8 323.3 325.0 326.6 326.7 328.2 328.3 337.1 339.5 341.0 342.6 344.2 345.8 346.6 349.8 352.2 358.9 359.7 360.4 361.0 361.1 361.2 363.4 363.6 384.2 386.6 420.40 (Also see listings for New River MCAS.)

Camp Merrill, Dalonega, GA (Army Rangers): Range 39.30 Medics 44.75 Army 38.50 40.00 40.20 41.00 49.00 49.95 67.50 (Also see Moody AHP.)

Camp Parks AHP/Camp Parks, Pleasanton, CA: T 40.50 41.50 Range 40.91 46.70 150.20 FD 41.50 150.775 Security 150.285 Medevac 38.90 Target Access 40.89 41.35 AF 139.70 316.625 359.3 397.2

Camp Pendleton MCAS, Oceanside, CA (Marine Air Grp 39; 1st Marine Amphibious Force; 1st Marine Div): S 267.6 AD 120.05 127.3 300.4 323.0 G 360.2 WX 344.6 T 41.95 126.2 340.2 382.2 VFR Advisories 360.1 FD 138.60 140.50 Northern Impact Area Control ("Crestline") 49.30 123.4 360.3 Southern Impact Area Control ("Long Rifle") 30.35 49.30 123.2 123.4 301.9 360.3 Splash OP 41.00 41.10 Medevac 38.80 Emergency 149.45 Weapons 149.37 SP 150.57 Security 138.025 138.375 139.675 140.00 149.09 149.275 149.50 Ambhibious OP 140.50 CID 139.58 140.64 Transportation 148.025 149.01 Civil Engineering 148.725 150.09 150.65 Pager 138.15 149.35 Base Traffic Control 149.025 Medic 149.45 148.625 Guards 138.025 138.375 139.675 Ambulances 149.625 Msc 167.85 168.45 AF 240.5 USMC 32.05 32.45 32.61 32.80 32.86 36.55 38.45 40.35 49.30 65.10 140.52 140.525 140.71 140.85 140.925 142.025 142.48 142.575 142.80 148.30 148.375 148.425 148.95 149.05 149.30 149.425 149.43 150.10 150.345 233.9 236.3 237.9 245.0 249.3 249.9 251.7 255.2 258.9 265.0 265.8 267.4 272.3 272.4 273.0 274.9 277.1 277.9 278.9 280.6 281.7 283.4 299.3 307.4 307.5 310.1 310.2 312.7 313.3 313.8 321.9 325.4 326.8 336.2 336.5 336.9 337.1 338.1 340.4 345.3 350.5 353.2 355.8 362.2 362.9 363.4 369.7 372.7 380.7 382.1 385.0 387.4 394.4 413.30

Camp Peary, Williamsburg, VA (CIA School): 135.975 166.035 162.375 163.15 164.865 164.975 226.4 229.9

Camp Perry ANG Sta., Pt. Clinton, OH: ANG 46.95 47.00 143.10 143.40

Camp Rapid, Rapid City, SD: NG 41.50 123.05 Emergency 129.05

Camp Ripley, MN: See Ray S. Miller AAF

Camp Roberts, Paso Robles, CA: T 40.95 41.50 126.2 241.0 Helicopters 229.4 Range 38.90 165.0875 FD 154.28 154.295 163.5375 165.0625 165.1625 Maintenance 38.90 MP 38.45 Army 42.85 49.00 150.725 163.5625 173.4625 275.4 320.2 Emergency Training 407.475 412.875 (Also see listings for Fritzche AAF & Ft. Hunter Liggett.)

Camp Robinson, Little Rock, AR: NG 41.50 122.8 139.20 241.0

Camp San Luis Obispo, CA: NG 42.00

Camp Shelby Annual Training Site, McLaurin, MS: T 126.2 241.0 NG 49.70 49.80 139.50 143.10 143.40 229.6 233.2

Camp Stanley, TX: Army 173.4625

Camp W. G. Wallace Total Force Field, Riverton, UT: AD 120.9 124.3 322.3 NG 49.65 243.8

Cannon AFB, Clovis, NM (ACC, 8th AF, 7th Bomb Wing, HQ 27th Tactical Fighter Wing): DI 372.2 S 119.1 269.9 AD 120.4 124.0 126.85 319.2 358.3 397.2 T 120.4 348.4 G 121.9 275.8 E 120.2 378.8 WX 344.6 CP ("Raymond 7") 381.3 (HF 3060 6730 9014 kHz) Msc 167.85 168.45 AF 41.45 46.85 139.70 148.905 148.545 149.205 149.265 149.505 150.315 163.4875 163.5375 163.5875 165.0125 165.0375 165.1125 165.1375 173.4375 173.5375 173.5875 259.4 282.2 286.5 289.3 296.1 296.2 321.2 344.9 347.2 359.3 361.6 381.1 390.1 396.9 413.15

Canyonlands Fld., Moab, UT: AD 307.9

Cape Canaveral AFS, FL: Skid Strip AD 119.25 134.95 340.9 358.3 Skid Strip T 118.625 393.0 Army OP 40.70 Security 150.15 163.4625 CP 165.1125 CG OP 143.28 FD 163.5625 OSI 40.17 40.19 NASA TV OP 148.035 Still Photographers 148.485 Pager 163.5875 165.0125 Radiation Monitoring OP 164.50 Range Safety 416.50 Loan Pool 139.30 139.90 Missile Launch OP 148.515 149.15 Cranes 142.50 142.86 143.04 Satellite Uplink 148.25 Telemetry 141.00 149.90 400.50 403.00 Msc 46.65 49.62 138.15 138.45 139.05 139.25 140.17 140.20 140.40 140.43 141.30 143.43 149.25 150.195 150.25

Cape Charles AFS, VA: AF 228.8 234.7 238.5 251.0 256.6 263.2 263.4 270.4 275.0 278.6 278.8 292.7 298.5 302.4 306.4 325.5 339.4 344.0 356.0 364.2 369.0 375.1 386.2 392.8 USN 363.4

Cape Girardeau Muni Apt., MO: FSS 255.4 AD 379.2

Cape Henry, VA: USN 347.8 CG 38.27 138.80

Cape Lisburne AFS, AK: T 121.5 126.2 364.2 AF 163.5875 165.1375 229.2 269.9 288.4

Cape May CGAS, NJ: CG OP 381.8 (HF 5692 8980 kHz) Security 171.3125 CG 171.2375 171.3625 274.8 393.9 407.625 415.825 Rescue 282.8 Ambulances 155.34

Cape May Co. Apt., NJ: AD 263.6

Cape Newenham AFS, AK: T 121.5 126.2 364.2 FSS 122.3 AF 122.205 163.5875 165.1375 229.1 269.9

Cape Romanzoff AFS, AK: T 121.5 126.2 364.2 FSS 122.1 AF 122.195 122.4 163.5875 163.1375 165.6375 229.1 254.7 269.9 293.2

Cape Sarichef AFS, AK: T 122.9

Capital Apt., Springfield, IL: S 270.1 AD 307.0 327.5 395.8 G 348.6 T 257.8 ANG OP (187 Tactical Fighter Grp) ("Sunspot") 165.1125 287.3 Security 163.4875 Maintenance 164.9625 165.1375 Medics 165.0375 FD/Crash 165.0125 ANG 163.4625 163.5875 164.10 297.1

Capital City Apt., Frankfort, KY: AD 285.4 298.9 NG 36.20 42.25 139.175 139.35 150.675 226.6

Capital City Apt., Harrisburg, PA: FSS 255.4 AD247.2 339.3 379.8 G348.6 T 257.8

Capital City Apt., Lansing, MI: FSS 255.4 AD 226.4 T 226.4 E 240.9

Carabelle, FL: USN 228.0 238.3 261.0 261.0 271.2 279.2 289.0 304.9 AF 287.5 293.1 297.9 301.7 304.9 311.2 343.4 349.7 351.3 354.3

Carbon Co. Apt., UT: AD 370.85

Carderock Naval R&D Center, MD: Security 140.35 USN 140.46 142.80

Caribou Muni Apt., ME: AD 359.3 363.8

Carlisle Barracks, PA (Army War College; Army Military Institute; Armed Forces Information School): T 126.2 Army 122.8 173.4875 173.5125

Carl R. Keller Fld., Pt. Clinton, OH: AD 307.9

Carroll Co. Regn'l. Apt./Potage Fld., MD: AD 307.9

Carroll Co.-Tolson Apt., Carrollton, OH: AD 226.4

Carswell AFB, Ft. Worth, TX (ACC; 8th AF; 19th Air Div; 7th Bombardment Wing; 7th Combat Support Grp; 301st Tactical Fighter Wing (AF Reserve)): **Base closing date 9/93.** S 271.6   AD 120.2 120.5 133.15 227.8 309.8 371.2 376.0   T 119.8 255.9   TAC CP 395.8   G 121.85 275.8   WX 342.5   AF Reserve 252.1   FD/Crash 173.5875   Commanders Net 149.565   General Dynamics Corp 284.1 292.5   FSS 284.1 292.5   AF 138.075 138.165 138.175 139.65 148.065 148.095 148.175 148.245 148.45 148.515 148.545 148.175 149.205 149.235 149.50 150.225 150.27 162.61 163.30 163.4875 163.5125 163.5875 164.50 165.1125 165.1375 173.4375 173.5125 173.5375 173.6875 262.05 271.6 291.0 340.7 383.2 407.45 413.025 413.075 413.10 413.125 413.15 413.20 413.30 413.375 413.45

Casa Grande Muni Apt., AZ: AD 269.3

Casco Cove CGAS, Attu, AK: T 122.9   AF 150.315

Casement Apt., Painesville, OH: AD 360.6

Casper, WY: USN 165.0125

Castle AFB, Merced, CA (ACC; 12th AF; 93rd Bombardment Wing; 84th & 318th Fighter Interceptor Sqdns) **Base closing date 9/95.**: AD 120.95 124.8 294.5 301.5 372.1 379.8 395.0   DI 372.2   WX 342.5   S 271.8   T 118.45 289.6   G 275.8   E 259.3   SAC CP 311.0 321.0   FD/Crash 173.4375 173.5875   Emergency 173.5375   Maintenance 149.205 149.325 164.9625 165.0125 165.1125   OSI 138.075 138.165 138.175   Base Commanders Net 148.065 148.175 149.175 149.75   PD 164.175   Civil Engineering 150.285   Security 163.4625 163.4875 164.70   Base Transportation 165.1375   Pager 138.325 413.45   Crew Alerts 413.45   Building Maintenance 165.1375   Flighline Fueling 148.152   Flighline (B-52) Maintenance 148.155   Link to McClellan AFB 165.0625   AF 149.505 162.225 163.5125 164.30 233.4 251.9 262.0 293.2 293.4 316.7 340.7 373.0 389.8 395.0 399.8

Castle Dome AHP, Yuma, AZ: OP 41.50 126.2 241.0 (See listings for Laguna AAF.)

Caswell AFS, Limestone, ME: AF 150.20 173.5375 228.7 228.8 234.7 235.8 239.2 251.0 254.8 256.6 263.2 265.4 275.0 278.4 278.6 282.5 287.8 288.0 292.7 292.8 298.5 298.6 302.4 303.9 306.4 316.2 325.5 326.4 338.8 342.1 344.0 347.4 351.6 356.0 364.2 369.0 371.8 376.2 378.1 386.2 389.2 392.8 394.8 399.0

Cavern City Air Terminal, Tupelo, MS: AD 343.6   NG 349.85 241.0

Cecil Field NAS, Jacksonville, FL (Commander, Service Fighter Wings, Atlantic; Light Attack Wing 1; Air ASW Wing 1; Carrier Wings 3 & 7): S 276.2   AD 119.85 124.9 284.6 319.9   G 118.35 384.4   T 126.1 340.2 360.2   E 268.7   WX 317.0   OP 361.9 (HF 6723 kHz)   USN 30.15 32.65 34.15 36.15 38.60 138.625 139.85 138.96 139.475 139.545 139.55 139.575 140.025 140.04 140.05 140.10 140.15 140.16 140.20 140.225 140.25 140.275 140.30 140.45 140.46 140.48 140.50 140.525 140.625 140.85 140.85 140.895 140.95 141.00 142.075 143.715 148.325 149.37 149.45 150.10 235.4 271.4 272.8 274.6 277.9 283.1 285.8 300.4 311.4 315.4 339.4 350.0 357.8 368.4 374.9 383.7

Cedar City Muni Apt., UT: FSS 255.4

Cedar Rapids Muni Apt., IA: FSS 255.4   AD 247.2 261.5   T 247.2   AF 290.0 316.625 316.785

Centennial Apt., CO: AD 307.3

Centerville Muni Apt., TN: AD 381.4

Central Fla. Reg'l. Apt., FL: AD 351.9   T 281.65   G 281.65

Centralia Muni Apt., IL: AD 317.7

Central Nebraska Regn'l. Apt., NE: FSS 255.4   AD 287.9   T 388.2   G 388.2

Central Wisc Apt., Mosinee, WI: AD 317.7   T 360.7   G 360.7

Cessna Aircraft Co., Wichita KS: 123.25 123.275 123.35 123.5 123.575 151.925 334.7 462.30

Chadron Muni. Apt., NE: AD 338.2

Chambersburg Muni Apt., PA: AD 339.3   Army 123.05 376.7

Chambers Co. Apt., Anahuac, TX: AD 396.0

Chambers Fld., VA: See Norfolk NAS.

Chandler Fld., Alexandria, MN: AD 269.2

Chan Gurney Muni Apt., SD:AD 269.0

Channel Island ANGB, CA: See Point Mugu NAS.

Chanute AFB, Rantoul, IL (3330th Technical Training Wing): Security 138.275 138.425 163.4875 Maintenance 165.0375 Engineering 165.1375 Civil Engineering 140.00 OSI 138.075 138.165 138.175 Base Commanders Net 149.175 Medics 139.725 Administration 150.225 FD 139.825 172.825 Pager 148.10 AF 138.275 138.325 139.65 142.155 150.275 150.285 163.5875 173.5375 236.0 251.9 254.7

Chanute Martin Johnson Apt., KS: FSS 255.4   AD 343.9

Charles L. Kelly AHP, San Antonio, TX: S 118.9   OP 41.50 142.35 233.2   (Also see listings for Ft. Sam Houston.)

Charleston AFB/Int'l Apt., SC (AMC; 437th Military Airlift Wing MAC): DI 372.2 S 124.75 FSS 255.4 AD 119.3 120.7 135.8 257.1 284.0 319.8 T 126.0 239.0 G 121.9 348.6 E 118.0 381.6 E 118.0 381.6 MAC CP 130.65 349.4 WX 344.6 FD/Crash 173.5875 Security 163.4625 163.5125 163.5875 Pager 150.23 Flightline Maintenance 165.0575 165.1125 165.1625 Loadmaster 148.075 Base Commanders Net 408.00 Civil Engineering 163.4875 Flightline OP 163.5875 36.85 138.075 138.165 138.175 138.525 138.55 139.65 141.70 148.275 148.35 148.95 149.05 149.125 149.20 149.325 150.225 150.275 150.315 165.0125 165.0375 165.1875 165.375 173.4375 236.0 238.8 251.9 283.4 289.0 340.6 341.5 342.3 407.375 410.00 413.00 413.40

Charleston Army Depot, SC: Army 163.5375

Charleston Naval Base, SC: Police/SP ("Charlie") 140.35 150.125 150.55 408.175 FD 143.575 150.55 Disaster Control 150.175 Medics 155.28 Shipyard Security 140.05 Shipyard Pager 138.975 140.22 Shipyard Transportation 138.65 Pier Sentries 140.275 NIS 140.46 Motor Pool 138.825 Fuel Shop 141.95 Dredge ("Gravel Gertie") 138.85 Base Transportation 139.15 Ship Services 139.95 FD/Crash 140.10 Base Radio Shop 409.90 Supply Center 140.125 Supply Delivery 140.150 Base Pager 140.22 SIMA 140.825 Nuclear Accident Response 142.03 Base Buses 142.50 Seabees 142.83 143.525 Supply 143.10 Polaris Missile Security 148.975 150.50 Tugboats 148.325 148.35 148.375 Hospital 148.80 Vessels in Port 409.025 Tugboats 148.325 148.35 148.375 Hospital Pager 149.45 USN 32.05 36.15 36.55 38.95 138.575 138.60 138.625 138.70 138.84 138.86 138.94 138.98 139.475 139.50 139.525 140.18 140.225 140.34 140.44 140.48 140.56 140.58 140.60 140.675 140.70 140.725 140.75 141.00 141.975 142.155 143.035 148.30 148.40 149.90 149.425 149.50 228.55 233.8 274.6 275.4 275.6 275.7 281.1 291.3 307.7 312.9 313.9 322.0 339.6 341.0 348.1 356.2 358.0 358.6 359.4 361.8 380.6 382.0 382.1 382.5

Charleston Naval Base Annex, SC: Security 140.35

Charleston Naval Weapons Station, SC: PD/FD 150.55/149.15   USMC Security 150.175/148.43 Pier Security 150.125 Weapons OP 150.40 Civil Engineering 150,375

Charles Wood AHP, Ft, Monmouth, NJ: OP 41.25 123.075 255.7   FD 123.075 (Also see listings for Ft. Monmouth.)

Charlotte/Douglas Int'l. Apt. NC: FSS 255.4 AD 257.2 316.7 T 257.8 G 348.6 E 397.7 ANG CP 292.2 ANG Administration 165.0125 ANG OP 165.1375 ANG Security 163.4875 ANG FD/Crash 148.225 ANG Medics 149.15 ANG 138.20 148.05 149.20 163.5875

Charlottesville-Albemarle Apt., VA: AD 284.7 T 242.7 G 242.7

Chase City Muni Apt., VA: AD 353.9

Chase Fld. NAS, Beeville, TX (Training Air Wing 3; Training Sqdns 24, 25 & 26): S 282.0 AD 121.3 128.15 134.1 134.6 264.2 281.9 322.5 337.8 G 336.4 T 126.2 350.8 360.2 E 312.4 WX 344.6 Rescue 282.8 USN 138.725 139.55 140.35 140.89 140.90 143.50 143.725 148.425 149.375 262.8 272.8 279.0 282.0 300.2 301.0 326.6 339.6 359.6 361.1 362.2 384.2

Chautaqua Co. Apt., Dunkirk, NY: AD 305.4

Chautaqua Co. Apt., Jamestown, NY: AD 323.2

Cheltenham, MD (USN Reserve Radio Station): FD 149.95 150.15 Medic 149.95 USN 138.65 139.48 229.9 292.95 294.2 294.65 296.35 297.95 299.45 302.7 306.35 307.75 307.85 309.25 310.75

Cheltenham, VA (USN Supply Center): 140.90

Chennault Indust'l. Airpark, LA: AD 319.9 381.6 T 286.6 G 275.8 AF ("Gumb OP") 258.2

Cherry Capital Apt., Traverse City, MI: FSS 255.4 AD 398.9 G 348.6 T 320.5 CG 381.8 383.9 Rescue 282.8

Cherry Point MCAS/Cunningham Fld., NC (2nd Marine Aircraft Wing; Naval Air Rework Facility): DI 306.6 S 354.9 AD 119.35 124.1 132.575 134.1 268.7 278.8 374.9 T 121.3 340.2 360.2 G 128.625 380.8 E 125.95 263.6 WX 344.6 OP 306.6 USN Air Reserve ("Camel Base") 383.4 VIP Aircraft 306.6 FD/Crash 138.525 149.10 PD 140.34 Target Control 140.15 317.1 337.0 Base Commanders Net 138.625 Harrier OP 333.3 Marine Air Grp 14 Guards 138.96 Officer of The Day 140.82 Training 382.0 AWACS OP 371.0 Maintenance 138.06 Ambulances 138.525 Survival/Escape School 45.70 NORAD 364.2 USMC 32.05 34.55 36.05 138.575 138.60 138.65 138.675 138.70 138.85 138.895 138.95 139.50 139.54 140.03 149.05 140.145 140.275 140.35 140.445 140.45 140.825 142.625 142.80 142.825 142.86 143.505 143.525 148.35 148.37 148.375 149.075 149.115 149.125 149.415 149.425 150.075 236.6 250.3 251.6 251.9 258.9 262.6 264.0 264.2 265.8 267.4 268.2 269.7 270.6 271.4 273.8 274.5 274.6 274.8 275.4 278.4 279.4 280.2 280.6 281.2 283.4 284.4 285.0 289.9 290.0 291.4 299.3 300.2 300.3 304.2 305.8 306.7 307.4 308.2 309.0 309.8 310.1 310.6 312.2 313.8 314.7 315.3 315.4 317.0 317.8 320.2 320.3 321.8 321.9 322.1 323.3 325.0 326.6 327.7 328.2 328.3 337.1 339.5 341.0 342.6 344.2 345.8 346.6 349.8 352.2 353.0 353.2 354.7 354.8 356.2 358.1 358.9 359.7 360.4 361.1 361.2 362.2 363.4 363.6 384.2 386.0 386.6 413.20 413.275 420.00

Chesapeake Beach, MD: USN 138.62 140.175 140,575 140.85 140.925 141.95

Chesapeake Portsmouth, VA: See Hampton Roads.

Chess-Lamberton Apt., Franklin, PA: AD 317.4

Chester Co. Carlson Apt., PA: AD 286.0

Chesterfield Co. Apt., VA: AD 307.2 371.1

Chevalier Fld. Naval Air Rework Facility, Pensacola, FL: T 126.2 340.2 Helicopter OP ("Fumble Base") 32.90 118.15 122.7 266.7 Fixed Wing OP ("Victor Base") 32.90 118.15 122.7 266.7

Cheyenne Mountain AFB, CO (Air Force Space Command): See listings for City of Colorado Springs Apt./Peterson AFB.

Cheyenne Muni Apt./F. E. Warren AFB, WY (4th Air Division; 90th Strategic Missile Wing): AD 124.55 133.0 265.0 281.5 S 134.425 278.3 T 118.7 257.8 G 121.9 348.6 CP 311.0 321.0 Base Cmdr's Net 148.545 FD/Crash 150.275 ANG OP 383.3 "Blade OP" 271.9 AF 34.10 138.075 138.325 148.065 148.455 148.95 149.175 149.235 149.535 149.565 150.10 150.25 150.35 163.5125 164.9625 165.1375 165.1875 173.175 173.4375 260.2 266.2 308.8 314.6 351.0 407.375 NG ("Steamboat Ops") 126.2 Army 141.40 242.4

Chicago, IL (33rd Infantry Bde; 85th Div Training; 86th Infantry Division; 416th Engineering Command); Army 164.20

31

Chicago CGAS, IL: See Glenview NAS.

Chicago Midway Apt., IL: AD 388.0   T 226.3   NG 47.00 123.05   Helo T 135.2

Chicago-O'Hare Int'l. Apt., IL: DI 372.2   S 269.9   AD 126.2 269.5 284.0 307.2 337.4 393.1   T 126.2 390.9   G 348.6   ANG   384.9   AF Reserve CP (928th Tactical Air Grp) 252.1 372.2   Security 163.4875   FD/Crash 163.5875   Commanders Net 143.80   Maintenance 149.15   ANG 138.30 138.40 149.30 165.1375 173.5125 173.4375 OSI 40.17 40.19   138.075 138.165 138.175   AF 149.15 149.265 163.00 164.50 165.0125 165.1125 173.5625 173.5875 235.5 311.0 369.5 371.5 372.5 394.5 398.5 407.375 407.45 413.10 413.20 413.30

Chickasha Muni Apt., OK: AD 393.1

Chico Muni Apt., CA: AD 350.3   T 239.3   AF 40.12 40.35 138.06 148.225 148.515 149.325 242.0 319.7 392.9 410.00

Chievres AB, Belgium: DI 255.5   AD 118.25 127.15 308.5 362.3   T 122.1 257.8 357.0   G141.75 378.55   SHAPE Helipad 39.80

Childress Muni Apt., TX: FSS 255.4   AD 389.6

China Lake Naval Weapons Center/Armitage Fld., Ridgecrest, CA: AD 133.65 348.7   T 120.16 340.2   G 360.2   VFR Advisory 126.55 127.5 133.65 291.6 348.7   WX 353.0   S 265.2   Transportation 148.275   FD/Crash 148.40 148.45   Security 140.125 140.70 141.175 143.375 143.50 143.575 149.075 149.175   Range 141.425   Base Electric Power 143.52   Weapons Test 141.15   Rescue 282.8   Nuclear Weapons Systems 122.9 167.85 384.8 406.9125 409.2125 411.075 416.725   USN 32.46 32.86 33.85 34.34 34.53 34.73 35.85 36.00 36.53 38.30 38.93 138.765 139.475 139.50 135.525 139.625 139.69 139.72 139.75 139.90 139.925 139.975 140.025 140.04 140.20 140.25 140.30 140.35 140.425 140.45 140.47 140.50 140.58 140.675 140.825 140.95 141.11 141.11 141.25 141.275 141.40 141.45 141.50 141.96 142.065 142.50 142.90 142.925 143.175 143.50 143.80 148.375 148.65 148.975 149.02 149.35 149.375 149.40 149.40 149.40 149.425 149.43 150.105 235.0 240.2 245.3 240.2 246.3 253.8 256.2 262.8 264.2 265.8 269.8 271.5 274.2 274.4 278.7 280.3 281.1 301.0 309.7 311.4 313.3 313.9 324.8 336.4 377.0 344.1 348.1 358.0 360.0 362.7 363.5 372.8 381.8 381.9 383.4 385.1 393.855 413.20

Chino Apt., CA: AD 295.7

Chippewa Co. Int'l. Apt., MI: AD 344.5

Chisholm-Hibbing Apt., MN: FSS 255.4 AD 255.9

Choctaw OLF, Milton, FL: AD 372.0   T 126.2 380.8   Msc 277.2 282.0 315.6

Chula Vista, CA: USN 143.50

Cincinnati, OH: USN 32.45 34.55 36.55 38.30 40.80 350.7

Cincinnati-Blue Ash Apt. & AFS, OH: AD 257.2   ANG (123rd Tactical Control Flight) 46.85 126.2 134.1 163.4875 259.4 267.8 283.8 303.0 308.9 314.2 340.8

Cincinnati Muni-Lunken Apt., OH: FSS 255.4   AD 257.2   T 257.8

Cincinnati/N. Kentucky Int'l. Apt., KY: AD 257.2   T 286.6

City of Colorado Springs Apt./Peterson AFB/Cheyenne Mountain AFB/Falcon AFB, CO (Air Force Space Command; Air Defense Command; North American Defense Command; SAC 46th Aerospace Defense Wing): DI 372.2   S 125.0 254.3   AD 118.5 124.0 362.3 380.2   T 119.9 133.15 335.55 360.6   G 121.7 348.6   E 134.45 385.5 AF Reserve OP ("High Country Control") 298.4   WX 342.5   FD/Crash 173.5625 Security 163.4625 163.5875   AF 148.185 149.175 149.275 149.505 150.075 163.5125 165.1375 173.5125 251.9 361.4 384.9 395.1 398.1 407.375 407.45 413.15

Clark Co. Apt., IN: AD 306.2

Clark Fld. Muni Apt., Stephenville, TX: AD 353.7

Clatsop Co. Apt., Astoria, OR: CG 381.8 383.9 416.6   Rescue 282.8   (HF 5692 8980 kHz)

Clay Kaserne AHP, Garlstedt, Germany: T 118.5 249.5   OP 30.10

Clemson-Oconee Co. Apt., SC: AD 307.9 385.4

Clermont Co. Apt., Batavia, OH: AD 257.2

Cleveland Army Tank-Automotive Plant, OH: 165.0875

Cleveland-Hopkins Int'l. Apt., OH: FSS 255.4 AD 360.6 T 257.8 NASA OP 122.85 123.3 AF Reserve 40.20 Army Reserve 40.40

Cleveland, OH: USN 34.15 34.95 36.15 36.55 41.10 275.4

Clinton Co. Apt., NY: AD 120.7 360.8 396.1

Clinton Muni Apt., IA: AD 257.8 351.7

Clinton Muni Apt., OK: AD 339.8

Clinton-Sherman Apt., OK: AD 256.9 339.8 T 256.9 G 239.0 AF 413.40

Clintonville Muni Apt., WI: AD 338.2 370.9

Cloquet Carlton Co. Apt., MN: AD 255.9

Cloudcroft Observatory, NM: Security 165.1125

Clovis Muni Apt., AD 319.2 358.3 397.2

Clow Int'l Apt., IL: AD 388.0

Coast Guard Academy, New London, CT: CG 171.2375 171.3375 171.3625 415.625

Coast Guard Depot, Curtis Bay, MD: Security 419.65 419.85 FD 419.65 419.85 OP 416.475 CG 407.125 415.775 416.6375

Coatesville, PA: USN 32.45

Cochran Apt., GA: AD 269.3 388.2

Coeur D'Alene Air Terminal, ID: AD 263.0 T 225.3 308.9 AF 271.3 379.9 390.8 391.2 398.1

Coffeyville Mini Apt., KS: AD 343.9

Cold Bay Apt., AK: AD 278.3 T 126.2 364.2 (HF 2866 5631 kHz) AF 229.1 236.6 269.9

Cold Regions Research Engineering Lab, Hanover, NH: Army 173.4625

Coleman AAF, Germany: DI 30.60 S 108.2 AD 143.75 276.4 T 31.80 40.80 122.1 142.65 291.5 G 141.30 250.55 Flight Following 139.50 Range 47.30 WX 140.30

Coles Co. Memorial Apt., Mattoon, IL: AD 291.0

Collins Radio Co.: See Rockwell International listings.

Colonial Beach, VA: USN 142.05 142.80

Colt Industries, Inc., Hartford, CT: 153.05 153.32; Beloit, WI: 153.08 153.38

Columbia Apt., CA: AD 319.9

Columbia Co. Apt., NY: AD 307.2

Columbia Metro Apt., SC: AD 285.6 338.2 G 348.6 T 257.8 Mil OP (498th MED & 120th ARCOM) 32.90 38.20 41.20 130.0 Medevac 49.65 (Also see Ft. Jackson listings.)

Columbia Regional Apt., MO: FSS 255.4 AD 363.25

Columbus AFB, MS (14th Flying Training Wing): DI 376.0 S 115.2 273.5 AD 120.4 127.95 135.6 226.0 229.15 324.5 389.8 T 128.65 289.6 E 126.25 338.6 G 275.8 WX 344.6 SOF 390.15 AF 139.65 139.85 139.875 143.825 148.065 148.10 148.145 148.45 148.485 149.15 149.425 149.565 163.4625 163.4875 163.5125 165.1125 165.1375 173.5625 173.5875 225.9 272.0 276.6 297.0 311.0 316.7 317.8 321.0 324.1 324.5 327.5 340.7 349.0 363.8 373.0 379.5 383.1 388.2 389.8 390.9 391.9 393.1 413.45

Columbus Army Depot, OH: Army 165.0875 173.4875

Columbus-Lowndes Co. Apt., MS: AD 226.0 269.4

Columbus Metro Apt., GA: FSS 255.4 AD 226.4 278.5 357.6 388.0 G 348.6 T 257.8 357.6

Columbus Muni Apt., IN: AD 317.8

Columbus Muni Apt., NE: FSS 255.4 AD 346.3

Compton Apt., CA: AF 149.15 149.265 235.5 252.5 372.5 375.5 388.5 394.5 396.5 398.5

Concord Airpark, Painesville, OH: AD 360.6

Concord Muni Apt., NH: FSS 255.4 AD 338.2 385.45 NG 32.10

Concord Naval Weapons Station, CA (Logistic Support Facility for Auxiliary Ammunition Ships): T 313.8 341.0   Security 140.175 140.85 149.07 149.35 149.375 149.425 150.10   FD 139.50   Emergency 40.00   Civil Engineering 140.175 140.85 149,425 150.025   Pager 148.375   Weapons Storage Area 140.325   Weapons Transport 140.125 140.925   Tidal Area OP 149.37   USN 36.53 36.57 36.63 36.87 45.24 140.13 140.46 140.82

Condron AAF, White Sands, NM: AD 120.6 324.3   OP 122.8 241.0   Range ("Cherokee") 126.95 294.6 (Also see listings for White Sands Missile Range.)

Connecticut ANG: 30.65 34.15 34.50 34.75 38.50 38.90 40.10 40.90 41.90 46.65 236.5 236.6 238.7 251.25 256.9 259.4 267.8 275.9 283.8 301.6 303.0 314.2 34.08 34.30 34.97

Connellsville Apt., PA: AD 307.1   USN 26.66

Conrad Apt., MT: AF 150.375 165.0125 165.0375 300.8 418.025

Controlonics Corp.: 151.625 461.85

Cornhusker Army Ammunition Plant, Grand Island, NE: 163.5875 173.4625

Corona Muni Apt., CA: AD 295.7

Coronado Naval Amphibious Base, CA (Commander Naval Surface Force Pacific Fleet; Naval Beach Grp 1; Naval Special Warfare Grp 1; Tactical Air Grp 1; SEAL Team 1; Underwater Demolition Teams 11 & 12): USN 36.55 40.80 140.00 273.3 413.00 413.15

Coronel Enrique Soto Cano AB/Palmerola AB, Honduras: FSS 65.77 89.10 123.9 124.1 126.7 126.9   AD 131.3 285.0   T 128.9 264.4   Security 32.00 41.00   CP ("Dusty OP") 319.4   Base OP & WX ("Carrot Top") 124.9 340.6 (HF 12220 kHz)

Corpus Christi Aero Depot Maintenance Center, TX: Army 229.4 248.2 407.225

Corpus Christi Int'l. Apt., TX: FSS 255.4   AD 233.7 307.9 319.8 363.1 385.6   T 257.8   G 348.6

Corpus Christi NAS/CGAS, TX (Chief of Naval Air Training; Training Air Wing 4; Corpus Christi Army Depot): S 138.60 284.2   AD 120.9 125.4 134.1 270.8 307.9 337.2 363.1 380.8 385.6 (HF 6835 kHz) T 126.2 340.2 360.2   G 135.3 348.0   E 314.8   WX 344.6   OP 346.8   CG 381.7 381.8 383.9 (HF 3123 5696 8984 11201 kHz)   Rescue 123.1 282.8   Army Air OP ("X-Ray Charlie") 49.70 139.20 386.6   Army Depot 32.20 36.10 46.80 49.80 141.20 141.30 141.40 143.10   USN 40.55 138.775 139.575 140.075 140.10 140.325 140.65 140.70 140.775 140.975 141.00 141.10 149.375 264.4 265.8 299.6 304.2 305.8 306.6 320.4 340.8 342.8 349.8 355.4 358.8 384.4

Corvallis Muni Apt., OR: AD 291.7 348.7

Costa Mesa ANG Sta., CA: ANG 149.15 235.5 240.5 252.5 369.5 375.5 388.5 390.5 394.5

Cotulla LaSalle Co. Apt., TX: AD 322.5

Craig Fld., Selma, AL: FSS 255.4   AD 270.25 319.9   AF 165.1375 165.1625 173.5125 173.5875

Craig Muni Apt., Jacksonville, FL: FSS 255.4   AD 347.8 351.8   T 242.7   NG OP 40.90 139.30 248.2   NG 40.50 139.15 241.0 263.2 273.8

Crane Naval Ammunition Depot, IN: USN 138.60 149.01 149.07 149.37 149.40 150.075   Security 42.26 42.42 148.275

Craney Island Naval Supply Center, VA: USN Security/FD: 149.425

Craven Co. Regn'l. Apt., NC: FSS 255.4   AD 374.9

Crawfordsville Muni Apt., IN: AD 317.8

Creech AAF, Lexington, KY: OP 126.2 241.0 229.9 (Also see Blue Grass Army Depot.)

Crest Apt., Kent, WA: AF 337.5   FD 154.25 154.34

Crisp Co.-Cordele Apt., GA: AD 226.8

Crissy AHP, San Francisco, CA: AD 120.9 124.3 323.2 (Also see Presidio of San Francisco listings.)

Crooked Island, FL: USN 138.55 139.95

Cross Co. Apt., FL: AD 352.0

Crossville Memorial Apt., TN: FSS 255.4   AD 254.3

Croughton USAF, UK: CP 344.85 (HF 4725 6738 11176 13201 13201 15015 17975 kHz)

Crows Landing NALF, CA: AD 124.8 126.5 294.5 379.8   T 125.05 126.2 328.1 336.4 337.8 340.2   NASA 170.125 170.20 170.35 171.00 173.6875   Security 140.25

Crystal Apt., Minneapolis, MN: AD 335.5

Cubi Point NAS/Radford Fld., Luzon, Philippines: DI 263.6   S 274.5   AD 132.3 256.6 267.6   T 122.2 340.2   G 134.4 360.2   E 118.2 343.0   OP 263.6   WX 344.6   MS ("Raspberry Cubi") (HF 3050 6763 8980 kHz)

Cudjoe Key Air Force Site, FL: AF 232.9 240.2

Cumberland Muni Apt., MD: FSS 255.4   AD 327.1

Curtis Wright Corp., NY: 154.60 158.295;   Woodbridge, NJ 451.525

Cushing Muni Apt., OK: AD 291.7

Cut Bank Muni Apt., MT: FSS 255.4

Cutler Naval Communications Station NAA, ME: USN 138.96 140.04   FD 154.31

Cuyahoga Co. Apt., Cleveland, OH: 360.6

Dade-Collier Training & Transition Apt., Miami, FL: AD 281.5

Dahlgren Naval Surface Weapons Command, VA: T 120.15 126.2 340.0   Aero OP 120.15   USN 138.525 138.575 138.825 140.475 140.825 141.95 142.075 142.05 142.80 142.90 148.975 149.025 150.15 164.10 233.9 250.0 300.0 350.0   Army 141.40 148.025 171.075

Dalhart Muni Apt., TX: FSS 255.4   AD 351.7

Dallas-Ft. Worth Int'l. Apt., TX: AD 225.7 227.8 256.7 322.1 364.0 397.2   E 348.6

Dallas Love Fld., TX: FSS 255.4   AD 255.7 372.1   T 239.3   G 348.6

Dallas NAS/Hensley Fld., TX: S 278.0   AD 118.55 120.5 123.9 124.5 125.2 127.75 227.8 252.9 265.8 364.0 372.1   T 126.2 336.4 340.2 360.2   G 143.60 382.8 Base OP 263.5 311.6   WX 263.5   Army Reserve 34.70 336.4   NG Helicopters 46.80 242.6 336.4 ANG OP 300.75   NASA OP 49.83   USN 30.45 32.45 34.15 36.15 36.55 36.85 38.30 40.80 140.15 140.075 140.65 140.775 143.675 252.3 265.8 308.4 344.2 345.4 353.4 355.6   Army 139.025 139.10 139.15 142.45 143.40 241.0 304.4   AF 148.245 149.15 149.265 163.4875 163.5625 389.1 413.325   FD/Crash 140.10

Dam Neck, VA (USN Guided Missiles School; USN Supply Depot): Security 148.425 148.45   Fire Control 140.565 140.84   Civil Engineering 140.85   Pager 150.175   USN 263.3 274.2 277.0 277.3 283.2 301.8 304.0 310.1 313.9 336.2 339.4 340.4 355.0 335.5 376.8 383.8

Danbury Muni Apt., CT: AD 319.8

Dan Daniels AAFES Distribution Center, Norfolk, VA: Security 149.575 Maintenance 148.875

Dane Co. Regn'l. Apt./Truax Fld., Madison, WI: S 278.3   G 348.6   AD 380.35 318.1 350.3 396.0   T 257.8   ANG OP 392.2   NG OP 40.80 123.4 347.7   ANG Medevac 41.94   FD/Crash 173.5875   MP 163.5625   ANG 34.10 34.55 34.60 36.80 36.86 138.25 138.275 138.35 138.45 139.80 143.80 148.075 163.4875 165.0125 173.4375 273.4625 173.5375 238.2 298.7 392.9 396.9

Daniel Fld., Augusta, GA: AD 270.3 323.0

Dannelly Fld., Montgomery, AL: AD 270.25 271.3 284.0 291.0 319.9 369.2　　FSS 255.4　G 348.6　T 360.85　E 257.8 270.3　NG OP 38.20 40.30 226.35　ANG (187th Tactical Fighter Grp) ("Bama Control") 286.5　Range OP 297.1　Aerial Refueling 276.1　Equipment Test 139.825　Civil Engnrng 140.00　FD/Crash 148.325　Maintenance 148.10 148.125 148.175　Medic 149.325　Training 139.925　ANG 148.035 148.235 148.45 149.235 163.5125 262.3 287.4 291.8 297.6 314.3 347.3 359.1 376.0

Danvers, MA: NG 34.70

Danville Muni Apt., VA: FSS 255.4　AD 307.0

Danville, IL: USN 36.85 41.90

Darlington Co. Apt., SC: AD 341.7　Range Control 349.1　AF 261.1 271.1 300.9 308.7 324.7 349.5 364.1 376.1 394.7

Darmstadt AAF, Germany: Advisories 30.75 122.2 242.45

Daugherty Fld., CA: See Long Beach

Dauphin Island, AL: AF 228.8 234.7 238.6 251.0 256.6 263.2 270.4 275.0 278.8 292.7 302.4 306.4 325.5 338.4 344.0 356.0 369.0 375.1 386.2 392.8

Davenport Muni Apt., IA: AD 257.8 351.7　NG OP 36.10 36.70 40.60 123.45 241.0 280.8

David W. Hooks Mem'l. Apt., Houston, TX: AD 290.2　G 348.6　T 393.1　E 393.1

Davis Fld., Muskogee, OK: AD 278.3

Davis-Monthan AFB, Tucson, AZ (ACC; HQ 12th AF as of 6/93; 836th Air Division; 355th Tactical Training Wing; 41st Electronic Combat Sqdn; Aircraft Maintenance & Reservation Ctr.): S 270.1　DI 372.2　AD 118.5 125.1 297.2 318.1　T 118.85 253.5　G 121.8 275.8　E 121.8 275.8　WX 239.8　41st ECS CP ("Raymond 8") 296.3 ("Zapper Ops") 304.8　Security 163.00　OSI 138.075 138.165 138.175　Police 164.9875　FD/Crash 173.5875　Pager 407.35　Base Commanders Net 149.55　Flightline Maintenance 148.185 148.45 148.475 148.50 150.325　Civil Engineering 163.5875　ANG 283.7　Aircraft Graveyard 165.1625 165.1875　Helicopters 32.85 34.60　Data 138.925 139.65　Range 341.5　Training 34.55 34.60 34.95 36.45 40.80 41.45 138.05 138.10 138.20 138.25 138.30 139.70 142.20 276.6 297.2 361.5　AF 30.15 30.55 32.45 32.65 34.15 34.20 36.15 36.25 36.50 36.54 36.80 38.30 41.65 41.90 41.95 46.65 46.75 46.80 49.75 49.80 49.90 138.625 138.90 139.00 140.40 141.575 141.625 141.75 141.90 141.925 142.575 143.425 143.76 143.80 143.88 148.065 148.095 148.225 148.245 148.455 148.515 148.545 149.15 149.175 149.25 149.31 149.535 150.15 150.35 162.25 163.4875 164.20 165.0125 173.4375 173.4875 225.3 251.2 255.7 255.8 259.4 259.6 262.3 266.2 268.1 271.1 271.9 285.2 286.2 286.4 289.3 292.5 300.8 308.8 311.0 314.3 321.0 321.2 327.7 347.2 351.4 358.2 359.3 361.5 361.6 364.2 378.0 379.4 381.3 407.375 407.40 407.425 407.45 407.475 413.00 413.05 413.125 413.15 413.175 413.20 413.30 413.375

Davison AAF/Ft. Belvoir, VA (Army Engineer School; Defense Mapping School; Information Systems Engineering Command; Defense Systems Management College; Army Ordnance School; HQ 310th Support Command): S 128.175　AD 118.1 119.85 322.3 347.3　T 126.3 229.4 241.0　G 121.9 245.2　E 142.35 245.2　OP 34.10 139.40　NG 52.75　WX 139.40　Security 142.40　MP 150.155 150.555　CID 141.325 150.155　R&D Center 148.605 148.755　FD 166.75 173.4375　Motor Pool 163.425　FEMA 167.975　Army 40.10 49.80 139.325 141.35 141.425 142.35 143.20 148.605 148.775 148.815 148.90 150.70 164.15 241.0 407.475　Pager 34.10 148.575

Daytona Beach Regn'l. Apt., FL: AD 322.3 381.5 387.0　G 348.6　T 257.8

Dayton General South Apt., OH: AD 327.1

Decatur Apt., IL: FSS 255.4　G 392.1　T 392.1　AD 291.0 392.1

Decibel Products Co., Dallas, TX: 149.225 151.145 458.05

Defense Construction Supply Ctr. Heliport, Columbus, OH: AD 119.15 125.95 338.8 392.1

Defense General Supply Center, Richmond, VA (Defense Industrial Security Institute): PD 165.1875   Pager 164.25   OP 139.00/139.40   Msc 139.65 150.625 165.1875 173.5125

Defense Logistics Agency, Houston, TX: Army 139.025 226.6

Defense Mapping Agency, DC: Security 165.0375

Defiance Memorial Apt., OH: 321.1

De Kalb, Peachtree Apt., Atlanta, GA: AD 381.65   T 228.3

De Kalb Taylor Muni Apt., IL: AD 371.9

Deland Muni-Taylor Field, FL: AD 322.3

Delaware Airpark, Dover, DE: AD 339.1

Delaware County-Johnson Fld., Muncie, IN: AD 318.2   T 379.8

Delaware Muni Apt., AD 267.9

Del Rio Int'l. Apt., TX: AD 259.1 346.4

Deming Muni Apt., NM: AD 285.5

Dept. of Commerce, Silver Spring, MD: 163.325 163.35 166.125 169.35

Desert Rock Apt., Mercury, NV: AF 255.8 261.1

Des Moines Int'l. Apt., IA: S 283.0   FSS 255.4   AD 252.9 360.7   T 257.8   G 348.6   E 321.1   ANG OP 41.45 260.4   ANG Maintenance 41.45 260.4   ANG 34.55 36.45 36.85 163.4625 163.5875 173.5625 252.1   Army Reserve 41.50

Detroit Arsenal Army Tank-Automotive Material Readiness Command, Michigan Army Missile Plant. MI: Army: 34.50 139.00 139.20 163.5375 165.0625 165.0875 173.4625 231.9 393.8   Chrysler Co 151.655 153.38 158.46 451.25 456.425 462.20 462.425 462.45 462.525 462.825 464.425 464.525 467.175 467.325 467.45   General Motors 35.90 151.625 153.20 153.32 158.46 334.7 461.1875 461.275 461.6175 462.225 462.275 462.30 462.50 462.70 462.825 462.85 462.875 462.90 464.925 466.275

Detroit City Apt., MI: FSS 255.4   AD 348.3 363.2   T 257.8

Detroit Metro Wayne Co. Apt., MI: T 287.1

Detroit, MI: USN 32.45 34.15 140.075 140.65 140.775 140.90 141.00 143.725 148.325 148.35 313.0 318.6 320.2 321.8 336.4 346.8 348.0

Dewitt Fld., Oldtown Muni Apt., ME: AD 390.9

Dickinson Muni Apt., ND: FSS 255.4   AD 380.3

Dillant Hopkins Apt., Keene, NH: AD 338.2

Dillingham Fld., HI (Army Support Command): AD 122.6 122.8 122.9   FSS 255.4 272.7   OP 123.0 225.4   ARMY 236.6 238.3 261.7 264.5 267.5 270.4 276.0 280.5 283.8 294.5 309.5 324.5 337.4 372.3

Dobbins ARB/Atlanta NAS, GA (Reserve training facilities): DI 372.2   AD 121.0 254.25   T 120.75 397.2   G 125.3 275.8   700 TAS CP ("Dapper Dan") 381.3   NG OP 47.00   WX 342.5   Maintenance 165.1625   FD/Crash 173.5875   Disaster 164.9625 172.30 173.15   Security Police 149.475 163.4875   Lockheed Security 165.0625   USN Air OP 340.2   30.51 49.95 138.025 138.10 138.36 142.155 142.20 148.10 148.525 148.55 149.15 150.66 165.0125 165.1125 165.1375 165.1625 173.025 173.4125 173.4375 173.5625 229.3 239.0 261.2 266.3 320.0 309.2 312.4 326.2 346.8 384.8 396.1 413.025 413.15 413.20   USN 36.85 138.96 139.545 140.895 150.09 279.2 295.1 360.2   Lockheed Aerospace 30.84 31.20 123.2 123.25 123.35 123.45 123.525 123.55 151.955 153.32 154.60 158.31 275.2 314.6 337.4 345.4 382.6 461.60 462.20 462.45 462.625 462.75 462.925

Dodge City Muni Apt., KS: FSS 255.4   AD 269.4

Dodge Co. Apt., Juneau, WI: AD 396.0

Donaldson Center Apt., SC: AD 257.9 385.4

Door Co. Cherryland Apt., Sturgeon Bay, WI: AD 338.2 370.9

Dothan Apt., AL: FSS 255.4   AD 234.4   T 257.6   G 348.6   DCASPRO Hayes ("Novel") 383.5

Double Eagle II Apt., NM: AD 301.5

Douglas Muni Apt., GA: AD 290.4

Dover, DE (261st Signal Command): NG 164.15

Dover, NJ: USN 34.95

Dover AFB, Dover, DE (AMC, 436th Military Airlift Wing; USAF Port Mortuary): S 273.5 DI 372.2 AD 125.9 128.0 135.15 142.20 324.5 339.1 359.3 T 126.35 327.5 G 121.9 225.4 E 125.55 289.4 WX 342.5 MAC CP 130.65 349.4 Security 172.30 Police 173.4375 FD/Crash 173.5875 Pager 173.5625 Migratory Bird Advisories (October to April) 142.20 359.3 Phone Patches 413.20 Maintenance 163.5875 Flightline 138.045 OSI 138.075 138.165 138.175 AF 138.20 138.275 138.405 139.65 139.90 148.45 148.545 149.475 165.1125 251.9 257.8 270.1 363.8 410.25 413.025 413.05 413.15 413.275

Doylestown Apt., PA: AD 291.7

Drake Fld., Fayetteville, AR: FSS 255.4 AD 269.0 T 369.0

Draughton-Miller Muni Apt., Temple, TX: AD 370.0

Dresden, NY: USN 34.73 34.93

Dubois-Jefferson Co. Apt., PA: FSS 255.4 AD 317.4

Dubuque Regnl. Apt., IA: AD 281.4 351.8 T 226.8

Dugway Proving Grounds: See Michael AAF.

Dulles Int'l. Apt., DC: AD 350.2 384.9 390.9 G 348.6 T 388.0 SAC CP 311.0 321.0 NASA 170.175 Dept. Agriculture 171.525 AF 409.20 Security/FD 165.50 165.6625 165.7125 408.825 410.25 FD 164.825 FAA OP 165.6375 FAA Aircraft Inspection 408.175 FAA Ground Transportation 409.30 415.125 416.875 419.025 FAA 162.35 165.5125 169.325 Maintenance 166.0875

Duluth Int'l. Apt., MN: DI 288.9 AD 255.9 285.6 T 257.8 WX 342.5 G 348.6 S 270.1 ANG OP 288.9 (HF 6735 kHz LSB) OSI 138,075 138.165 138.175 ANG 148.065 148.095 148.185 148.245 148.455 148.485 149.15 165.1125 173.5375 251.9 298.3 348.8 379.0 413.15

Du Page Apt., IL: FSS 255.4 AD 371.9 T 257.8

Du Pont Company
  Wilmington, DE: 151.085 153.08 461.15 466.0375 466.2375 466.3375
  Antioch, CA: 153.08
  Louviers, CO: 171.025

Durango-La Plata Co. Apt., CO: AD 363.05

Dutchess Co. Apt., NY: FSS 255.4 AD 387.15 T 357.4

Dyersburg Muni Apt., TN:FSS 255.4 AD 317.4

Dyess AFB, Abilene, TX (ACC. 8th AF, 12th Air Division; 96th Bombardment Wing; 463rd Tactical Airlift Wing): DI 372.2 S 385.7 AD 121.3 124.1 126.5 127.45 269.4 322.3 338.3 379.1 T 126.2 236.6 295.7 G 275.8 WX 344.6 MAC CP 349.4 SAC CP 311.0 321.0 Tactical 300.6 303.0 AF 129.7 139.825 141.80 148.065 148.095 148.125 148.225 148.455 148.545 149.475 149.505 149.565 150.25 163.00 163.4625 163.4875 163.5125 163.5875 164.20 164.50 164.70 164.9875 165.0125 165.1625 169.60 172.975 173.5375 173.5875 235.1 295.8 314.2 351.1 340.8 370.4 381.3 385.7 413.15 413.20 413.40 413.45

Eagle Lake Apt., TX: AD 360.8

Eagle River Union Apt., WI: AD 281.5

Eaker AFB, Blytheville, AR (ACC; 8th AF; 42nd Air Division; 97th Bombardment Wing) **Closing date 12/92.**: DI 376.0   AD 135.5 350.3   T 127.2 255.9   G 275.8   E 121.8 225.4   WX 342.5   Security 163.5125   Engineering 163.4875   OSI 138.075 138.165 138.175   CP 311.0 321.0   AF 138.875 143.825 148.065 148.185 148.485 149.15 149.20 149.565 162.6125 163.5625 164.50 165.0125 165.1375 163.4375 173.5625 173.5875 225.4 353.8 371.2 379.3 392.0 395.8 398.2 407.425 413.15   Crew Alerts 413.45

Eaker Fld., OK: AD 377.1

Earle Naval Weapons Station, NJ (Support & home port for Atl Fleet ammunition ships USS Nitro, USS Suribachi, & USS Butte): Security 140.50 141.95   Railroad 140.025   USN 32.45 140.45 141.00 143.50 340.2 360.2 394.0   Army 231.0 304.5

Eastern West Virginia Regn'l. Apt./Shepherd Fld., Martinsburg, WV: AD 126.1 128.75 140.00 296.2 384.9   FSS 255.4   G 275.8   T 124.3 236.6   167 Tactical Air Grp ANG ("Pikeside Control") 297.0   FAA 406.0625 409.4875 416.6375

Easterwood Fld., College Sta., TX: FSS 255.4   AD 371.9   G 284.7   T 257.8

Easthampton Apt., NY: AD 288.1

Eastman Dodge Co Apt., GA: AD 290.4

Easton, MD: USN 142.155

Eau Claire Co Apt., WI: FSS 255.4 AD 335.6

Edgewood Arsenal, MD (Army Chemical Center): T 126.2 229.4 241.0   Air OP 38.40   Security 165.0625   MP 165.5875   EOD 49.70 49.80   (Also see Phillips AAF.)

Edo-Aire Co., Fairfield, NJ: 123.2

Edo Corp., College Point, NY: 471.1125

Edward F. Knapp State Apt., Montpelier, VT: FSS 255.4   AD 282.2

Edwards Air Force Auxiliary North Base, CA: AD 127.8 133.65 307.2   T 120.7 236.6 318.1

Edwards AFB, CA (6510th Test Wing; AF Test Pilot School; AF Rocket Propulsion Lab; Army Aviation Flight Activity; Utah Test & Training Range; NASA Dryden Research Center): DI 372.2   S 116.4 269.9   AD 126.1 133.15 133.65 269.2 284.7 290.3 348.7   T 120.7 236.6 318.1   G 121.8 390.1   CP ("Conform") 304.0   Army OP 141.10 339.9   USN OP 235.0   Police 149.925 163.4875   OSI 138.075 138.175   Security 148.05 148.87 149.91   FD/Crash 173.5875   Medics 173.4875 173.5125   Engineering 149.565   Base Transportation 149.98   Tow Trucks 149.76   Pager 413.50   Convoy Control 164.10   Maintenance 149.985 163.4625 163.6375   Flightline Maintenance 163.5375   Runway Maintenance 148.095   Communications Maintenance 173.4125 Rocket Control 173.4125   EOD 163.5875   Red Flag OP 295.1   Range Control ("Dagrat") 148.245 148.485   Range Cleanup ("Sport" & "Downfall") 148.48   Crew Alerts 413.45   Nuclear Systems 122.9 123.3 168.45 230.4 259.7 384.0   SAC CP 311.0 TV Pool Coverage 169.60   Still Photogs 148.84   Purge Network 162.625   Cooling Network 168.00   Fueling 148.905   Northrop Co 123.3 123.35 123.5 123.525 153.11 Boeing Co 153.38   McDonnell Douglas Co 123.2 123.55   Rockwell Int'l. 123.35 123.425 123.525 464.875   NASA CP 38.45   NASA 49.83 120.7 121.3 122.85 138.40 155.28 162.025 162.60 162.6125 164.10 165.6125 166.225 169.40 170.35 170.40 171.00 171.15 240.2 240.4 240.6 241.4 241.6 241.8 259.7 278.9 290.0 296.0 296.8 318.0 348.7 371.7 382.6 384.8   AF 38.65 138.05 138.25 139.80 141.55 148.55 148.675 148.90 149.15 149.225 150.15 150.28 173.4375 228.2 229.6 236.0 239.4 245.3 248.6 251.9 257.0 260.7 262.5 264.6 266.3 267.9 268.1 272.0 274.2 275.9 279.9 280.1 284.1 286.4 286.8 287.2 289.1 289.4 290.6 291.8 294.6 296.8 297.4 304.0 308.7 311.2 311.4 314.4 315.2 315.9 318.1 319.6 322.7 325.9 337.0 341.6 349.3 349.6 351.4 358.4 359.2 378.1 379.7 383.0 385.9 390.1 395.1 398.1

Edwards Co. Apt., Rocksprings, TX: AD 346.4

Eglin Air Force Auxiliary #3 Duke, Valparaiso, FL: DI 372.2 AD 120.9 124.05 391.2 393.0   T 133.2 338.7   G 251.2   AF Reserve ("Spectre") 225.3   AF 142.275

142.625 142.80 143.80 173.5125 173.5875 225.3 261.1 262.5 294.4 296.2 314.2 321.2 327.7 337.0 348.9 349.4 351.4 375.8 397.2 407.375 413.425

Eglin Air Force Auxiliary #6, Valparaiso, FL: AF 173.5875

Eglin Air Force Auxiliary #9, Mary Esther, FL: AF 32.65 34.15 36.45 36.85 41.45 46.65 46.75 138.10 138.275 138.50 139.90 140.40 142.125 143.75 148.075 148.215 148.245 148.455 150.135 150.225 150.375 163.4875 170.575 173.5125 173.6375 242.0 390.0 392.2 410.00

Eglin AFB, Valparaiso, FL (ACC. 9th AF; Air Warfare Centre; AF Systems Command/Armament Division; Eglin Gulf Test Range; 79th Test & Evaluation Grp.; 441 TAG Training Grp; Air/Ground Operations School; 33rd Tactical Fighter Wing; HQ Strike Command; McKinley Climatic Lab): DI 122.85 372.2 S 273.5 AD 125.1 132.1 322.6 358.3 T 118.2 348.4 G 121.8 335.8 E 127.7 388.9 CP 318.05 328.025 TAC CP ("Raymond 11") 381.3 390.9 WX 342.5 Security 163.375 163.4875 164.175 Transportation 163.4625 FD/Crash 173.5875 173.6375 Medics 173.5125 Disaster Control 150.315 163.5875 Emergency 280.5 Mission Control 290.9 Radar Control 398.2 Aircraft Maintenance 148.575 150.15 Fuels 150.255 Explosive Ordnance 165.1125 Weapons Test 173.5625 Helicopter Rescue 150.195 Federal Prison 170.65 170.875 170.925 Nuclear Systems 138.61 140.61 143,41 143.86 167.85 168.45 239.4 242.0 248.6 252.4 259.7 410.00 411.00 AF 32.10 32.43 32.95 34.60 46.85 49.85 138.015 138.045 138.14 138.24 138.40 138.90 139.14 139.65 139.80 141.20 141.42 141.48 141.55 141.66 141.90 142.155 142.20 142.30 143.15 143.46 143.035 148.065 148.185 148.515 148.575 148.075 148.755 148.815 149.175 149.205 149.235 149.265 149.31 149.475 149.535 149.565 149.825 150.165 150.285 150.345 163.5125 165.5375 164.9625 165.0125 165.0375 165.1625 165.1375 165.1875 167.825 171.3875 173.4375 173.5375 173.6125 232.15 234.1 237.4 239.4 240.2 250.9 251.2 251.9 252.525 257.0 259.2 260.7 262.3 264.7 266.0 268.0 272.0 276.0 277.0 279.7 282.0 284.1 287.2 289.0 291.8 292.2 293.4 294.5 294.6 295.1 295.2 299.5 301.7 311.0 311.2 314.2 314.4 315.0 315.2 315.9 316.62 317.27 317.9 319.6 323.2 324.15 324.7 325.5 325.9 333.55 335.55 340.9 341.6 341.9 344.8 347.3 349.5 349.6 357.3 359.2 361.5 364.0 376.0 378.0 377.8 379.7 383.0 384.8 385.7 385.9 388.1 389.1 391.2 394.8 397.0 399.75 407.00 407.40 407.50 409.00 410.00 412.00 413.00 413.075 413.15 413.175 413.20 413.30 413.275 413.45 415.00 418.00 Army 40.10 46.70 46.90 139.08 142.925 143.175 148.90

Eielson AFB, Fairbanks, AK (343rd Tactical Fighter Wing): DI 372.2 AD 118.1 126.5 271.3 290.9 363.8 T 117.0 127.2 126.5 255.6 290.9 G 121.8 275.8 WX 344.6 ANG OP ("Chena Cntrl.") 292.4 AF 32.45 36.85 38.65 40.12 40.35 119.9 121.185 121.195 122.205 120.8 124.7 125.4 125.9 126.65 138.06 139.20 139.85 141.625 141.725 141.80 148.065 148.215 148.545 149.175 149.31 149.565 150.15 150.195 150.285 163.4875 163.5875 164.10 164.50 165.0125 165.0375 165.1125 165.1375 165.1875 173.5375 173.5625 173.5875 225.52 225.56 225.6 225.64 225.72 225.76 225.8 226.9 227.3 227.5 228.0 229.4 229.5 229.7 230.5 231.5 231.9 232.2 236.6 242.0 243.3 255.2 255.6 259.1 268.8 271.3 275.8 289.4 294.2 300.9 301.6 318.2 320.1 324.3 327.3 350.9 381.0 389.9 391.7 392.5 396.1 407.45 408.00 408.80 409.125 409.325 413.00 413.025 413.375 413.45 413.575 OSI 138.075 138.165 138.175

El Campo Metro Apt., TX: FSS 255.4 AD 306.9

El Centro Naval Air Facility, CA (Attack Squadron 174): S 271.4 T 119.1 340.2 360.2 G 126.2 263.4 Security 140.90 148.35 FD/Crash 139.80 140.525 Nuclear Weapons Systems 122.9 167.85 168.45 230.4 239.4 248.6 259.7 384.0 NASA 240.2 240.4 240.6 241.4 241.6 241.8 USN 140.10 140.28 140.60 142.48 252.4 271.4 276.4 277.2 283.2 350.0 384.2 AF 46.75 142.25

Electrocom Inc., San Diego CA: 35.98 123.3 123.4 123.45 123.5 151.985 153.26 158.43 462.15 464.55 471.5625 471.5875 471.6125; Montrose, CA: 464.05; Compton, CA: 464.05; Pomona, CA: 153.08; San Francisco, CA: 462.80; Needham, MA: 464.40; Boston, MA: 461.4875; No. Andover, MA: 461.4875; Quincy, MA: 153.32 153.335; LA & IL: 462.675; Groton, CT: 153.08 153.26 462.50 FD 33.74 33.78 33.90 33.92 33.94 33.96

Elizabeth City CGAS, NC: AD 323.0 T 355.6 G 121.6 Copters 123.05 Ambulances 155.28 155.34 155.40 Security/FD 171.2375 Rescue 282.8 CG 171.3625 381.3 381.7 381.8 383.9

Elizabeth Fld., Fishers Island, NY: AD 307.9 380.25 USN 143.275 149.01 149.37

Elkhart Muni Apt., IN: AD 257.8 263.1

Elko Muni Apt-Harris Fld., NV: FSS 255.4

Ellington Fld., Houston, TX: S 269.9 AD 257.7 284.0 307.1 379.1 T 109.4 126.2 253.5 G 121.6 275.8 USN 363.5 Army 36.11 36.53 36.69 NG 41.00 135.00 242.4 NORAD 313.6 364.2 AWACS OP ("Dragnet") 313.6 CG 157.05 157.075 381.7 381.8 383.9 (HF 5692 8980 15084) Rescue 282.8 FD/Crash 165.5875 173.5875 Aircraft Fuel Delivery 154.57 463.2375 Tower to Ground Crews 163.5375 ANG Security 162.6125 163.00 163.4875 163.5625 ANG Crew Alerts 164.50 ANG Aircraft Maintence 165.1375 Disaster 163.5125 Base Commanders Net 163.00 Building Maintenance 163.4625 Aircraft Fueling 165.1875 Aircaft to Maintenance ("Lonestar") 293.7 ANG CP ("Lonestar") 261.8 Runway Maintenance ("Ramp Rats") 173.6125 Damage Assessment Team 163.00 NASA OP ("Candy") 235.4 NASA Security 164.9875 ANG Training 138.10 140.40 228.8 234.7 251.0 263.2 292.7 306.4 338.4 344.0 ANG 138.325 148.575 163.5625 163.5875 163.6125 173.6125 225.4 238.5 251.9 270.4 275.0 279.1 287.5 287.8 302.4 325.5 351.8 356.0 369.0 370.9 375.1 386.2 392.8

Ellisville, FL: USN 228.55

Ellsworth AFB, Rapid City, SD (ACC; 8th AF; 321st Strategic Missile Wing; 44th Strategic Missile Wing; 28th Bombardment Wing): DI 372.2 AD 119.5 125.3 271.3 396.0 T 126.05 236.6 253.5 G 121.8 275.8 E 121.1 289.4 WX 375.2 VIP Aircraft OP ("Sky Bird") 311.0 321.0 Copter OP ("Beaver Operations") 266.2 Air Police 163.5375 Security 163.4875 Snow Plows 148.575 Base Commanders Net 149.565 Civil Engineering 150.175 150.315 171.775 Medics 172.725 173.5625 FD/Crash 173.5875 OSI 138.075 148.065 148.245 148.35 148.455 148.485 148.95 149.15 149.225 149.275 150.10 163.00 163.375 163.4625 164.50 165.0625 174.455 260.2 271.9 301.75 308.8 314.3 375.2 409.90 413.15 413.45

Ellyson Field NAS, Pensacola, FL: USN 148.29

Elmendorf AFB, Anchorage, AK (343rd Tactical Fighter Wing): DI 134.8 372.2 S 124.3 AD 118.6 290.9 T 127.2 255.6 G 121.8 275.8 E 121.8 275.8 MAC CP "Denali") 128.0 349.4 (HF 11480 kHz) Rescue 123.1 282.8 WX 344.6 OSI 138.075 138.165 138.175 AF 34.11 34.35 121.185 121.195 122.205 124.7 125.4 125.9 134.1 134.8 139.85 139.875 148.035 148.095 148.185 148.245 148.455 148.465 148.485 148.515 148.545 149.285 150.295 150.225 150.345 163.4625 163.4875 163.5125 163.5875 164.10 164.175 164.9625 165.0125 165.0375 165.1125 165.1375 165.1626 165.1875 172.675 173.4375 173.5125 173.5375 173.5625 173.5875 173.7125 225.52 225.56 225.6 226.9 227.3 228.0 228.8 229.4 229.5 229.7 230.5 231.5 231.9 232.2 234.3 236.6 242.0 243.3 250.345 259.1 259.3 271.3 274.0 281.8 290.9 300.9 301.5 318.2 320.1 324.3 327.5 338.6 349.4 389.0 391.7 395.1 407.45 407.475 413.025 413.20 413.30 411.45 416.50 (HF 4725 6738 8967 11176 13201 15015 17975 kHz)

Elmira/Corning Regn'l. Apt., NY: AD 257.8 372.0 T 257.8 FSS 255.4 NG 142.155 142.275 143.775

El Monte Apt., CA: AD 351.1

El Paso Int'l. Apt., TX: FSS 255.4 AD 263.0 307.0 343.6 353.5 S 254.3 G 348.6 T 257.8 E 379.1 AF 228.9 260.8

El Reno Muni. Apt., OK: 393.1

El Toro MCAS, Santa Ana, CA (3rd Marine Air Wing; MAG-11, -13, VMF-314, -323, -531; VMFP-3; VMA-211, -214, -311; VMA(AW)-242; VMGR-352; HAMS-13): DI 117.2 284.2 328.1 AD 121.3 124.1 124.65 128.1 132.1 132.7 263.1 281.4 323.1 343.9 380.2 T 133.1 271.7 360.2 G 120.45 383.8 E 120.45 301.3 WX 344.6 Medics ("Delta") 138.74 139.55 Motor Pool 148.355 OP 328.1 Rescue 41.95 139.50 326.8 Fueling 142.625 148.40 Flightline Trucks 138.72 Ramp OP 138.72 140.425

Transportation 148.35   Civil Engineering 138.72 143.50 148.305   MAG-13 OP 38.40
FD/Crash 40.82 140.10   FD ("Station 16") 138.74 138.94 139.55 139.60 142.86
PD/Security ("Station 30") 138.025 138.60 138.74 138.95 140.30 140.575 142.86   Base
Traffic 149.025   Pager 148.35   Ordnance 140.80   USMC 32.05 138.575 138.625
138.835 139.475 139.525 139.575 140.05 140.22 140.425 140.515 140.715 140.85 140.925
141.925 142.025 142.575 142.75 143.525 143.575 143.625 143.725 148.325 148.375
148.425 148.975 149.075 149.125 149.40 149.425 150.345 233.9 236.3 237.9 255.1 258.9
262.6 263.1 268.7 269.6 272.3 272.4 273.0 273.8 274.9 277.0 277.1 277.9 279.3 281.0
281.2 281.7 281.9 283.4 293.1 299.3 299.5 304.0 305.4 307.5 310.2 310.6 310.9 312.4
312.7 313.7 313.8 318.7 324.0 325.4 336.3 336.4 336.5 338.1 340.2 340.4 343.9 344.2
345.0 347.8 348.0 349.9 350.1 352.3 353.6 359.5 362.2 380.8 385.0 387.4 413.20 (HF
6723 kHz)

Ely, NV: AF 275.9 279.9 296.8

Emanuel Co Apt., Swainsboro, GA AD 343.75

Emery AAF, Wurzburg, Germany: OP 122.175

Empire, MI: AF 229.1 233.6 239.4 251.8 254.4 258.0 273.4 276.4 278.2 284.4 292.4
297.7 309.5 312.8 318.4 327.2 348.8 357.2 364.2 371.0 379.0 384.0 396.8

Emporia Muni. Apt., KS: AD 269.2

Emporia Muni. Apt., VA: AD 323.0

Encino, CA: AF 345.5 375.5 377.5 394.5

Enewetak Aux. AF, Enewetak Atoll (Pacific): OP 126.2

England AFB, Alexandria, LA (ACC; 9th AF; 23rd Tactical Fighter Wing) **Closing
date 12/92.**: DI 372.2   E 289.4   S 270.1   AD 118.2 121.2 289.1 301.5   T 127.2 255.6
G 138.90 275.8   CP ("Raymond 12") 381.3   Supervisor of Flying ("Tiger") 233.4
WX 239.8   Hurricane Hunters 304.8   AF 34.20 34.50 36.10 36.85 38.70 40.55 40.90
41.45 41.90 46.85 49.85 148.035 148.095 148.455 148.50 148.454 149.175 149.205
149.265 149.505 150.135 150.195 150.255 150.285 150.315 162.6125 165.1125 173.5375
173.5625 173.5875 225.4 259.3 270.1 280.5 283.8 290.9 291.1 301.5 316.9 371.8 385.9
388.2 391.9 413.05 413.15   OSI 40.17 40.19

Enid Woodring Muni Apt., OK: AD 291.1 319.1   T 398.2

Enstrom Helicopters, Menominee, MI: 123.2 123.4 123.45

Enterprise Muni Apt., AL: AD 237.5

Environmental Research Labs, Boulder, CO: 162.125 165.5625 167.1875 167.90
165.4125

Ephrata Muni Apt., WA FSS 255.4   AD 385.5   AF 413.45

Eppley Airfield, Omaha, NE: AD 263.0 281.5 363.8   T 257.8

Erie Int'l. Apt., PA: AD 263.0 323.2   T 257.8

Ernest A. Love Fld., Prescott, AZ: FSS 255.4   AD 298.9   T 288.1

Essex Co Apt., Caldwell, NJ: AD 379.2 379.9

E-Systems, Inc., St. Petersburg, FL: 462.20

Evansville Regn'l Apt., IN: AD 226.4 363.0   T 257.8

Evanston-Uinta Co. Burns Fld., WY: AD 387.05

Eveleth-Virginia Muni Apt., MN: AD 255.9

Evergreen OLF, Evergreen, AL: AD 120.2 346.4   USN OP 122.7

Fairbanks Int'l. Apt., AK: FSS 255.4 AD 271.3 327.5 363.8 T 257.7

Fairchild AFB, Spokane, WA (ACC; 12th AF; 47th Air Division; 92nd Bombardment Wing (Heavy); 3636th Combat Crew Training Wing): DI 372.2 AD 124.3 124.7 263.0 384.9 T 126.2 289.6 G 275.8 SAC CP 311.0 321.0 ANG OP 396.9 WX 375.2 OSI 138.075 138.165 138.175 AF 138.025 138.75 143.825 148.065 148.10 148.185 148.225 148.545 149.175 149.25 149.565 150.195 150.225 150.345 163.075 163.275 163.4875 163.5625 163.5875 236.0 251.9 260.6 286.8 293.7 413.15

Fairchild Industries, Germantown, MD: 153.05 153.08 153.125

Fairfield, MT: AF 150.375 165.0375 165.1625 412.975 413.025

Fairfield Co Apt., OH: AD 279.6

Fairford USAF, UK: DI 378.0 AD 119.0 122.1 133.75 134.3 246.45 308.75 360.2 362.3 T 142.225 257.8 380.0 G 276.55 CP 307.8 371.2 WX 259.4 Medic 31.30 32.80 Security 30.025 30.55 30.9875 31.00 31.1825 32.20 32.30 76.45 Msc 39.90

Fairhope Muni Apt., AL: AD 269.3 288.15

Fairmont Muni Apt., MN: AD 257.7

Falcon AFB (Strategic Defense Initiative Nat'l. Test Facility): See listing for City of Colorado Springs.

Falcon Fld., Mesa AZ: AD 379.8 McDonnell Douglas Corp 462.425 Pager 465.00

Falcon Jet Corp., Little Rock, AR: 123.2 123.35; Teterboro, NJ: 334.7 462.625

Fallbrook Naval Weapons Station, CA: USN 138.84 138.85 140.28 140.50 140.52 140.60 140.90 142.50 142.675 142.775 142.825

Fallon Muni Apt., NV: AD 126.2 285.5 360.2

Fallon NAS/Van Voorhis Fld., NV (Weapons delivery training facility): S 284.3 AD 126.2 285.5 360.2 T 119.25 134.1 340.2 G 382.8 E 271.5 Target Control ("Desert Control") 263.6 WX 324.8 CG 165.3375 USN 40.30 41.10 139.55 140.04 140.28 140.52 140.60 170.70 149.90 142.575 142.80 143.725 143.825 149.07 150.40 245.0 267.2 263.6 265.8 267.4 271.4 272.3 272.9 273.2 279.9 281.2 284.5 312.4 313.7 314.9 340.5 341.0 360.2 384.2

Falls Int'l. Apt., MN: AD 377.1

Fanning Fld., Idaho Falls, ID: FSS 255.4 T 257.8

Farmington Regn'l. Apt., MO: AD 291.7

Farmville Muni Apt., VA: AD 284.7

Fayette Co Apt., Washington CH, OH: AD 279.6

Fayetteville Muni Apt./Grannis Field, NC: FSS 255.4 AD 288.3 295.0 340.7 393.0 T 269.2 G 348.6

Federal Cartridge Corp., Anoka, MN: 467.35

Federal Signal Corp.: Shelby, OH & Park Forest, IL Pagers 154.625; All US: 35.04 151.625 154.57 464.50 464.55

Federal Sign & Signal Corp.: Chicago, IL 463.55; Burr Ridge. IL 463.35 464.725

Felker AAF/Ft. Eustis, VA (Army Transportation Center & School): AD 125.7 395.8 T 126.3 241.0 248.2 G 121.35 229.4 OP 38.40 41.50 MP 150.575 163.725 407.475 412.875 FD 173.4125 Motor Pool 165.0875 Post Transportation 173.4675 Messengers 170.35 CID 141.325 Army Reserve ("Trident OP") 40.35 Medics 149.80 173.5125 Civil Engineers 173.4625 AF 415.00 Army 139.025 139.10 141.05 141.10 141.15 141.25 142.325 142.35 142.40 142.45 148.70 148.925 149.65 150.575 150.765 165.0875 172.30 173.5125

Felts Fld., Spokane, WA: FSS 255.4 AD 263.0 T 241.0

Fentress Auxiliary Landing Fld. (USN), VA: AD 119.6 279.2 (Also see listings for Oceana NAS.)

Feucht AAF, Germany: AD 124.775 342.6 T 31.80 33.60 122.1 142.20 314.8 G 138.95 250.55

Findlay Apt., OH: FSS 255.4 AD 228.4 269.3

Finland, MN: AF 149.235 229.1 233.6 239.4 251.8 254.4 258.0 262.2 273.4 276.0 278.2 284.8 289.0 292.4 297.7 309.5 312.8 318.4 327.2 348.8 357.2 364.2 371.0 379.0 384.0 396.8

Finley, ND: AF 150.285 173.5625 228.8 228.9 234.6 234.7 238.4 238.5 251.0 254.2 256.6 260.8 263.2 267.0 269.9 270.2 270.4 274.4 275.0 279.4 281.6 287.8 292.9 298.5 302.4 306.4 309.4 316.3 320.6 324.0 235.5 327.7 336.6 338.4 341.8 344.0 346.2 356.0 364.2 369.0 375.1 377.0 386.2 387.8 392.8 398.0 407.475

Finthen AAF, Mainz/Finthen, Germany: AD 119.15 120.15 120.5 122.925 127.5 231.25 341.8 367.15 T 31.80 40.50 40.80 122.1 139.05 341.8 G 141.30 315.85 WX 140.30

Firebaugh Apt., CA: AD 379.8

Fitzsimmons Army Hospital, Denver, CO: Security 148.575 FD 149.115

Fitzgerald Muni Apt., GA: AD 259.3 379.2

Flagstaff Pulliam Apt., AZ: AD 298.9 226.3

Fleming-Mason Apt., KY: AD 343.65

Fletcher Apt., Clarksdale, MS: AF 300.6

Florence City/Co Apt., SC: FSS 255.4 AD 306.3 309.7 341.7 T 379.8 G 379.8 E 379.8

Floyd Bennett Fld., NY: See Brooklyn CGAS.

Floyd W. Jones Apt., Lebanon, MO: AD 317.5

Flying Cloud Apt., Minneapolis, MN: AD 284.7 357.4

FMC Corp.: Camp Roberts, CA 154.60 410.00 416.60 462.275; Fridley, MN 153.065

Folly Beach, SC: USN 393.855

Fond du Lac Co Apt., WI: AD 387.1

Forbes Fld., Topeka, KS: AD 290.2 G 275.8 T 255.9 190th AREFG ANG OP 286.5 NG OP 41.70 304.6 SAC CP 311.0 321.0 ANG 148.05 148.545 163.375 163.4625 163.4875 164.50 165.0125 173.5375 173.5625 173.5875 413.45

Ford Aerospace Corp.: US 151.625; TX 464.8875; AZ 463.70 464.8875

Ford Apt., Iron Mtn, MI: AD 322.5

Ford Island NALF, HI: DI 122.8 FSS 255.4 T 126.2 340.2 USN 142.675 143.55 264.3 270.6 275.7 277.8 328.2 339.7 342.9 350.9 352.1 361.3 380.4 386.9 395.7

Forney AAF/Ft. (Leonard) Wood, MO (Army Engineers & Basic Training Center): S 110.0 T 40.95 110.0 125.4 126.2 229.4 241.0 Routing Control 364.5 Security 165.0625 Maintenance 165.0875 93rd Evac Hospital 163.25 164.50 Ambulance 173.10 Ammo Section 148.575 150.45 Artillery Range 163.4625 Engineering & Housing 143.20 165.0875 EOD 49.70 49.75 49.80 FD 171.575 171.975 173.9625 Forney OP 172.75 Hospital Pager 172.75 Hospital 173.4125 Switchboard 143.415 MP 139.20 163.5375 165.0625 165.1875 169.575 Gate Guards 139.30 Range Cntrl. 36.45 148.025 TMC 173.7125 Transp Motor Pool 163.5625 Transrail 173.6125 CID 164.9875 Army 32.00 32.50 40.90 138.925 139.00 139.125 141.325 142.325 142.905 143.05 173.4875 392.1 396.1

Forrest-Sherman Fld., FL: See Pensacola NAS.

Ft. Allen, PR: USN 148.10 149.01

Ft. Amador, Panama: Army 165.1375 165.225 165.335 USN 143.00 164.17 164.25

Ft. A.P. Hill, VA: AD 119.85 322.3 T 38.50 126.2 241.0 Security 150.75 MP 148.65 150.555 165.5375 Civil Engineering 165.0875 Range Control 38.50 Army 38.35 38.50 40.10 139.175 139.325 141.40 142.90 148.605 148.775 148.80 148.815 173.4875 266.6

Ft. Baker & Ft. Barry, Sausalito, CA: Army 164.775

Ft. Belvoir, VA: See Davison AAF.

Ft. Benning, GA: See Lawson AAF.

Ft. Bliss, TX: See Biggs AAF.

Ft. Bragg, NC: See Simmons AAF.

Ft. Buchanan, PR (Subpost of Ft. McPherson): Army 149.775 150.675

Ft. Campbell, KY/TN: See Campbell AAF & Sabre AHP.

Ft. Carson, CO: See Butts AAF.

Ft. Chaffee, AR (Detention Camp): AD 120.9 228.4 398.9 T 41.50 124.5 241.0 Airfield OP 36.60   Range 38.50 141.30 242.6 Msc 36.11 36.53 36.69 41.40 126.2 139.00 141.175 141.35 142.35 143.35 148.75 165.5625 241.8 300.0 356.4 366.6 399.8

Ft. Clayton, Panama: Army 163.75 164.55

Ft. Collins-Loveland Muni Apt., CO: FSS 255.4 AD 284.7

Ft. Custer, MI: Army 41.90 143.10 143.40

Ft. Davis, Panama: Army 37.70 169.325 USN 163.10

Ft. De Russy Military Reservation, HI (HQ 9th Corps): Army 143.415

Ft. Detrick, MD (East Coast Telecommunications Center; Defense Medical Materiel Board; Army Medical Research Institute of Infectious Diseases; Army Medical Bioengineering R&D Laboratory; Tri-Service Medical Logistics Systems Office): Army 36.05 165.0625 165.3375 171.475 237.4

Ft. Devens, MA: See Moore AAF.

Ft. Dix, NJ (Army Personnel Center; Infantry Training Center): Helicopter OP 30.50 139.30 265.6 Security 38.85 38.91 MP 141.40 EOD 49.70 49.80 Ambulances 148.675 155.28 155.34 155.355 Range 34.00 148.625 148.875 FD 141.20 Civil Engineering 165.0625 Pager 148.25 Duty Officer 141.05 Motor Pool 150.425 Army 38.69 139.10 139.20 139.40 141.40 141.325 142.325 148.025 148.60 148.625 173.4875

Ft. Dodge Regn'l. Apt., IA: AD 288.3 Army 143.05 233.4 AF 311.2

Ft. Douglas, UT (HQ 96th Army Reserve Command): EOD 49.70 49.80

Ft. Drum, NY: See Wheeler-Sack AAF.

Ft. Eustis, VA: See Felker AAF.

Ft. Fisher AFS, Kure Beach, NC: AF 165.0125 165.1625 NORAD CP 364.2 NORAD 228.8 234.7 238.5 251.0 256.6 263.2 270.4 275.0 278.6 287.8 292.7 298.5 302.4 306.4 325.3 338.4 344.0 356.0 369.0 375.1 386.2 392.8 Security 165.1625 Disaster 165.0125

Ft. Gillem, Forest Park, GA (Subpost of Ft. McPherson, GA): S 119.65 122.55 T 119.5 Helicopter OP 122.95 MP/Security 165.0875 EOD 49.70 49.80 Army 141.075 142.95 143.055 148.925 149.80 163.0375 163.5625 (Also see Ft. McPherson.)

Ft. Gordon, GA (HQ Army Signal Corps; National Science Center of the Communications & Electronics Foundation; Provost Marshal General Center): AD 119.5 125.4 231.1 270.3 Helipad OP 46.70 Motor Pool 163.5625 Medevac 32.50 Army 40.10 139.00 139.425 148.605 148.775 148.815 148.85 150.435 165.5375 165.0375 165.1625 165.1875 165.3375 169.175 170.125 173.4125 173.4626 173.4875 173.5125 226.6 366.5 371.5 374.5 376.3 376.5 377.5 380.5 387.5 389.5 391.5 392.5 393.5 395.5 397.5 407.25 407.30 412.85 412.90 412.95 413.05 413.475 413.525

Ft. Greely AK: See Allen AAF.

Ft. Hamilton, Brooklyn, NY (Long Island Recruiting Battalion; Military Entrance Processing Station for NY City; also 300+ Reserve & NG units): Security 46.79 143.15 164.025 Army 141.325 407.35 407.525

Ft. Hancock, Highlands, NJ: USN 34.15 39.65

Ft. (Bejamin) Harrison, Indianapolis, IN (Maj. Gen. E. J. Bean Finance Center; Adjutant Generals Corps; Finance Corps; Soldier Support Institute; Defense Information School; Intelligence School): Security 142.45 164.025 164.15 Ambulances 155.34 FD 165.0625 Maintenance 165.1875 OP 173.5125 NG 36.50 Army 139.45 141.325 142.25 150.525 165.5375 165.1875 407.325

Ft. Hase, HI: Army 139.095 143.15 165.0875 165.1875

Ft. Holabird, Baltimore, MD (Minimum Security Prison): Army 139.15 148.695

Ft. Hood, TX: See Hood AAF, Robert Gray AAF, Longhorn Auxiliary Landing Strip, & Shorthorn Auxiliary Landing Strip.

Ft. Huachuca, AZ: See Libby AAF.

Ft. Hunter-Liggett: See Hunter-Liggett.

Ft. Indiantowngap, PA: See Muir AAF.

Ft. Irwin National Training Center, Barstow, CA (1st Battalion; 6th Battalion; 31st Infantry; 73rd Armor): Aero OP Advisories 41.50 126.2 241.0 Range Control & Dust Off 32.10 32.70 38.45 38.89 38.90 Medevac 38.90 40.90 123.05 Ambulances 148.675 MP 164.70 Range Control Security 164.005 Blackhawk Range 48.00 Bike Lake WX 32.40 32.45 49.05 Live Fire Control ("Dragon Cntrl.") 37.80 48.45 Crash Inspectors 33.55 Air-to-Air 32.45 MILES Teams 34.09 34.11 34.29 34.31 34.49 Maintenance ("Thunderdome") 32.35 VIP Escorts 32.25 32.35 32.60 CBW Training ("Nerve") 31.70 33.85 35.00 35.85 36.00 Wargames Training 30.03 30.25 30.35 30.65 30.85 31.00 31.55 31.75 31.85 31.90 32.00 32.10 32.15 32.25 32.35 32.50 32.60 32.70 32.95 33.00 33.05 33.15 33.25 33.35 33.40 33.45 33.80 33.95 34.70 34.95 36.40 36.50 36.90 36.95 37.00 37.50 37.85 39.65 39.85 44.25 48.85 56.60 56.65 56.85 72.00 Post Taxi 164.575 Army 30.30 32.00 141.225 141.275 141.375 143.00 143.075 143.125 143.175 143.25 143.30 143.475 148.575 148.625 148.675 148.80 148.875 148.90 148.925 149.60 149.625 149.65 149.675 149.70 149.725 149.75 149.775 150.225 150.75 150.775 165.0625 413.575 AF 138.12 143.975 150.225 321.2 347.3 (Also see Bicycle Lake AAF.)

Ft. Jackson, Columbia, SC (Infantry Training Center; 120th Army Reserve Command): Helipad 38.20 Medevac 49.65 Air-to-Air 130.0 Army Reserve CP 41.20 130.0 Aero OP 38.20 130.0 Range 32.90 Motor Pool 163.5625 EOD 49.70 49.80 Army 139.075 139.15 139.225 142.155 142.35 142.875 143.35 148.25 148.925 149.80 150.525 150.55 164.9875 165.0875 165.5375 165.4375 173.4125 173.4625 173.5125 173.8125 387.9 412.90 413.525 (Also see Columbia Metropolitan Apt.)

Ft. Kahehameha Military Reservation, HI: 139.525

Ft. Knox, KY: See Godman AAF.

Ft. Lauderdale Executive Apt., FL: AD 306.3 T 239.3

Ft. Lauderale Hollywood Int'l. Apt., FL: AD 251.1 255.6 257.8 285.6 306.3 380.2 T 257.8 AF 142.155 USN 138.525 140.16 313.9

Ft. Lawton, Seattle, WA (HQ 124th Army Reserve Command): EOD 49.70 49.80 NG 32.30 34.05 Army 36.10 49.75 49.85 150.735 163.5625 164.20

Ft. Leavenworth, KS: See Sherman AAF.

Ft. Lee, Petersburg, VA (Army Quartermaster Center & School; Army Logistics Management Center; 1st & 22nd Field Army Support Command; Army Information Software Ststems Agency Development Center Lee (USAISSDCL)): AD 119.9 121.1 257.8 307.2 Helipad #3 OP 126.2 Medevac 32.50 Medics 142.375 149.80 EOD 49.70 49.80 FD 409.375 CID 141.325 MP 163.5625 165.0625 Engineer 173.6125 Post Transportation 150.465 Installation Supply 173.4875 Army 138.925 139.65 141.235 142.325 142.35 163.0375 163.4125 163.5625 165.075 165.0875 173.5375 407.275 (Also see Blackstone AAF & Ft. A.P. Hill.)

Ft. Leonard Wood, MO: See Forney AAF.

Ft. Leslie J. McNair, Washington, DC (HQ Military District of Washington; National War College; Industrial College of the Armed Forces; Inter-American Defense College): Security 36.71 MP 36.69 414.825 419.65 Armed Forces PD 453.55 Transportation 148.665 Motor Pool 36.91 139.00 Special Events 139.10 Public Affairs 139.35 Couriers 150.65 Army 36.31 36.63 139.065 139.125 139.15 139.175 139.20 407.30 409.925

Ft. Lewis, WA: See Gray AAF.

Ft. Mason, San Francisco, CA: Army 36.71 148.025 148.575 148.60 148.625 148.675 148.90 149.575 149.625 149.70 150.425 173.4125 173.4875 173.5125 407.225 413.575

Ft. Mc Arthur Annex, San Pedro, CA: AWOL Network 163.5375 Army 412.90 413.425

Ft. Mc Clellan, Anniston, AL (Military Police School; Army Chemical Corps Center & School): Security 164.50 165.0625 FD 165.0875 Range 34.90 41.50 MP Training 30.20 Medic 165.1625 Motor Pool 163.5625 Disaster Control 139.075 EOD 49.70 49.80 Army 34.90 36.10 139.32 140.25 141.075 141.125 141.165 142.305 142.905 143.385 143.40 148.70 149.65 169.60 170.125 173.025 173.4625 412.90 413.525

Ft. Mc Coy, WI: See Mc Coy AAF.

Ft. Mc Pherson, Atlanta, GA (HQ Army Forces Command; HQ 2nd Army; HQ 3rd Army; Army Southeast Recruiting Command): MP/Security ("Blue Knight") 165.0625 165.1875 FD 149.75 Bdlg Maintenance 165.0375 Army 139.35 148.575 148.70 150.575 163.5875 165.0625 412.90 423.525 (Ft. Mc Pherson operates Ft. Gillem & Ft. Buchanan.)

Ft. Meade, MD: See Tipton AAF.

Ft. Monmouth, NJ (Army Communications-Electronics Command; Joint Tactical Command; Control & Communications Agency; Army Information Systems Management Activity; Army Chaplain Center & School; U.S. Military Academy Prep School): Helipads 41.25 255.7 Security 164.55 165.0875 EOD 49.70 49.80 FD 123.075 EOD 49.70 49.80 Army 36.70 38.70 40.15 41.50 46.70 139.08 139.20 141.025 143.10 148.025 148.925 149.80 163.5875 164.50 336.3 229.6 231.0 232.2 248.3 267.1 280.8 304.5 320.7 321.5 321.7 368.7 369.8 394.0 399.0

Ft. Monroe, Hampton, VA (HQ Continental Army Command; HQ Training & Doctrine Command (TRADOC)): Helipad 122.9 Security 165.0625 FD 163.5375 165.0625 Civil Engineer 163.5375 165.0625 Transportation 173.4875 USN 139.55 150.39 AF OP ("King Cole") 292.3 321.2 363.9 AF 138.05 250.5 253.2 308.8 325.4 339.0 355.1 373.1 381.1 385.7 390.0 Army 139.65 143.00 143.40

Ft. Myer, Arlington, VA (3rd Infantry; Army Band): Security 36.71 FD 36.55 36.99 CID 412.95 Escorts 36.71 Official Ceremonies 148.665 Army 38.95 49.80 139.65 141.125 142.325 142.35 150.60 164.15 407.275 407.55 409.075 409.925

Ft. Norfolk, VA: Army 149.775

Ft. Ord, CA: See Fritzche AAF.

Ft. Pickett, VA: See Blackstone AAF.

Ft. Polk, LA: See Polk AAF.

Ft. Randall, SD: Army 164.525 165.0625 407.25 413.55

Ft. Richardson, AK: See Bryant AHP.

Ft. Riley, KS: See Marshall AAF.

Ft. Ritchie, Cascade, MD (7th Signal Command of Army Information Systems Command): Security ("Base 240") 149.865 Army 139.175 143.355 148.60 149.60 149.85 150.435 241.0

Ft. Roots, AR: Army 406.9375 407.2375 407.525 407.5625

Ft. Rosecrans, CA: EOD 49.70 49.80

Ft. Rucker, AL (Army Aviation Center & School): Army 40.90 41.30 139.05 139.10 139.25 139.30 141.25 141.30 141.35 141.40 141.45 141.50 142.40 142.455 142.90 142.935 142.975 143.00 143.025 143.05 143.075 143.10 143.125 143.175 143.225 143.30 143.35 143.40 148.605 148.65 148.70 148.755 148.80 148.815 148.85 149.06 149.65 149.70 149.75 149.85 150.425 150.475 150.60 150.70 163.5375 164.70 165.0375 165.0875 165.1875 226.9 232.2 232.8 233.1 242.4 244.8 248.0 249.2 261.3 267.2 299.1 300.0 304.7 321.5 321.6 339.9 340.0 340.1 347.6 356.9 365.2 366.2 367.5 373.7 386.3 389.4 393.3 397.4 412.90 413.525 (Also see Cairns AAF, Hanchey AAF, Lowe AHP, Knox AHP, & Shell AHP.)

Ft. Sam Houston, San Antonio, TX (HQ 5th Army; Army Health Services Command; Brooke Army Medical Center; Academy of Health Sciences; 90th Reserve Command; Medical Field Service School): S 118.9 Helipad 41.50 142.35 233.2 Security/MP 165.1875 507th Medical Co ("MAST Ops") 30.50 Brooke Pager 149.775 EOD 49.70 49.80 Duty Officer 164.775 Army 139.025 139.20 139.325 139.40 141.025 141.15 141.30 141.45 142.475 142.875 142.95 143.05 148.815 149.675 150.525 150.675 164.9625 165.0375 165.0875 165.4875 165.6125 173.5125 226.3 227.1 227.3 227.5 229.3 229.5 229.7 229.9 230.1 230.9 248.2 407.25 412.90 412.425 413.525 (Also see Camp Bullis.)

Ft. Scott, IL: Range 38.91 38.98 Pager 173.4125

Ft. Scott Muni Apt., KS: AD 327.0

Ft. Shafter, HI: Army 30.30 30.50 32.10 32.30 32.42 32.46 32.50 32.54 32.66 32.70 32.86 32.90 32.94 34.10 34.30 34.34 34.46 34.50 34.74 34.90 36.10 36.30 36.46 36.50 36.54 36.70 36.86 36.90 36.94 38.10 38.30 38.50 38.54 38.70 38.86 38.90 40.06 40.10 40.26 40.50 40.90 40.94 40.98 41.02 41.50 41.60 41.80 139.095 139.305 141.405 142.335 142.905 143.055 143.085 143.235 148.905 149.595

Ft. Sheridan, Highland Park, IL (HQ 4th Army; HQ Army Recruiting Command; Army Communications Command; Army Readiness & Mobilization Command): Aviation OP 123.45   FD 154.265   Army 141.20 141.325 142.325 163.4625 163.5625 165.0375 165.0875 165.0875 165.1625 165.4125 165.6125 173.4875

Ft. Sill, OK: See Henry Post AAF.

Ft. Smith Muni Apt., AR: FSS 255.4   AD 228.4 317.55 393.0 398.9   G 275.8   T 381.6   ANG CP 268.1   ANG 163.375 163.4875 163.5875 165.1375

Ft. Snelling, St. Paul, MN (88th Infantry Division): Army 139.125 143.05

Ft. Stewart, GA: See Wright AAF.

Ft. Stockton-Pecos Co. Apt., TX: AD 343.6

Ft. Story, Virginia Beach, VA: Spier Helipad 41.50   Security 140.125 407.475   FD 173.4125   Army 141.05 141.10 141.25 142.40 142.45 149.85 173.4125   USN 36.85 40.55 138.55 138.95 138.975 140.025 148.33 148.35 149.095 150.15 233.7 273.0 274.8 291.3 342.8 347.8 352.2 356.2 361.2 380.6 370.7 385.1 385.3 405.50 413.00

Ft. Thompson, SD: Army 163.5625 168.275

Ft. Totten, Bayside, NY: 38.30 38.83 38.91

Fortuna, ND: AF 173.4375   NORAD CP 364.2   NORAD 228.8 228.9 234.6 234.7 238.4 238.5 251.0 254.2 256.6 260.8 263.2 267.0 270.2 270.4 274.4 275.0 278.4 281.6 287.8 292.7 298.5 302.4 306.2 309.4 316.3 320.6 324.0 325.5 327.9 336.6 338.4 341.8 344.0 346.2 369.0 375.1 377.0 386.2 387.8 392.8 398.0

Ft. Vancouver, WA: Army 165.0625

Ft. Wadsworth, Staten Island, NY: USN 38.83 38.91

Ft. Wainright, AK: See Wainright AAF.

Ft. Walton Beach, FL: USN 149.37

Ft. Wayne Muni Apt./Baer Fld, IN: FSS 255.4 349.0   S 349.0   AD 260.6 284.6 369.2 398.2   G 348.6   T 257.8   122nd Tactical Fighter Wing ANG CP ("Snake Pit") 289.3   ANG 148.40 148.175 148.55 149.275 150.15 150.225 150.34 311.0 321.0 340.8 369.2 398.2

Ft. Wayne, IN: USN 34.35 36.15 38.30 40.80

Ft. William Harrison, Helena, MT: NG Helicopters 36.50

Ft. Wingate Army Depot, Gallup, NM: Army 141.00 165.1625 280.8 304.3 409.00 409.65 412.975

Ft. Worth Meacham Apt., TX: FSS 255.4   AD 227.8 379.9   T 257.8

Ft. Yukon, AK: AD 122.5 135.0 370.1   T 126.2   AF 148.845 163.5875 229.1 238.4 260.8 269.0 287.5 292.5 315.8 364.2

Four Corners Regn'l. Apt., NM: FSS 255.4   AD 257.8 363.05   T 257.8

Four Lakes Communications Station, Cheny, WA: AF 141.80 143.80 150.15 253.4 377.4 349.1 359.0 412.825 412.90

Fox Lake, IL: CG 142.08 142.38

Frakes Aviation, Cleburne, TX: 123.225

Frances E. Warren AFB, WY: See Cheyenne, WY.

Frances E. Warren Auxiliary #2, NE: AF 149.265 149.565

Frankford Arsenal, Philadelphia, PA: Army 139.15 164.0375 165.1875 173.4625

Frankfurt Main USAF, Rhein Main, Germany: DI 140.45   S 114.2 118.025   AD 119.15 120.15 120.8 127.5 203.3 231.25 359.8 367.15   T 119.9 124.85 249.5   G 121.8 121.9   Apron 121.7 122.05   Ramp 121.6 121.7   WX 259.4   CP 131.625 260.9 366.95 VFR Advisory 123.2 124.475 124.725 130.975   Hospital Heliport 30.75   Area MIL Heliports 31.80 33.20 122.1 142.90 251.2

Franklin Co State Apt., VT: AD 360.8 396.1

Franklin Muni-J. B. Rose Apt., VA: AD 249.9

Frasca Fld., Urbana, IL: AD 397.9

Frederick Muni Apt., MD: AD 307.9 AF 142.155

Freeman Fld., KS: AD 388.8

Freeman Muni Apt., IN: AD 269.4

Fremont Apt., OH: AD 307.0

Fresno Air Terminal, CA (ANG 14th Fighter Intercept Wing): S 273.6 FSS 255.4 AD 288.1 297.2 315.6 G 348.6 E 288.1 ANG OP ("Griffin Ops") 298.3 NG OP ("Shark Ops") 30.50 132.0 255.8 Emergency 163.4875 Maintenance 163.5875 FD/Crash 163.4625 Medics 163.5375 Security 163.375 165.1625 ANG 163.275 163.375 163.5625 163.8625 251.9 298.7 399.8 NG 148.65 USN 275.4 320.2

Fritzche AAF/Ft. Ord, Monterey, CA (7th Infantry Division): DI 38.80 S 124.6 AD 127.15 128.7 133.0 133.5 263.6 302.0 307.0 309.2 T 40.95 41.50 125.15 229.6 G 121.8 241.0 WX 344.6 OP 123.05 125.15 229.6 Medevac ("MAST Ops") 36.50 130.05 Ambulances 407.225 413.025 Range 32.25 32.75 34.40 38.90 PD 141.225 141.375 143.10 143.25 163.3375 Security 172.30 173.4125 173.5875 CID 150.675 407.575 412.90 413.425 Engineering 141.025 142.325 148.025 408.125 Maintenance 413.025 EOD 49.70 49.80 Pager 173.4875 Emergency Training 407.475 412.875 Army 38.00 140.325 141.245 141.50 141.80 142.45 142.92 143.375 143.40 143.975 149.375 150.25 163.5625 165.0375 165.0875 Msc 30.00 34.90 AF 139.70 321.2 347.3 (Also see Camp Roberts & Hunter Liggett Military Reservation.)

Fulda AAF, Germany: DI 33.20 AD 127.725 138.25 242.55 306.7 T 31.80 122.1 142.90 251.2 G 141.30 251.2 WX 140.30

Fullerton Muni Apt., AD 343.9

Fulton Co. Apt., IN: AD 362.3

Fulton Co.-Brown Fld, Atlanta, GA: FSS 255.4 AD 254.25 T 257.8 348.6 G 348.6 VIP OP ("Forscom") 141.35 FAA 162.275 164.60 165.75 166.175 Army Aviation 122.975 149.75 Lockheed 464.925

Furth AHP, Montieth Barracks, Nurnberg, Germany: T 118.3 356.1

Futenma MCAS, Okinawa: DI 307.4 S 230.8 AD 119.1 126.5 254.8 258.3 335.8 T 123.6 340.2 360.2 WX 290.6

Gadsden Muni Apt, AL: AD 231.1

Gage Apt., OK: FSS 255.4 AD 379.2

Gainesville Regn'l Apt., FL: FSS 255.4 AD 385.6 T 353.7

Gaithersburg, MD (220th MP Bde, Army Reserve): 164.9625

Galena Apt, AK (5072nd Combat Support Sqdn): DI 372.2 AD 259.3 290.9 T 255.6 G 275.8 AF 163.4875 165.1375 173.5125 173.5875 255.6 275.8 324.3 327.5

Galesburg Muni Apt., IL: AD 257.8 316.1

Galion Muni Apt., AD 317.7 390.8

Gallatin Fld., Bozeman, MT: FSS 255.4 AD 338.3

Gallia-Meigs Regn'l. Apt., Gallipolis, OH: AD 257.8
Gallup Muni-Senator Clarke Fld., NM: FSS 255.4
Garden City Muni Apt., KS: FSS 255.4 AD 269.4
Garden City, NY (HQ 1st USMC District): 138.55
Gardner Muni Apt., MA: AD 338.2
Garland ANG Sta., TX: ANG 148.20 148.475 235.5 240.5 252.5 372.5 388.5 396.5
Garner Fld., Uvalde, TX: AD 285.4
Gary, IN: USN 32.45 36.55
Gary Muni Apt., IN: AD 285.6
Gastonia Muni Apt., NC: AD 288.15
Gates Learjet Company: Wichita, KS 123.2 123.425 123.45 153.17 462.15; Tucson, AZ: 123.2 334.7 461.825; Reno, NV 123.45
Gateway Army Ammunition Plant, St. Louis, MO: Army 38.69 38.89 163.5375 165.1625 173.4625 173.5125
Gateway North Industr'l Apt., Anoka, MN: AD 355.5
Geilenkirchen NATO, Germany: S 398.3 AD 143.35 259.85 268.9 T ("Frisbee") 122.1 140.075 257.8 280.05 361.65 G ("Frisbee") 350.95 CP ("Magic") 139.875 259.65 375.8
General Aviation Electronics Co., Indianapolis, IN: 151.585 151.685
General Brees Fld., Laramie, WY: FSS 255.4 AD 281.5 Dept. Commerce 121.6 122.9
General Dynamics Company: Pomona, CA Pager 154.625; Shippingport, PA 461.10; Goose Creek, SC 461.175; San Diego, CA 462.225; Southfield, MI 463.40; Chelsea, MI 148.60 149.625; Troy, MI 148.60 148.625; Utica, MI 148.60 148.625; Denver, CO 148.40 148.60 148.625; TX 154.60
General Electric Company: Lynchburg, VA 151.865 153.32 158.235 158.265 158.31 159.075 159.135 461.65 462.30 462.65 857.625; Missile/Armament Division, Burlington, VT 462.375 (Also see specific location listings.)
General Edward L. Logan Int'l. Apt., Boston, MA: FSS 255.4 AD 263.1 279.6 343.6 382.0 E 257.8 ANG 321.0 413.45 FD/Crash 453.75 Security 156.015 Maintenance 453.875 464.825
General Lyman Fld., Hilo, HI: AD 269.2 T 263.1 WX 272.7
General Mitchell Fld., Milwaukee, WI: FSS 255.4 AD 307.0 379.8 G348.6 T 325.8 95th Tactical Air Sqdn AF Reserve CP ("Sweet") 376.1 440th Tactical Air Wing ANG CP ("Instigator") 148.175 376.1 413.15 440th TAW Security 163.4625 440th TAW FD/Crash 173.5875 440th TAW Maintenance 165.1375 440th TAW Cargo 150.20 440th TAW Civil Engineering 148.10 413.20 440th TAW Civil Engineering 148.10 413.20 128th AREFG ANG CP ("Upset Control") 139.50 351.2 128th AREFG OP 163.0125 128th AREFG Security 163.4875 163.9625 128th AREFG FD/Crash 163.5125 128th AREFG Maintenance 163.5625 163.5875 128th AREFG Crew Alerts 413.45 SAC CP 311.0 321.0 ANG 41.45 139.70 141.80 148.245 150.195 164.50 165.1375 311.3 314.2 322.7 361.4 384.7 413.30
General Motors Research: Indianapolis, IN 123.2 123.5 158.28 461.10 462.275 462.375; Maywood, IN 151.745
General Services Admin. Depot, Curtis Bay, MD: 163.075 163.175
General W.J. Fox Fld., Lancaster, CA: FSS 255.4 AD 284.7 290.3 G 256.9
Genesee Co Apt., Batavia, NY: AD 322.3
George AFB, Victorville, CA (ACC; 12th AF; 37th Fighter Wing; 55th Training Wing; 831st Air Division; 27th Tactical Air Support Sqdn. **Closing date 12/92.** DI 372.2 AD 124.05 133.15 269.2 340.9 T 118.35 348.4 G 148.545 275.8 E 225.4 CP ("Raymond 6") 381.3 WX 344.6 CP 165.1125 Security 148.545 149.30 163.4875 165.0125 165.0875 OSI 138.075 138.165 138.175 AF 46.65 139.05 142.155 148.45 149.40 149.325 150.20 150.315 166.25 173.4625 173.5625 173.5875 267.8 276.6 283.8 288.7 292.3 293.2 324.5 342.2 364.1 369.2 381.1 388.8 396.1 396.9 407.5 413.025 413.05 413.275 413.35 413.40

George M. Bryan Fld., Starkville, MS: AD 226.0 269.4

Georgetown Co. Apt., SC: AD 343.6

Georgetown Muni Apt., TX: AD 363.8

Gibbsboro AFS, NJ: AF 163.4875

Giebelstadt AAF, Germany, DI 33.70 AD 129.85 140.75 258.95 275.35 G 141.30 276.55 E 141.30 276.55 Info 122.5 WX 140.30 Leighton Barracks Medevac 30.75

Giessen AHP, Germany, Cooke Baracks, Germany: AD 11.2 125.5 Advisory 40.20 141.50 399.85

Gila Bend Air Force Auxiliary Fld., AZ: T 126.2 324.1 Range 120.55 272.1 AF 38.65 40.15 148.245 148.275 148.425 148.53 148.575 148.95 149.05 149.175 149.375 149.45 149.875 150.135 150.225 150.725 171.375 295.3 295.9 296.5 298.6 305.6 308.7 311.3 316.7 407.325 413.275 Army 40.90 (Auxiliary to Luke AFB, operates only during Luke flying periods. Emergency use only.)

Gillette, WY: SAC 238.6

Glacier Park Int'l. Apt., MT: AD 285.4

Glasgow Int'l. Apt., MT: AD 272.75

Glasgow Muni Apt., KY: AD 263.1

Glenview NAS, IL: DI 372.2 S 281.0 AD 119.0 120.55 125.0 125.7 126.9 134.4 290.2 337.4 353.9 363.8 T 126.2 340.2 360.2 G 118.45 382.8 WX 341.3 Army Aviation 123.45 Security 140.025 FD/Crash 140.10 140.895 154.265 OP 140.075 CG 381.8 383.9 (HF 5692 8980 kHz) Rescue 282.8 USN 30.45 32.45 32.65 32.85 34.15 34.35 34.55 36.55 36.85 41.10 138.60 139.55 140.65 140.775 140.90 142.85 264.2 281.0 302.6 311.6 314.8 336.4 346.8

Glynco Jetport, Brunswick, GA: AD 277.4

Godman AAF/Ft. Knox, KY (Armor Center & School; 194th Armored Brigade; Cavalry Center; Bullion Depository): S 109.6 AD 120.5 123.7 124.5 306.2 327.0 388.2 T 32.10 126.2 229.6 G 121.9 241.0 OP 125.125 Range #14 33.00 WX 127.475 344.6 Security 165.0875 Bullion Depository 411.675 Bldg Maintenance 164.70 EOD 49.70 49.80 Army 32.10 139.035 139.15 139.275 139.30 141.12 141.175 141.325 142.45 142.90 142.925 142.975 143.00 143.05 143.10 143.125 143.175 143.225 143.235 143.275 143.325 143.35 143.375 143.40 143.975 148.575 148.675 148.90 148.925 149.575 149.725 149.80 165.5375 163.5625 164.625 165.4375 173.5125 226.3 226.8 227.0 227.2 227.6 321.7 347.5 347.7 356.3 356.5 356.7 361.6 390.9 399.3 399.7 407.275 407.475 407.575 412.975 AF 46.65 49.75 138.40 139.70 260.7 292.3 349.3

Gold Creek AFS, AK: T 126.2

Golden Triangle Regn'l. Apt., Columbus, MS: AD 226.0 269.4

Goliad NALF, TX: AD 121.3 264.2 T 126.2 345.2 355.8 USN 138.55

Goodfellow AFB, San Angelo, TX (Electronic Security Command): AF 163.4625 173.125 173.5625 173.5875

Goodwin Fld., Eldorado, ARL FSS 255.4 AD 269.1

Goodyear Aerospace Company: Akron, OH 151.625 153.32 462.05 462.225; Suffield, OH 462.05; Litchfield Park, AZ 153.17 153.26

Goose Bay AAF, TX: OP 122.9

Goppingen AAF, Cooke Barracks Germany: AD 119.2 125.05 Advisory 40.20 141.50 399.85

Goshen Muni Apt., IN: AD 257.8 317.6

Governors Island CG Base, NY: Security 40.39 162.5625 CG 165.2625 171.3625 406.5625 407.625 419.975

Grafenwohr AAF, Germany: AD 138.25 275.45 T 31.80 122.1 142.45 250.55 369.8 G 141.30 250.55 OP 44.30 WX 140.30 Range 30.40 46.65

Grand Canyon Nat'l. Park Apt., AZ: AD 343.6

Grand Forks AFB, ND (ACC; 8th AF; 321st Strategic Missile Wing; 319th Bombardment Wing; 321st Combat Support Grp): AD 132.3 294.7 318.1 371.2 T ("Red River Tower") 124.9 349.0 DI 372.2 G 119.15 359.3 E 118.1 318.1 WX

344.6 SAC CP 311.0 321.0 OSI 138.075 138.165 138.175 AF 148.065 148.45 148.50 149.515 148.545 148.95 149.235 149.475 149.525 149.565 150.025 150.10 150.15 150.195 150.225 150.255 150.315 150.35 163.5875 164.50 173.4375 173.5375 173.5875 228.3 266.2 271.9 294.7 300.8 314.3 323.8 324.5 335.9 339.1 349.5 359.3 379.4 413.05 413.15 413.325 413.45

Grand Forks Mark Andrews Int'l Apt., ND: FSS 255.4 AD 394.7 T 388.8

Grand Haven Mem'l Airpark, MI: AD 269.6

Grand Island, LA: AF 228.8 234.7 251.0 256.6 263.2 270.4 275.0 287.8 302.4 306.4 325.5 338.4 344.0 356.0 364.2 369.0 375.1 392.8

Grand Rapids Itasca Co Apt., MI: FSS 255.4 AD 290.5

Grand Rapids, MI: USN 32.45 36.55 40.80 148.35

Grand Strand Apt., N. Myrtle Bch, SC: AD 321.1 343.6 T 397.2 G 397.2

Granite Mtn. AFS, AK: FSS 122.1

Grant Co. Apt., NM: AD 351.8

Grant Co Apt., Moses Lk, WA: AD 257.8 291.6 385.5 AF 46.75 138.10 139.60 142.25 311.0 340.6 341.5 342.3

Grant Co Apt., Platteville, WI: AD 351.8

Gratiot Community Apt., Alma, MI: AD 307.8 381.5

Gray AAF, TX: See Robert Gray AAF.

Gray AAF/Ft. Lewis, Tacoma, WA (1st Corps; 9th Infantry Division (Motorized); 4th ROTC Region; 2nd Battalion of 75th Rangers; 1st Special Forces Grp; 15th Support Brigade) S 124.65 248.2 AD 119.5 126.5 391.9 T 41.50 126.2 242.4 248.2 G 121.9 229.5 E 121.9 229.5 OP 32.30 WX 38.45 38.90 342.5 Airspace Cntrl. 34.50 Range 40.20 Flight Following 34.60 141.50 393.3 NG 34.50 34.60 123.075 141.50 Medevac ("MAST Ops") 40.55 47.50 FD 165.0875 173.4125 173.4875 EOD 49.70 49.80 Security 36.50 149.525 149.575 149.875 150.435 150.725 407.375 412.875 413.075 413.425 CID 32.80 407.375 413.4125 413.425 Medic Pager 407.325 Civil Engineering 412.875 Army 139.025 148.575 150.425 150.525 150.675 164.20 165.0625 171.375 300.1 347.7 367.4 393.3 407.425 AF 32.45 36.85 40.15 46.75 138.10 139.60 139.70 141.80 142.25 282.2 290.6 319.3 340.6 341.5 342.3 347.3

Grayling AAF/Camp Grayling, MI: FSS 122.65 AD 132.9 398.9 T 36.50 41.85 126.2 241.0 G 121.9 Unicom 122.8 AD 132.9 398.9 OP 41.90 126.2 Range 41.80 41.85 Security 42.00 FD 42.00 Guide Net 41.90 Pager 42.10 Maintenance 42.40 NG 37.00 139.125 139.30 141.35 143.05 143.10 143.35 143.40 229.4 248.2 347.7 381.8 385.7

Grayson Co Apt., Sherman, TX: AD 377.1

Great Barrington Apt., MA: AD 307.2

Great Bend Muni Apt., KS: AD 337.4

Greater Buffalo Int'l Apt., NY: FSS 255.4 AD 236.5 257.8 305.4 317.6 G 257.8 T 257.8 E 257.8 AF 255.5 236.0 257.0

Greater Peoria Apt., IL: S 282.2 AD 269.2 326.2 G 346.6 T 252.9 NG 32.30 ANG 40.15 163.4875 163.40 169.4625 165.1375 173.5375 285.5 297.1 ANG OP 34.15 141.55 286.5

Greater Pittsburgh Int'l Apt., PA: AD 126.2 337.4 338.2 360.8 363.8 388.0 G 348.6 T 258.3 291.7 ANG Tanker OP ("Shake Control") 303.0 (HF 14652 kHz) ANG OP ("Trice") 303.0 ANG Fighter OP ("Steel") 36.35 293.7 E 305.4 911th Tactical Air Grp AF Reserve ("Trice") 252.1 Security 163.4875 Maintenance 148.515 ANG 149.00

Greater Portsmouth Regn'l Apt., OH: AD 257.8

Greater Rochester Int'l. Apt., NY: AD 296.6 322.3 T 254.3

Greater Rockford Apt., IL: AD 287.1 327.0 379.2 G 348.6 T 239.0

Great Falls Int'l Apt., MT: FSS 255.4 S 269.0 AD 259.1 285.4 290.3 380.3 T 282.2 E 363.8 G 348.6 ANG OP 288.9 ANG Maintenance 288.9 ANG 148.125 148.215 148.455 149.235 149.275 150.195 163.4625 287.5 288.9 387.5 399.9

Great Lakes Naval Training Center & Base: SP 140.65 148.35 148.95 149.45 FD 148.275 148.29 150.075 Pager 150.10 "Trouble Base" 149.37 Base Transportation 140.70 Medics 150.10 USN 138.95 140.075 140.65 140.775 148.35 149.01 336.4 363.4 407.475 413.075

Greeley AHP, Ft. Monmouth, NJ: OP 41.25 255.7 FD 123.075 (See listings for Ft. Monmouth, NJ.)

Greeley-Weld Co Apt., CO: AD 284.7

Greenbriar Valley Apt., WV: AD 353.9

Greene Co Apt., Xenia, OH: AD 327.1

Greenham Common USAF, UK: AD 126.7 134.3 250.6 264.5 308.75 T 122.1 257.8 266.8 G 276.55 Security 32.20 76.40 76.55 Msc 76.625

Greensboro, NC: USN 275.4 320.2

Greenville Apt., IL: 317.7

Greenville Downtown Apt., SC: AD 257.9 385.4 T 257.7 AF 413.0

Greenville Muni Apt., MS: AD 269.35 T 256.9 G 256.9

Greenville, MS: USN 143.50

Greenville-Spartanburg Apt., Greer, SC: FSS 255.4 AD 257.9 350.2 385.4 T 257.8

Greenwood Co Apt., SC: AD 322.4 350.2 Army 231.5 232.5 243.5 245.5 247.5 248.5 356.5 364.5 365.5 367.5 368.5 370.5 399.5

Greenwood-Leflore Apt., MS: FSS 255.4 AD 259.1 T 367.6 G 373.4

Gregg Co Apt., Longview, TX: AD 270.3 T 377.05

Grenada Muni Apt. MS: AD AD 252.7

Grider Fld., Pine Bluff, AR: FSS 255.4 AD 353.6

Griffing-Sandusky Apt., OH: AD 327.0

Griffiss AFB, Rome, NY (ACC; 1st AF; NE Air Defense Sector; 9th AF; 416th Bombardment Wing; Rome Laboratory): DI 122.95 372.2 S 284.7 AD 118.5 120.9 126.65 269.5 353.6 363.8 395.0 T 126.25 236.6 289.6 291.7 E 295.0 G 121.8 275.8 WX 344.6 MAC ALCE 228.2 Base Op 165.1375 Security 163.30 163.4625 163.4875 163.5875 164.10 164.60 FD/Crash 154.25 161.25 173.5125 173.5875 OSI 40.13 40.17 40.19 138.075/141.525 138.175/141.525 138.275 138.375 Pager 138.325 Crew Alerts 413.45 Rome Air Development Center 143.925 150.225 162.225 Commanders Net 149.565/148.065 Flightline Maintenance 148.515 SAC Flightline Maintenance 148.175 148.55 149.20 149.50 Maintenance/Supply 173.5625 173.8625 Base Transportation 150.345 Railroad OP 161.07 162.015 Petroleum/Oils/Lubrication 173.4375 Materials Handling 407.40 Ramp Control 165.1375 Civil Engineering 165.0125 165.1375 Disaster Preparedness 150.345 Communications & Navaid Repair 163.30 163.5875 164.10 165.0125 485th Engineering Geodetic Survey 150.195 413.025 413.10 413.40 416th Bombardment Wing Commanders Net 148.075/149.525 49th FIS Maintenance 148.215 150.165 165.1875 Medics 173.4125 173.5125 Air Refueling 264.9 24th AD Commanders Net 407.45/411.35 AF 138.165 138.90 139.90 141.90 143.85 148.545 150.255 164.50 173.5375 173.7125 238.8 251.9 257.9 259.2 284.1 291.8 293.2 293.4 302.7 303.4 319.6 349.6 379.9 383.0 384.8 399.8 413.15 SAC CP 311.0 321.0

Grimes Fld., OH: AD 316.7

Grissom AFB, Peru, IN (AMC; 305th Air Refueling Wing; 931st Air Refueling Grp; 434th Tactical Fighter Wing; 46th Tactical Fighter Sqdn AF Reserve): DI 372.2 S 271.8 AD 120.0 121.05 351.1 363.8 T 133.7 295.7 G 275.8 E 324.3 WX 344.6 Security 163.5125 163.5625 164.05 164.075 FD/Crash 173.5875 WX 344.6 Base Commanders Net 149.525 149.575 Civil Engineering 163.4875 Emergencies 163.5875 Job Control 165.0125 Base Transportation 163.5875 Pager 138.325 Medics 173.5625 Air-to-Air 46.75 49.85 Baker Net 165.1625 AF 123.0 138.075 138.925 139.875 143.825 148.065 148.45 148.525 149.235 149.565 164.50 164.9625 165.1125 165.1375 173.4375 252.1 318.2 339.3 372.9 388.8 392.2 407.475 413.075 413.15 413.175 413.20 413.30 413.425 SAC CP 311.0 321.0 Crew Alerts 413.45

Groton Submarine Base, CT: Security 153.22 Cranes 462.225 FD 33.74 33.78 33.90 33.92 33.94 33.96 153.32 USN 143.675 236.2 236.35 237.85 277.8 Dept of Agriculture 171.525 Msc 153.08 153.26 153.32

Groton-New London Apt., CT: AD 307.9 346.0 380.25 T 352.8 NG 40.90 122.75 G 352.8

Grumman Aerospace Company: Bethpage, NY 36.90 123.2 123.25 123.4 123.45 151.865 153.35 154.625 162.25 164.50 165.625 166.75 168.25 169.00 169.75 170.125 171.25 173.50 462.375 256.5 268.8 275.2 309.8 314.6 345.4 360.4 372.3 382.6 398.6 399.8 (HF 3280 3283 6585 kHz); Calverton, NY 36.90 123.2 123.45 123.55 268.8 275.2 309.8 340.2 345.2 360.2 382.6 462.375 Security 153.35 (HF 3280 3283 kHz (Also see Calverton NWIRP listings.); Florida 34.10 38.90 46.90 49.65; Savannah, GA 123.2 123.3 123.35 123.475 153.35

Grumman-Bethpage Apt., NY (Inactive): AD 269.0 388.0 396.1 T 121.3 126.2 340.2 E 340.2

Guadalupe Co Apt., Seguin, TX: AF 271.2

Guam Naval Station, GU: USN 140.15 140.25

Guantanamo Bay NAS/Leeward Pt. Fld., Cuba: AD 134.1 263.6 289.4 T 126.2 340.2 G 118.45 360.2 WX 344.6 (HF 6723 kHz)

Guernsey Apt., WY: AF 126.2

Gulfport-Biloxi Regional Apt., MS: AD 287.1 288.15 354.1 G 348.6 T 379.8 ANG 138.025 138.375 148.215 148.545 149.475 234.8 235.5 249.5 279.1 377.8 388.5 395.5 NG 139.15

Gulfport Naval Seabee Center, MS: Transportation 138.55 FD 138.50 Security 149.10 USN 138.84 140.10 143.60 148.30

Gunter AFB, Montgomery, AL (Air University; HQ Standard Systems Center of AF Communications Command; AF Logistics Manpower Center; AF Extension Course Institute; AF Senior NCO Academy): AF 139.65 163.4875 164.175 165.1375

Gunter AFS, Montgomery, AL (AF Data Systems Design Center): See Gunter AFB.

Guthrie AAF, Ft. Rucker, AL: AD 125.8 232.5 T 127.95 254.6 E 120.325 304.45 OP ("Warlord OP") 41.30 (Also see listings for Cairns AAF.)

Guyamon Muni Apt., OK: AD 290.8

H-108 Hpt, Camp Howze, S. Korea: Advisories ("Warrior Cntrl.") 37.60 123.3 255.8

H-127 Hpt, JSA Rear, S. Korea: Advisories ("Warrior Cntrl.") 37.60 123.3 255.8

H-128 Hpt, JSA, S. Korea: Advisories ("Warrior Cntrl.") 37.60 123.3 255.8

H-172 Hpt, Camp Pelham, S. Korea: Advisories ("Warrior Cntrl.") 37.60 123.3 255.8

H-173 & H-173A Hpts, Hill 496, S. Korea: Advisories ("Warrior Cntrl.") 37.60 123.3 255.8

H-207 Hpt, Cochran AHP/Camp Stanley, S. Korea: T 37.20 118.9 266.4 OP ("Apache OP") 31.75

H-208 Hpt, Yongsan, S. Korea: OP 46.90 WX 37.30 Advisory 42.50 141.50 233.8

H-209 Hpt, Camp Red Cloud, S. Korea: AD ("Cobra OP") 65.15 ("LaGuardia OP") 36.45 127.0 254.1 Advisories ("Summit Noble") 36.75

H-210 Hpt, Camp LaGuardia, S. Korea: T 36.45 127.0 254.1 OP ("Cobra OP") 65.15

H-211 Hpt, Camp Mosier, S. Korea: Advisories ("LaGuardia OP") 36.45 127.0 254.1

H-220 Hpt, Camp Casey, KS: DI 35.40 T 35.40 122.5 227.1 WX 37.30 OP 45.80

H-221 Hpt, Camp Casey East, S. Korea: Advisories 35.40 123.3 227.1

H-245 Hpt, Camp Colbern, S. Korea: AD 35.80

H-247 Hpt, FOC North, S. Korea: Advisories 36.45 127.0 254.1 Msc 45.95

H-248 Hpt, S. Korea: Advisories 36.45 127.0 254.1

H-250 Hpt, Camp Merser, S. Korea: Advisories 35.40 122.5 227.1

H-253 Hpt, S. Korea: AD 45.95

H-263 Hpt, Camp Hovey, S. Korea: Advisories 35.40 122.5 227.1

H-310 Hpt, Evenreach, S. Korea: OP 36.90 120.5 245.9

H-401 Hpt, Camp Eagle, S. Korea: AD ("Hoengsong Approach Cntrl.") 141.20 T ("Hoengsong Tower") 126.2 236.6 265.5 OP 35.80

H-416 Hpt, Camp Long, S. Korea: OP 35.25

H-503 Hpt, Camp Ames, S. Korea: OP ("Tango Cntrl.") 50.20

H-508 Hpt, Highpoint, S. Korea: AD ("Vanderbilt Foxtrot") 38.65

H-608 Hpt, Salem Top, S. Korea: AD ("Vanderbilt Hotel") 38.65

H-805 Hpt, Camp Walker, S. Korea: Flight Following ("Taegu Radio") 32.25 T 41.40 122.5 233.8 OP 49.85 51.20 62.45

H-809 Hpt, S. Korea: AD ("Vanderbilt Kilo") 38.65

H-811 Hpt, Dartboardm S. Korea: AD ("Vanderbilt India") 38.45

H-830 Hpt, Hialeah Compound, S. Korea: OP ("Protector") 41.45 41.75

H-831 Hpt, S. Korea: AD ("Busan Radio") 32.25

H-832, Camp Carrol Cargo, S. Korea: AD ("Banker Charlie") 41.75 OP ("Classic Python") 49.20 ("Longbow") 40.30

Hagler AAF, Camp Shelby, MS: T 126.2 241.0 (Also see Camp Shelby listings.)

Hahn AB, Germany: DI 367.4 S 262.6 AD 233.6 370.6 T 122.1 139.375 257.8 315.55 G375.0 E 306.25 CP 342.25 WX 259.4

Hale Co., Apt., Plainview, TX: AD 335.6

Haley AHP, IL: AD 120.5 337.4 VFR Advisory 126.2 340.2 (Also see Ft. Sheridan listings.)

Hall ANG Station, Dothan, AL: ANG 138.20 303.0 321.2 354.4 373.1

Halliburton Fld., Duncan, OK: AD 248.2

Hamilton AAF, San Rafael, CA: AD 127.8 353.5 VFR Advisory 34.50 124.95 241.2 T 128.0 241.2 OP 40.10 139.20 FD/Crash 149.70 150.425 Army Reserve ("Marathon Market") 34.50

Hammond ANG Communications Sta., LA: ANG 149.235 235.5 236.6 240.5 252.5 275.8 349.3 375.5 381.1 388.5 390.1 398.5

Hammond Barracks AHP, Mannheim, Germany: AD 31.80 33.60 122.1 142.20 257.8 314.8

Hammond Muni Apt., LA: AD 284.7

Hammonton Muni Apt., NJ: AD 385.5

Hampton Roads, VA: USN 359.4

Hanau AAF, Germany: AD 119.7 120.15 120.8 299.1 359.8 366.3 367.15 DI 72.10 T 31.18 37.60 122.1 142.45 234.8 G 141.30 250.55 WX 140.30 141.30 250.55

Hampton Roads Apt., Portsmouth, VA: AD 257.3

Hanchey AHP/Ft. Rucker, AL: S 141.375 AD 125.4 232.5 T 148.70 149.60 248.4 365.4 G 321.5 373.3 E 120.325 304.45 Army 143.10 163.5625 241.6 249.4 265.6 291.0 367.3 373.3 (Also see Ft. Rucker listings.)

Hancock Co.-Bar Harbor Apt., ME: AD 390.9

Hanover Co Muni Apt., Ashland, VA: AD 307.2 371.1

Hardy-Anders Fld./Natches-Adams Co. Apt., MS: AD 291.7

Harold Davidson Fld, Vermillion, SD: AD 269.0

Harold OLF, Milton, FL: OP 237.9

Harrell Fld., Camden, AR: AD 269.1

Harrisburg Int'l.-Olmstead Fld., PA: FSS 255.4 AD 247.2 339.3 379.8 T 231.1 E 307.0 OSI 40.17 40.19 Msc ("Warlock Base") 127.2 231.1 ANG OP 395.1 FD/Crash 33.80 33.84 33.90 ANG 149.175 148.225 148.45 148.545 150.20 173.5375 173.5875

Harry Clever Fld., New Philadelphia, OH: AD 226.4

Harry Diamond Army Labs, MD: Army 38.45 141.40 142.90 164.9625

Harry P. Williams Mem'l. Apt., Patterson, LA: AD 256.9

Hartford-Brainerd Apt., CT: AD 327.1 T 248.2

Hartford Muni Apt., WI: AD 307.0

Hartsfield Apt., Atlanta, GA: See **The** William Hartsfield Atlanta listings.

Hartsville Muni Apt., SC: AD 327.3

Harvard Observatory Agassiz Station, Cambridge, MA: 33.14 151.835 151.925 Security 467.2625

Haskell Indian College, Lawrence, KS: 162.025

Hastings Muni Apt., NE: AD 287.9 AF 354.3

Hattiesburg-Laurel Regn'l. Apt., MS: AD 281.5

Havre AFS, ME: AF 173.5625

Hawkins Fld., MS: AD 259.1 319.2 317.7 T 257.8 G 239.0 NG 241.0

Hawthorne Muni Apt., CA: AD 269.0 360.7 363.2 381.6 385.4 T 257.8 Northrop Company 31.04 123.3 123.35 123.5 123.525 158.28 334.7 462.20 463.35 462.85

Hayes International Corp: Birmingham, AL 123.2 151.835 451.8625 451.875 452.125; Dothan, AL ("Novel") 123.45 260.4 383.5

Hays Army Ammunition Depot, Pittsburgh, PA: 163.5875

Hays Munic Apt., KS: AD 322.4

Hayward Air Terminal, CA: AD 317.6 350.8 351.8 354.1 T 257.8 Rescue 139.70 390.0 ANG 138.90 148.20 149.15 150.05 150.025 150.30 150.35 163.4875 165.1125 235.5 240.5 252.5 359.3 375.5 388.5 394.5 397.2 398.5

Hayward Muni Apt., WI: AD 278.5

Hazeltine Company, Long Island, NY: 464.625

Hazelton Muni Apt., PA: AD 256.7 319.9

Heber Springs Muni Apt., AR: AD 286.6

Hector Int'l. Apt., Fargo, ND: DI 262.0 S 271.6 AD 255.6 395.9 G 348.6 T 290.4 E 348.6 ANG OP 262.0 ANG 143.75 149.525 163.00 164.9625 164.9875 165.1375 238.2 251.9 Dept Energy 122.9

Helena Regn'l Apt., MT: AD 226.3 285.4 T 257.8 NG 40.65 126.2

Hemet-Ryan Apt., CA: AD 278.3

Henderson, MS: USN 34.15

Henderson City/Co. Apt., KY: AD 226.4 284.65

Henryetta Muni Apt., OK: FSS 255.4 AD 278.3

Henry Post AAF/Ft. Sill, OK (Army Field Artillery Center & School; 11th Corps Artillery; Army Missile Center): DI 376.7 S 123.8 241.0 AD 118.6 120.55 121.0 134.1 227.3 233.2 248.2 T 124.95 229.4 G 121.7 231.4 E 118.6 248.2 WX 375.2 Duncan Sector 118.6 248.2 MP/Security 163.125 164.10 173.5625 FD 173.4625 Billeting 407.275 Engineer 173.4875 Artillery Range 30.50 Motor Pool 165.0875 Maintenance 173.4875 NG 40.10 41.15 46.90 EOD 49.70 49.80 AF 142.25 292.0

297.0 340.6 341.5 342.3   Army 138.60 139.00 139.10 139.15 139.20 139.30 139.325
139.40 139.60 141.05 141.15 141.125 141.175 141.40 142.90 143.05 143.10 143.15
143.25 143.35 143.40 148.575 148.60 148.65 148.875 148.90 148.925 149.775 149.80
149.875 150.425 150.60 163.00 164.50 164.50 164.70 165.0375 165.1875 166.20 170.125
226.5 227.0 229.8 231.2 234.3 237.7 238.8 241.8 242.4 244.3 356.8 373.8 376.3 386.4
393.4 396.6 397.7 399.7 407.325 407.525 412.825 412.90 412.975 413.275 413.425
413.525

   Henry T. Myers Apt., Tifton, GA: AD 285.6 259.3
   Herbert Smart Downtown Apt., Macon, GA: AD 324.3 348.7   AF 255.9 287.1 393.1
   Hercules Inc.: Bacchus, UT 153.125 461.775; Hopewell, VA 153.17 154.57 462.225;
Magna, UT 153.08 153.125 153.28 158.28 158.375 461.775
   Hereford Muni Apt., TX: AD 307.0 307.9 351.7
   Hermiston Muni Apt., OR: AD 343.9 380.2
   Hesler-Noble Fld., Laurel, MS: AD 281.5
   Hewlett-Packard Corp., Cupertino, CA: 151.655 153.11 462.275 464.475 464.925
   Hickam AFB, HI (HQ Pacific Air Forces; 15th Air Base Wing): DI 372.2   WX 344.6
Rescue 282.8   AD 285.4   T 257.8   G 348.6   FD/Crash 173.5625   Security 163.4625
164.20   Medics 172.775   Transportation 149.55   OSI 138.075 138.165 138.175   AF
125.1 125.5 128.0 138.3 139.65 139.75 139.875 139.95 141.80 143.825 148.05 148.065
148.125 148.185 148.475 148.455 149.175 149.535 150.225 150.285 150.31 150.345
163.5125 164.9625 165.0125 165.1125 165.1375 166.225 170.175 171.3875 172.225
173.4125 173.4375 173.5875 225.4 225.6 228.2 231.0 235.0 235.4 236.6 238.3 239.0
240.2 245.0 253.4 256.2 261.7 264.5 267.5 270.4 276.0 280.5 283.8 292.5 293.1 294.5
300.6 305.4 309.5 324.5 327.4 337.4 339.2 349.4 354.2 372.3 407.325 407.525 408.15
408.80 413.05 413.15   SAC CP 311.0 321.0   Nuclear Weapons Systems 150.45 163.075
164.375 230.4 248.6 259.7 293.0 315.1 410.00   USN 148.905 149.00   (USAF HF 6738
8967 11176 13201 kHz)
   Hickory Regn'l Apt., NC: FSS 255.4   AD 263.0
   Highland Co. Apt., Hillsboro, OH: AD 281.4
   Hill AFB, Ogden, UT (ACC; 12th AF; 388th Fighter Wing; Ogden Air Logistics
Center): DI 122.85 372.2   S 396.0   AD 121.1 124.9 126.0 126.8 290.3 301.5 307.2
316.7 381.2 389.8   T 127.15 236.6 289.6   G 121.6 275.8   E 124.1 335.8   419th OP
252.1   CP ("Convoy") 381.3   TAC CP ("Raymond 23") 381.3   WX 375.2   49th OP
251.2   Range 148.45 149.35 163.225 163.5125 164.05 164.165 164.1625   FD/Crash
148.485   F-16 Close Range Support Training 34.15 40.15   OSI 40.17 40.19
Maintenance 40.64   Utah Training Range Air/Ground 118.45   IFF Control 139.51
Helicopter Range Control & Rescue 139.60   PD/Security 149.165 149.265 163.4625
163.65   Base OP 173.4375   Crew Alerts 413.45   Medics 149.565   Life Support 150.135
Disaster Preparedness 163.5875   SAC CP 311.0 321.0   AF 40.65 119.9 123.9 134.1
148.05 148.185 148.225 148.545 149.175 149.205 149.225 149.265 149.40 149.50 150.20
150.25 150.285 150.345 163.375 165.0125 165.1375 173.5875 239.9 240.2 242.0 269.9
275.8 317.8 327.4 327.6 337.6 339.0 347.3 351.0 361.4 375.9 381.3 389.0 396.0
407.375 407.45 413.00 413.025 413.125 413.15 413.20 413.30
   Hilton Head Apt., SC: AD 387.1
   Hitco, Gardena, CA: Security 462.375
   Hobart Muni Apt., OK: AD 290.9 348.3
   Hohenfels AAF, Germany: T 31.80 40.20 122.1 141.95 399.85   Msc 48.80 139.20
250.9
   Holley OLF, Ft. Walton Beach, FL: OP 264.2
   Holloman AFB, Alamogordo, NM (ACC; 20th Fighter Sqdn.; 49th Tactical Fighter
Wing; 479th Tactical Training Wing of the 833rd Air Division); DI 372.2   S 273.5
AD 120.6 128.1 134.1 284.0 324.3   T 119.3 255.9   G 119.3 275.8   WX 344.6   E 128.1
289.4   TAC CP ("Raymond 14") 41.90 381.3 381.6 397.0   Army Aviation 123.3 229.3
167.175   Dept. Commerce 121.6   AF ("23 Alpha") 41.90   T-38 Supply 119.5   T-38

Red 148.175 150.075   T-38 White 148.095   T-38 Yellow 148.50   T-38 149.50   T-38-Blue 149.525   T-38 Silver 149.525   FMS/AGE 150.325   T-38 Motor Pool 150.35   48th CRS Sqdn 138.90   F-15 Maxi (Maintenance) 138.90   F-15 Yellow 141.55   F-15 Red 141.775 163.375   F-15 Blue 142.20   Balloon Br. 138.125 141.60 148.50   Balloon Br. Selenas 149.50   MOBB Squadron 148.85   Test Track A 148.485   Test Track B 149.175   Flight Tests 260.8 264.9   Guid. SAC Peak 149.295   Guid. (Bldg. #1262) 150.165   R&D (Bldg. #1080) 163.4625   OSI 163.00   PD/Security 163.3375 163.4875 165.0125   Civil Engineering (Bldg. #55) 163.5125   Ramp Control (Bldg. #571) 163.5875   Communications (Bldg. #221) 164.70   Base Commander Net 165.1125 173.5375 173.5375   Base Transportation 173.4375   Drone (Bldg. #1088) 173.5125   FD/Crash 173.5875   Medics (Bldg. #15) 173.7125   Flight Test 324.4   AR-644 OP 293.0   AR-310 OP 319.5   Launch Filming 34.85 163.4625   Telemetry 40.35   Hypersonic Test Track 163.00 163.4875   AF 189.4 251.1 353.6 364.2 376.1 397.9 (Also see White Sands Missile Range.)

Holly Springs-Marshall Co. Apt., MS: AD 313.2 338.3

Homestead AFB, FL (ACC; 9th AF; 31st Tactical Fighter Wing) **Virtually destroyed by Hurricane Andrew, 8/92; very limited operation status.** DI 372.2   S 269.9   AD 123.8 125.5 317.7 354.1 363.8   T 133.45 295.7   G 275.8   E 275.8   WX 344.6   TAC CP ("Raymond 15") 381.3   TAC Supervisor of Flying ("Wyvern") 280.5   301st Air Reserve Rescue Sqdn ("Homestead Rescue") 139.75 252.8 (HF 6712 11440 kHz)   93rd Tactical Fighter Sqdn AF Reserve ("Mako Ops") 364.0   Base Commander 148.065 149.565   Base OP 148.20   AF Reserve 163.5625   PD/Security 32.45 163.5875   Perimeter Security 163.4875   VIP OP 148.20   Transient OP 163.4625   OSI 163.5125   Medics 173.5625   CP 311.0 331.0 413.45   MAC 413.45   Training 139.975 142.20   Disaster Preparedness 173.4375   Fuel 163.5375   Helicopter Maintenance 163.1375   Communications Maintenance 148.85   Maintenance 148.455 148.545 149.15 150.195 150.25   FD/Crash 173.4125 173.5875   Port OP 156.60 413.00   Army 31st Air Defense Artillery Brigade 139.025   AF 122.85 122.9 139.65 139.875 141.00 143.025 149.20 149.25 149.475 149.525 149.525 149.925 163.5125 163.5375 165.0875 165.1125 266.4 281.2 283.8 286.2 289.3 289.6 292.3 294.9 318.2 321.2 327.7 337.0 347.6 351.4 358.4 371.1 372.9 379.4 384.8 385.9 388.8 389.0 413.20 413.30

Honolulu Int'l. Apt., HI: AD 285.4   DI 372.2   T 257.8   G 348.6   S 279.4

Honolulu, HI (29th Inf Bde; 442 Regimental Combat Team): NG 149.745 163.5625

Hood AAF/Ft. Hood, TX: AD 111.8 118.0 244.0   T 119.65 229.6   G 133.85 225.4   Flight Following 143.10 231.6 357.9   E 255.4   Ranges 30.45 34.30 38.30 293.9   WX 41.20 304.4   Army 234.4   MP/Security 45.00 165.0875 165.1625   Medevac 38.00   Helicopter OP 46.65   (Also see Robert Gray AAF listings.)

Hook Fld Muni Apt., Middletown, OH: AD 327.1

Hope Muni Apt., AR: AD 381.4

Hopkinsville-Christian CO Apt, KY: AD 255.6

Horace Williams Apt., Chapel Hill, NC: AD 256.9 307.9

Hornell Muni Apt., NY: AD 239.35

Hot Springs, AR: AF 235.5 252.5 369.5 388.5 396.5

Houghton Co Mem'l Apt, Hancock, MI: FSS 255.4   AD 379.1

Houlton Int'l Apt., ME: FSS 255.4   AD 346.4

Houma-Terrebonne Apt., LA: AD 256.9   T 346.3

Houston CGAS, TX: See Ellington AFB.

Houston Intercontinental Apt., TX: AD 257.7 284.0 379.1 385.65 396.0   T 290.2   Terminal Control Area 257.7 284.0 396.0

Howard AFB, Panama (ACC; 12th AF; 24th Wing; AF Southern Air Division; 24th Combat Support Grp; Army 193rd Infantry Brigade): DI 297.0   AD 119.7 120.9 121.2 125.5 263.0 270.6 289.4 317.7 335.8 352.0   T 126.2 257.8   G 130.8 275.8   Msc 40.50   WX 373.1   AF 119.0 122.7 122.8 129.7 162.985 163.45 164.00 165.30 236.6 265.0 272.3 305.2   (Also see listings for Albrook AFB.)

Hughes Apt., Culver City, CA: T 126.2 Hughes Aircraft Co 123.375 123.45 123.4 153.38 153.88 462.45 462.50 Army 34.10 34.90 36.10 36.90 40.10 41.90 46.90 142.95 149.95 225.3 242.7 265.5 280.0

Hughes Aircraft Co: Carlsbad, CA 35.08 123.375 123.45 462.50; Fullerton, CA: 153.38 461.625; LaCanada, CA 462.45 462.50; Los Angeles, CA: 153.38 462.45 Malibu, CA 153.38; Santa Monica, CA: 462.45 Seattle, WA: 334.7; Tucson, AZ: 153.32; Newport Beach, CA: 451.625; Lake Hughes, CA 462.45; Long Beach, CA 462.50 (Also see specific location listings.)

Hulman Regn'l Apt, Terre Haute, IN: FSS 255.4 S 284.4 AD 288.15 339.8 ANG OP ("Racer") 392.2 G 348.2 T 239.0 ANG 148.45 148.50 148.55 149.30 163.4875 280.5 295.1

Hunter AAF, Savannah, GA: DI 126.375 S 111.6 AD 118.4 120.4 120.85 121.1 125.3 322.5 354.0 387.1 388.8 T 46.70 133.55 229.6 241.0 G 121.8 248.2 CG 381.7 381.8 393.9 (HF 5692 kHz) Rescue 282.8 WX 344.6 Security 165.0625 NG OP 32.60 41.05 126.25 NG 139.15 139.30 139.40 141.40 143.65 173.4875 AF CP 311.0 321.0 413.15

Hunter Liggett Military Reservation/Ft. Hunter Liggett, Jolon, CA: T 40.95 41.50 Helicopter OP 229.5 Base OP 148.575 Emergency Training 407.475 412.875 FD 165.0625 165.5375 Security 173.4125 Civil Engineering 165.1875 NG 40.10 Army 34.90 138.025 138.10 138.275 138.325 138.45 138.65 138.75 138.80 139.00 139.005 139.065 139.10 139.125 139.185 139.245 139.275 139.30 139.305 139.365 139.425 139.475 139.65 139.75 139.95 140.00 140.275 140.625 140.725 140.85 140.975 141.075 141.135 141.195 141.225 141.35 141.40 141.45 141.50 141.65 141.75 142.335 142.425 142.475 142.90 142.935 142.975 143.025 143.075 143.125 143.20 143.35 143.40 143.50 143.55 148.08 148.38 148.65 148.79 148.90 149.36 149.43 149.575 149.63 149.69 149.775 149.87 149.96 150.03 150.09 150.32 150.56 150.74 163.5375 235.5 240.7 241.0 245.0 245.5 264.1 283.25 297.95 312.65 321.7 365.4 368.1 373.4 393.4 (Also see Fritzche AAF/Ft. Ord listings.)

Huntingburg Apt., IN: AD 226.4 284.65

Huntsville-Madison Co-Carl T. Jones Fld., AL: AD 239.0 307.0 354.1 T 126.2 350.35

Huntsville Muni Apt., TX: AD 269.6

Hurlburt (USAF) Field, Mary Esther, FL (AMC; 1st Special Operations Wing; 4442nd Tactical Control Group; Air Ground Operations School; 823rd Civil Engineering Squadron; Special Operations Control Team; Strike Force): DI 372.2 AD 109.8 125.1 132.1 133.0 315.9 322.6 358.3 T 126.2 126.5 139.60 291.1 TAC CP ("Raymond 10") 140.40 320.7 G 275.8 WX 375.2 AF 32.85 34.35 34.53 46.95 138.30 139.60 139.65 148.20 149.15 162.6125 163.5625 234.8 272.1 291.9 305.7 325.7 371.1 413.05

Huron Regn'l Apt., SD: FSS 255.4 AD 306.2

Hutchinson Muni Apt., KS: AD 325.8 T 363.0

Hutchinson Muni-Butler Fld., MN: AD 290.2

Hyattsville, MD: USN 138.65 139.48

Hyde Apt., Clinton, MD: NASA 123.2

Idaho Falls Naval Avionics Center, ID: USN 163.30

Ie Shima Aux. AB, Je Ie Shima Isl., Japan: T 250.9 287.3 OP 44.80

Igor I. Sikorsky Memorial Apt., Bridgeport, CT: AD 288.1 T 36.90 123.55 257.8 305.8 359.4 G 257.8

Illesheim AAF, Storck Barracks, Germany: T 31.80 33.20 122.1 142.90 251.2 OP 45.00

Imperial Beach OLF/Ream Fld., CA: S 276.2 AD 125.15 285.2 T 120.65 271.4 G 271.4 285.9 Crash 140.03 140.30 FD 140.975 USN 138.64 138.72 138.725 139.515 140.10 140.62 148.33 256.3 269.1 340.2 343.8 356.8 360.8

Imperial City Apt., CA: FSS 255.4 AD 291.7

Incirlik AB, Turkey: DI 294.9 AD 123.025 126.5 134.1 242.1 281.325 T 122.1 129.5 257.8 276.8 G 382.05 OP 234.4 360.06 360.05 WX 259.4 CP 232.85 (HF 4725 6738 8993 11176 15015 17975 kHz)

Independence Muni Apt., KS: AD 343.9

Independent Hill, VA: USN 140.275 Army 149.995 AF 150.20

Indiana Army Ammunition Plant, Charlestown, IN: Army 138.925 128.025 165.1625 172.525 173.4875 407.325

Indiana Co. Apt./Jimmy Stewart Fld., PA: AD 307.1

Indianapolis, Brookside Airpark, IN: AD 317.8 Army Reserve 123rd USARFFAC OP 34.70

Indianapolis Downtown Apt, IN: AD 317.8

Indianapolis, IN: USN 140.46 357.8 363.5 408.025 412.95

Indianapolis Int'l. Apt., IN: FSS 255.4 AD 317.8 T 257.8 G 257.8 E 257.8

Indianapolis Metro Apt., IN: AD 317.8

Indianapolis-Terry Apt., IN: AD 317.8

Indian Head Naval Ordnance Station, MD: USN 138.85 138.94 139.425 139.475 139.525 140.84

Indian Mountain AFS, Utopia Creek, AK: AD 121.5 T 126.2 364.2 Msc 122.6 AF 122.195 163.5875 165.1375 229.1 269.9 289.1 297.8

Indianola Muni Apt., MS: AD 269.35

Indian Springs AF Auxiliary Fld., NV: DI 372.2 T 118.3 126.2 358.3 G 118.3 275.8 Nellis Control 119.35 253.4 AF 138.20 138.50 138.90 139.74 141.64 148.05 148.225 148.40 149.15 149.31 150.225 150.275 150.60 173.4125 173.4375 173.5875 268.0 289.6 337.7 358.3 407.40 407.50 413.20 413.40 (Also see Nellis AFB listings.)

Ingalls Fld., Hot Springs, VA: AD 317.7 353.9

Intergraph Cprp.: Huntsville, AL 462.35 462.425 464.40; Union Hall, AL 462.60

Intermountain Regn'l Apt, Mena, AR: AD 398.9

Iosco Co. Apt., E. Tawas, MI: AD 301.5

Iowa Army Ammunition Plant, Burlington, IA: Army 165.0375 165.0625 165.1875 173.4125 173.4625

Iowa City Muni Apt., IA: AD 247.2 261.5

Iwakuni MCAS, Honshu, Japan: DI 258.6 S 283.0 AD 128.0 236.2 283.0 363.8 T 123.8 340.2 G 141.60 360.2 E 134.1 310.6 WX 344.6 Msc 126.7 128.2

Jack McNamara Fld., Crescent City, CA: FSS 255.4
Jackson Co.-Reynolds Fld., MI: FSS 255.4 AD 357.6 T 257.8
Jackson Hole Apt., WY: AD 285.6
Jackson Int'l. Apt, MS: FSS 255.4 AD 259.1 317.7 319.2 T 352.0 G 348.0 ANG 172nd TAG 264.6 ANG 148.20 163.4875 163.5875 165.1375
Jackson, MS: NG 213rd Medical Brigade 41.80 149.865 AF 139.70 148.075
Jackson Muni Apt., MN: FSS 255.4 AD 257.7
Jacksonville Int'l Apt., FL: FSS 255.4 AD 319.9 322.4 335.6 351.8 T 317.7 G 348.6 E 348.6 ANG CP & Maintenance 300.8 Security 165.0125 Medics 164.50 ANG 164.9625 228.8 234.7 236.4 238.5 251.0 251.9 268.9 271.5 275.0 292.7 292.95 295.35 298.5 302.4 306.4 309.25 325.5 338.4 339.7 344.0 356.0 361.0 369.0 375.1 383.4 386.2 392.8
Jacksonville NAS/Towers Fld., FL (Commander, Helicopter Wings Atlantic; Patrol Wing 11; Helicopter Antisubmarine Wing 1): S 281.0 AD 119.85 124.9 284.6 319.9 T 124.0 340.2 355.8 E 135.9 352.4 OP 310.2 (HF 6723 kHz) VFR Advisory 120.75 124.4 G 128.6 336.4 WX 344.6 SP/Security 140.575 142.50 142.88 143.50 CID 142.84 FD 140.46 Fleet Area Control & Surveillance Facility ("Sealord" & "Bristol") 120.95 134.65 267.5 284.5 (HF 3130 6723 6742 11252 kHz) USN 32.05 36.15 138.525 138.72 138.84 139.545 140.07 140.10 140.25 140.35 140.46 140.58 140.72 140.80 140.82 142.60 148.235 148.35 149.01 165.0125 165.1125 165.1375 165.1625 250.2 251.3 253.2 256.2 256.6 261.9 263.5 294.05 294.95 296.35 296.45 297.95 298.05 299.45 299.6 303.6 305.1 306.0 305.35 306.45 307.85 307.95 309.25 310.75 310.85 311.5 311.7 312.4 312.9 314.8 315.4 317.3 320.5 323.4 341.1 345.8 355.4 360.2 361.15 361.3 362.5 364.2 384.2
James Clements Muni Apt., Bay City, MI: AF 142.25 143.775
James M. Cox-Dayton Int'l Apt., OH: AD 291.1 294.5 316.7 324.5 327.1 353.7 T 257.8 FSS 255.4
Jamestown Muni Apt., ND: FSS 255.4 AD 270.3
Jasper Co. Apt., IN: AD 272.7
Jeffco Apt., Denver, CO: AD 381.5 388.0
Jefferson City Mem'l. Apt., MO: AD 363.25 T 41.95 NG OP 41.65 46.70 118.55
Jefferson Co. Apt., Beaumont, TX: AD 251.1 322.3 T 251.1
Jekyll Island Apt., GA: AD 277.4
Jerome Co. Apt., ID: AD 363.0
Jerry Tyler Mem'l Apt., Niles, MI: AD 257.8 263.1
Jesup-Wayne Co Apt., GA: AD 277.4
Jim Creek USN Communications Station NLK, WA: USN 140.85 143.01 149.00 149.01 416.4125
Jim Hogg Co. Apt., Hebronville, TX: AD 307.2
Jim Taylor Fld., FL: See Ocala Muni Apt.
J. Lynn Helms Sevier Co. Apt., AR: AD 381.4
Joe Foss Fld., Sioux Falls, SD: AD 267.9 317.4 353.6 G 348.6 T 257.8 317.8 ANG OP ("Lobo Ops") 253.4 ANG Maintenance 253.4 ANG Ordnance 163.375 Security 163.4875 Civil Engineering 163.5875 ANG 34.20 34.55 36.85 41.95 163.00 163.4625 163.5125 300.8 390.1
Joe Williams OLF, MS: AD 276.4 T ("Bravo Tower") 279.2 355.8 Msc 340.2
Joe Zerby Apt., PA: See Schuylkill Co. Apt.
John F. Kennedy Int'l. Apt., Jamaica, NY: AD 269.0 280.1 388.0 T 258.3 G 348.6 Postal Svc 173.6125 408.675 Security 453.375 453.65 FD/Crash 453.65 Dept. Agriculture 169.1875 Customs Service 165.2375
John F. Kennedy Mem'l Apt., Ashland, WI: AD 278.5
John H. Batten Fld., WI: AD 379.8
Johnson Atoll USAF, Pacific: OP 122.8 WX 344.6
Johnson Barracks AHP, Nurnberg, Germany: AD 31.80 33.60 122.1 142.20 314.8
Johnson Co. Executive Apt., Olathe, KS: AD 294.7 T 241.1

Johnson Co. Indust'l. Apt., Olathe, KS: AD 294.7 T 367.7 Army Reserve 46.90 368.1

Johnstown-Cambria Co. Apt., PA: FSS 255.4 AD 307.1

John Wayne/Orange Co. Apt., CA: AD 263.1 343.9 380.2 381.4 T 379.9

Joliet Army Ammunition Plant, IL: 139.025 139.125 141.025 142.375 14305 150.645 163.5375 164.20 165.0625 165.1875 412.85 413.5625

Joliet Park District Apt., IL: AD 388.0

Jonesnoro Muni Apt., AR: FSS 255.4 AD 319.3

Joplin Muni Apt., MO: FSS 255.4 AD 320.1 343.9

Joseph G. Lapointe Helipad, Martin Army Hospital, Ft. Benning, GA: Medevac 49.65 (Also see Lawson AAF/Ft. Benning listings.)

Jupiter Inlet, FL: USN 393.855

Kadena AB, Okinawa: DI 266.0 S 124.2 280.5 AD 119.1 126.5 258,3 335.8 T 126.2 236.6 315.8 G 118.5 275.8 E 123.3 235.0 CP 128.0 349.4 WX 344.6 Base OP 313rd Air Div Hpt (Same freqs as airfield.)

Kahului Apt., HI: AD 343.8 T 279.6 G 348.6

Kalakaket Creek AFS, AK: Msc 118.3

Kalamazoo Muni Apt., MI: AD 255.9 263.1 340.9

Kalispell AFS, Lakeside, MT: AF 148.095 NORAD CP 364.2 NORAD 228.8 234.6 344.7 238.4 238.5 251.0 254.2 256.6 260.8 263.2 267.0 270.2 270.4 274.4 275.0 278.4 281.6 287.8 292.7 298.5 302.4 306.4 309.4 316.3 320.6 324.0 235.5 327.9 336.6 338.4 341.8 344.0 346.2 356.0 369.0 375.1 377.0 386.2 387.8 392.8 398.0

Kaman Aerospace Corp., Bloomfield & Moosup, CT: 158.28 158.31

Kaneohe Bay MCAS, HI: S 284.5 AD 125.0 263.6 T 32.45 120.7 349.9 360.2 G 382.8 E 310.8 Security 140.55 OP 41.15 Helicopter OP 36.50 40.80 41.15 WX 344.6 Naval Investigative Service 140.075/140.775 USMC 138.55 138.60 138.70 138.775 138.80 138.85 138.975 139.575 140.025 140.05 140.10 140.45 140.60 140.65 140.75 140.92 140.975 142.00 142.05 142.525 142.60 142.65 142.725 142.825 148.375 163.4875 263.5 263.7 267.5 271.7 274.9 284.5 299.3 308.2 323.4 328.3 337.2 344.1 346.0 348.0 352.4 354.8 255.4 361.2 364.8 374.9 380.8 384.4 Army 139.305 AF 163.6375

Kansas Army Ammunition Plant, Parsons, KS: Army 163.5375 165.0625

Kansas City Downtown Apt: MO: FSS 255.4 AD 294.7 T 257.8

Kansas City Int'l. Apt., MO: AD 318.1 T 267.9 Security 165.175 USN 32.45 34.65 36.55 38.30 40.80 263.4 362.5

Kastner AAF/Camp Zama, Honshu, Japan: AD 120.7 123.8 261.4 367.0 T 122.5 126.2 288.8 340.2 OP 36.80 WX 344.0

Keahole Apt., Kailua-kona, HI: AD 290.5 T 254.3

Kearney Muni Apt., NE: AD 287.9

Keesler AFB, Biloxi, MS (ACC; 9th AF; 7th Air Base Command; 3300th Technical Training Wing; 3380th Air Base Grp; 7th Airborne Command & Control Sqdn; 35th Weather Recon Sqdn): S 256.0 AD 124.6 127.5 287.1 354.1 387.05 T 120.75 320.1

DI 372.2 G 121.8 275.8 E 121.8 275.8 WX 342.5 Medevac 236.6 WX Recon Op ("Gull") 304.8 349.9 TAC 7th ACCS OP 283.7 AF Reserve 403 TAW ("Accountant") 381.0 (HF 11440 kHz) Medics 173.5375 Base Commanders Net 148.225 150.225 FD 173.5875 Security 163.4875 Flightline Maintenance 165.125 OSI 138.075 138.165 138.175 AF 38.65 40.15 46.65 123.0 138.10 139.65 141.60 143.75 148.05 148.10 148.45 153.5875 165.0375 165.1375 165.1875 225.7 227.8 234.8 275.8 280.5 288.8 305.6 383.2 384.9 396.9 398.1 407.40 413.15 413.20 413.30

Keflavik NAS, Iceland: S 112.0 311.6 AD 119.3 363.8 T 118.3 257.8 G 121.9 359.8 Terminal 131.1 349.4 WX 120.3 344.6 Msc 131.9 CP 349.4

Kegelman AF Auxiliary Fld., Cherokee, OK: OP ("Dogface") 289.1 (Also see Vance AFB listings.)

Kelly AFB, San Antonio, TX (Air Logistics Center): DI 130.65 372.2 S 113.8 273.5 AD 118.05 125.1 127.1 289.2 307.0 353.5 381.4 T 113.8 124.3 320.1 G 121.8 149.175 289.4 AF Reserve 433rd Tactical Air Wing 143.80 252.1 WX 239.8 Flightline Maintenance 149.175 165.1375 413.125 Gate Guards 164.20 Security 173.4375 OSI 40.19 40.19 138.075 138.165 138.175 Escort Net 171.3875 Civil Engineer 149.225 AF 46.65 143.95 143.99 148.155 148.215 148.455 148.55 149.00 149.15 149.205 149.295 149.30 149.505 149.535 150.165 150.345 163.5375 165.0125 173.025 173.5625 252.1 260.4 266.3 314.2 357.0 377.8 390.1 394.9 407.375 407.425 407.50 408.80 413.05 413.10 413.15 413.20 413.45 Army 413.10 413.125 413.30 413.40

Kelso-Burnett Co., Rolling Meadows, IL: 151.625 151.925

Kelso-Longview Apt., WA: AD 317.6

Kenai Muni Apt., AK: AD 379.1 T 239.3

Kenmore Air Harbor Seaplane Base, WA: AD 306.9

Kendall-Tamiami Executive Apt., FL: AD 354.1

Kennedy Space Center, FL: Shuttle Landing Facility (SLF) OP 117.8 121.9 126.4 148.40 162.60 170.10 (HF 7675 7765 10780 13213 20390 kHz SLF Advisory 123.6 SLF T 126.3 284.0 SLF G 121.75 126.3 284.0 Shuttle Ground OP 408.15 408.80 Van Escorts 173.6875 Pad OP 173.6625 Orbiter OP 165.4125 Launch Support OP ("Alpha Control") 148.485 162.6125 Space Shuttle 259.7 279.0 296.8 Skid T 393.1 WX 126.65 Base OP 170.15 Transportation 170.175 Manned Flight Emergency & Search/Rescue 121.5 123.1 148.50 149.10 156.80 157.10 162.10 164.80 243.0 252.8 282.8 (HF 2182 3023 5680 10003 14993 19993 kHz) NASA Helos 46.40 60.25 Vessels 148.50 149.10 162.00 162.0125 (HF 2625 5190 5696 5810 9125 11407 kHz) Aircraft 164.80 (HF 6693 6896 6983 7461 8891 9043 9131 10780 11205 15015 18200 kHz) Disaster Preparedness 155.715 158.94 167.975 SRB Recovery 148.455 149.175 162.0125 Medics 173.4375 462.925 463.875 NASA Safety 1734.6625 173.6875 EOD 49.70 49.80 NASA OP 162.6125 Radiation Monitoring 164.00 Security 163.4625 163.4875 163.5125 173.175 173.6875 FD/Rescue 154.10 163.5625 173.175 173.5625 173.7875 Base OP 170.15 VIP Escort Net 170.35 Check Points 165.1875 Motor Pool 170.175 Vehicle Maintenance 170.40 Parking Control ("Bravo Control") 171.00 Public Relations 170.15 170.35 Photo Units 148.485 TV Camera Coordination 171.2625 Loan Pool 173.5375 Fuels & Maintenance ("Nova") 171.15 Railroad 170.175 Crawler OP 148.455 149.175 Convoy Command 407.325 Convoy Purge 408.15 Convoy Cooling 409.175 Cranes 142.50 142.86 143.04 148.155 149.175 407.475 408.15 408.175 409.05 Mobile Cranes 412.95 GSA 170.40 National Park Service 164.75 Wildlife Control 43.88 Nuclear Materials 167.85 168.45 Barge Supply 162.0125 "Thinker 1" 264.8 "Barracks 9" 294.6 "Variety 1" 294.6 Pagers 43.56 43.60 163.0125 165.5375 170.35 454.60 Data 165.1875 165.6125 Industrial Area 412.825 413.025 413.15 413.25 413.375 413.525 413.55 Contractor Security 163.4625 TW Services Co 154.515 Lockheed Corp 153.20 Rockwell 123.475 Com-Tech 151.955 Bendix Engineers 461.30 Federal Express 859.8625 IBM Research 152.48 855.8375 Grumman Aerospace 36.90 276.2 314.5 360.0 461.20 461.975 Harris Corp 152.48 153.32 462.25 462.30 462.35 Utilities 171.00 Fla Power & Light 37.74 37.86

158.25 451.10 451.125 451.175 451.20 451.25 451.275 451.375 451.475 Southern Bell Telephone 151.985 Msc 41.45 46.65 49.62 138.15 138.45 139.05 139.25 139.30 139.425 139.90 140.17 140.20 140.40 141.00 141.30 142.86 143.28 143.43 143.035 148.21 148.25 148.515 148.56 149.15 149.25 149.90 150.15 150.195 150.25 156.185 162.60 163.5875 164.50 164.65 165.0125 165.0375 165.1125 165.6125 170.10 171.15 173.5375 232.9 239.4 240.6 240.4 240.6 240.8 241.2 241.4 241.6 241.8 242.0 259.7 284.0 296.6 310.6 328.2 331.0 341.6 349.6 350.6 358.3 379.9 406.50 407.325 407.475 409.125 409.175 413.125 413.15 413.40 416.15 (Also see Cape Canaveral AFS, Patrick AFB listings, & Malabar listings.)

Keno AFS, Klamath Falls, OR: NORAD CP 364.2 NORAD 228.6 235.9 238.6 239.7 252.0 260.9 265.4 271.0 277.6 279.4 282.6 287.7 288.4 293.6 293.8 328.0 348.2 351.5 359.8 374.0 386.0 390.2 394.2 397.8

Kenosha Regn'l. Apt., WI: AD 379.8

Kent City Int'l. Apt., Grand Rapids, MI: AD 257.6 287.9 T 257.6

Kent Island, WA: USN 138.525 148.55

Kerrville Muni Apt./Schreiner Fld., TX: AD 291.7 Mooney Aircraft Co 123.15 123.25 123.35 123.45

Key Fld/Meridian, MS: FSS 255.4 AD 269.6 323.0 G 348.6 395.8 T 257.8 186th TRG ANG OP & CP 292.3 (HF 8989 kHz) ANG 163.4875 165.1375 165.1625 173.5375 235.5 255.8 375.8 388.5 396.5 407.425 NG 36.25 Msc 374.9

Keyport Naval Station, WA: USN 36.53 36.57 36.63 36.87 122.85 122.9 139.50 139.525 140.00 140.025 140.325 140.35 140.725 140.875 140.90 141.575 142.85 240.2 246.3 253.1 257.3

Keystone Apk., FL: AD 379.9

Key West Int'l Apt., FL: FSS 255.4 AD 289.4 323.1 T 257.8 G 257.8

Key West NAS/Boca Chica Fld., FL (Base for tactical electronic warfare & attack fighter sqdns): S 277.2 AD 119.25 124.45 132.2 289.4 313.2 323.1 T 126.1 305.2 340.2 360.2 G 121.7 336.4 E 121.2 355.6 OP 139.50 338.0 WX 344.6 VFR Advisories 119.25 313.2 WX 344.6 CG 139.50 SP/Security ("Danger Hilltop") 149.01 Hurricane OP 139.50 Tactical Nets 140.715 140.815 140.87 141.00 USN 30.45 32.05 34.74 36.15 138.60 138.72 139.545 139.55 140.025 140.04 140.10 140.175 140.32 140.575 150.58 140.82 140.825 140.895 142.50 142.85 143.715 149.37 149.375 149.79 228.8 265.0 269.8 270.6 275.1 275.4 277.2 277.8 280.2 285.0 289.9 306.4 307.4 309.0 318.5 318.8 326.8 342.8 344.2 352.2 354.6 362.6 363.6 364.2 369.2 383.4 385.0 AF 234.7 238.5 238.8 251.0 256.6 236.2 270.4 275.0 278.6 287.8 292.7 298.5 302.4 325.5 338.4 344.0 356.0 364.2 375.1 386.2 392.8

Kickapoo Downtown Airpark, Wichita Falls, TX: AD 308.6 E 289.0

Killeen Muni Apt., TX: AD 244.0

King of Prussia Nuclear Weapons Plant & Storage Facility, PA (GE Company): 153.23 AF 300.0

King Radio Corp., KS: 123.375 123.4 151.625 151.925 463.225 464.50

King Salmon Apt., AK: FSS 255.4 DI 372.2 AD 259.1 T 255.6 AF (5071st Combat Support Sqdn) 165.1375 173.5125 173.5875 229.1 254.6 255.6 269.9 288.4 324.3 327.5 364.2

Kings Bay Naval Submarine Base, GA (Fleet Ballistic Missile Submarine Sqdns): USN 138.575 140.15 140.175 140.20 140.325 140.35 140.475 318.6 385.0

Kings Land O'Lakes Muni Apt., WI: 281.5

Kingston Regn'l. Jetport/Stallings Fld., NC: AD 338.6 T 338.0

Kingsville NAS, TX (Training Air Wing 2): S 314.0 AD 119.9 226.8 383.6 T 126.2 340.2 346.0 G 352.4 E 328.4 OP 274.8 WX 344.6 Rescue 282.8 USN 141.95 142.00 142.05 142.50 149.375 276.2 287.8 314.0 315.4 344.2 350.6 AF 228.8 234.7 238.5 251.0 256.0 263.2 270.4 275.0 292.7 302.4 306.4 325.5 338.4 344.0 356.0 364.2 369.0 375.1 386.2 392.8

Kirksville Muni Apt., MO: AD 370.9

Kirtland AFB, NM: See Albuquerque International.

K.I. Sawyer AFB, Gwinn, MI (ACC; 8th AF; 410th Bombardment Wing; 2001st Communications Sqdn; AF Hospital): DI 372.2 AD 116.3 119.1 259.3 363.8 T 126.8 236.6 255.6 G 148.225 150.195 275.8 WX 344.6 Security 149.205 150.315 163.4875 173.5625 173.5875 OSI 138.075 SAC CP 311.0 321.0 Crew Alerts 413.45 AF 142.275 143.775 148.065 148.45 148.55 149.265 149.325 149.565 163.4875 163.5875 164.50 165.0125 165.1375 165.1625 163.4375 251.9 262.0 289.0 290.9 293.4 341.9 372.8 388.2 391.9 395.9 398.2 399.8 413.15

Kissimmee Muni Apt., FL: AD 259.1

Kit Carson MOA, CO: AF 281.2 344.2 363.4

Kitt Peak Nat'l. Observatrory, AZ: 164.35 164.50 168.375 409.20 (HF 10190 20875 kHz)

Kitzingen AAF, Harvey Barracks, Germany: DI 33.70 AD 129.85 140.75 258.95 275.35 T 31.80 111.4 126.1 142.65 245.75 G 141.30 250.55 WX 140.30

Klamath AFS, Requa, CA: AF 165.0125 228.6 235.9 238.6 239.7 252.0 260.9 261.4 265.4 271.0 277.6 278.4 280.1 282.6 287.5 287.7 288.4 293.6 293.8 328.0 348.2 351.5 355.2 358.4 359.8 364.2 374.0 386.0 390.2 394.2 397.9

Klamath Falls Int'l. Apt./Kingsley Fld., OR: AD 351.7 T 257.8 G 348.6 ANG 114th Tactical Fighter Training Sqdn CP "Killer Ops" 298.4 ANG OP "Spud Ops" 138.10 258.1 OSI 1238.075 ANG 46.65 46.85 46.95 139.70 143.80 149.175 150.315 163.4875 163.525 163.5875 165.0125 165.1125 173.4375 173.5375 251.9 253.4 261.9 291.2 298.4 337.4 355.2 358.2 359.0 364.2 371.2 379.1 386.0

Kleberg Co. Apt., Kingsville, TX: AD 291.6

Knapp State Apt, VT: see Edward F. Knapp State.

Knox AHP, Ft. Rucker, AL: AD 125.4 234.4 T 36.60 148.75 389.6 E 120.325 304.45 Army Reserve 38.10 141.05 (Also see Ft. Rucker listings.)

Knox Co. Apt., Mt. Vernon, OH: AD 267.9

Knox Co. Regn'l Apt., Rockland, ME: AD 263.6 290.5 322.4

Kodiak Apt., AK: AD 281.4 T 239.0 CG 381.8 (HF 2182 2678 5696 kHz)

Kokee AFS, HI (ANG 150th AC&W): ANG: 259.0 264.8 269.9 270.1 271.2 271.6 273.5 275.8 279.8 280.5 283.0 303.8 340.6 354.2 358.2 364.2 364.7

Kokomo Muni Apt., IN: AD 363.8

Kosciusko-Attala Co Apt., MS: AD 263.0

Kulis AFS, Anchorage, AK: FSS 255.4 AD 134.1 225.1 259.3 290.9 363.8 T 257.8 G 121.9 E 316.7 OP ("Camper") 134.5 292.4 (HF 4898 kHz) ANG 150.135 150.165 150.275 150.325 292.9 295.4

Kunsan AB, S. Korea: DI 247.1 S 304.8 AD 128.1 287.8 370.9 T 126.5 286.6 307.6 G 126.5 275.8 CP 277.2 CP ("Brickwall") 141.675 291.8 WX 346.5

Kupper Apt., Manville, NJ: AD 379.9

Lackland AFB & Training Annex, TX (Officer Training School; Defense Language Institute English Center; AF Pararescue School; also basic airmen training as well as basic/advanced training for law enforcement & security personnel): Security 163.4625 165.5375 Security 163.4625 165.5125 165.5375 FD 166.225 Motor Pool 163.5875 Ambulances 163.5625 Medic Pager 409.60 413.425 Motor Pool 163.5875 Medic Helipad 130.65 372.2 AF 139.65 149.475 150.225 165.15 289.4 290.8 320.1 336.2 376.1 407.475 409.05 409.90 413.175

Laconia Muni Apt., NH: AD 338.2 385.45

LaCrosse Muni Apt., WI: AD 363.0 T 248.2

Lafayette, LA: NG (256th Infantry Brigade) 38.89 163.00 163.025 163.5375 408.865

Lafayette Regn'l. Apt., LA: FSS 255.4 AD 263.1 278.5 363.0 T 257.8 Army Reserve ("Cajun Ops") 34.30

LaGuardia Apt., Flushing, NY: AD 263.0 T 263.0 G 263.0 Security 453.375 453.65 FD/Crash 453.65

Laguna AAF/Proving Ground, AZ: AD 120.0 314.0 336.4 374.8 T 41.50 127.65 241.0 G 121.8 229.4 Range Control 119.0 248.4 Security 165.0375 165.1125 173.4125 173.5125 EOD 49.70 49.80 Army 30.10 30.30 30.50 32.50 32.70 32.85 32.90 34.10 34.50 34.70 34.90 36.10 36.30 36.90 38.45 38.70 40.90 46.90 139.025 139.10 139.425 141.40 142.90 150.50 163.4125 163.4625 163.4875 163.5125 163.5375 163.5625 163.5875 173.5625 173.5875 226.4 226.8 227.8 229.7 230.2 242.4 248.2 282.8 299.05 304.4 356.4 365.1 407.30 407.35 407.45 407.525 407.575 416.60 Nuclear Weapons Systems 167.85 168.45

Lajes AB #4, Azores: DI 349.4 S 120.93 356.95 AD 112.3 135.0 362.3 T 118.1 122.1 142.40 257.8 269.0 G 121.9 340.3 CP 130.65 349.4 (HF 6738 8967 15015 kHz)

LaJolla, CA; USN 138.525

LaJunta, CO: AF 258.2 300.6

Lake Charles AFS, LA: AF 228.8 234.7 238.3 238.5 251.0 256.6 263.2 270.4 275.0 287.8 292.7 302.4 306.4 325.5 338.4 344.0 356.0 364.2 369.0 375.1 386.2 392.8

Lake Charles Regn'l. Apt., LA: FSS 255.4 AD 319.9 381.6 T 257.8 Helos 119.75

Lake City Army Ammunition Plant, Independence, MO: Army 412.825 412.975 413.075 413.125 413.275

Lake City Muni Apt., FL: AD 134.4 385.6 T 119.2 123.45 G 121.9 123.2 Government Rep ("Logic Control") 314.6 (HF 6550 kHz) Unicom 122.7 Aero Corp 123.2 123.4 123.45 (HF 5572 5823 kHz) (Contract maintenance facility for military aircraft.)

Lake Elmo Apt, MN: AD 335.5

Lakefield Apt., Celina, OH: AD 316.7

Lakefront Apt., New Orleans, LA: FSS 255.4 AD 256.9 290.3 T 257.8 NG OP 40.90 122.95 241.0 NG 38.69 139.025 163.6375

Lake George, FL: USN 140.125

Lakehurst Naval Engineering Center, NJ: AD 120.25 127.5 259.3 363.8 T 126.2 127.5 259.3 340.2 360.2 G 121.0 352.4 WX 355.3 Flightline Maintenance 236.4 VIP Aircraft OP 255.7 Army Aviation OP 41.25 255.7 PD/FD 139.50 USN 138.72 139.55 140.55 140.075 140.125 140.65 140.775 143.525 148.40 149.45 241.0 250.6 267.35 274.8 301.8 337.2 352.4 383.4 Army 229.4 339.4 339.9 AF 36.85

Lakeland Muni Apt., FL: AD 290.3 NG 40.90 241.0 Piper Aircraft Co 123.2 123.35 123.55

Lakenheath USAF, UK: DI 375.0 S 284.8 AD 129.05 135.275 253.1 268.2 355.35 362.3 378.9 Crash 34.15 T 122.1 231.5 257.8 G 75.325 75.575 248.45 CP 398.2 WX 259.4 Transportation 31.375 Security 32.20 34.90 75.45 75.675 76.05 76.525 76.575 76.675 76.725 Msc 33.25 33.50

Lake Tahoe Apt., S. Lake Tahoe, CA: AD 316.1 T 257.8

Lakewood Apt., NJ: AD 363.8

Lamar Muni Apt., CO: FSS 255.4 AD 380.15

Lambert-St. Louis Int'l. Apt., MO: S 277.2 AD 289.1 324.1 335.5 360.6 T 257.7 284.6 289.1 E 363.1 G 348.6 ANG OP 297.1 ANG FD 148.20 ANG 163.4875 163.5125 163.5875 228.2 235.8 245.3 266.6 275.2 314.6 345.4 347.3 373.5 USN 140.075 140.775 357.8 McDonnell Douglas Corp 42.98 123.2 123.55 153.29 382.6 462.225

Lampassas Apt., TX: AD 244.0

Lanai City, HI: AD 307.2

Lancaster Apt., PA: AD 379.8 T 251.1

Landstuhl AHP, Germany: Advisories 30.60 30.75 138.60 266.65

Langdon, ND: AF 165.1125

Langlade Co Apt., Antigo, WI: AD 317.7

Langley AFB, Hampton, VA (HQ ACC; 1st Fighter Wing; 9th AF; 1st Combat Support Grp; 5th Weather Wing; 48th Fighter Intercept Sqdn; 6th ACCS; 552nd Airborne Warning & Control Wing; Air Defense Force; Tactical Communications Division): DI 122.9 376.0 S 271.8 AD 124.9 125.7 126.05 127.9 249.9 372.1 379.1 395.8 T 125.1 253.5 G 121.7 275.8 E 118.85 271.3 TAC CP ("Raymond 16") 287.45 344.8 WX 239.8 Security & Law Enforcement 149.565 150.165 163.4875 163.5125 163.5875 164.975 165.825 173.6125 FD/Crash 165.1625 173.4875 173.5875 173.6125 Supervisor of Flying 280.5 OSI 40.17 40.19 138.075 138.165 138.175 Motor Pool 150.315 Base OP 163.4625 Base Supply 141.925 Base Fuels 149.55 Base Transportation 150.325 Base Hospital 149.35 155.28 173.5625 Civil Engineers 165.0125 Weapons 150.275 1st TFW Commanders Net ("Eagle") 165.1125/173.4375 1st TFW Maintenance 148.175 Blue/148.225 Red/149.30 Gold/149.30 1st TFW Eqpt Maintenance Sqdn 148.475 1st TFW Munitions Net 150.225 48th FIS Weapons 148.45 48th FIS Maintenance Net A 149.265 1913rd Communications Grp 149.475 1st TAC 149.265 6th ACCS 413.275 SAC CP 311.0 321.0 Crew Alerts 413.45 AF 34.15 139.65 141.525 141.60 142.155 143.45 143.95 148.065 148.05 148.095 148.125 148.185 148.215 148.475 149.205 149.225 149.535 149.675 165.4375 173.4375 173.7625 251.9 262.9 289.1 293.4 294.9 342.7 344.8 351.0 358.2 364.0 383.2 389.1 391.1 396.9 397.1 399.8 407.425 413.025 413.15 NASA Langley Research Center OP 122.85 314.6 NASA Security 170.00 173.6875 173.8875 NASA FD 46.06 173.6125 NASA Duty Officer 173.5625 173.6625 NASA Inspectors 173.6875 NASA Trucks 170.35 NASA Pager 170.40 NASA Building Maintenance 171.15 NASA 40.87 49.83 166.225 170.125 171.00 173.6375 311.2 362.6

Lansdowne Apt., Youngstown, PA: AD 306.3 381.4

Lansing, MI: USN 30.45 41.90

LaPlata, MD: USN 140.275

Laredo Int'l. Apt., TX: FSS 255.4 AD 307.2 T 257.9

Las Animas Co. Apt., Trinidad, CO: FSS 255.4

Las Cruces Int'l Apt., NM: AD 285.5

Las Vegas, NV: AF Range Control 126.65 343.0

Las Vegas Muni Apt., NM: FSS 255.4 AD 299.3

Laughlin AFB, Del Rio, TX (47th Flying Training Wing/ATC; Air Training Command): S 114.4 269.9 AD 119.6 125.75 259.1 264.8 346.4 T 114.4 125.2 396.0 G 257.8 E 335.8 WX 344.6 OSI 138.075 138.165 138.175 AF 139.65 148.475 149.125 150.225 150.325 163.4875 163.5125 165.0125 165.1625 173.4375 173.5375 173.5875 228.9 234.6 238.4 253.5 254.2 259.1 260.8 261.7 264.8 267.0 269.9 270.2 271.3 274.4 275.8 280.1 281.6 284.0 290.9 309.4 316.3 320.6 321.1 323.9 234.0 326.2 327.9 336.6 338.6 340.7 340.9 341.8 346.2 352.8 358.3 364.2 369.2 377.0 383.1 387.8 388.9 390.8 395.1 396.0 398.0 398.1 407.45 413.15

Lawrence G. Hanscom Fld., Bedford, MA: AD 279.6 T 236.6 AF Electronics Systems CP 397.1 Security 163.4625 FD/Crash 173.5875 Medic 236.6 General Aircraft Corp 123.4 AF 32.35 32.70 123.0 123.2 149.175 149.205 149.475 164.70 165.1625 257.0 259.2 284.1 287.2 291.8 294.2 294.6 295.3 295.9 316.625 316.785

317.175 317.275 319.6 341.6 349.6 379.7 383.0 384.8 413.00 Army 46.70 261.3 262.5 277.5 345.4 347.5

Laurinburg-Maxton Apt., NC: AD 295.0 AF 260.4 294.9 327.7

Lawrence J. Timmerman Apt., Milwaukee, WI: AD 307.0

Lawrence Muni Apt., KS: AD 290.2

Lawrence Muni Apt., MA: AD 279.6

Lawrenceville-Vincennes Int'l Apt., IN: AD 339.8

Lawson AAF/Ft. Benning, Columbus, GA (Infantry School of Arms; 197th Infantry Brigade; Infantry Center & School; Army Jump School; Airborne & Ranger Schools): DI 128.15 372.2 S 134.375 AD 120.45 125.5 126.0 126.55 226.4 278.5 357.6 388.0 T 36.70 41.50 126.2 229.4 241.0 G 121.05 340.1 E 121.7 248.2 Base OP 128.15 372.2 MAC CP 141.80 340.8 WX 127.4 344.6 Range 165.0375 Rescue 123.1 282.8 Medics 46.90 149.75 Medevac 49.65 VIP Aircraft 372.2 Security 165.0875 165.4375 FD 165.0375 EOD 49.70 49.80 Army 40.10 40.50 46.90 139.005 139.025 139.125 139.175 139.325 139.70 141.175 141.425 142.875 143.05 143.075 143.15 148.605 148.65 148.775 148.415 148.925 149.00 149.575 149.625 149.70 149.80 149.825 165.6375 163.5875 164.375 164.80 164.9875 165.5875 173.4125 173.4625 173.4875 173.5125 173.5625 226.5 227.4 229.8 231.9 234.1 241.0 244.4 267.1 277.475 302.3 321.7 344.7 356.6 387.9 412.90 413.525 AF 141.80 300.9 303.1 304.5 338.3

Lawton Muni Apt., OK: AD 233.2 T 257.8

Lea Co Apt., Hobbs, NM: FSS 255.4 AD 385.6

Lebanon Muni Apt., NH: FSS 255.4 AD 338.2 381.4 T 385.5

Lee Bird Fld., N. Platte, NE: FSS 255.4 AD 269.6 FAA 41.59 41.69

Lee C. Fine Mem'l Apt., Kaiser, MO: AD 353.7

Lee Gilmer Mem;l Apt., Gainesville, GA: AD 307.9

Leesburg Muni Apt/Godfrey Fld., VA: AD 384.9

Lemoore NAS/Reeves Fld., CA (Commander, Light Attack Wing/Pacific Fleet): S 267.6 AD 118.15 124.1 134.1 279.2 286.0 318.8 T 128.3 340.2 260.2 G 128.3 305.2 E 124.1 380.8 OP 239.55 299.3 (HF 6723 kHz) WX 317.0 Data Links 323.5 USMC OP 272.4 Crash 138.75 140.35 FD 140.10 USMC Security 139.575 142.775 148.375 Pagers 138.975 140.85 CID 140.075 140.65 Ordnance 140.124 140.925 Ramp 140.10 Security 139.575 141.00 142.775 USN 122.9 149.85 140.90 142.55 250.2 255.0 256.3 258.6 258.8 263.9 275.5 290.0 299.7 306.0 309.1 358.0 360.4 361.9 SAC CP 311.0 321.0

Lenawee Co Apt., MI: AD 321.1

Letterkenny Army Depot, Chambersburg, PA: Helipad 123.05 376.7 Army 163.5375 165.0125 165.0875 165.1875 173.4125 173.4875

Lewes, DE: USN 139.50

Lewiston-Nez Perce Co Apt., ID: AD 335.5 T 318.8

Lewiston, MD: AD 155.0375 268.0 287.6 293.5

Lewistown AFS, MT: AF 150.315 150.375 165.1625 413.025

Lewisville, AR: USN 143.50

Lexington-Blue Grass Army Depot, KY (Chemical-Biological Warfare storage area): Aero OP 126.2 241.0 229.8 Army 143.0 163.5625 155.0125 163.0375 163.4626

Lexington, KY: USN 32.45 36.55 40.80

Libby AAF/Sierra Vista Muni Apt., Ft. Huachuca, AZ (Army Information Systems Command; 11th Signal Brigade; Army Intelligence Center & School): S 134.75 265.7 AD 127.95 351.8 T 41.50 118.9 229.6 G 121.7 248.2 OP 135.85 Unicom 122.95 MP/Security 36.10 163.5625 165.0625 173.025 173.4125 FD 173.325 EOD 49.70 49.80 Army 30.30 30.50 32.05 32.10 32.30 32.50 32.60 32.70 36.30 36.70 36.90 38.20 38.50 38.53 40.90 41.80 46.70 139.00 139.005 139.05 139.15 139.20 139.25 139.40 139.45 139.75 141.425 142.40 142.875 142.40 142.875 143.10 148.32 148.605 148.665 148.70 148.85 148.975 149.625 149.685 149.685 149.715 149.775 149.825 150.075 150.425 150.525 150.725 150.775 162.225 163.5375 165.0875 169.575 172.30 172.325 173.10

173.15 173.4625 173.4875 173.5125 173.5625 241.0 242.6 245.5 267.2 280.8 290.6 315.2 338.9 340.1 391.5 393.3 412.90 413.425

Liberal Muni Apt., KS: AD 290.8 Beech Act Co 123.2

Lihue Muni Apt., KS: AD 269.4 T 263.1

Lima Allen Co Apt., OH: AD 269.0

Lincoln Muni Apt., NE: FSS 255.4 AD 270.3 338.3 346.3 G 275.8 S 302.2 T 253.5 E 396.0 NG OP 38.80 123.075 ANG OP 236.85 ANG 138.925 149.30 149.475 150.135 150.255 150.325 150.35 173.4375 259.6 305.77 (HF 4280 kHz) SAC CP 311.0 321.0

Linden Apt., NJ: AD 379.9 E 257.6 379.9 NG 41.00 241.0

Litchfield Apt., IL: AD 388.0

Litchfield Muni Apt., MN: AD 323.1

Little America, WY: AF 385.7

Littlebrook Apk., ME: AD 322.4 363.8

Little Creek Naval Amphibious Base, Norfolk, VA: Security & FD 138.65 138.85 138.96 Master at Arms 149.03 Medics 155.34 155.40 Navy Exchange 138.525 Billeting 143.575 Pager 150.10 Assault Craft Unit #2 34.20 38.30 307.4 (HF 4802 5382 kHz) Disaster Control 34.15 36.50 138.96 139.625 140.00 354.6 (HF 3237 8304 kHz) Tactical Air Control Exercises 30.55 41.30 277.2 299.7 305.0 339.7 (HF 3149.5 kHz) USN 32.65 34.35 38.35 38.50 38.55 138.525 138.65 140.075 140.65 140.775 148.325 149.01 149.05 233.8 267.4 274.9 312.2 313.1 325.0 326.8 328.2 350.1 353.4 361.8 363.4 375.0 380.7 382.1 385.0 394.5 398.4

Little Falls-Morrison Co Apt., MN: AD 323.1

Little Rock AFB, Jacksonville, AR (AMC; 314th Tactical Airlift Wing; 308th Missile Wing): DI 372.2 S 271.3 AD 119.5 125.35 306.2 T 120.6 348.4 G 132.8 275.8 E 275.8 CP 349.4 WX 239.8 INDIS Link #F-10L 46.95 INDIS Link #F-20L 49.95 INDIS Link F-40H 165.25 INDIS Link F-45H 164.50 INDIS Link F-49H 173.95 NSA E-Com Net 49.81 NSA E-Com Net 49.91 Security 163.4875/163.5875 (PL-91.5) Titan II Silos 140.40 149.31 Crew Alerts 413.45 OSI 138.075 138.175 (PL 103.5) 314th TAW Tactical Cntrl. 142.30 (PL 114.8) 314th OMS (Gold) 148.05 (PL 114.8) 314th OMS (Blue) 149.50 (PL 114.8) 314th TAW/LGX 149.535 (PL 131.8) Fuels Distrib POL 165.0125 (PL 131.8) 314th Commanders Net 165.1125/173.5375 (PL 131.8) EOD 173.10 (PL 100.0) Disaster/Crisis Control 173.4125 (PL 91.5) Civil Engnrng 173.4375 (PL 91.5/100.0) Base Hosp/Ambulance 173.5625 FD/Crash 173.5875 (PL 100.0) Pager 407.375 Spec OP Intercom 417.75 Intersysten Common Link 453.10/458.10 314th APS/ATOC 150.05 (PL 141.3/156.7/173.8) 314th FMS 150.20 150.20 (PL 114.8) Base Taxi 150.35 (PL 91.5) 314th AMS 148.10 (PL 114.8) Base Supply & Munitions Maint 148.455 314th Comms Sqdn 148.30 Base OP Ramp Net 149.225 (PL 91.5/100.0) AF 41.90 49.80 138.70 139.60 139.65 139.70 141.80 142.20 142.25 143.80 143.88 148.085 148.065 148.095 148.20 148.515 148.55 148.95 149.20 149.26 149.475 149.505 149.565 150.15 150.315 163.4625 163.5125 173.4375 173.5375 173.5625 173.5875 255.7 262.3 266.2 271.1 271.9 284.0 303.0 308.8 314.2 314.3 340.6 340.8 341.5 342.3 369.2 413.10 413.425

Little Rock, AR: Army 165.06

Litton Systems Company: Canoga Park, CA 232.0 241.0 349.0 Pascagoula, MS 462.625; Van Nuys, CA 152.23; Agoura, CA 153.185; Woodland Hills, CA 153.185 153.335

Livermore Muni Apt., CA: AD 278.3 319.9 354.1 T 368.7

Lockheed Aerospace/Missiles Company: Beaumont, TX 35.70; Los Angeles, CA 123.15 123.25 123.325 123.425 123.45 166.75 173.50 462.425 464.925; Palo Alto, CA 153.20; Redlands, CA 35.70; Seattle, WA 153.05 153.20 462.30 464.925; Greenville, SC 123.2 464.525; Burbank, CA 123.425 153.20 464.925 FD 154.265 154.28 154.295; San Jose, CA, 462.425; Claremont, CA 462.425; Ontario, CA 462.425; Watchung, NJ 123.2 123.45 451.375 462.325; Sunnyvale, CA 153.20 153.32

451.475; Saugus, CA 153.20 158.295 462.425; Helendale, CA 153.20 158.295; Austin, TX 153.14 460.65 462.40; Charlotte, NC 464.925; Albuquerque, NM 464.475 464.925; Chicago, IL 463.825; Atlanta, GA 461.60; Calbasas, CA 462.525; Salt Lake City, UT 464.925; Bastrop, TX 461.275; Copperas Cove, TX 463.35; Kennedy Space Center, FL 461.7625 (Also see specific location listings.)

Lockport AFS, NY: Emergency 148.45 NORAD 228.7 235.8 239.2 254.8 270.1 278.4 282.5 288.0 292.8 298.8 303.9 316.2 326.4 338.3 338.8 342.1 347.4 351.6 371.8 376.2 389.2 394.8 399.0 NORAD CP 364.2

Logan Int'l Apt., MA: See General Edward L. Logan Int'l Apt.

Logansport Muni Apt., IN: AD 351.1 363.8

Lompoc Apt, CA: AD 339.1

London-Corbin-Magee Fld, KY: FSS 255.4 AD 246.0

Lonely D.E.W. Line Station, AK: T 123.0 236.6 288.4 Msc 122.4 126.2

Lonesome Pine Apt., VA: AD 253.5

Lone Star Army Ammunition Plant, Texarkana, TX: Army 149.70 150.75 163.5625 164.05 165.0625 165.0875 165.1875 165.7175 173.4125 176.4625

Long Beach Apt/Daugherty Fld., CA: AD 269.6 343.9 T 257.6 G 257.6 McDonnell Douglas Company 30.05 32.50 41.95 49.80 122.0 123.2 123.275 123.3 123.4 123.425 123.45 123.55 124.4 125.95 130.0 132.1 135.6 153.05 153.08 156.00 158.28 314.6 360.6 382.6

Long Beach Naval Station, CA: Electronics Maintenance 142.55 Security 138.46 140.975 141.975 SP 140.975 141.975 Base OP 150.075 Command Early Warning Network 328.2 Range 143.675 149.07 149.13 Dept of Defense Security 140.025 FD 140.325 Naval Investigations 162.375 Medics 140.325 Pager 148.275 Shipyard OP 139.575 142.55 149.30 150.075 Heliport 381.8 USN 36.53 36.63 36.87 40.53 40.79 138.65 138.75 138.775 138.79 138.825 140.175 140.32 140.34 140.48 140.76 140.80 142.00 142.025 142.075 142.10 142.525 142.775 148.99 149.43 149.49 250.9 251.4 272.9 273.0 277.1 277.9 283.3 300.5 308.5 312.7 313.7 313.8 318.5 321.8 323.5 326.5 336.2 339.7 340.4 340.5 342.6 342.6 345.1 345.8 346.6 353.0 353.1 353.4 354.6 355.0 357.8 358.0 358.1 358.7 359.4 359.7 360.4 361.0 361.8 362.0 362.5 380.7 380.9 382.2 382.5 382.9 383.4 383.5 384.1 384.2 385.0 385.3 387.4 406.375 409.125 CG OP 381.8

Longhorn Army Ammunition Plant, Marshall, TX: Army 149.145 163.5875 165.0125

Longhorn Army Auxiliary Landing Strip, Ft. Hood, TX: T 143.35 237.4 (Also see Robert Gray AAF and Hood AAF listings.)

Long Island MacArthur Apt., Islip, NY: FSS 255.4 AD 367.2 T 239.3 335.5 Army Aviation Support Facility ("Long Island Guard") 41.00 122.475 241.0 242.4

Lorain Co Regn'l Apt., Elyria, OH: AD 360.6 Army Reserve 38.10

Loral Corp.: Akron, OH 158.415 462.05 462.225; Suffield, OH 123.125 123.25; AL 123.325 151.955 153.26; US 154.57

Loring AFB, Limestone, ME (ACC; 9th AF; 42nd Bombardment Wing/Heavy **Closing date 9/94.**): DI 372.2 AD 124.7 359.3 363.8 T 128.75 236.6 294.7 G 275.8 CP 149.565 311.0 321.0 WX 342.5 Security 163.375 163.4875 163.5625 164.10 165.0125 173.4375 OSI 138.075 138.165 138.175 FD/Crash 173.5875 Medics 173.4375 Crew Alerts 413.45 Emergency 165.5375 Transients 165.3125 Air/Air 235.1 Pager 138.325 Flightline Fuel 165.1125 Flightline Maintenance 149.25 165.0125 165.1375 165.1625 165.1875 Bldg Maintenance 148.175 Field Maintenance 165.0375 Motor Pool 163.5375 Job Control 165.0125 Commanders Net 148.525 Nuclear Weapons Systems 122.9 167.85 168.45 384.8 AF 120.85 124.7 140.065 148.245 149.205 149.25 149.565 163.4875 163.625 164.50 165.0375 236.6 238.8 318.1 324.5 335.8 339.1 349.0 363.8 413.15 (HF 6738 11176 15015 kHz)

Lorton, VA: FEMA 167.975 GSA 163.075 163.175 168.575

Los Alamitos AAF, CA (Armed Forces Reserve Center): AD 124.65 343.9 T 123.85 347.5 G 126.95 356.6 OP 127.95 237.2 ARASF ("Arcom Ops") 30.10 139.05

230.9 NG 65.05 142.95 233.8 Army 41.50 142.375 143.05 230.2 340.1 346.8 352.4 356.6

Los Angeles AFB, El Segundo, CA (Space Division): AF 243.725 243.885 316.625 316.785 Hughes Aircraft Co 153.38 461.625 462.40 462.45 Pager 465.00 Rockwell 462.275 462.325 462.7375 Pager 154.625 Aerospace Corp 151.775 Northrop 158.28 508.8125 Xerox Corp 151.865 153.14 153.26 153.335

Los Angeles CGAS, CA: See Los Angeles Int'l. Apt.

Los Angeles Int'l. Apt, CA: AD 269.0 360.7 363.2 381.6 385.4 T 239.3 379.1 G 327.0 VFR Advisory & Helicopter OP 120.35 122.75 E 327.0 AF OP ("Orbit Ops") 372.2 CG 122.75 162.125 381.7 381.8 383.9 (HF 3120 5692 8980 8984 kHz) Rescue 282.8 AF 138.075 138.175 148.145 149.205 163.4625 163.4875 165.0125 252.4 USN 264.1 314.6 382.6

Los Angeles, CA: USN SP/Security 141.975 NG 139.325 143.375 143.415 150.46 150.525 165.1875 169.425 412.925 413.235

Los Banos Muni Apt., CA: AD 287.1

L. O. Simonstad Apt., Osceola, WI: AD 319.2

Louisiana Army Ammunition Plant, Shreveport, LA: Army 38.89

Louisville, KY: NG 38.89 163.00 163.025 USN 142.50

Lovell Fld., Chattanooga, TN: AD 321.2 353.8 379.1 G 348.6 T 257.8 353.8 AF 150.15 150.225

Lowe AHP/Ft. Rucker, AL: S 364.9 AD 133.45 237.5 T 46.95 141.30 237.3 G 265.6 Army 143.375 173.4125 229.4 (Also see Ft. Rucker listings.)

Lowry AFB, Aurora, CO (Technical Training Center/Air Training Command): CP 253.675 Finance/Accounting Office Security 413.125 OSI 40.17 40.19 138.075 138.165 138.175 Commanders Net 164.9625 Medics 173.5625 FD 173.5875 Motor Pool 163.5875 Disaster Response 163.5875 AF 139.65 163.00 163.4625 163.4875 164.9625 165.1375 409.60 413.00

LTV Aerospace Corp.: Dallas, TX 122.725 153.08 153.14 153.215 153.245 153.32 158.28 462.25 462.225 462.50; Alamogordo, NM 464.60; Grand Prairie, TX 153.23 153.29 153.32 158.31; Camden, AR 153.305 153.35; Horizon City, TX 153.065 153.155 153.23

Lualualai Naval Reservation, HI: USN 140.60

Lubbock Int'l. Apt, TX: AD 279.9 335.6 351.8 T 239.3 G 348.6

Ludwigsburg AAF, Germany: Msc 122.1

Luke AFB, Glendale, AZ (ACC; 12th AF; 58th Fighter Wing; Gila Bend Gunnery Range): DI 372.2 S 269.9 AD 120.5 125.45 128.45 298.9 301.5 391.2 T 119.1 289.6 G 121.4 335.8 E 119.9 395.0 WX 375.2 TAC CP ("Raymond 18") 381.3 Maintenance 148.40 FD/Crash 173.7875 Security 163.4875 NORAD ("Sierra Pete") 254.2 260.8 270.2 364.2 Gunnery Range 120.55 272.1 296.3 Nuclear Weapons Systems 167.85 168.45 OSI 138.075 139.165 138.175 AF 36.50 41.95 13.40 139.65 148.036 148.10 148.175 148.185 148.30 148.45 148.545 149.00 149.10 149.15 148.20 149.265 149.40 149.565 150.20 150.315 150.35 165.0125 165.0875 165.1125 173.5375 173.5625 242.1 242.3 252.9 254.5 257.2 259.0 259.4 264.7 266.4 276.0 276.9 279.9 283.8 285.2 287.1 288.7 291.1 294.9 295.3 296.1 301.4 301.5 301.6 308.9 311.2 316.9 321.2 322.6 324.4 325.7 335.9 337.7 338.5 338.9 343.0 343.4 347.2 349.0 351.0 352.8 361.6 369.1 371.1 372.9 373.1 384.7 388.9 398.9 390.1 391.2 413.15 (Also see Gila Bend AF Auxiliary listings.)

Lumberton Muni Apt., NC: AD 288.3 295.0 340.7

Lumpkin Co. Apt., Dahlonega, GA: Army 139.025 226.5 227.4 244.4

Lynchburg Muni Apt./Preston Glenn Fld., VA: AD 317.7 T 257.8

Lynn, MA: NG 34.70 40.95 42.80

Lynn Haven AFS, FL: AF 150.20

Lyons-Rice Co Muni Apt., KS: AD 337.4

MacDill AFB, Tampa, FL (ACC; 9th AF; HQ US Central Command; US Special Operations Command; Avon Park AF Range; 56th Fighter Wing **Closing date 9/94.**): DI 372.2 S 270.1 AD 118.8 129.45 134.25 269.1 279.6 354.0 T 126.2 294.7 G 275.8 TAC CP ("Raymond 19") 238.35 381.3 WX 344.6 Hurricane Hunters 304.8 Security 163.4875 FD/Crash 173.5875 Maintenance 149.175 Medics 173.5625 Runway Maintenance 165.1875 Global HF System 292.1 (HF 6738 8993 11176 15015 kHz) Base Transportation 149.175 Telemet 149.55 150.285 SAC CP 311.0 321.0 NORAD 364.2 Crew Alerts 413.45 AF 139.875 139.975 141.80 142.20 143.80 143.825 148.095 148.145 148.455 148.485 149.275 149.325 150.20 150.315 163.5125 163.5875 165.0125 165.1125 165.1875 173.4375 173.5125 173.5375 228.8 234.7 238.5 251.0 256.6 263.2 268.1 270.4 271.1 272.0 275.0 276.8 278.6 280.5 287.3 287.8 283.7 292.7 297.1 297.5 298.5 300.9 302.4 306.4 316.9 321.2 325.5 325.8 327.3 338.4 344.0 348.1 356.0 369.0 375.1 376.1 381.0 386.2 389.1 392.8 397.1 398.1 407.375 407.50 413.15 413.20 413.30 USN 275.7 283.4 307.7 339.6 358.6 Army 407.30 (Also see MacDill AFB Aux Fld./Avon Park AF Range listings, below.)

MacDill AFB Auxiliary Fld/Avon Park AF Range, Avon Park, FL: T 126.15 276.6 292.2 Range 264.6 271.1 372.0 276.8 283.7 286.4 282.2 309.9 316.9 327.3 340.6 341.5 342.3 349.3 359.4 361.4 376.1 397.0 AF 139.60 142.25 149.225 150.135 150.225 150.345 163.375 164.9625 409.425 413.325 413.425

Mackall AAF/Camp Mackall, NC: AD 119.55 127.8 132.4 340.7 346.4 393.0 T 41.75 121.0 304.6 G 41.75 Range 38.90 246.0 OP 141.40 VFR Advisories 39.95 141.40 (Also see Simmons AAF listings.)

Madigan Hospital, Ft. Lewis, Tacoma, WA: Medevac 40.55 (Also see Gray AAF listings.)

Madison Co Apt., OH: AD 327.1

Madison Forest Products Lab, WI: Dept Agriculture 164.9375

Madison Muni Apt, GA: AD 306.9

Madison Muni Apt, IN: AD 306.2 327.0

Madison Muni Apt, SD: FSS 255.4 AD 317.4

Madison, WI: Army 141.40 142.90 413.875 413.95 415.20 AF 165.0625 165.1125 343.0 390.1

Madisonville Muni Apt., KY: AD 226.4

Magnavox Gov't. & Electronics Corp.: Ft. Wayne, IN 153.36 462.25 462.40; Garrett, IN 153.365 462.30; Edgerton, IN 153.095; Columbia City, IN 462.30

Mahlon Sweet Fld., Eugene, OR: FSS 255.4 AD 291.7 298.9 348.7 T 371.9 E 269.5 G 269.5

Majors Fld., Greenville, TX: AD 254.3 T 383.1 G 335.8 AF 257.0 291.8 293.25 319.6 348.95 AFL/CIO OP 349.6 (HF 15044 kHz)

Makah AFS, Neah Bay, WI: AD 228.6 235.9 238.6 239.1 239.7 252.0 260.9 261.4 265.4 271.0 277.6 278.4 282.6 287.7 288.4 293.6 293.8 328.0 348.2 351.5 355.2 359.8 364.2 374.0 386.0 390.2 394.4 397.8

Malabar, FL NASA: HF/USB Space Shuttle Support comms-- SRB Booster Recovery 2622 2764 3187 4510 7765 11407 11621 Tracking Vessels 5180 5187 ETR Range Cntrl 2678 5190 5810 10780 20390 Launch Support Vessels 5680 11104 11252 18009 19303 Launch Support Aircraft 5350 7461 7676 9022 9043 9132 13227 13878 Cape Radio 4856 6837 6896 11414 11548 19640 23413 USCG Cutter comms 4992 Search/Rescue 3024 4376 6720 7412 Backup comms 2664 USN Harbor net 2716 Launch Tracking Net 7525 20186 Space Missile Tactical net 10305 OCC Shuttle Mission Audio 20190 NASA/USAF comms 4510 4760 4855 4992 5350 5810 6727 6740 8993 9315 9974 10780 11104 11414 11548 14615 19303 19984 20191 20475 kHz

Malcom-McKinnon Apt., Brunswick, GA: FSS 255.4 AD 277.4

Malden Muni Apt., MO: AD 350.3

Malmstrom AFB, Great Falls, MT (AMC; 20th AF; 341st Missile Wing; 301st Air Refueling Wing): DI 372.2 AD 119.3 121.1 124.15 259.1 290.3 G 257.8 T 126.55

252.9   SAC CP 311.0 321.0   NORAD 364.2   WX 239.8   OSI 40.17 40.19 138.075
138.165 138.175   Helicopter OP 271.9   AF 138.235 138.925 148.065 148.95 149.235
149.265 149.505 149.535 149.565 150.10 150.275 150.50 163.375 163.4875 163.5125
163.5375 163.5625 163.5875 164.50 165.1125 165.1375 173.4375 173.5375 173.5625
173.5875 228.8 228.9 234.6 234.7 238.4 238.5 251.0 254.2 256.6 260.8 263.2 266.2
267.0 270.2 270.4 274.4 275.0 281.6 287.8 288.6 292.7 298.5 300.8 302.4 306.4 308.8
309.4 314.3 316.3 320.6 324.0 325.5 327.9 336.6 338.4 341.8 344.0 344.9 346.2 351.35
356.0 369.0 375.1 377.0 386.2 387.8 392.8 398.0 407.325 407.375 407.425 407.525
412.875 413.15 413.325 413.425 413.525

Manassas Muni Apt./Davis Fld., VA: AD 360.75 390.9

Manchester Apt./Grenier Indst'l Airpark, NH: AD 305.4 324.3 338.2 385.45 T
324.3

Manhattan Muni Apt., KS: FSS 255.4 AD 388.8

Manitowoc Co Apt., WI: AD 338.2 370.9

Mankato Muni Apt., NM: AD 306.9

Mansfield Lahm Muni Apt., OH: AD 317.7 390.8   T 325.8   G 325.8   ANG
("Buffoon") 297.5   ANG 163.4875 163.5125 164.10 165.0125 165.1375 301.6

March AFB, Riverside, CA (AMC; 1st AF; Southwest Air Defense Sector; 452nd
Air Refueling Wing/AF Reserve; 22 & 100 Air Refueling Wings; 163rd Tactical
Fighter Grp/ANG; 5, 22, 28, 43, 92, 93, 96, 319, & 320th Bombardment Wings; 44,
90, 91, 321, 341, & 390 Strategic Missile Wings; 6, 43, & 376 Strategic Wings; 9 &
55 Strategic Recon Wings; 7 & 13 Missile Warning Sqdns; 16th Surveillance Sqdn;
46th Aerospace Defense Wing; US Customs Service Intelligence Center): DI 372.2 S
134.75 270.1   AD 119.65 125.5 127.25 134.0 134.4 135.4 278.3 295.7 306.3 318.2
327.5 351.1   T 127.65 253.5   G 121.65 335.8   WX 239.8   Security 150.175 163.4625
163.4875 164.70   FD/Crash 150.345   Medics 150.225 150.255 150.265 168.00 406.975
413.00   Crew Alerts 413.45   SAC CP 311.0 321.0   AF Reserve 138.45 252.1 298.45
413.325   AF Reserve Commanders Net 413.075   1st Air Force Commanders Net
173.5125/149.535   22nd Air Refueling Wing Commanders Net 149.535   Pagers 163.4875
173.5625   Flightline OP 149.235 150.175 413.025   ANG OP ("Grizzly Ops") 293.7
Maintenance 148.175 148.515 148.70 149.175 407.475 413.425   Groundskeeping 148.515
149.175   Civil Engineering 413.20 413.30   Base Transportation 149.475   FAA Flight
Service ("Homeland Radio") 113.4/122.1   OSI 138.075 138.165 138.175   AF 37.60
138.125 138.30 139.875 143.825 148.065 148.245 150.05 163.5375 164.20 164.50
165.0625 165.1625 242.0 242.0 335.8 324.1 359.0 413.35

Mare Island Naval Complex, CA (Naval Station; Naval Shipyard; Combat Systems
Technical Schools Command; Engineering Duty Officer School): Security 138.95
140.95 406.358.70 140.025   Crash 138.70   CID 140.075 140.65 140.775   Utilities
148.345   Medics 142.075 149.40   Special Boat Unit 11 (SBU-11) Narc Enforcement OP
("Chambers Grill") 30.15 35.50 49.80 157.025 (HF 5426 6512.5 8476 10448.5 11113.5
12118.6 kHz)   SBU-11 Maintenance ("Solar Lobster") 30.15 35.50 49.80   USMC
Security 149.375   Industrial 148.305   Pager 148.85 149.10 149.45 150.40   Shipyard
Security 138.575 140.15   Port OP 138.525 140.625 140.875 149.37 156.45 156.50
156.60 156.65 156.80 156.90   Shipyard OP 32.25 32.75 138.80 139.575 140.20 140.35
140.45 140.475 140.50 140.525 140.975 142.10 142.50 142.525 142.55 143.61 148.35
150.375   USN 36.53 36.57 36.63 36.87 149.235 148.375 149.43 149.81 243.6 257.8
262.6 270.6 275.0 281.0 309.0 310.6 386.8 412.975

Marianna Muni Apt., FL: AD 370.3

Marinette Marine Corp., WI: 158.31 158.35

Marion Co Apt., Hamilton, OH: AD 269.4

Marion Co Apt., SC: AD 306.3 341.7

Marion Co Regn'l Apt., AR: AD 286.6

Marion Muni Apt., IN: AD 318.2

Marion Muni Apt., OH AD 269.3 390.8

Marquardt Corp., Van Nuys, CA: 154.57

Marquete Co Apt., MI: FSS 255.4   AD 259.3

Marshall AAF/Ft. Riley, Junction, KS (HQ 1st Infantry Division-Mechanized): S 109.4   AD 127.35 388.8   T 41.50 126.2 248.2   G 121.7 229.4   OP 30.30   WX 344.6 MP 166.225   Medevac 36.90   Army 139.125 139.30 143.05 143.175 143.225 163.25 163.5625 164.20 164.50 164.9875 165.0125 165.0625 165.1875 173.4625 173.5125 226.5 228.9 233.2 237.3 242.4 265.6 278.8 286.2 347.2 407.575 412.90 413.15 413.425   AF 32.45 36.85 139.70 141.80

Marshall Muni Apt/Ryan Fld, MN: FSS 255.4   AD 290.2

Marshfield Muni Apt, WI FSS 255.4   AD 317.7

Marthas Vineyard Apt., MA: AD 387.1

Martin ANG Station, Gadsden, AL: ANG 150.20

Martindale AAF, San Antonio, TX: NG Helicopters 123.05

Martin Marietta Company (selected listings): Belgrade, NC 153.02; Cedar Rapids, IA 43.10; Deer Park, FL 153.245; Charlestown, IN 154.49 157.025; Englewood, CO 153.32; Goldendale, WA 151.955 151.715 462.375 462.425; Littleton, CO 153.14 153.32; Lyons, CO 43.52; Maitland, MO 43.10; Rock Springs, WY 154.49; Vandenberg AFB, CA 153.05 153.065; Waterton, CO 153.14 153.32; Maitland, MO 43.10; Moegon, MO 43.10; Moline, KS 43.10; Orlando, FL 123.2 123.3 153.20 153.32 153.245 461.375 Pager 157.74; Savannah, GA 43.10; Topeka, KS 43.10;

Martinsburg ANG Station, WV: Security 163.4875 165.1125   FD/Crash 163.5125 Disaster Preparedness 163.5875   ANG 165.0125 165.1375 165.1625 390.1

Martin State Apt., Baltimore, MD: AD 228.4   T 297.2   G 297.2   CP 135th Tactical Air Grp 385.9   CP 175th Tactical Fighter Grp ("Colt Control") 347.2   MAC CP ("Witch Ops") 385.9   ANG Security 163.4875   ANG FD 149.225 149.545   ANG 34.40 34.60 36.80 40.15 41.45 41.95 139.70 143.80 148.50 149.15 149.325 149.525 150.15 150.175 150.225 235.0 253.4 257.5 268.1 272.5 297.2 301.6 335.7 343.0 371.5 384.7 385.9 389.0 392.2

Maryland Shipbuilding & Drydock Co., Baltimore, MD: 154.60 461.275

Mason City Muni Apt., IA: FSS 255.4   AD 380.2

Massena Int'l. Apt-Richards Fld, NY: FSS 255.4 AD 377.1

Mather AFB, Sacramento, CA (323rd Air Base Grp; 320th Bombardment Wing): DI 296.0   S 119.15 270.1   AD 123.7 124.5 127.4 233.5 259.1 284.0 285.6 363.8 372.8   T 120.65 126.2 348.4   G 120.65 275.8   E 120.65 239.15   SAC CP 311.0 321.0   AF Reserve OP ("Baker Control") 351.2   NG ("Spartan Control") 49.95 340.1   WX 344.6 VIP OP 163.5625   Security 148.125 148.175 148.275 148.525 148.575 149.575 163.4875 FD/Crash 173.5875   Base OP 165.1375 165.4125   OSI 138.075 138.165 138.175   Base Commander 138.025 138.425 148.065 149.565   Civil Engineering 149.50   Medics 173.5625   Ramp Control 163.4875 413.175 413.20 413.30   Flightline Maintenance 149.375 165.1625 163.5625   320th BW Flightline Maintenance 148.425 149.175 149.265 Pager 138.025   Crew Alerts 413.45   Base Transportation 149.50   AF 138.265 139.05 139.85 148.475 149.175 164.50 165.1375 173.5125 267.9 379.5 413.35

Mathis Fld., San Angelo, TX: FSS 255.4   AD 322.55 354.1   G 348.6   E 319.0   T 257.8

Maurice Rose AHP, Germany: T 31.80 33.20 122.1 142.90 251.2

Maury Co. Apt., Columbia, TN: AD 381.4

Maxwell AFB, Montgomery, AL (Air University; Air War College; Air Command & Staff College; Squadron Officer School; AF Senior NCO Academy): DI 122.85 372.2 S 269.9   AD 118.45 120.55 121.2 124.0 132.45 255.6 270.25 319.9 322.5 369.2   T 118.15 253.5   G 127.15 289.4   AF Reserve CP 908th Tactical Air Grp ("Toil Ops") 396.9   WX 342.5   OSI 40.17 40.19 138.075 138.165 138.175   Base Cmdr's Net 163.4625   Base OP 148.075   908th Maintenance 149.075 149.475 150.275   Security 164.175   Power Utilities 139.65   Disaster Net 138.025   Civil Engnrng 148.525   A/C Fueling 149.125   FD 172.5375   Medics 171.4875   AF 34.20 38.65 46.85 139.65 139.70

141.80 148.065 148.125 148.51 149.175 149.525 150.275 150.315 163.4875 163.5375 164.15 164.1376 165.1375 173.4375 173.5375 307.8 314.2 363.8 413.20 413.30 413.40 (Also see Gunter AFB listings.)

Mayport Naval Station, FL (Carrier Grp 6; NATO Standing Naval Force Atlantic; Cruiser Destroyer Grp 12; Naval Surface Force Atlantic Readiness Support Grp; Fleet Training Center): DI 301.3 S 268.6 AD 124.4 347.8 T 118.75 126.2 265.8 350.5 G 126.5 233.7 FD/Crash 140.125 Security 142.525 WX 301.3 Harbor Patrol 149.075 USN 138.525 139.525 140.025 140.05 140.25 140.60 140.675 140.75 140.825 140.925 140.95 140.975 141.00 141.95 142.575 142.80 148.325 149.075 149.37 150.075 237.8 250.8 264.3 268.6 267.4 273.0 275.7 280.6 283.4 289.8 300.5 307.7 315.7 326.6 338.1 339.6 344.5 348.1

McAlester Muni Apt., OK: FSS 255.4 AD 278.3

McAlester Army Ammunition Depot, OK: Railroad 143.52 Army 139.50 140.00 140.125 148.29

McCain Fld., MS: See Meridian NAS.

McCarran Int'l Apt., Las Vegas, NV: FSS 255.4 AD 353.7 379.15 380.05 T 257.8 G 319.95 E 379.95 SAC CP 311.0 321.0

McChord AFB, Tacoma, WA (AMC; 1st AF; Northwest Air Defense Sector; 62nd Military Airlift Wing; 25th Air Division; 446th Military Airlift Wing/Reserve; HQ 25th NORAD Region): DI 372.2 S 109.6 270.1 AD 126.5 391.9 T 124.8 236.6 259.3 G 121.65 275.8 MAC CP 130.65 349.4 SAC CP 311.0 321.0 NORAD CP 364.2 Security 165.1625 413.125 MAC OP 407.425 413.125 WX 342.5 OSI 40.17 40.19 138.075 138.165 138.175 FD/Crash 173.5875 Base Commanders Net 165.1125 Motor Pool 163.5875 Flightline Fueling 148.095 Flightline Maintenance 149.265 Crew Alerts 413.45 AF 46.75 138.10 139.00 142.20 142.275 143.775 148.175 148.175 148.215 148.40 148.48 148.55 148.71 149.175 149.205 149.325 149.475 149.505 150.195 150.25 150.345 163.4625 163.5375 165.1625 173.4375 173.5375 228.6 235.9 238.6 239.7 251.9 252.0 260.9 261.4 261.9 265.4 271.0 277.6 282.6 287.7 288.4 294.4 293.6 293.8 298.1 298.4 338.0 340.6 341.5 342.3 348.2 348.4 351.5 355.2 359.8 374.0 386.0 390.2 394.2 397.8 399.8 413.075 413.125 413.15 413.30 413.525 413.825

McClellan AFB, Sacramento, CA (Air Logistics Center; 1155th Technical Opns Sqdn; 2049th Communications Grp; 431st Test & Evaluation Sqdn): 41st Rescue & Weather Recon Wing): DI 122.85 372.2 S 109.2 269.9 AD 118.8 119.1 120.45 124.5 125.25 125.6 127.4 257.9 271.3 285.6 320.1 340.9 381.2 383.1 385.5 G 118.2 225.4 E 121.85 225.4 T 124.6 236.6 369.2 CP ("Fosdick") 377.8 Global HF System CP 292.1 (HF 4725 6738 8967 11176 13201 15015 17975 kHz) 41st Rescue CP ("Lark Cntrl.") 276.0 CG 169.25 381.7 (HF 3123 5696 8984 11201 kHz) CG Rescue 282.8 WX 344.6 Security 163.4875 Base FD 163.4375 Crash Trucks 173.4875 173.5875 OSI 138.075 138.165 138.175 Base OP 150.285 Civil Engineering 149.025 Medics 168.00 Castle AFB link 165.0625 Pager 407.475 Commanders Net 150.225 165.1125 407.425 413.00 AF Rescue 143.15 143.35 148.845 Disaster Preparedness 148.845 163.5875 Supply OP 149.475 Flightline Maintenance 148.215 148.40 148.45 148.515 148.545 150.285 173.5375 407.40 409.05 409.125 410.20 413.125 413.275 413.325 413.375 Nuclear Weapons Systems 168.45 CG Ground Support 150.285 SAC CP 311.0 321.0 Crew Alerts 413.45 AF 46.85 138.20 139.05 139.725 150.195 167.85 173.4375 233.6 236.0 251.9 252.22 252.42 252.8 254.8 259.0 287.4 303.0 314.6 327.2 339.0 351.6 372.8 379.0 382.6 384.7 391.2 399.8 399.9 409.05 413.025 413.20 413.30

McClellan-Palomar Apt., CA: AD 323.0 T 392.0 WX 344.6

McComb-Pike Co Apt./Lewis Fld, MS: FSS 255.4 AD 327.05

McConnell AFB, Wichita, KS (ACC; 8th AF; 384st Bombardment Wing; 91st Strategic Missile Wing): DI 372.2 S 119.5 269.9 AD 120.6 127.45 126.7 134.8 269.1 281.5 290.3 353.5 T 126.2 236.6 295.7 G 118.0 275.8 WX 375.2 Security 163.4625 Crew Alerts 413.45 SAC CP 311.0 321.0 ANG OP 301.6 OSI 138.075 138.165 138.175 Boeing Mil Aircraft (BMA) FD 154.25 154.295 BMA OP 123.2 123.325

123.35 153.20 462.275 462.45 462.50 463.875 AF 30.10 32.90 34.50 38.90 41.50 48.90
140.40 148.065 148.30 148.545 149.205 149.31 149.325 149.475 149.565 150.195 150.315
150.35 163.4875 163.5125 163.5875 164.50 173.5625 173.5875 255.7 262.3 266.2 271.1
271.9 275.2 295.7 302.2 308.0 308.8 314.3 339.3 351.1 390.0 413.15

McConnell Auxiliary AFB #9, KS: AF 140.40

McCoy AAF/Ft. McCoy, WI (Army Reserve): AD 128.6 363.0 T 38.50 41.70 124.6
229.4 241.0 Range 41.90 46.80 124.6 247.4 Army Reserve 36.11 36,53 36.69 49.80
139.125 139.30 141.30 143.05 143.225 143.25 143.40 143.5625 165.0375 165.0625
165.0875 165.1875 AF 314.2

McDonnell Douglas Corp. (Selected listings; also see specific locations):
Huntington Beach, CA Security ("Echo Base") 153.305 Pager 153.08 Msc 158.28;
Knob Noster, MO 123.55; Robertson, MO 153.29; St. Louis, MO: 33.14 35.02 35.14
35.92 42.98 154.57 153.29 173.20 173.395 462.225; Tulsa, OK 123.375 123.45 123.55
153.20; Wrightwood, CA 123.2 123.275 123.3 123.4 123.425 123.45 123.55 275.2;
Long Beach, CA 158.28 275.2; Patuxent River, MD 123.55; Edwards AFB, CA
123.275 123.55; Yuma, AZ 123.275 123.425 123.55 278.2 314.6 282.6; Monrovia, CA
151.655; Culver City, CA 462.20; Torrance, CA 153.08 158.28; Kennedy Space
Center, FL 153.395; Palmdale, CA 153.08; Mt. Wilson (repeater), CA 462.225; W.
Orange, NJ 471.8375

McEntire ANG Base, Columbia, SC: DI 298.3 AD 118.85 124.7 133.4 298.9 306.3
358.3 T 132.4 253.5 G 395.8 NG OP 41.30 246.7 WX 342.5 Security 149.475
FD/Crash 148.515 ANG 32.65 34.15 34.55 40.15 138.40 148.065 149.19 149.30 253.5
287.7 298.3 365.5 379.5 388.5 395.1 398.5

McGhee Tyson Apt., Knoxville, KY: FSS 255.4 AD 353.6 360.8 T 257.8 G 348.6
NG OP 49.80 313.0 ANG OP 143.80 303.0 SAC CP 311.0 321.0 ANG 163.4625
163.4875 163.5125 163.5375 164.50 154.0125 165.1125 235.5 375.5 388.5 398.5

McGregor Range, NM: Army 30.45 32.05 38.71 139.325 139.35 141.175 141.30
149.37 165.1375 172.825 241.1 250.7 264.5 277.5 303.3 310.5 315.5 323.5 326.5 336.5
346.5 367.5 370.5 389.5 416.425

McGregor Muni Apt., TX: AD 269.4 363.0

McGuire AFB, Wrightstown, NJ (AMC; 21st Air Force; 514th Military Airlift
Wing/Associate; NJ National Guard): DI 372.2 S 110.6 AD 120.0 120.25 127.5
259.3 318.2 363.8 388.2 T 119.8 236.6 255.6 G 121.8 275.8 E 135.2 335.2 MAC
CP 130.65 319.4 SAC CP 311.0 321.0 NORAD CP 364.2 NG & Army OP 41.35
122.85 265.6 Ft. Dix Range 34.00 41.00 Ft. Dix OP 41.25 41.30 122.85 139.30
265.6 ANG 150.20 Security 149.00 163.4625 163.4875 FD/Crash 407.45 Crew
Alerts 413.45 Civil Engineering 150.325 Base Commanders Net 148.175 165.1125
Flightline Maintenance 149.20 149.40 Fueling 149.225 AF 36.85 139.65 139.85 142.40
140.065 148.215 148.45 148.475 148.515 149.15 149.175 149.265 149.30 149.35 149.50
149.55 150.165 150.225 150.25 150.275 150.30 150.345 163.5375 165.5625 165.0125
166.20 173.5375 228.7 228.8 234.7 235.6 238.5 239.2 251.0 254.8 256.6 263.2 270.4
271.8 275.0 278.4 278.6 282.5 286.7 287.8 288.0 292.7 292.8 298.8 302.4 303.0 303.9
306.4 316.2 325.5 326.4 338.4 338.8 342.1 344.0 347.4 351.6 356.0 363.8 369.0 371.8
375.1 376.2 386.2 388.2 389.2 390.1 392.8 394.8 408.125 409.05 413.025 413.05 413.15
413.175 413.20 413.30

McKellar Fld., TN: FSS 255.4 AD 317.4

McMillan Assault Strip, San Miguel, CA: OP 41.50 126.2 241.0 Medevac 38.90

McMinn Co Apt., Athens, TN: AD 353.6

McMinnville Apt., OR: AD 284.6 291.7

McMullen, TX: USN 277.8

McMurdo Station/Williams Fld, Antarctica: T 126.2 134.1 270.6 340.2 CP (HF 8997
13251 kHz) Msc (HF 4718 5726 11255 kHz)

McNary Fld., Salem, OR: AD 257.2 291.7 T 257.2 NG 40.90 148.575 241.6 244.8

McPherson Apt., TX: AD 325.8

Meadows Fld., Bakersfield, CA: AD 270.3 317.7 362.3   T 257.8
Medford-Jackson Co Apt., OR: FSS 255.4   AD 306.3   T 257.8
Melbourne Regn'l. Apt., FL: FSS 255.4   AD 340.9 370.9   T 257.8
Memorial Fld., Hot Springs, AR: AD 348.7
Memphis Defense Depot, TN: Security 173.4125   Pager 173.4625   Army 38.89 164.10 412.835 413.235
Memphis Intl. Apt., TN: FSS 255.4   AD 284.7 291.6 313.2 338.3   G 257.8   T 257.8   ANG CP 138.10 341.6   ANG Security 163.4875   ANG 140.65 140.775 141.00 150.345 163.4625
Memphis NAS, NAS (Naval Air Technical Training Center): S 374.8   AD 119.1 120.7 122.5 124.15 124.65 125.8 126.7 284.7 291.6 313.2 338.3   T 120.25 340.2 360.2 G 126.2 382.8   OP 274.5   WX 274.5   FD/Crash Trucks 149.10   Medics 138.95 Ambulances 155.28   CID 139.58   Construction Crews 140.82   Civil Engineering 141.00   Gate Guards 142.50   Security 142.55   Recreation 142.86   Pager 148.325 Base Maintenance Emergency 38.30   USN 138.525 138.96 139.45 139.545 140.075 140.50 142.075 143.275 143.675 143.70 143.725 282.0 285.2 299.6 301.3 321.8
Mena Intermountain Muni Apt, AR: AD 398.9
Menominee Marinette Twin City Apt., MI: AD 338.2
Merced Muni Apt., CA: AD 379.8
Mercer Co Apt., Trenton, NJ: AD 291.7   T 257.8   E 257.8   NG 40.10 41.00 121.95 242.4
Mercer Co Apt., Bluefield, WV: FSS 255.4   AD 381.6
Merchant Marine Academy, Kings Point, NY: 40.29 162.125 166.025
Meridian NAS/McCain Fld, MS (Training Air Wing 1; Naval Technical Training Center; Alpha OLF; Bravo OLF; Sea Ray Target Facility): S 273.2   AD 119.2 120.5 120.95 124.8 269.6 276.4 314.8 343.7 374.9   T 126.2 340.2 360.2   G 336.4   E 336.4 WX 312.4   Training Sqdn 7 (VT-7) 263.0 282.1 285.2 299.6 323.0 377.2   VT-7 Ground Support 139.545   Training Sqdn 9 (VT-9) Ground Support 140.34   Medics 150.075   PHE 280.1   Base OP 352.2   USN 138.60 138.85 139.85 139.55 140.025 140.15 140.32 140.325 140.70 140.90 141.00 142.50 266.8 274.8 300.4 301.0 308.2 342.8 348.0 356.1 363.6
Merrill Fld., Anchorage, AK: FSS 255.4   AD 134.1 290.9   E 316.7
Merrill Muni Apt., WI: FSS 255.4   AD 317.7
Mesa AZ McDonnell Douglas Heliport: S ("Falcon ATIS") 118.25   T ("Falcon Tower") 124.6   G ("Falcon Ground") 121.3   Pager 465.00   OP ("Apache Control") 123.35 226.3   Msc 123.25 123.475 153.08 462.425 (Production, training & experimental helicopter flight test operations.)
Metcalf Fld., Toledo, OH: AD 307.0
Metro Oakland Int'l. Apt., CA: FSS 255.4   AD 307.2 317.65 323.2 338.2 346.05 350.8 354.1 398.9   T 256.9 395.9   SAC CP 311.0 321.0 413.45
Mettel Fld., Connersville, IN: AD 316.7
M. Graham Park Apt., MO: AD 286.6
Miami CGAS, FL: See Opa Locka.
Miami Int'l. Apt., FL: FSS 255.4   AD 301.5 319.9 322.3 354.1 379.9   G 348.6   T 256.9   US Customs Svc aero OP (see US Customs listings elsewhere in this edition)
Miami University Apt., Oxford, OH: AD 257.2
Michael AAF/Dugway Proving Ground, UT: T 41.50 126.2 241.0 248.2   FD 126.2 248.2   OP ("Clover Control") 134.1 301.7   Range Control 36.10   Army 34.30 40.20 118.45 149.315 149.575 149.625 149.655 149.685 149.715 162.225 163.4125 163.4875 163.5375 165.0375 165.1875 173.4125 173.4625 173.4875 173.5375 225.7 226.7 228.2 230.4 231.9 234.0 235.0 237.8 244.3 245.8 255.8 274.0 274.2 300.0 311.4 407.425 413.525   USN 337.0   AF 46.95 49.65 49.75 148.125 148.815
Michael J. Smith Fld, NC: AD 268.7
Michiana Regn'l. Apt., So. Bend, IN: FSS 255.4   AD 257.8   T 257.8

Michigan ANG: 267.8 385.9 389.0 391.2

Middle Georgia Regn'l. Apt., GA: AD 324.3 348.7 388.2 T 257.8

Middleton Fld/Evergreen OLF, AL: AD 346.4 OP 122.7

Midland Int'l. Apt., TX: FSS 255.4 AD 290.4 372.1 385.6 T 257.8 G 348.6

Midland Int'l. Corp., Kansas City, MO: 151.625 461.775 464.35

Mid-State Apt., Phillipsburg, PA: AD 272.7 NG 30.50 122.85 242.4

Midway NAF/Henderson Fld, Midway Isl.: OP 126.2 257.8 340.2

Mifflin Co. Apt., PA: AD 272.2

Milan Army Ammunition Depot, TN: Army 165.0375 165.1875 173.4625 173.5125

Miliard Apt., PA: AD 379.9

Military Ocean Terminal, Bayonne, NJ (Military Traffic Management Command/Eastern Area): Security 142.305 Msc 139.15 139.155 141.195 142.035 165.0375 275.7 283.4 307.7 339.6 348.1 358.6 407.225

Miller Int'l. Apt., McAllen, TX: FSS 255.4 AD 276.3 T 256.9

Miller Muni Apt, SD: AD 269.1

Millinocket Muni Apt., ME: FSS 255.4 AD 346.4

Mill Valley AFS, CA: 148.545 228.9 234.6 238.4 254.2 260.8 267.0 270.2 274.4 279.4 281.6 309.4 316.3 320.6 324.0 327.9 336.6 341.8 346.2 377.0 387.8 398.0

Millville Muni Apt., NJ: FSS 255.4 AD 263.6

Miltope Corp., Melville, NY: 154.57 929.9625

Mineral Wells Apt., TX: FSS 255.4 AD 360.6

Minneapolis-St. Paul Int'l. Apt/Wold-Chamberlain Fld., MN: DI 351.2 FSS 255.4 AD 284.7 335.5 357.4 G 348.6 T 257.6 CP 934th TAG ("Abstain") 252.1 351.2 CP 133rd TAW 240.15 SAC CP 311.0 321.0 Crew Alerts 413.45 ANG 141.80 148.10 148.20 148.545 149.265 163.4875 163.5125 163.5625 163.5875 164.30 165.1375 413.20 413.30

Minot AFB, ND (ACC; 57th Air Division; 91st Missile Wing; 5th Bombardment Wing; 5th Fighter Interceptor Sqdn; 91st Security Police Grp; 91st Combat Supply Grp): DI 372.2 S 375.8 AD 119.6 259.1 363.8 T 120.65 236.6 253.5 G 275.8 E 134.0 275.8 SAC CP 311.0 321.0 Crew Alerts 413.45 WX 342.5 OSI 138.075 138.165 138.175 AF 148.035 148.065 148.215 148.30 148.45 148.515 148.545 148.95 149.175 149.235 149.265 149.325 149.375 149.475 150.10 150.135 130.345 163.00 163.5125 164.10 164.50 165.0125 165.1125 165.1375 165.1625 173.5125 173.5375 173.5625 173.5875 234.95 236.0 251.9 266.2 271.3 271.9 284.0 292.5 293.4 297.2 298.1 308.8 314.3 318.2 323.8 326.2 335.9 379.4 386.2 387.8 392.8 395.0 398.0 399.8 413.00 413.15

Minot Int'l. Apt., ND: FSS 255.4 AD 259.1 363.8 T 393.1 G 393.1

Minuteman III Missile Sites:

Colorado 148.54 148.55 148.935 149.265 150.35 407.375

Kansas 149.31 149.325 149.475 149.505

Missouri 148.095 148.05 149.175 149.205 149.235 149.265 150.10 150.375 407.375

Montana 148.455 148.54 148.935 148.95 149.175 149.265 149.505 149.535 150.10 150.375 150.50 407.375 407.40

Nebraska 148.455 148.54 148.935 148.95 149.175 149.265 149.565 150.35 407.375

North Dakota 138.50 148.30 148.455 148.50 148.54 148.935 148.95 149.175 149.475 149.535 150.10 150.195 150.225 150.25 150.285 407.375 407.40

South Dakota 148.095 148.455 148.475 148.54 148.935 149.275 150.10 406.375 407.40

Wyoming 148.455 148.545 148.935 149.175 149.235 149.265 149.565 150.10 150.35 407.375

Miramar NAS/Mitscher Fld., San Diego, CA (Fighter Weapons "Top Gun" School; Pacific Fleet fighter, recon, & early warning squadrons): S 280.4 282.0 AD 119.6 120.05 132.2 135.2 269.1 281.8 363.1 T 133.625 315.6 340.2 G 380.8 E 301.3 WX 362.1 Data Link 305.1 FD/Crash 141.10 140.22 Medics 143.525 Fleet Area Control

& Surveillance Facility ("Beaver") 118.65 120.85 266.9 272.6 285.7 289.9 314.7 344.1 Ordnance 301.3 Security ("Bravo") 150.105 ("Charlie") 150.15 Public Works ("Alpha") 141.00 Pacific Fighter Wing ("Echo") 150.55 Top Gun Base 262.7 OPFOR OP ("Hassle Base") 311.9 Top Gun Tactical 333.25 "Happy Hunter" 255.3 ACM Range ("War Wag") 279.2 ACM Range Chocolate Mtns 272.9 Base OP 150.105 150.15 FD 140.25 VC-12 291.3 VF-1 263.7 VF-2 291.3 VF-24 322.1 VF-51 254.5 VF-111 250.2 VF-114 299.7 VF-124 253.1 VF-126 275.5 VF-211 361.9 VF-213 250.2 VF-301 344.4 VF-302 323.5 VX-4 265.3 USN 38.40 138.855 139.545 140.895 142.515 143.715 150.20 249.8 250.8 253.1 253.3 255.0 263.5 263.7 265.2 267.7 283.3 284.5 284.6 285.2 290.4 291.3 299.7 300.2 300.4 301.3 304.1 325.2 350.8 354.7 355.6 355.7 360.8 362.5 362.6 366.8 376.8 381.5 382.0 383.7 385.5

Misawa AB, Honshu, Japan: DI 313.6 S128.4 366.2 AD 120.7 125.3 317.8 363.8 T 118.1 123.1 126.2 138.05 236.6 236.8 247.0 315.8 G 118.65 126.2 275.8 E118.65 275.8 432nd Fighter Wing ("Falcon OP") 141.60 277.2 394.4 WX 344.6

Missoula County Apt., MT: FSS 255.4 T 381.7 AD 285.4 387.1

Mitchell Muni Apt, SD: AD 317.4

Mobay Chemical Corp., Baytown, TX: 457.525 457.55

Mobile Downtown Apt, AL: AD 288.15 269.3 T 367.7 NG 41.05 125.525

Mobile Regn'l Apt, AL: AD 288.15 269.3 307.1 T 239.0 G 348.6 CG 381.8 (HF 3123 5696 8984 kHz)

Modesto City/Co. Apt./Harry Sham Fld., CA: AD 278.3 284.6 294.5 319.9 T 257.8

Moffett Fld. NAS, Mountain View, CA (2 ASW Patrol Wings & 8 ASW Patrol Sqdns): S 283.0 AD 120.1 121.3 134.5 317.6 322.0 346.0 350.8 T 126.2 340.2 353.2 G 121.85 142.575 336.4 E 380.8 WX 341.3 PD/Security ("Dover Popgun") 139.575 140.05 140.225 141.00 141.25 142.02 142.04 USMC Security 138.675 FD/Crash 140.25 140.525 143.42 CID 140.075 140.65 140.775 Base OP 140.05 149.125 251.7 ANG 40.13 127.05 139.70 390.0 (HF 6715 kHz) Medics 139.575 149.125 Civil Engineering 141.95 Officer of the Day ("Multibarter") 140.04 VIP Escorts 138.675 Supply Net 138.675 139.545 Ramp 140.05 142.575 Base Transportation 149.03 FD 140.25 Ordnance 140.125 140.925 Msc 1240.91 142.575 EOD 140.225 Building Maintenance 139.525 Communications Technicians 140.55 Pager 149.03 166.225 Flightline Maintenance 138.675 ANG Maintenance 150.025 150.05 150.25 150.35 Patrol Sqdn 19 (VP-19) 339.5 Patrol Sqdn 31 (VP-31) 263.5 Patrol Sqdn 46 (VP-46) 384.5 Patrol Sqdn 47 (VP-47) 149.03 380.6 Patrol Sqdn 48 (VP-48) 266.7 Patrol Sqdn 50 (VP-50) 148.35 354.7 Patrol Sqdn 91 (VP-91) 149.03 250.1 USN 139.55 140.04 140.13 140.25 140.65 141.00 149.03 163.1125 163.4875 253.9 256.5 263.7 266.8 270.7 283.3 292.95 293.05 294.65 294.95 295.35 295.45 297.95 298.05 299.45 300.2 305.0 306.35 306.45 307.85 307.95 309.25 309.35 310.75 310.85 312.3 341.0 NASA Ames Research Center Security 170.35 171.15 NASA OP 123.3 162.025 163.025 171.25 170.20 170.35 170.40 171.00 171.15 173.6675 173.6875 314.6 406.225 407.125 408.00 408.15 408.80 409.20 409.35

Moisant Fld., LA: See New Orleans Int'l.

Molokai Apt., HI: AD 317.5 T 306.2

Monroe Co Apt., AL: AD 267.9

Monroe Co Apt., IN: AD 339.8

Monroe Co Apt., MS: AD 269.4 299.15

Monroe Muni Apt, WI: AD 327.0 379.2

Monroe Regn'l Apt., LA: FSS 255.4 AD 271.2 388.0 T 257.8

Monterey, CA: CG 416.85; USN Postgraduate School 138.525 140.04 149.075 149.425 305.8 FD 140.50

Monterey Peninsula Apt., CA: AD 263.6 302.0 307.3 309.2 T 257.8 G 348.6

Montevideo-Chippewa Co Apt., MN: FSS 255.4

Montgomery, AL: USN 34.55

Montgomery Co Apt., MD: NASA 123.2

Montgomery Co Apt, TX: AD 396.0

Montgomery Fld., San Diego, CA: AD 306.7 363.1 T 269.4

Monticello Muni Apt., IA: 247.2

Moody AFB, Valdosta, GA (ACC; 9th AF; 68, 69 & 70 Fighter Sqdns of the 347th Fighter Wing): DI 372.2 S 256.0 AD 124.6 125.95 126.6 127.925 259.3 285.6 306.3 316.7 379.2 T 128.45 289.6 G 275.8 E 121.25 225.4 TAC CP ("Raymond 17") 381.3 WX 342.5 FAA 162.275 Security 163.00 173.025 FD/Crash 173.5875 AF 149.175 150.225 165.0125 165.1125 165.1375 165.1625 166.10 173.4375 174.5375 295.0 296.9 311.3 379.5 413.15

Moore AAF/Ft. Devens, Ayer, MA (1st Army/Forward; 39th Engineer Battalion/Combat; 36th Medical Battalion; 46th Combat Support Hospital; 10th Special Forces Grp/Airborne; Army Intelligence School; Army Readiness & Mobilization Region 1): AD 119.45 279.6 T 119.35 229.4 241.0 OP 30.10 38.40 38.51 46.95 WX 46.95 Range 38.50 Msc (CSMS) 40.60 49.85 142.35 Security 38.85 40.93 FD 34.33 34.83 38.85 Medics 46.95 49.70 148.785 150.70 Maintenance 150.685 Army Engineers 163.025 163.125 163.4875 167.925 168.125 168.325 Army Reserve ("Trident North") 41.90 Army 38.75 49.80 141.325 142.325 163.5625

Moore-Murrell Apt., Moorestown, NJ: AD 360.8

Moorestown, NJ: USN 122.75 123.3 123.4 233.75 262.6 280.6 305.9 314.6 364.8 384.55 RCA Corp 310.0 323.5 384.5

Morey Apt., Madison, WI: AD 396.0

Morgantown Muni Apt./Hart Fld., WV: FSS 255.4 T 257.8

Mormon Mesa, NV: AF Bombing Range 122.65 343.0

Moron AB, Spain: AD 120.0 120.8 128.5 132.47 133.35 134.55 271.8 284.8 292.0 296.4 342.8 T 122.1 323.0 G242.0

Morris Muni Apt, IL: AD 388.0

Morris Muni Apt, MN: AD 269.2

Morristown Muni Apt., NJ: AD 379.9 T 353.9

Mosby AHP, Dahlonega, GA: Range ("Mountain Ranger") 34.10 Army 38.50 139.025 226.5 227.4 244.4 (Also see listings for Camp Merrill.)

Moscow, MS: USN 141.00 355.8

Motorola Corp. (Selected listings): Bensenville, IL 151.955; Schaumburg, IL 151.865 151.955 151.965 152.48 152.495 152.925 154.56 173.3375 173.35 173.5625 453.025 453.125 454.00 454.725 454.85 461.975 462.15 462.25 464.55 471.1635 471.2875 851.1875 851.25 851.3375; Cherry Valley 151.955; Chicago, IL 151.865 151.955 461.975 462.25 462.90 463.35 851.3375; Des Plaines, IL 151.955; Dixon, IL 151.955; Franklin Park, IL 151.865 151.955 154.625 461.975 462.25; Lombard, IL 151.955; Mesa, AZ 158.31; Ottawa, IL 151.865; Phoenix, AZ 153.935 157.74 461.125 461.15 461.975 462.20 464.95 851.1375; Rolling Meadows, IL 462.90; Salem, IL 461.90; Scottsdale, AZ 151.955 157.74 462.20; Tucson, AZ 461.90 462.10; Coltville, UT 461.90; Cleveland, OH 463.95; Escondido, CA 857.50; Edgewood, IA 461.80; New York, NY 463.90; Meriden, CT 463.70; Pelham, MA 463.675; Boston, MA 463.95; Arlington, VA 463.80; Atlanta, GA 363.375; Palo Alto, CA: 462.675; Walnut Creek, CA 462.675

Motor Vehicles Emission/MPG Test Lab (EPA): Ann Arbor, MI: 173.9125 408.00

Moultree Muni Apt., GA: AD 259.3 285.6

Mountain Home AFB, IA (ACC; 12th AF; 336th Fighter Wing; 389th Tactical Fighter Training Sqdn; 390th Electronic Combat Sqdn; Air Intervention Composite Wing): DI DI 372.2 S273.5 AD 124.8 134.1 259.1 371.2 T 120.5 253.5 G 275.8 E 127.1 373.0 TAC CP ("Raymond 27") 292.2 381.3 SAC CP 311.0 321.0 WX 342.5 376.0 391st TFS Launch & Recovery 30.50 148.85 276.6 Security 163.495 163.5875 FD/Crash 173.5875 Medics 155.28 155.34 389th TFS Yellow Section 148.20 391st TFS Blue Section 148.45 390th ECS Red Section 148.075 389th TFTS Flightline

Maintenance 148.20 289.3   390th ECS Flightline Maintenance 148.075 268.1   Orchard NG Artillery Range 39.80 127.8   Range 292.2   Supervisor of Flying 381.3   Fighter Weapons Integrated Command 300.05 392.2   In-Flight Emergencies 124.5 132.5 271.3   Channel #'s: Ch 1 273.5;   Ch 2 126.2/275.8;   Ch 3 126.2/253.5;   Ch 4 128.4/371.2;   Ch 5 126.35/360.6;   Ch 6 292.2;   Ch 7 381.3;   Ch 8 (individual sqdn's OP, a/c, & launch/recovery metro vans);   Ch 9 127.1/373.0;   Ch 10 255.4;   Ch 11 134.1/263.8;   Ch 12 124.3/259.1;   Ch 13 271.3;   Ch 14 284.0;   Ch 15 287.4/349.0;   Ch 16 297.6/369.2;   Ch 17 314.3/317.7;   Ch 18 359.1/269.0;   Ch 19 376.0/342.5;   Ch 20 300.05/392.2   Nuclear Weapons Systems 167.85 168.45   AF 139.65 148.065 148.125 148.455 148.515 148.545 149.30 150.255 150.315 163.4625 163.5375 169.4625 165.06 165.1125 173.7375 173.5625 268.1 283.8 284.0 305.7 395.1 413.15

Mountain Home Muni Apt., ID: AD 259.1

Mountain View Apt, MO: AD 317.5

Mt Hebo, OR: NORAD CP 364.2   AF 163.4875 228.6 235.9 238.2 238.6 239.7 252.0 260.9 261.4 265.4 271.0 277.6 279.4 282.6 287.7 288.4 293.6 293.8 328.0 348.2 351.5 355.2 359.8 374.0 386.0 390.2 394.2 397.8

Mt Laguna, CA: AF 163.4875 228.9 234.6 238.4 254.2 260.8

Mt Olive, NC: Army 277.0 242.0 249.0 364.5 391.5

Mt Pleasant Apt., MI: AD 381.5

Mt St Helens Volcano, WA: GSA 164.675 167.025 168.50 169.825   Federal Highway Admin 40.26 40.39 40.97   Forestry 170.50 171.425 172.225 172.325 409.65   National Park Service 171.425   Army Engineer Corps 164.50 165.0375   Geodetic Survey 167.425/167.10 168.425/167.075

Mt Vernon Outland Apt., IL: AD 317.7

Mt Washington Regn'l. Apt., NH: 282.2

Mt Wilson Observatory, Pasadena, CA: 30.84 31.24 33.14 33.40 35.02 35.04 154.60 508.1875

Muir AAF/Ft. Indiantown Gap, PA (HQ FTIG; PA Dept. of Military Affairs; Army Readiness Grp; Sr Army Advisor to PA NG; 56 Ordnance Detachment/EOD): AD 118.25 247.2   T 126.2 241.0   G 40.90 139.00 265.6   NG 41.50 49.95   NG Flightline 41.20   Flight Following 40.90   MP/Security 412.875   Gate Guards 412.40   56th OD 49.70 49.80   Range 247.2   Army & NG 32.53 38.45 40.77 40.83 46.79 46.93 143.075 143.15 148.065 163.4625 165.0875 232.7 235.5 237.4 267.1 299.1 375.5   AF 149.275 235.5 388.5 398.5

Muldrow NG Heliport, Lexington, OK: OP 46.90 142.45 387.9

Murphy Dome AFS Heliport, AK: T 126.2   NORAD CP 364.2   AF 173.4375 229.1 254.4 269.9 298.9   FSS 122.3

Muscle Shoals Apt., AL: FSS 255.4   AD 307.0

Muskegon Co Apt., MI: AD 269.6 339.1   T 285.4

Mustin Fld NALF Helipad, Philadelphia, PA: T 118.5 135.1 263.0

Myrtle Beach AFB, SC (ACC; 9th AF; 354th Fighter Wing; 17 & 19 Tactical Fighter Sqdns; 16th Tactical Recon Sqdn **Closing date 3/93**): DI 372.2   S 124.5 269.9   AD 119.2 127.4 128.7 225.4 294.5 321.1 343.6   T 126.05 255.9   G 121.2 275.8 TAC CP ("Raymond 21") 343.0 381.3   WX 239.8   Emergencies 40.50 363.8   Security 149.505 163.375   FD/Crash 173.5875   Medics 173.5625   Refueling 260.2   17th TFS 138.90 139.925 140.375 141.675 141.75 398.1   19th TFS 138.025 138.25 138.475 138.925 139.90 344.9   16th TRS 276.9   OSI 138.075 138.165 138.175   AF 32.85 34.20 34.35 34.60 36.45 36.80 38.70 40.20 40.55 41.70 46.65 46.90 46.95 47.65 47.95 49.90 49.95 51.50 60.10 138.10 138.30 138.425 138.65 139.80 139.975 141.60 142.30 148.05 148.095 148.215 148.375 148.455 149.175 149.225 149.565 150.165 150.315 163.5875 165.1375 236.0 239.8 251.9 259.0 262.3 266.3 270.1 276.8 280.5 286.5 286.7 289.3 289.6 290.7 294.5 295.9 304.9 318.2 321.0 321.2 339.1 371.2 379.3 381.0 383.1 389.4 392.0 413.15

Nahbollenbach Quartermaster Depot AHP, Germany: Msc 32.20 142.90 251.2

Nampa Apt., ID: AD 269.4

Nanoose Bay, WA: USN Test Range 139.50

Nantucket Mem'l. Apt, MA: AD 387.1 T 257.9 CG 165.2625

Napa Co. Apt., CA: AD 323.0 T 257.8

Narco Avionics, Ft. Washington, PA: 123.2

NASA Shuttle Landing Facility, FL: AD 134.95 358.3 T 128.55 284.0 G 121.75 Advisories 123.6 (Also see Kennedy Space Center listings.)

NASA Wallops Island Flight Center, Chincoteague, VA: AD 127.95 132.55 134.1 314.0 353.6 T 126.5 394.3 E 121.7 Security 171.00 NOAA 140.00 165.4375 CG 416.55 417.00 Nuclear Systems 226.7 230.4 239.4 248.6 259.7 AF 149.15 149.325 NASA 40.87 46.73 49.83 122.8 122.85 123.175 123.175 123.2 123.225 123.25 123.3 123.375 123.4 123.45 148.25 148.56 148.98 149.15 149.52 164.70 166.225 166.25 170.35 170.40 171.15 171.3875 311.2 314.6 326.3 326.6 412.00 416.80 412.00

Nashville, TN: NG 148.925 150.465 150.765 164.9625

Nashville Int'l. Apt., TN: FSS 255.4 AD 317.45 385.55 388.0 G 348.6 379.95 T 257.8 307.2 ANG OP 335.7 ANG Maintenance 138.10

Natchitoches Regn'l. Apt., AL: AD 381.5 395.9

Natick Laboratories, MA: Army 40.89 40.95 41.49

National Center for Atmospheric Research, Boulder, CO: 164.20 165.6625 409.825

National Climatic Center NOAA, Asheville, NC: 416.375

National Environmental Satellite Service, Suitland, MD: 410.50

National Hurricane Center, Miami, FL: 122.925 123.05 Environmental Lab 169.025 Hurricane Network 162.50 Data Exchange 162.075 Msc 165.4375 165.5125 166.075 166.125 304.8 (HF ("Miami Monitor") 3407 5562 6673 6824 8876 8918 10015 11398 11396 13267 13354 14325 17901 18019 21937 kHz)

National Institutes of Health, Bethesda, MD: Security 164.775 411.45 FD 419.80 Transportation 41.83 Maintenance 36.75 Pagers 164.625 171.2375

National Naval Medical Center, Bethesda, MD: Mercy Net 140.275 Security 41.83 140.725 164.30 FD 140.275 140.725 Medevac 267.6 296.0 Ambulances 140.275 Disaster ("Magic Swimmer") 138.65 142.225 142.45 Pagers 140.275 148.275 Maintenance 142.525 Heliport 120.75 257.2 USN 140.075 140.20 140.225 140.55 140.58 140.65 140.675 140.775 140.82 142.00 143.335 148.525

National Severe Storms Forecast Center, Kansas City, MO: 163.225 172.10

National Severe Storms Laboratory, Norman, OK: Aero OP 122.9 122.925 122.95 123.05 123.075 Mobile Vans (HF 2010.5 4464 5769 7342.5 10218.5 14380 18171 23488 kHz) Mobile Vans Satellite comms (NFM mode) 268.7/251.5 OP 163.275 173.10 403.15 403.75 409.75

National Steel & Shipbuilding Co., San Diego, CA: 31.04 462.25 462.45 466.0125 466.0875 466.1125 466.2375 266.2625 466.3125 466.3375 466.6875 466.7125 477.7625 477.7875 477.9125

Natrona Co. Int'l. Apt., Casper, WY: FSS 255.4 AD 239.0 354.1

Navajo Army Depot, Flagstaff, AZ: 409.65 412.925

Naval Coastal Systems Heliport, Panama City, FL: OP 354.6

Naval Communication Area Master Station Atlantic, Driver, VA: USN 140.175 149.35

Naval Electronics Test Facility, St. Ingoes, MD: AD 120.05 261.8 T 126.2 358.0 USN 139.55 294.2 294.65 295.0 295.35 297.95 299.45 306.35 307.85 309.25 310.75

Naval Intelligence Support Center, Suitland, MD: Guards 415.20 417.20 USN 138.65 139.48 140.075 140.10 140.775 148.31 Army 36.69 FAA 415.55

Naval Investigative Service, Tidewater, VA: USN 138.70 140.075 140.65 140.775

Naval Petroleum Reserve #4, AK: 32.05 49.85 122.2 122.3 122.6 123.6 139.50 141.00 AF 126.2 162.60 236.6

Naval Research Laboratory, Chesapeake Beach, MD & Washington, DC: Medics 140.98 Security 140.95 USN 138.62 138.80 138.82 140.175 140.575 140.85 140.925 140.975 141.95

Naval Security Group (NAVSECGRU), Northwest, VA: Security 143.65 USN 149.075

Naval Ship Research & Development Command, Carderock, MD: Medics 140.46

Naval Surface Weapons Center/White Oak Lab, Silver Spring, MD: Medics 149.35 Security 139.50 Administrative 139.50 Base OP 142.50 Disaster Control 139.65 USN 138.72 140.22 140.45 140.58

Naval Weapons Laboratory, VA: Security 149.075

Navasota Muni Apt., TX: AD 338.3 394.1

Neil Armstrong Apt., Wapakoneta, OH: AD 316.7

Nellingen AHP, Germany: T 118.8 122.7 249.5 Msc 30.60 30.75 138.60 358.2

Nellis AFB, Las Vegas, NV (ACC; Fighter Weapons Center; 554th Combat Support Sqdn; 554th Operations Support Wing; 57th Fighter Weapons Wing; 4477th TES Red Eagles; USAF Thunderbirds Team; 4450th Tactical Grp; 99th Tactics & Training Wing; 4440 Fighter Training Grp; Fighter Weapons School; 552nd Tactical Operations Force; 26, 64, 65, 527, & 5021 Tactical Operations (Agressor) Sqdns): DI 372.2 S 270.1 AD 135.1 279.7 352.6 T 125.1 324.3 G 121.8 275.8 E 120.9 289.4 TAC CP ("Raymond 22") 320.0 381.3 (HF 4742 kHz) MAC ALCE 257.35 259.95 WX 239.8 344.6 Flight Space Control 34.60 Inflight Emergencies 321.1 385.5 Search/Rescue 259.0 282.2 Supervisor of Flying ("Bullseye") 303.2 Base OP 148.545 FD/Crash 173.5875 Medics 173.5625 Area #2 Security 163.375 165.0625 Housing Security 163.4875 Flightline Security 148.30 Nuclear Area Security 165.065 OSI 40.17 40.19 138.075 138.175 Post Engineer 163.4625 Communications Technicians 138.30 148.50 Post Transportation 150.30 150.315 Pagers 138.325 168.00 173.5625 Commanders Net ("Vegas 1") 173.15 173.5375 407.45 Ground Emergency Crews 413.275 413.625 Ground Refueling 148.075 Flightline Supervisor 150.30 Flightline Decontamination 148.15 148.175 411.85 Flightline 57th Agressor 148.45 Flightline 474th OMS 149.275 149.325 149.475 Flightline 474th AMS 149.50 Flightline 474th MMS 149.55 165.1875 Flightline 148.175 148.30 148.455 148.70 149.265 149.505 149.565 Range Air/Air 138.275 139.10 139.70 257.2 259.4 268.2 294.9 357.1 364.0 Range Control-Air ("Blackjack") 377.8 Range Control-Ground ("Roulette") 293.5 383.3 Range #61 320.1 Range #62 292.2 Range #63 361.6 Range #64/64A 319.7 Range #65 288.8 Range #71 344.8 Range #74/74A 228.0 Range #75 363.9 Range #76 354.3 EOD Teams 36.33 36.39 410.35 4477th TES Red Eagles 36.80 Wilson Creek MOA 124.95 392.1 Tonopah MOA 126.95 338.7 Beatty MOA 119.35 253.4 Las Vegas MOA 126.65 343.0 Caliente MOA 124.45 392.1 Mormon Mesa MOA 126.65 343.0 Groom Lake MOA 361.1 Dreamland MOA 118.7 126.15 255.8 261.1 Dart East MOA 292.2 Dart West MOA 319.7 Dart South MOA 319.7 Watertown Strip/S-4 MOA 297.65 Sally Corridor MOA 343.0 Pahute Mesa MOA 118.7 126.15 255.8 261.1 Yucca MOA 118.7 126.15 255.8 261.1 AF 30.15 32.35 32.45 32.65 32.85 34.17 34.33 34.73 36.45 36.85 40.15 40.65 41.31 41.45 41.95 138.165 138.40 139.65 139.80 139.90 140.65 141.30 142.30 142.75 142.925 143.175 148.03 148.215 148.40 148.485 148.525 149.10 149.175 149.205 149.25 149.425 150.15 150.225 150.25 150.275 150.60 163.5125 165.0125 165.1125 225.6 227.8 234.8 234.9 236.7 252.1 257.1 260.1 264.6 266.6 271.6 274.8 276.4 283.0 287.6 288.6 290.6 290.8 295.2 296.1 297.5 304.9 308.6 313.9 315.2 326.2 349.5 361.5 377.7 397.2 409.025 413.15 413.425 413.45 415.625 (Also see Nevada Test Site, Tonopah AFS, Indian Springs, & Roswell AFS listings.)

Neosho Mem'l Apt., MO: AD 343.9

Neubruecke Hospital AHP, Germany: OP ("Eagle Cntrl.") 40.10 Msc 132.20 142.90 251.2

Nevada Muni Apt, MO: AD 327.0

Nevada Test Site (NTS), NV: Net #1 148.47; Net #2 148.35 Transportation; Net #3 167.925 FD/Medics/Radiation Safety; Net #4 170.75; Net #5 173.5125 Los Alamos test ops & dry runs; Net #6 173.7125 Livermore test ops & dry runs; Net #8 173.6125 Sandia test ops & dry runs; Net #11 168.475 Weather/Crane Maintenance & Electrical; Net #12 36.33/34.99 & 36.39/34.99 & 410.35 Weather, EOD, EPA; Net #14 167.875 Control & Administration; Net #37 416.20; Desert Rock Airport 118.7 122.8 255.8 261.1 Pahute Mesa Airstrip 118.7 126.15 255.8 261.1 Yucca Airstrip 118.7 126.25 255.8 261.1 Transportation 41.03 41.31 173.7125 Control 169.00 Security 167.825 416.85 Construction 407.35 408.025 416.30 Communications Technicians 416.925 Carpenters 408.175 Vehicle Maintenance 408.95 Small Arms Range 409.50 Pager 410.80 Computer Tones 411.025 EG&G Corp 153.025 FEMA 167.975 Msc 36.05/34.99 126.15 139.77 141.68 142.23 150.45 150.555 162.10 162.225 162.475 163.00 164.025 164.10 164.175 164.225 164.275 164.40 164.475 164.525 164.675 164.70 164.75 164.775 164.9625 166.20 166.225 166.275 167.19 167.85 167.875 169.00 169.075 169.275 169.85 170.025 170.70 170.75 171.20 171.2375 171.3875 171.95 172.725 172.30 173.175 173.6625 225.8 239.4 240.2 260.3 292.1 406.30 406.425 406.50 406.525 406.625 406.9125 408.10 408.55 409.2125 410.00 410.05 411.075 411.15 411.60 412.65 415.15 416.025 416.25 416.50 416.7125 419.35 419.565 (Also see Nellis AFB listings.)

Newark AFB, OH (AF Logistics Command; Aerospace Guidancer Metrology Center): AF 165.1125 165.1625 403.375 407.45

Newark-Heath Apt., OH: AD 267.9

Newark Int'l. Apt., NJ: AD 379.9 T 257.6

New Bedford Muni Apt., MA: AD 307.9 385.6 T 239.0

New Boston AFS, NH (Tracking Station): Security 170.60 173.4875 AF 165.4125 374.53 375.36 375.855 375.90 376.185

New Braunfells Apt., TX: AD 381.4 392.1

New Castle Apt., PA: NG 33.78

New Castle Co. Apt., DE: AD 323.1 T 305.4 G 275.8 ANG OP ("Seabee") 343.0 NG 38.60 46.90 ANG 34.15 148.125 148.20 149.25 150.25 FD/Crash 33.78 33.94

New Castle-Henry City Apt., IN: AD 317.8

New Cumberland Army Depot, PA: Security 165.0625 FD 33.90 Motor Pool 148.675 Railroad 148.675 Pager 163.5625 Army 34.10 229.4

New Garden Flying Fld., Toughkenamon, PA: AD 286.0

New Hanover Co. Apt., Wilmington, NC: AD 276.3 343.9 T 239.3 E 348.6 Army 139.15 148.725

New Haven, CT: USN 32.45 36.55

New London CT (Naval Submarine Base; New London Lab; Naval Underwater Systems Center Detachment): 38.30 38.40 138.72 140.075 140.46 140.58 140.65 140.775 141.00 149.075 149.125 149.40 233.8 266.7 275.7 283.4 284.4 299.4 300.3 306.0 309.0 314.9 320.5 328.1 336.2 336.3 304.4 348.1 355.0 358.0 385.0 386.9 (Also see Groton, CT listings.)

New Orleans, LA: Army Reserve (337th Support Brigade): 38.89 150.75 163.00 163.025 163.5375

New Orleans Int'l. Apt./Moisant Fld., LA: FSS 255.4 AD 256.9 269.2 284.7 290.3 T 254.3 FAA 165.875 169.30

New Orleans NAS/Alvin Callender Fld., LA (5 Commands, Naval Reserve, CGAS, Customs Service Air Support Branch): S 276.2 AD 123.85 256.9 T 123.8 340.2 360.2 G 121.6 382.8 CG 165.2625 165.3375 171.2375 171.3375 381.7 381.8 383.9 (HF 5696 8984 kHz) WX 265.8 Search/Rescue 282.8 Security ("Sandpoint") 139.50 Security 138.70 140.82 FD/Crash 140.10 140.25 142.48 Base FD 138.30 139.575 140.10 Naval Support Activity Security 148.275 148.35 Naval Investigative Service 140.075 140.775 CP 267.8 Base OP 138.03 142.625 Pager 148.325 150.75 ANG

Security 163.5125   Master at Arms 140.625   Ordnance 142.75   Gate Guards 140.55
Duty Office 149.025   Shipyard Security 140.25   Shipyard FD 140.70   Shore Patrol
138.70 150.075   Piers 139.475   ANG Security 163.5125   Fueling 138.725 138.82   Air
Terminal 138.80   Ferry 149.35   Port & Harbor 142.65   Supply Center 140.90
Facility Maintenance 138.75 139.75 140.16   Flightline 140.80   Naval Reserve VA-204
Sqdn 301.3   ANG Medevac 271.2 351.2   ANG Ambulances 155.28 413.30 413.40   ANG
OP 138.10 148.575 149.235 150.225 163.4875 163.5125 165.0125 165.1125 165.1375   AF
34.60 36.35 36.80 148.575 413.20   Supply Center OP 140.90   Supply Center Security
140.04   Cranes 140.45 148.35   USN 32.45 34.15 34.35 36.85 38.30 40.80 41.10 41.90
138.82 138.85 140.50 140.65 140.80 142.675 148.35 148.575 149.01 150.375 261.8 271.4
275.4 275.7 277.4 283.4 285.8 287.1 290.9 305.8 307.7 312.2 313.8 320.2 355.8 339.6
348.1 358.6 413.025

  Newport Army Ammunition Depot, IN: Army 139.075 140.025 165.5375 173.4625
  Newport AFS, NC: AF 228.8 234.7 238.5 251.0 256.6 263.2 270.4 275.0 278.6 287.8
292.7 302.4 306.4 338.4 344.0 356.0 364.2 369.0 375.1 386.2 392.8
  Newport Naval Education Training Center (NETC), RI (Underwater Systems
Center): Heliport AD 135.4 257.7 385.0   Heliport T 121.2 252.9 385.0   Heliport OP
& Medevac 385.0   FD/Crash 140.35   Medics 138.60 155.28   Port Control 385.0   USN
32.45 36.55 138.60 138.62 138.975 140.075 140.04 140.34 140.65 140.725 140.75
140.775 140.82 140.85 143.50 143.70 148.27 148.325 149.40 162.25 163.00 163.75
164.50 233.8 266.7 276.7 283.4 284.4 300.3 306.0 314.9 320.5 336.3 339.6 340.4 348.1
355.5
  Newport News, VA: USN 138.95 140.25 141.175 143.525 150.39 262.8 273.0 305.8
356.2 387.4 394.4   Newport News Shipbuilding/Drydock Co: Security 462.275   OP
150.405 153.08 153.11 156.30 156.35 456.10 456.25 461.475 463.5125 464.0125 464.9625
465.7125 465.7875 465.8875 466.0125 466.0875 466.1875 466.3125 466.3125 466.3875
466.4875 466.6125 466.6875 466.7875 466.9125 466.9875 467.0875 467.65 468.4875
468.5125 468.5375 468.5625 468.5875 468.6125 469.0125 470.425
  Newport News/Williamsburg Int'l. Apt, VA: AD 379.1 395.8   T 280.1   G 348.6
  Newport State Apt., RI: AD 385.6
  New Raymer MOA, CO: AF 303.0 340.8
  New Richmond Muni Apt., WI: AD 353.7
  New River MCAS(H)/McCutcheon Fld., Jacksonville, NC (Marine Air Grps 26 &
29): S 265.2   AD 119.35 362.2 379.4   T 41.95 120.0 340.2 360.2   G 121.8 352.4   OP
236.4   WX 250.6   FD/Crash 140.01   USMC 30.15 34.65 41.93 138.95 138.96 139.09
139.475 139.50 139.52 139.525 140.04 140.125 140.16 140.175 140.20 140.30 140.55
140.55 140.70 140.82 142.725 142.80 143.505 143.525 143.675 143.715 143.725 148.37
148.375 148.425 148.45 149.01 149.025 149.05 149.07 149.09 149.10 149.35 149.37
149.40 236.0 243.9 250.3 251.9 258.9 264.0 274.5 274.8 299.3 300.2 374.9   (Also see
Camp Lejeune listings.)
  New River Valley Apt., Dublin, VA: AD 319.9 339.8
  Newton City/Co. Apt., KS: AD 325.8
  Newton Muni Apt., IA: AD 252.9
  New Ulm Muni Apt., MN: AD 290.2
  New York ANG: 41.95 42.50 46.70 46.75 46.85 49.75 251.9 261.9 287.5 340.4 355.6
379.5
  New York, NY: AF OSI 40.17 40.19   AF 407.475   Army 34.90 141.15 141.25 149.91
163.00   Army CID 412.90 413.425 413.525   Armed Forces PD 46.79   USN Harbor OP
149.40   USN 32.65 34.35 34.95 36.15 140.075 140.65 140.775 233.0 266.7 275.7 283.4
284.4 300.3 308.0 314.9 320.5 336.3 340.4 348.1 355.5   CG Intelligence 163.4125
165.0125 165.3375   CG 40.39 171.3625 406.5625 407.975 419.975
  Niagara Falls Int'l. Apt., NY: S 269.4   AD 317.6   G 275.8   T 349.0   ANG 914th
Tactical Air Grp ("Carbonate") 340.8   E 251.1   Security 149.15 150.025 150.325
FD/Crash 173.5875   Emergency 150.15 407.375   NG OP 41.00   SAC CP 311.0 321.0

ANG OP 261.9 AF 164.025 164.50 164.8625 165.1375 165.1625 165.2875 251.9 275.8 298.4 349.0 351.2 413.15 413.20 413.40 413.45

Niland, CA: USN 142.80 245.0

NOAA Environmental Research Labs, Boulder, CO: 122.9 122.925 162.075 162.125 165.5625 166.05 172.025

NOAA Mt. Washington Weather Station, NH: 34.02 463.95

NOAA Rockville, MD (HQ): 34.98 36.22 166.05 169.35 FEMA 167.975

Norfolk Int'l. Apt., VA: AD 257.3 395.8 T 257.8

Norfolk NAS/Chambers Fld. & Naval Base: S 118.425 341.0 AD 118.9 125.2 125.7 257.3 389.9 395.8 G 121.8 352.4 T 124.3 126.375 318.7 340.2 Helipad T 126.375 237.8 380.4 Helipad G 312.4 E 120.7 348.0 Air Terminal 130.65 349.4 WX 271.6 OP 268.8 Flightline Fueling 140.345 Aircraft Maintenance 268.8 Range 141.975 Parachute Riggers 143.58 Naval Air Reserve ("Razz Base") 385.1 Ground Support 140.125 142.025 Shore Patrol 138.70 Police 140.25 140.825 143.425/140.525 143.60/140.575 Naval Investigative Service 140.075/140.775 140.125 140.65 USMC Gate Guards 140.36 140.925 Base OP 142.625 268.0 268.8 Medics ("Tribe Control") 143.50 143.625/140.875 Pagers 140.05 148.375 150.125 NOB Duty Officer 142.625 149.025 NATO 138.775 CINCLANTFLEET Mobilephones 142.50 Base Transportation 140.60 Vehicle Repair 149.40 Public Works 139.50 140.16 Electricians 138.75 149.30 Gate 140.55 Base FD 139.575 139.975 140.10/138.575 Fuels 138.725 Navy Exchange 138.525 Forklifts 407.25 Piers 138.475 140.275 148.35 Ordnance Handling 140.975 142.75 Base Master at Arms 140.625 Shop #26 142.85 Shop #56 143.675 Port/Harbor OP 385.0 (HF 2716 kHz) Base Tugs 140.76 141.90 141.95 142.00 142.05 142.65 Degaussing Station 356.2 Radcon 140.875 Nuclear Inspection 141.975 Shipyard Security 140.25 Shipyard FD 140.70 USS L.Y. SPEAR 139.525 140.25 USS TEXAS 140.275 USS DAHLGREN 140.275 USS RICHARD E. BYRD 139.475 USS YELLOWSTONE 139.475 Armed Forces College Security 142.85 Naval Supply Center 140.90 142.60 148.775 Naval Supply Center Security 138.525 140.04 Naval Supply Center Pickup/Delivery 140.05 FACSFAC ("Giant Killer") 127.65 135.225 125.725 135.875 233.7 249.8 251.6 255.0 305.0 310.1 350.0 (HF 2252 4373 kHz) USN 30.15 30.53 32.05 32.85 36.15 36.55 36.85 38.30 40.82 123.3 138.55 139.525 139.75 140.30 140.325 140.35 140.36 140.475 140.50 140.675 140.72 140.725 140.75 141.00 142.00 142.075 142.425 142.525 142.575 142.775 143.55 148.305 149.00 149.01 149.05 149.07 149.09 149.10 149.35 149.75 149.90 150.175 150.39 162.25 162.325 162.875 163.625 163.75 163.925 164.125 165.625 167.125 167.15 167.875 168.25 169.00 169.75 170.075 170.50 172.325 172.75 173.125 235.4 262.9 263.5 264.2 266.9 270.6 270.8 274.3 274.6 275.4 277.8 283.1 284.2 284.5 291.2 292.95 293.05 294.65 294.75 296.35 296.45 297.95 298.05 299.45 299.55 300.5 301.0 302.2 303.4 304.1 304.2 306.0 306.35 306.45 307.85 307.95 309.35 310.75 310.85 312.9 313.8 320.5 328.3 337.0 341.0 344.1 345.1 347.8 349.8 350.6 350.8 353.1 354.6 355.3 358.95 359.6 361.0 362.5 382.0 384.2 405.30 408.20 (HF 6723 kHz) Army 149.775

North AF Auxiliary Field, SC: OP "North DZ" 139.60 341.5 (Also see Charleston AFB listings.)

North Bend AFS, OR: 165.0125 228.6 235.8 238.6 238.7 239.7 252.0 260.9 261.4 265.4 271.0 276.4 277.6 282.6 374.0 390.2 394.2 397.8

North Bend Muni Apt., OR: FSS 255.4 AD 239.0 CG 381.8 383.9 413.45 (HF 5692 8980 kHz)

North Brookfield, MA: Army 38.40 49.80 149.75 226.3 299.1

North Central State Apt., Pawtucket, RI: AD 307.9 385.6

Northeast Philadelphia Apt., PA: FSS 255.4 AD 291.7 T 349.0

Northern Maine Regn'l. Apt., Presque Isl., ME: AD 359.3 363.8

North Island NAS/Halsey Fld., San Diego, CA: S 283.0 AD 125.15 285.2 T 135.1 336.4 340.2 G 118.0 352.4 OP 140.375 140.575 355.5 E 128.4 356.8 WX 344.6 Security 140.375 140.575 148.35 FD/Crash 140.05 Search/Rescue 282.8

Training OP 142.80   USN 36.55 138.675 139.545 140.05 140.125 140.58 140.76 140.895 143.58 143.715 148.29 163.75 166.00 167.50 269.00 170.50 172.75 238.0 250.4 253.0 253.9 256.4 263.4 268.3 272.6 273.1 273.7 275.6 275.7 280.2 281.3 285.1 285.7 289.9 291.2 301.1 305.8 307.6 308.1 310.3 311.7 315.3 325.1 326.9 342.7 342.9 344.0 346.7 347.9 349.9 352.5 354.9 355.5 360.2 375.0 376.8 384.4 (HF 6723 kHz)

North Pier Army Heliport, Honshu, Japan: OP 36.80 122.5 288.8

Northrop Corp: Pico Rivera, CA 462.85 473.8375 508.8875; El Segundo, CA 158.28 508.8125 511.8125; Anaheim, CA 123.35 123.525 153.245 158.28 462.85; Hawthorne, CA 123.35 123.525 158.28 462.35 462.85; Palmdale, CA 123.35 123.525 451.475 451.525 462.35 462.85; Edwards AFB 123.35 123.5 123.525 158.28 451.625; Rosamond CA 451.475 451.625 462.35; Los Angeles, CA 158.28 451.475 461.475; Inyokern, CA 122.9 314.6; Rolling Meadows, IL 461.30 462.925 464.575; Mojave, AZ 123.35 123.525; Long Beach, CA 123.35 123.525; Perry, GA 462.20 462.30 462.375; Norwood, MA: 462.35; Arlingon, IL 464.575; Elk Grove, IL 464.575; La Habra, CA 462.85; Rolling Hills, CA 462.85; Palos Verdes, CA 158.28; Newbury Park, CA 158.28; La Canada, CA 462.35; Downey, CA 508.8875

North Truro AFS, MA: AF 165.0125 228.7 235.8 239.2 254.8 270.1 278.4 282.5 288.0 292.8 298.8 303.9 316.2 316.4 338.8 342.1 347.4 351.6 371.8 376.2 389.2 394.8 399.0

Northumberland Co. Apt., PA: AD 247.2

North Vernon Apt., IN: AD 269.4

Norton AFB, San Bernardino, CA (AMC; 63rd Military Airlift Wing): DI 132.55 372.2 AD 119.65 125.5 127.25 134.0 134.4 135.4 278.3 295.7 306.3 318.2 327.5 351.1 T 119.45 320.1 G 121.8 289.4 E 121.8 289.4 MAC CP 130.65 349.4 WX 344.6 Mountaintop Transmitter for long range air/ground 349.4 OSI 138.075 138.175 141.525 63rd MAW/MAM Secure Comm 139.70 63rd MAW/DOX ALCS Air/Ground 142.30 63rd MAW/DOX ALCS 413.075 413.275 413.40 413.55 63rd MAW/DOX Air Drop 340.6 341.5 342.3 63rd MAW/DOC CP Link 163.5625 63rd MAW/CCE Commanders Net 407.375 413.125 (Link 163.5875) 63rd MAW/MAO 63 OMS Aircraft Maintenance 173.5375 63rd MAW/MAF 63FMS Aircraft Maintenance 173.5375 63rd MAW Life Support 173.4875 63rd MAW/LGS Supply 176.5625 63rd MAW/DOT Rescue/Survival Training 251.9 63rd MAW/DOC Base OP 290.95 63rd MAW/MAA 63AMS 325.7 63rd MAW/LGT Taxi 407.35 63rd MAW/TR CAPS 407/425/413.175 63rd MAW/LGSF POL 407.45 63rd MAW/TR OP 413.10 63rd MAW/TR Port Training 413.15 445th MAW/DE Training 143.425 445th MAW/DE Prime Beef Training 413.20 63rd CSG/SC Base Pager 150.60 63rd CSG/SC Comm/Navaids Maintenance 165.0375 63rd CSG/DEM Civil Engineer 165.1375 63rd CSG/SC Local Cntrl 320.1 63rd CSG/SP Security PD 408.00 408.175 63rd CSG/SG Nedic 413.00/416.425 63rd CSS/DEF Fire Tactical 413.225 63rd CSS/DED FD/Crash 413.375 1722nd CCS C3 (HF 4491.5 4501.5 5733.5 6801.5 7461.5 7633.5 kHz) 1722nd CCS Drop Zone Training (HF 7861 9017.5 kHz) 1722nd CCS Tactical Training (HF 9271 10268,5 11611.5 14906.5 17488.5 20108.5 26813.5 kHz) McDonnell Douglas OP 123.525 AF 138.175 150.225 413.425

Norwood Mem'l. Apt., MA: 263.1 343.6

Novato, CA: USN 138.525

Noxubee, MA: USN 140.10 384.4

Nuclear Regulatory Commission Emergency Teams: 168.05 168.20 168.60 168.625 169.10 170.00

Nuclear Regulatory Commission Office of Inspection, Bethesda, MD: 167.275 167.875 411.20

Nurnberg Hospital AHP, Standort Lazarette, Germany: AD 31.60 33.60 122.4 142.20 314.8

Oakdale AHP, Pittsburgh, PA: AD 360.8 363.8

Oak Grove Heliport, Ft. Worth, TX (Army Reserve): OP 122.7

Oakland Supply Center (USN), CA: Security 142.825 148.26 412.95 Emergency 140.34 Base Commanders Net 142.86 Disaster Preparedness 140.16 Storage Facilities 142.06 142.60 Fuel Tank Area 143.70 Base Transportation 140.46 Motor Pool 138.625 138.84 150.09 162.875 Pager 139.475 Ambulances 142.86 148.35 Maintenance 138.55 138.65 FD 46.06 142.825 142.86 143.50 Medic USN 36.53 36.63 36.87 141.00 148.375

Oakland Supply Depot, CA: Heliport OP 126.2 340.2 Security 149.775 FD 149.775 Base Commanders Net 149.725 Motor Pool 148.275 149.75 163.5375 407.275 413.525 Army 149.875 150.45 412.95

Oakland-Pontiac Apt., MI: AD 348.3 363.2

Oberursel AHP/Camp King, Germany: OP ("Throttle Cntrl.") 45.00 Msc 31.80 33.20 122.1 142.90 251.2

Ocala Muni Apt., FL: AD 377.2

Oceana NAS/Soucek Fld., Virginia Beach, VA (3 training sqdns; 23 attack & fighter sqdns): S 315.4 AD 119.6 125.2 126.05 279.2 372.1 374.8 389.9 T 126.2 336.4 340.2 360.2 G 336.4 E 300.4 Base OP 284.9 WX 387.4 Fleet Area Control & Surveillance Facility ("Giant Killer") 127.65 135.225 135.725 135.875 233.7 249.8 251.6 255.0 305.0 310.1 350.0 (HF 2252 4373 kHz) Security 140.15 140.225 141.00 142.675 FD 142.725 Crash Trucks 141.00 Ground Support 142.075 Flightline Refueling 142.80 VAQ-209 Sqdn 140.90 VC-12 Sqdn 138.55 USN 32.86 138.95 139.835 139.52 140.125 140.55 140.895 143.275 148.035 148.305 149.115 149.375 149.49 235.4 238.1 250.2 250.5 251.3 253.2 256.4 267.2 264.2 265.1 265.8 266.7 267.4 271.4 273.8 274.7 281.2 285.8 289.9 291.2 295.5 301.0 308.7 311.4 311.5 313.0 315.3 315.75 320.2 323.4 325.4 328.4 337.0 339.5 341.2 342.6 342.9 344.3 344.5 345.0 345.0 346.6 349.0 349.8 350.0 352.2 352.3 353.2 355.1 355.8 357.8 358.6 338.8 359.5 361.0 361.3 362.4 363.5 383.4 384.1 384.2 413.45 (HF 6723 kHz) SAC CP 311.0 321.0

Oceanside Muni Apt., CA: AD 323.0

Oconto Muni Apt., WI: AD 338.2

OCS Security Co., New York, NY: 154.60 851.8375

Odessa, TX: AF 228.9 260.8

Offutt AFB, Omaha, NE (ACC; 2nd AF; HQ Strategic Command; 544th Intelligence Wing; AF Global Weather Center): DI 372.2 S 373.5 AD 118.0 120.1 124.5 134.1 263.0 281.5 363.8 T 123.7 236.6 348.4 G 121.7 275.8 WX 342.5 Royal Air Force OP ("Plainsman") 318.7 OSI 40.17 40.19 138.075 138.165 138.175 SAC CP ("Aksarben Cntrl.") 311.0 321.0 Crew Alerts 413.45 Global HF Network (HF 6738 8967 11176 17975 kHz) AF 139.65 139.825 139.875 143.825 148.035 148.225 148.485 148.50 149.05 149.235 149.535 150.195 150.285 163.4625 163.4875 163.5125 163.5625 163.5875 164.50 165.0125 165.1125 165.1375 165.1625 173.5875 255.15 225.6 228.55 238.85 240.5 240.6 252.5 226.05 272.0 276.9 280.05 288.55 294.2 295.3 315.5 316.5 316.785 317.175 317.275 326.0 327.4 337.55 342.2 343.35 357.0 358.45 359.95 361.6 364.5 369.5 372.5 375.95 378.5 385.85 389.15 390.5 391.5 392.5 397.05 398.1 399.05 407.375 407.425 413.15 413.20 413.275 413.35 419.90

Ogden Defense Depot, UT: Army 163.5625 165.0625 165.0875 173.4125 417.20 419.175

Ogden-Hinkley Apt., UT: AD 301.5 T 324.1

Ohio State University Apt., Columbus, OH: AD 267.0 T 258.3 NG 46.80 123.075

Ohio University Apt., Athens, OH: AD 257.8

Ohio Wesleyan University Radio Astronomy Observatory, Delaware, OH: 154.54

Okmulgee Muni Apt., OK: AD 338.3

Oktibbeha Apt., Starkville, MS: AD 226.0 269.4

Olean Muni Apt., NY: AD 239.35

Oliktak D.E.W. Station, AK: T 126.2 288.4 Msc 122.5 236.6

Olive Branch Apt., MS: AD 313.2 338.3

Olympia Apt., WA: AD 290.9 T 233.2

O'Neal Apt., Vincennes, IN: AD 339.8

Oneida Co. Apt., Utica, NY: FSS 255.4 AD 269.5 353.6 363.8 G 241.0 T 241.0 291.7

Oneonta Muni Apt., NY: AD 279.5

Onizuka AFB, Sunnyvale, CA (Consolidated Space Test Center; 2nd Satellite Tracking Grp; 1004th Space Support Grp; AFSPACECOM Base; 1999th Communications Sqdn; 6594th Air Base Sqdn): Security 148.25 148.50 Emergency 148.50 Maintenance 148.50 AF 148.245 148.515 226.3 228.2 229.5 235.0 245.3 375.9 376.5 Army 227.5 321.0 232.5 234.5 239.5 242.0 242.6 244.0 245.0 246.0 247.0 248.0 249.0 261.3 265.5 277.5 280.9 300.0 302.3 304.5 321.5 347.5 357.4 365.0 367.0 367.8 370.0 370.5 374.5 374.53 386.5 388.0 389.5 349.5 395.5 397.5 Lockheed 153.20 153.32 451.475 TRW 153.35 Hewlett Packard 462.20 AT&T 153.23 Ford Communications 151.195 153.095 153.29 Westinghouse 154.54 462.20

Onslow Beach, NC: USN 138.975 140.025

Ontario Int'l. Apt., CA: FSS 255.4 AD 278.3 295.7 306.3 318.2 351.1 T 385.6 G 257.8 AF 36.85 40.15 125.85 138.50 142.15 149.485 149.505 165.1125 165.1375 173.5625 173.5875 173.6125 251.9 293.7 397.1 Lockheed 123.0 153.20 462.425 Inbound Big Safari aircraft going to Lockheed use 138.40 & 275.2 (HF 11215.5 kHz)

Ontario Muni Apt., OR: AD 387.15

Opa Locka Apt., Miami, FL: AD 255.6 T 360.8 G 336.4 CG 123.1 171.2375 381.7 381.8 383.9 (HF 3123 5686 8984 11201 kHz) CG Intelligence 172.30 Aero Design Associates 123.55 also see National Hurricane Center Listings.

Opheim, MT: AF 165.1125 NORAD CP 364.2 NORAD 228.8 228.9 234.6 234.7 238.4 238.5 251.0 254.2 256.6 260.8 263.2 267.0 270.2 274.4 275.0 281.6 287.8 292.7 298.5 302.4 306.4 309.4 316.3 320.6 324.0 325.5 327.9 336.6 338.4 341.8 344.0 346.2 356.0 369.0 375.1 377.0 386.2 387.8 392.8 398.0

Orange ANG Communications Station, CT: ANG 141.80 143.80 259.4 267.8 283.8 301.6 303.0 314.2 340.8

Orange Co Apt, Montgomery, NY: AD 363.1

Orange Grove NALF, TX: S 265.2 AD 119.9 383.6 T 119.35 344.4 G 126.2 267.4 E 126.2 267.4 WX 344.6 USN 141.95 265.2 318.8

Orlando Executive Apt., FL: FSS 255.4 AD 351.9 284.7 307.0 351.9 397.85 T 239.0 259.1 G 239.0

Orlando International Apt., FL: FSS 255.4 AD 259.1 284.7 307.0 338.2 339.8 351.9 397.85 G 275.8 T 252.5 288.15 E 341.7 Army 32.70 34.90 36.10 36.40 38.40 40.05 41.81 46.60 49.60 226.4 231.3 245.3 252.4 339.7 Army Reserve 143rd Transportation Brigade OP 38.45 148.80

Orlando Naval Training Center NTEC-N5, FL (NTC Recruit Training, NTC Service School; NTC Administration; NTC Personnel Service Support School Command): Security 149.075 149.375 FD 150.075 USN 148.275 149.39 150.07 150.11 150.125

Ormond Beach Muni Apt, FL: AD 381.5

Osan AB, S. Korea: DI 232.9 S 128.425 272.7 AD 120.7 127.9 130.2 234.3 267.6 268.3 327.3 363.1 T 122.1 315.8 G 129.1 300.8 E 127.3 343.0 CP 227.525 276.2 277.2 WX 346.5 MAC CP ("Brickwall") 120.0 141.675 291.8 349.4 Rescue CP 282.8 381.0

O'Sullivan AAF, Camp San Luis Obispo, CA: NG 42.00

Otis ANG Base, Falmouth, MA (567th USAF Band; 101st & 102nd Weather Flight; 102nd Fighter Interceptor Wing): DI 372.2 AD AD 118.2 118.75 126.3 132.9 284.6 291.1 318.1 387.1 T 121.0 236.6 294.7 G 121.6 275.8 CG 164.30 164.55 381.7 381.8 383.9 419.125 (HF 3123 5696 8984 11201 kHz) CG Search/Rescue 282.8 CG Medics 173.3375 Security 150.165 165.0375 165.1375 165.5375 173.5875 ANG 102 FIW

OP ("Cape Fox") 262.0   FD/Crash 173.5625 173.5875   Ramp 150.255   Ordnance 150.195 163.5375   EOD 173.5875   Flightline Refueling 150.165   SAC CP 311.0 321.0   Crew Alerts 148.515 413.45   NG ("Yankee Ops") 51.15 122.85   Ground Engineers 150.255   Civil Engineers 165.1125   Fuel Trucks 150.165   Maintenance 150.195   Base Transportation 163.5125 165.1125   Dept. Agriculture 170.45   NORAD 364.2   USN 138.525 138.55 143.725 385.3   ANG 255.8 228.7 229.5 233.5 233.6 237.15 239.2 251.8 251.9 255.8 258.0 259.4 267.8 273.4 278.4 283.8 288.0 282.5 288.2 289.0 292.8 301.6 303.1 303.9 305.0 312.8 313.6 318.4 320.6 328.0 338.0 355.2 357.2 361.4 361.6 364.2 375.0 382.0 388.1 391.2 420.0   (Also see Camp Edwards listings.)

   Otsego Co. Apt. MI: AD 323.0

   Ottumwa Indust'l. Apt., IA: FSS 255.4 AD 354.1

   Outagamie Co. Apt., Appleton, WI: AD 338.2 370.9

   Outlaw Fld, Clarksville, TN: AD 255.6

   Owatonna Muni Apt., MN: AD 307.3

   Owego Satellite Tracking Station, NY: USN 228.85 252.3 298.55 336.675 369.05 398.775

   Owensboro-Daviess Co. Apt., KY: AD 226.4 284.66   T 241.0

   Oxnard Apt., CA: AD 325 327.1   T 257.8

   Ozarkcom Army Helipad, St. Louis, MO: S 120.45 277.2   AD 123.7 125.15 126.5 324.1 360.6   T 118.5 120.05 257.7 284.6

   Pace OLF, Wallace, FL: OP 250.0

   Pacific Beach Naval Reservation, CA: USN 139.50 140.275 140.525 140.60 140.90

   Pachino USN Heliport, Italy: T 344.15

   Page Fld., FL: AD 306.2 322.8 327.8   T 316.7

   Page Field Muni Apt., AZ: AD 343.6

   Pahute Mesa Airstrip, Nevada Test Site, NV: AD 118.7 126.15 255.8 261.1 (Also see Nevada Test Site listings.)

   Palacios Muni Apt, TX: FSS 255.4   AD 306.8

   Palm Bay NASA, FL: See listings for Malabar NASA, FL

   Palm Beach Int'l. Apt., FL: AD 317.4 343.6 387.1 397.9   G 257.8   T 257.8 384.6 AF 138.175 138.50   USN 141.00   United Technologies 36.90 38.90 123.275 123.325 123.425 123.525 153.14 304.6 314.6 462.30 464.825

   Palmdale Production Flight Test Installation AF Plant #42, CA: AD 126.1 290.3   G 121.9 348.6   T 123.7 317.6   FD 154.40   AF 148.625 149.25 149.505 150.345 163.5875 173.4125 385.7   USN 30.15 252.4 264.1 314.6 382.6   Rockwell Int'l 128.8 123.075 123.475 123.525 464.875 472.8375   Northrop 123.35 123.525 451.475 451.525 451.625 Lockheed 123.325 123.425 153.20 158.295 334.7   McDonnell Douglas 153.08   Hughes 472.2125

   Palm Springs Regn'l. Apt., AD: 257.8 285.6   T 257.8

Pal-Waukee Apt., Chicago, IL: AD 290.2

Panama Canal, Panama: 31.75

Panama City-Bay Co. Apt., FL: AD 379.3   T 257.1

Pangborn Mem'l. Apt., WA: FSS 255.4

Papago AAF, Phoenix, AZ: S 121.2   NG OP 49.95 126.05 244.3

Parris Island USMC Depot, SC (Recruiting & Training Base): AD 123.7 251.7 301.7   Heliport OP 32.07   USMC 38.30 41.10 140.16 148.29

Pascagoula, MS: USN 32.2 32.65 36.56 38.28 38.30 40.80 138.525 138.975 139.00 139.15 139.30 139.45 139.60 139.75 140.85 141.95 141.975 142.075 148.25 148.65 148.80 149.25 149.40 263.4 340.3 346.6 347.8 360.4 382.1

Paso Robles Muni Apt., CA: FSS 255.4   AD 307.0

Patrick AFB, Cocoa Beach, FL (ACC; 9th AF; USAF Eastern Space & Missile Center; HQ Eastern Test Range; 2nd Combat Comms Grp; 6555th Aerospace Test Grp; Defense Equal Opportunity Management Institute:) DI 122.85 372.2   S 273.5 AD 132.65 134.95 335.8 340.9 358.3   T 133.75 173.125 348.4   G 124.35 173.125 335.8 E 118.4 289.4   TAC CP ("Raymond 20") 138.30 383.0   Eastern Test Range OP ("Cape Radio") (HF 10780 20390 kHz)   TAC OP (HF 4449 4760 kHz)   MAC OP 413.40 (15575 kHz)   NORAD CP 364.2   SAC CP 311.0 321.0   SAC OP 150.225 312.0 396.9 (HF 4560 kHz)   Fleet Area Control & Surveillance Facility ("Sealord") 120.95 135.825 267.5 369.9   WX 344.6   USCG 126.4 263.8 282.0 381.8   USCG Search/Rescue 282.8 NASA 141.30 163.5125 264.8 324.7   Disaster Preparedness 173.4375   Security 163.4875 173.025 173.175 413.275   FD/Crash 173.5875   Medics 155.16 163.4375 173.4375   Pager 148.275 149.535   OSI 138.075 138.175   Plane-to-Plane 38.65 41.95 46.65 46.85 138.40 139.70 340.8 351.0   AF Reserve 40.15 (HF 3183 kHz)   Air Refueling 228.9 260.2 322.8 366.3   Fuels 165.1625   Supply 148.265   Flightline Maintenance 148.225   Civil Engineering 173.4125   Base Transportation 165.1375 Communications Technicians 148.125   Base Commanders Net 148.065   Data 141.60 Msc 138.35 139.65 139.70 141.60 141.70 142.30 148.065 148.095 148.185 149.265 149.535 163.4875 165.125 165.1375 165.1625 173.025 173.125 173.4125 228.8 234.7 238.5 251.0 251.9 252.8 256.6 263.2 270.4 275.0 278.6 287.8 292.7 294.6 297.2 298.5 302.4 306.4 325.5 338.4 343.0 344.0 351.2 356.0 363.9 369.0 375.1 383.2 383.3 385.7 386.2 392.8 395.1 407.85 413.10 415.70   Cocoa Beach Hospital 462.925   Cocoa Beach Shuttle 463.225   Motorola 463.825   IBM Corp 856.8375   (Also see Kennedy Space Center, Malabar, & Cape Canaveral AFS listings.)

Patuxent River NAS/Trapnell Fld., MD (Naval Air Test Center): FSS 117.6/122.1 DI 276.2   AD 120.05 127.95 132.55 281.8 314.0 353.6   T 123.65 340.2 344.4   G 120.6 336.4   E 126.2 384.4   WX 356.2   VFR Advisories 270.8 354.8   ASW OP 341.1   Medics 140.1 140.70   SAC CP 311.0 321.0   McDonnell Douglas 123.55   SAC CP 311.0 321.0 Crew Alerts 413.45   USN 30.45 32.05 32.45 36.05 40.55 49.95 123.3 138.60 138.625 138.70 138.725 138.84 138.95 138.975 139.50 139.525 140.16 140.20 140.25 140.30 140.50 140.55 140.58 140.75 140.895 140.90 140.925 141.00 142.02 142.50 142.575 142.70 142.80 143.725 148.27 148.375 149.125 149.425 164.50 172.00 229.0 223.8 236.3 250.6 250.1 254.0 262.8 264.8 265.3 271.5 272.9 274.2 277.0 278.0 283.1 285.2 291.3 299.4 300.0 300.2 301.3 304.1 308.1 313.0 314.0 320.5 321.8 326.5 326.5 337.9 341.35 345.1 348.0 350.0 350.9 353.4 355.4 355.6 359.6 363.6 364.875 369.9 376.6 376.85 381.7 381.9 382.2 382.9 383.4 384.3 385.2 387.9 398.0

Pearl Harbor USN, HI (Naval Station; Submarine Base; Navy Ship Yard; Naval Supply Center; Fleet Training Group): Security 142.625/141.925   Shore Patrol 141.00/138.80 142.55   Base PD 138.625 140.50   Naval Intelligence 140.075/140.775 Special Operations 140.65   Fleet Area Control & Surveillance Facility ("Hula Dancer") 127.0 132.0 280.7 308.1   Public Works 148.325   Underwater Demolition Teams 32.45   USN 32.05 38.36 138.55 138.60 138.70 138.775 138.975 138.975 140.04 140.10 140.125 140.22 140.30 140.35 140.52 140.575 140.70 140.80 140.825 140.975

141.00 141.95 142.02 142.10 142.50 143.55 148.235 148.325 148.905 149.125 150.15 233.8 309.0 328.2 340.3 353.0

Pearson Airpark, Vancouver, WA: AD 284.6 360.8 Army 49.70 49.80 165.0625

Pease Int'l. Trade Port, Portsmouth, NH: S 273.5 AD 322.4 363.8 T 255.9 G 275.8 E 335.8 157th Air Refuel Gp ANG ("Pack Cntrl") 134.1 287.3 390.1 ANG 148.20 149.265 149.30 150.25 150.30 150.35 162.6125 164.50 173.15 316.7 324.1 351.1 363.8 371.2 379.3 392.0 413.15

Peconic Field, NY: See Calverton NWIRF listings.

Pecos Muni Apt., Ft. Stockton, TX: AD 343.6

Pellston Regn'l. Apt., MI: FSS 255.4 AD 323.0

Pendleton Muni Apt., OR: FSS 255.4 AD 343.9 380.2 T 257.8 G 257.8

Pennsylvania: ANG 279.6 303.0 319.2 348.4 392.1 NG 247.2 255.8 263.0 265.6 303.0 322.3 344.6 381.4

Penn Valley Apt., PA: AD 247.2

Pensacola NAS/Forrest Sherman Fld., FL (Chief of Naval Education & Training; Blue Angels; USS Lexington AVT-16): S 267.6 AD 120.05 120.65 125.35 270.8 314.0 372.0 376.8 T 126.2 340.2 G 121.7 336.4 E 134.1 268.7 Fleet Area Control & Surveillance Facility ("Seabreeze") 118.425 274.2 280.7 303.8 306.8 313.2 346.5 353.2 362.8 382.0 383.8 385.2 (HF 6835 kHz) Base OP 312.1 VFR Advisories 118.8 270.8 WX 359.6 Security 140.04 150.11 Emergency 150.75 Medics 155.28 Naval Air Rework Facility Chevalier Field helicopter OP ("Fumble Base") fixed wing OP ("Victor Base") 32.90 118.15 122.7 266.7 Search/Rescue 282.8 USN 30.47 31.09 32.05 32.45 34.93 36.15 36.55 38.30 40.53 40.83 41.11 41.93 41.95 122.75 138.525 138.575 138.58 138.70 138.72 138.75 138.80 138.84 138.85 138.95 139.52 139.525 139.545 140.025 140.075 140.10 140.15 140.20 140.25 140.34 140.65 140.675 140.775 140.82 140.895 142.00 143.60 143.715 149.35 149.37 235.4 251.6 263.5 265.8 271.4 272.2 274.6 275.35 275.7 277.0 277.8 278.4 283.4 300.2 301.0 307.7 312.9 315.4 320.2 326.6 337.0 339.6 348.1 355.4 358.0 358.6 359.6 360.4 376.8 380.5 360.6 385.0

Pensacola Regional Apt., FL: FSS 255.4 AD 286.0 376.8 380.6 E 348.6 G 348.6 T 257.8

Pentagon, Washington, DC (HQ Department of Defense): Mobile Telephones ("Ginger Copy") 143.35 Helipad 143.10 231.1 FEMA 167.975 Security 36.71 36.79 FD 36.99 VIP Limos 36.63 36.69 36.91 Taxi Service ("315") 32.87/32.53 142.10 Naval Intelligence 140.64 Army 30.49 32.53 36.51 36.63 36.91 40.50 141.025 141.375 141.475 143.025 149.60 150.465 150.51 150.60 150.725 162.45 165.0375 165.0875 241.0 407.25 407.225 413.225 413.475 AF 138.025 138.05 142.55 143.025 143.10 148.85 149.85 USN 30.15 34.15 40.55 138.575 138.65 138.675 138.72 138.74 138.775 138.80 138.96 139.025 139.48 140.075 140.10 140.125 140.14 140.175 140.22 140.225 140.25 140.30 140.45 140.46 140.58 140.625 140.65 140.775 140.95 140.975 141.00 142.48 142.60 143.55 143.70 148.40 149.07 149.10 150.11 311.6 357.8

Perry AHP, Camp Perry, OH: OP 46.95 47.00

Perry Foley Apt., FL: AD 343.8

Perry-Ft. Valley Apt., GA: AD 324.3

Perry Stokes Apt, CO: AD 362.35

Peru Muni Apt., IN: AD 351.1 363.8

Peter O. Knight Apt., Tampa, FL: AD 279.6

Petersburg Muni Apt., VA: AD 371.1 398.2 Ft. Lee Army Air Detachment 126.2 (Also see Ft. Lee listings.)

Peterson AFB, CO: See City of Colorado Springs Muni Apt.

Phelps-Collins ANG Base/Alpena Co. Regn'l. Apt., Alpena, MI: AD 121.35 127.75 134.8 236.6 279.6 351.1 383.1 G 121.9 275.8 T 121.35 127.75 134.8 279.6 383.1 SAC CP 311.0 321.0 Crew Alerts 413.45 AF 148.035 148.245 148.515 149.475 149.535 150.345 165.1375 173.5375 173.5875 236.6 275.8 286.0 291.7 297.1 318.1 320.1 348.4 351.1 358.2 369.2 379.3

Philadelphia Int'l. Apt., PA: FSS 255.4   AD 281.3 307.2 343.6   G 348.6   T 263.0
E 348.6

Philadelphia Naval Base, PA (Naval Shipyard; Ship Systems Engineering Station;
4th USMC District & Recruiting Station; Navy Damage Control Training Center;
Destroyer Sqdn 30 NRF): Security 138.975/140.455   FD 148.40   Hospital 150.10
Medics 148.29   USN 30.45 32.05 341;50 41.90 138.525 138.575 138.60 138.625 138.775
140.075 140.525 140.65 140.675 140.725 140.75 140.775 140.825 149.025 149.82 229.0
250.2 275.7 283.4 300.3 307.7 339.5 339.6 348.1 358.6 375.0 386.6 396.4 396.5

Philip Apt., SD: AD 338.2

Philip Ballard Muni Apt., Topeka, KS: AD 290.2   T 257.8

Phillips AAF/Aberdeen Proving Ground, MD (Army Test & Evanuation Command;
Ordnance Command; Ordnance School): S 108.4   AD 126.75 307.9   T 126.15 229.6
241.0   G 121.9   MP/Security 36.89 37.18 37.30 165.0625 165.1875 173.4375   FD 33.74
407.475 416.10   Weapons Testing 416.25   Emergency Vans 36.69 36.89 165.1875
165.5875   Medics 165.0375 165.0625   Pager 149.835 173.4875   Base Transportation
36.69   Air OP 36.10 126.15   EOD 49.70 49.80   Engineers 148.815   MTD 38.45   Range
Control 30.45 38.40 40.90 148.315 165.0875 170.025 170.525 170.575 248.4   Armored
Vehicle Testing 150.315   Army 30.51 32.30 36.21 36.89 40.10 46.70 49.90 139.035
141.30 141.40 142.90 143.055 143.205 148.025 148.605 148.725 148.755 148.845 148.875
149.715 149.835 149.85 149.875 150.50 150.695 150.69 150.775 173.4125 226.4 230.9
234.5 237.6 240.5 373.8 407.275 412.275 412.90 412.975 413.25 413.475 413.525
413.575 415.425 416.65 416.95

Phillipsburg Muni Apt., KS: AD 353.7

Phoenix-Sky Harbor Int'l. Apt., AZ: FSS 255.4   AD 239.0 256.9 296.6 353.8 363.0
379.8   T 254.3 385.4   E 269.2   AF 164.50   SAC CP 311.0 321.0   ANG 140.00

Picatinny Arsenal, Dover, NJ (Armament Research & Development Command): AD
127.6 379.9   Heliport OP 41.05 121.95 241.0   Security 165.1875   Army 143.10 149.60
163.5125 165.5375 165.1875 173.5125 406.625 412.975

Picayune Pearl River Co. Apt., MS: AD 327.05

Pickaway Co. Mem'l. Apt., Circleville, OH: AD 279.6

Piedmont Triad Int'l. Apt., NC: AD 233.2 247.2   T 226.3   G 348.6

Pierre Muni Apt., SD: FSS 255.4   AD 269.1

Pinal Apk, Marana, AZ: NG 41.50 123.05 245.1

Pine Bluff Arsenal, AR (Chemical-Biological Warfare storage depot): EOD 49.70
49.80   Army 38.89 141.475 149.85 150.705 150.765 163.5375 165.0625 165.0375
165.0875 165.1625 165.1875 412.975 413.235 413.525

Pine Castle, FL: USN 267.4 315.1 321.8 326.8 357.0 380.7

Piper Aircraft Corp., Vero Beach, FL: 72.48 72.60 72.56 72.60 123.35 123.55
462.20 462.40

Pipestone Muni Apt., MN: AD 317.4

Piqua Apt., OH: AD 316.7

Pirmasens AHP, Germany: VFR Advisories 40.20 142.90 251.2

Pittsburgh, PA (99th Army Reserve Command): Army 163.025 163.5875

Pittsfield Muni Apt., MA: AD 307.2

Pittsfield Muni Apt., ME: AD 239.3

Plainville, KS: AF 289.5

Planes Inc., Atlanta, GA: 123.4

Plattsburgh AFB, NY (AMC; 380th Bomb Wing): FSS 255.4   DI 372.2   S 388.2
AD 126.3 360.8   T 120.7 122.7 236.5 255.6   G 121.8 275.8 353.8   WX 239.8
Security 163.4875 164.9875 165.0125 165.1375 170.175   OSI 40.17 40.19 138.075
138.165 138.175   FD/Crash 173.5625 173.5875   Range Cntrl. 34.50   Base OP 149.485
149.565 303.0   SAC CP 311.0 321.0   NORAD CP 364.2   Base Commanders Net
148.075 149.575   380th Bomb Wing OP 393.0   Crew Alerts 413.45   Pager 138.325   Air
Refueling 238.9 318.0 360.8   Ground Services 163.5875 164.175   Flightline Fuels &

Oils 164.50 Base Transportation 173.5375 AF 32.85 41.70 141.525 143.925 148.065 148.495 148.50 149.565 163.125 163.25 163.4875 163.5125 163.5375 163.5875 170.175 173.4125 209.9 290.9 305.6 338.6 372.9 388.2 391.9 395.9 413.15

Pleasanton Muni Apt., TX: AD 353.5 381.4

Plymouth Muni Apt., ID: AD 323.0 T 257.8

Plymouth Muni Apt., IN: AD 257.8 317.6

Plymouth Muni Apt., MA: AD 387.1

Pocatello Regn'l. Apt, ID: AD 381.6 T 257.8

Pocono Mountains Muni Apt., PA: 256.7

Point Arena AFS, CA: NORAD CP 364.2 AF 148.095 228.9 234.6 238.9 254.2 260.8 267.0 270.2 274.4 278.4 280.0 281.6 287.7 293.8 299.0 309.4 316.3 320.6 324.0 327.9 336.6 341.8 346.2 359.4 377.0 387.8 398.0

Point Barrow LRRS, AK: AD 135.3 385.6 FSS 122.2 122.6 123.6 (HF 2866 5631 kHz)

Point Lay LRRS, AK: T 126.2 278.0 FSS 122.4

Point Loma Naval Reservation, CA: USN 30.45 32.05 40.15 40.53 40.79 41.09 138.96 140.275 140.35 140.54 140.825 142.00 142.025 142.075 142.10 142.85 149.07 149.17 149.13 149.43 149.43 149.49 236.4 238.1 253.2 262.9 267.4 272.8 277.7 280.5 285.8 292.95 293.05 293.15 294.65 294.75 294.85 295.35 295.455 295.55 297.95 298.05 298.15 299.45 299.55 299.65 306.35 306.45 306.55 307.85 307.95 308.05 309.25 309.35 309.45 310.75 310.85 310.95 317.045 317.06 317.065 317.07 317.075 317.08 317.085 317.07 317.095 317.1 317.11 317.145 317.155 317.16 317.165 317.17 317.175 317.18 317.185 317.19 317.195 317.2 317.21 317.245 317.255 317.26 317.265 317.27 317.275 317.28 317.285 317.29 317.295 317.3 317.31 352.2 355.9 358.0 362.0 380.5 390.3 AF 378.5

Point Mugu NAWS, CA (Pacific Missile Test Center): S 125.55 277.2 AD ("Plead") 124.7 128.65 135.5 327.1 325.0 T 124.85 126.2 340.2 382.8 G 121.6 360.2 E 120.75 339.4 OP 267.5 WX ("Plead 13") 341.3 ANG OP 303.0 Aircraft Emergency 269.8 Search & Rescue 282.8 USN 30.55 32.05 32.86 34.35 34.35 133.25 138.825 138.84 138.835 139.80 140.145 140.25 140.34 140.48 140.52 140.55 140.625 140.94 141.00 142.50 142.80 143.52 143.575 143.715 148.325 148.325 149.00 149.055 149.085 149.40 235.0 236.2 236.4 245.0 253.2 254.9 257.4 262.8 263.3 263.8 264.4 265.3 268.9 270.5 272.8 274.2 277.7 277.8 280.7 292.95 293.05 293.15 294.65 294.75 294.85 295.35 295.45 295.55 297.95 298.05 298.15 299.45 299.55 299.65 301.8 302.7 305.0 306.35 306.45 306.55 306.6 307.85 307.95 308.05 308.2 309.25 309.35 309.45 310.75 310.85 310.95 311.4 311.6 312.2 313.0 313.3 323.3 328.4 337.0 338.0 342.8 344.5 353.0 358.8 361.2 362.8 364.8 380.6 383.6 384.4 393.855

Point Reyes Naval Reservation, CA: 32.65 38.30 139.525 140.05 140.975 262.6 264.2 301.8 304.2 309.0 384.5 CG 415.825

Point Sur Naval Facility, CA (Oceanographic Research Station-- security restricted facility): USN 138.96

Polk AAF/Ft. Polk, Leesville, LA (5th Infantry Division/Mechanized): S 108.4 AD 135.7 381.5 T 41.50 108.4 119.0 248.2 G 121.8 248.0 OP ("Poe Ops") 41.30 123.45 374.2 Medevac 42.50 WX 40.35 118.45 126.2 342.5 EOD 49.70 49.80 Range 40.95 143.20 373.3 Army 30.10 138.40 139.00 139.05 139.10 139.15 139.20 139.20 139.30 139.325 139.40 139.45 141.05 141.10 141.15 141.175 141.175 141.20 141.255 141.25 141.30 141.40 141.425 141.50 142.325 142.35 142.40 142.425 142.45 142.875 142.90 142.925 142.95 143.00 143.05 143.225 148.20 148.71 148.90 149.73 150.675 150.70 150.70 162.225 163.375 163.5625 165.0375 165.0625 165.0875 165.1875 173.4125 173.4875 226.35 226.5 226.7 227.3 227.7 229.5 229.8 230.0 230.2 230.8 231.3 231.5 232.0 232.1 232.3 245.0 248.0 249.0 302.2 302.3 304.3 321.5 327.1 347.5 356.35 356.9 357.35 364.9 365.95 366.95 368.0 370.0 370.05 370.5 371.1 374.5 376.0 379.4 389.0 407.275 412.90 413.525 AF 32.35 41.90 138.30

Pompano Beach Airpark, FL: AD 306.3

Ponca City Muni Apt., OK: FSS 255.4 AD 319.1

Pope AFB, Fayetteville, NC (ACC; 9th AF; 23rd Wing; 317th Tactical Airlift Wing; AF Airlift Center; 317th Combat Support Grp): DI 372.2 S 132.3 AD 127.8 295.0 340.7 T 135.025 236.6 291.1 G 124.55 275.8 MAC CP 130.65 319.4 WX 344.6 JA/ATT Controller 340.8 OSI 138.075 138.165 138.175 163.00 Security 148.20 163.4875 163.5375 FD/Crash 173.5875 Medics 173.5625 AF 38.65 41.45 46.75 138.30 139.70 139.975 140.40 141.80 142.20 143.80 148.245 148.45 148.455 148.515 148.545 149.00 149.30 149.475 149.505 149.535 149.55 150.195 150.225 150.285 150.315 150.345 165.1125 173.6375 265.7 272.0 286.6 297.2 301.6 305.4 314.2 317.8 321.2 324.6 326.2 341.5 342.3 342.4 359.3 379.4 389.4 393.0 393.3 413.15 413.30 413.40 Army 32.10 139.025 227.1 244.7

Poplar Bluff Muni Apt., MT: AD 350.3 AF 289.5

Portage Co. Apt., Ravenna, OH: AD 226.4

Portage Muni Apt., WI: AD 350.3 396.0

Portales Muni Apt., NM: AD 319.2 358.3 397.2

Port Angeles CGAS, WA: CG 127.7 381.8 383.9 416.585 (HF 2182 2702 3120 5692 8980 kHz) FSS 122.6 USN 233.7 233.8 273.0 277.1 291.4 314.8 317.0 347.9 384.2 396.3

Port Austin AFS, MI: NORAD CP 364.2 AF 165.1625 229.1 233.6 239.4 251.8 254.4 258.8 273.4 278.2 279.4 284.0 289.0 292.4 297.7 309.5 312.8 318.4 327.2 348.8 357.2 371.0 379.0 384.0 396.8

Port Clarence USCG, AK: OP 122.8 (HF 2182 5696 kHz)

Port Columbus Int'l. Apt., OH: AD 267.9 279.6 353.9 388.8 392.1 G 348.6 T 257.8 ANG 38.60 163.5625 SAC CP 311.0 321.0 Army Reserve 38.10 Rockwell Int'l. 36.60 123.525 275.6 305.8 314.6 345.4 382.6

Porter Co. Muni. Apt., Valparaiso, IN: AD 257.8 317.6

Port Hueneme Naval Construction Battalion Center, CA (3rd, 4th, 5th, & 40th Naval Mobile Construction Battalions; Reserve Naval Mobile Construction Battalion 17): USN 36.53 36.57 36.63 36.87 38.31 140.075 140.65 141.00 142.075 142.575 143.20 149.01 150.225 150.275 150.325 406.375 409.125 413.00 413.15

Portland, OR: USN 36.53 36.57 36.87 Army 165.0375

Portland-Hillsboro Apt., OR: FSS 255.4 AD 284.6 G 239.3 T 239.3

Portland Int'l. Apt., OR: FSS 255.4 S 269.9 AD 284.6 290.3 294.7 299.2 360.8 T 257.8 G 348.6 E 318.1 Security 163.4875 FD/Crash 173.5875 SAC CP 311.0 321.0 939th ARRG Rescue ANG CP 288.9 ANG Base OP ("Portland Guard Ops') 163.525 280.5 AF Reserve ("Acclimate") 67.12 138.45 252.8 (11440 kHz) NG 163.4875 163.5875 Flight Line 165.1625 Flight Line Maintenance 165.0125 298.3 Flight Line Fueling 165.1625 Crew Alerts 413.45 AF 46.65 46.85 46.95 149.175 163.225 173.5375 235.5 240.5 251.9 252.5 233.4 289.3 337.4 349.1 352.8 359.0 369.5 372.5 375.5 378.5 388.5 390.5 394.5 397.0 396.5 398.5 413.15 Lockheed 464.925

Portland Int'l. Jetport, ME: AD 322.4 353.9 381.2 T 257.8

Port of Astoria/Clatsop Co. Apt., OR: CG 381.8 (HF 5696 8984 kHz)

Portsmouth, ME: USN 141.00 141.95 149.425 223.9 255.0 280.2 305.0 335.3 355.4 380.5 385.0 394.3

Portsmouth Naval Shipyard, NH (Repair/overhaul facility for nuclear submarines): Security 138.72 138.85 138.975 Naval Investigative Service 140.65 140.75 Pager 148.31 Maintenance 140.05 Base Transportation 140.46 Base Utilities 148.29 Cranes 140.55 Radiation Monitoring 142.50 149.39 USN 140.06 140.55 142.85 149.375 149.40 150.07 150.11 150.15 150.28 CG 143.28 162.125 162.25 162.375 165.2625 165.3125 166.4375 171.3625

Portsmouth Naval Base, VA: Hospital 143.625 Hospital Security 140.25 Crane Testing 138.675 USN 34.35 138.60 138.675 140.075 140.125 140.675 140.725 140.75 140.775 140.825 141.975 142.20 142.50 142.525 142.60 142.68 142.825 143.675 150.775 328.8 CG 165.3375 (HF 5696 kHz) CG Security 165.2625

Potsdam Muni Apt., NY: AD 377.1

Pottstown Limerick Apt., PA: AD 281.3

Prairie du Chien Muni Apt., WI: AD 281.4

Pratt & Whitney Aircraft Co.,: Rocky Hill, CT 153.38 461.3125 466.3125 466.6125; Columbus, GA 462.20 462.375 462.50

Presidio of Monterey, CA: (Army Defense Language Institute): Security 173.4125 FD 173.4625 (Also see Ft. Ord listings.)

Presidio of San Francisco/Ft. Scott, CA (HQ 6th Army; Letterman Army Medical Center; Army Defense Language Institute; HQ 91st Division): Aero OP 36.60 120.9 124.3 323.2 Security/MP 148.60 148.90 149.575 150.70 173.4125 CID 412.90 413.025 413.425 FD 149.70 150.425 173.4625 Medics 141.00 155.34 407.225 Emergency 139.075 141.465 142.355 148.75 149.825 150.50 EOD 49.70 49.80 Civil Engineering 149.625 150.625 Pager 173.4125 Recreational Facilities 148.825 Army 148.925 413.475

Prescott Muni Apt., AZ: See Ernest A. Love Fld.

Princeton Apt., NJ: AD 379.9

Princeton Muni Apt., ME: 290.5

Prospect Harbor, ME: USN 143.52

Providence, RI: USN 32.45

Provincetown Muni. Apt., MA: AD 387.1

Provo Muni Apt., UT: 322.3

Pryor Fld., Decatur, AL: AD 239.0 307.0

Public Health Center for Disease Control, Atlanta, GA: 30.34 32.14 32.22 34.02 36.22 40.38 40.58 40.70 40.97 41.14 41.35 155.3125 171.2375

Pueblo Army Depot, CO (Chemical-Biological Warfare agent storage depot): 142.395 142.455 142.965 149.115 150.555 409.65 409.85 412.925 412.975

Pueblo Mem'l. Apt., CO: FSS 255.4 AD 290.5 362.35 T 257.8

Puget Sound Naval Shipyard, Bremerton, WA: Railroad 148.325 (Also see Bremerton Naval Center listings.)

Purdue University Apt., Lafayette, IN: FSS 255.4 T 393.0 G 393.0

Putnam Hall, FL: USN 267.4

Quad City Apt., Moline, IL: AD 257.8 351.7 T 257.8 G 257.8 Army 302.5

Quakertown Apt., PA: AD 291.7

Quantico MCAF/Turner Fld., VA (HQ USMC Development & Education Command; Officers Candidate School; Officer Basic School; Amphibious Warfare School; Command & Staff College; USMC Disciplinary Barracks; FBI Academy; DEA Academy): AD 118.95 126.2 257.2 312.2 S 265.0 T 41.95 118.6 340.2 360.2 G 340.2 WX 355.3 Security 149.10 149.13 FD 149.35 Crash Trucks 149.10 Medics 149.35 149.45 FBI Academy 149.37 Army 40.10 148.605 USMC 29.90 30.45 32.05 32.80 34.15 34.20 34.35 36.15 36.55 36.60 38.30 38.65 38.80 38.85 41.10 140.04

140.05 140.075 140.10 140.20 140.25 140.48 140.65 140.775 140.80 143.65 148.275 148.605 148.775 148.815 148.95 149.075 149.10 149.375 149.39 149.45 149.49 256.4 261.2 265.2 265.8 270.5 277.7 279.0 318.0 326.4 328.4 337.2 339.6 340.4 345.2 358.1 359.7 362.0 382.8 383.6 419.50

Quincy Muni Apt.-Baldwin Fld., IL: FSS 255.4 AD 319.9

Quonset State Apt., N. Kingstown, RI: AD 257.7 307.9 380.25 385.6 T 252.9 G 275.8 ANG OP ("Rhody 80") 141.80 383.3 SAC CP 311.0 321.0 NG OP 47.00 49.70 244.1 NG 139.10 141.40 141.80 242.7 247.9 383.3

Radford Army Ammunition Plant, VA: Security 163.5875 Safety 163.4625 Railroad OP 173.4125 Propellant OP 163.5625 Chemical OP 412.85 Pager 163.5375 Maintenance 165.1875 Army 138.925 139.035 165.0625 407.325 413.225 413.45

Raleigh Co. Mem'l Apt., Beckley, WV: AD 398.95

Raleigh-Durham Apt., NC: FSS 255.4 AD 256.9 307.9 388.0 392.1 T 257.8 G 348.6 NG 49.95

Ralph Wein Mem'l. Apt., Kotzebue, AK: AD 263.0 T 126.2 364.2 AD 163.5875 229.1 269.9 288.2 288.4

Ramey AFB, PR: AF 34.10 36.35 36.85 165.2125 272.6 299.0 304.8 337.4 NORAD CP 364.2 National Science Foundation 30.325 143.835

Ramstein AB, Germany: S 138.775 140.90 277.7 AD 129.05 140.90 358.5 378.4 T 122.1 123.55 257.8 263.6 277.2 G 130.4 375.0 E 250.55 MAC 234.4 235.15 CP 315.35 360.55 385.15 WX 259.4 SOF 379.5

Randolph AFB, Universal City, TX (HQ AF Training Command; AF Military Personnel Center; AF Recruiting Service; 12 Flying Training Wing): S 271.8 DI 372.2 AD 109.7 112.3 124.45 125.1 125.7 353.5 381.4 392.1 T 120.5 258.3 G 134.05 275.8 WX 344.6 Students T ("Hangover Tower") 128.25 291.1 Students G ("Hangover Ground") 124.75 316.8 OSI 138.075 138.165 138.175 AF 138.50 138.90 139.25 139.65 149.25 149.265 150.195 163.4875 163.5625 164.50 165.1125 173.5375 173.5875 236.6 297.4 308.9 311.3 318.1 320.9 324.5 325.8 337.4 341.5 349.0 359.3 407.525 413.00 413.15 413.375 Army 139.00 139.10 139.15 227.2 230.8 231.2 231.7

Randolph AFB Auxiliary Fld, Sequin, TX: OP ("Charlie Brown") 271.2

Range 72, FL: AF 139.74

Rapid City Regn'l Apt., SD: AD FSS 255.4 AD 271.3 396.0 T 257.8 NG 41.50 123.05 165.0625 173.4625

Raton Muni. Apt./Crews Fld., NM: AD 299.3

Ravenna Ordnance Depot, OH: Army 143.10 143.40 165.0625 173.4625 384.7

Rawlins Muni Apt., WY: FSS 255.4

Ray Brook, NY: Army 163.2625 166.16 168.025 168.435 169.90

Ray S. Miller AAF/Camp Ripley, MN: AD 125.3 312.3 T 49.20 126.2 241.0 OP 49.65 NG 32.10 36.70 40.90 139.125 139.30 141.35 143.05 143.10 143.35 143.40 229.4 248.1 347.7 Range 36.10 304.3

Raytheon Company: Andover, MA 158.46; Billerica, MA 462.275; Bristol, TN 152.39 462.40; Framingham, MA 153.335; Goleta, CA 462.25; Mtn. View, CA 462.525; Pelham, NH 123.2 123.4 123.45 314.6 382.6; Portsmouth, RI 153.155 156.45; Rochester, NY 451.225 451.525; San Angelo, TX: 463.30; Torrance, CA 156.55; Waltham, MA 153.20 153.23; Weston, MA 153.335

RCA Corporation: Arlington, TX: 463.30; Atlanta, GA: 461.80; Baileys Crossroads, VA 851.4875; Bloomington, IN 35.90 153.14 153.32 451.175 451.375 451.475 464.85; Brecksville, OH 462.025; Bridgeton, NJ 461.325; Bridgewater; NJ 154.625; Burlington, MA 464.325; Camden NJ 153.32 451.225 462.85 463.85 464.05 464.85 472.2125 Security 461.25; Canonsburg, PA 157.74 462.15 462.70; Cedar Hill, TX 852.1375; Charlotte, NC: 463.475; Chery Hill, NJ 151.625 463.85; Chicago, IL: 464.625 853.9375; Chicopee, MA 462.05; Chula Vista, CA 461.025; Clayton, MO 461.325 851.3625; College Park, MD 461.125 461.975; Cornwells, ME 463.85; Dallas, TX 463.325; Des Plaines, IL 464.625 853.9375; Dewitt, MI 462.175; Dunmore, PA 257.74 462.85; East Orange, NJ 475.2125; Ft. Lauderdale, FL 463.90; Freeland, PA 461.80; Golden, CO 461.475 851.9375; Gretna, LA 30.88 156.45; Hazleton, PA 461.80; Hightstown, NJ 151.655; Holly, MI 463.275; Houston, TX 462.15; Indianapolis, IN 153.14 153.32 461.225 462.425 464.525 464.95; Irving, TX 463.30; Kansas City, MO 851.26; Lancaster PA 31.20; Lansing, MI 462.175; Lexington, KY 461.375; Los Angeles, CA 461.925 851.3375; Marion, IN 153.08 153.14 461.225; McMurray, PA 462.15 462.70; Meadow Lands, PA 30.58 35.24 35.26 156.65 159.42 159.45 159.48 159.51 161.575 451.1375 454.55 464.65 462.15 462.70 471.1125 494.3125 494.3375 851.0125 851.0375 851.0625 865.0125 865.9375 865.9625; Memphis, TN 153.52 463.85; Moorestown, NJ 462.85 310.0 323.5; Mountaintop, PA 462.275; Mount Laurel, NJ 463.85; Mount Wilson, CA 461.925; New Augusta, IN 461.225; New Hyde Park, NY 472.2125; New Orleans, LA 462.025 851.4385; New York, NY 472.2125; Noblesville, IN 461.225; Oakland, CA 464.225 851.4375; Oklahoma City, OK 464.225 851.4375; Oneonta, NY 464.975; Philadelphia, PA 464.85 853.01; Pittsburgh, PA 462.70 861.1375; Portland, OR 851.2875; Princeton, NJ 151.715 153.14 462.70; Quilcen, WA 463.225; Richmond, VA 461.25; Rochester, NY 461.25; San Antonio, TX: 461.475; Sherman Oaks, CA 851.3375; Skokie, IL 464.625; Southfield, MI 461.175; Springfield, VA 464.775; Strongsville, OH 462.025; Sudbury, MA 461.3525 463.525; Somerville, NJ 153.335; Van Nuys, CA 123.2 123.45; Venetia, PA 462.15; Wheatridge, CO 461.475; Wichita, KS 123.2; Wilbraham, MA 462.05

Reading Muni Apt./Spaatz, Fld., PA: AD 257.9 339.3 T 288.3

Reading, PA: USN 30.15 32.05 34.35

Ream Fld.: See Imperial Beach OLF.

Redbird Apt., Dallas, TX: AD 372.1 T 257.8

Red Bluff Muni. Apt., CA: FSS 255.4 AD 350.3

Redding Muni. Apt., CA: AD 350.3 T 226.3

Red Lion Apt., PA: AD 259.3

Red River Army Ammunition Depot, Texarkana, TX: Helipad 125.7 257.8 Army 139.00 139.05 139.125 139.175 143.40 148.65 277.55 407.275 (Also see Lone Star Army Ammunition Plant listings.)

Redstone AAF/Redstone Arsenal, Huntsville, AL (Army Missile Command/MICOM; NASA Marshall Space Flight Center): AD 118.05 120.8 125.6 239.0 307.0 354.1 T 126.2 241.0 Guards 165.0125 165.02 165.1375 MP/Security 165.1375 DoD Security 165.0875 CID 163.5125 FD/Crash 165.0125 OP 128.15 Emergencies 139.20 Medics 163.5625 Base Commanders Net 165.1875 Pager 173.5375 Base Transportation 165.0375 Research & Development 172.875 173.175 173.4625 173.4875 Army 30.10 30.50 32.10 32.30 34.90 36.10 40.10 40.50 46.80 46.90 139.025 139.10 139.375 139.425 141.00 141.30 148.605 148.755 148.815 150.435 150.765 162.225 163.5375 163.6125 164.10 165.1125 165.1625 169.925 173.4125 173.4375 173.5125 225.4 226.3 227.1 227.3

229.8 230.8 232.7 233.3 237.3 239.5 243.8 244.7 260.3 299.1 304.6 153.305 NASA Marshall Space Flight Center Security   Aero OP 118.2   NASA Maintenance 122.85 NASA Security 164.975 FD 165.0125   NASA Railroad 163.4875   NASA Mobile Phones 167.675   NASA 162.125 164.175 164.20 164.275 165.375 166.225 167.875 168.45 170.10 170.20 170.35 170.40 171.00 171.15 172.225 173.025 173.6125 173.6625 173.6875 173.7365 173.7875 314.6 382.6

   Red River D.E.W. Line Station, Greenland: AF 122.2 236.6 (HF 5295 kHz)

   Red Wing Muni Apt., MN: AD 353.7

   Redwood Falls Muni Apt., MN: FSS 255.4   AD 290.2

   Reedsburg Muni Apt., WI: AD 380.35

   Reese AFB, Lubbock, TX (64th Flying Training Wing): S 270.1   DI 376.0   AD 119.2 119.9 123.75 275.8 335.6 351.8   T 125.45 291.1   G 125.45 275.8   E 335.8   T-37 Student OP 287.6   T-38 Student OP 289.1   SOF ("Watchman") 390.15   WX 375.2   AF 139.65 149.175 150.225 163.4875 165.5375 163.5875 164.10 164.9625 165.1375 173.4375 173.5875 271.8 292.1 297.2 321.1 326.2 393.0 413.15

   Reidsville Apt., GA: AD 290.4

   Remington Arms Co.: Bridgeport, CT 153.23 462.45; Ilion, NY 153.05 153.14 466.8125; Lonoke, AR 152.42 153.395

   Renner Fld/Goodland Muni. Apt., KS: AD 353.7

   Reno-Cannon Int'l. Apt., NV: FSS 255.4   S 277.2   AD 298.9 353.9   T 257.8   G 348.6   E 343.9   ANG OP 388.85   ANG CP ("Caprock") 280.0 280.5 (HF 4341 8780 kHz)   ANG 149.25 149.30 149.50 149.55 163.4875 165.0125 165.1375 165.1875 280.5 292.3   USN 320.3 376.8

   Reno/Stead Apt., NV: NG ("Rocky Ops") 32.30 40.40 118.05 122.8 277.5   NG 139.20 141.20 302.3

   Renton Muni Apt., WA: AD 263.1 284.7 338.2 385.2   T 256.9   G 256.9   AF 245.0 262.5 270.1 280.2 287.2 290.0 298.1 300.0 328.0 337.5 341.6 349.6 350.0 360.0 370.0 Boeing Company 123.35 123.55 153.245 451.425 462.225 464.775 (HF 3444.4 kHz)   FD 154.25 154.34

   Rentschler Airport/United Technologies Company, East Hartford, CT: AD 125.65 327.1   T 119.9 275.2   G 121.7   FD/Crash 460.60   Unicom 122.95   Msc 31.24 119.5 151.745 151.805 151.865 153.08 153.17 153.32 153.38 462.225 462.30 462.40

   Republic Apt., Farmingdale, NY: AD 269.0 388.0 396.1   T 229.5   G 269.6   AF 377.8 397.0   Beechcraft 130.575 130.60   Fairchild Republic Aircraft Co 153.11

   Reston, VA: USN 138.585 138.75

   Rexburg-Madison Co. Apt., ID: AD 381.6

   Rhinelander-Oneida Co. Apt., WI: AD 281.5

   Rice Lake Muni. Apt., WI: AD 335.6

   Richard B. Russell Apt, GA: AD 353.7

   Richard Downing Apt., Coshocton, OH: AD 323.0

   Richard I. Bong Apt., Superior, WI: AD 255.9

   Richard Russell Apt., Rome, GA: AD 353.7

   Richards-Gebaur Apt., Kansas City, MO: DI 372.2   AD 294.7   T 236.6   G 289.4 AF Reserve 442 Tactical Fighter Wing ("Frontline") 252.1   AF Reserve 303rd Tactical Fighter Sqdn Supervisor of Flying ("Ground Hog") 227.8 321.4   FD/Crash 166.135 173.5875   Army Reserve 36.85 42.15 46.90   Air/Air 141.10   Security 150.195 Commanders Net 165.1125   Hospital 173.4375   Truman MOA 305.1   AF Reserve 148.125 148.175 148.225 148.45 148.50 148.545 148.55 149.30 149.47 149.975 150.225 150.445 163.225 163.5625 164.175 173.025 173.175 173.4875 242.4 252.1 289.4 399.8 413.15 413.20 413.30 413.40

Richland Apt., Richland Ctr., WI: AD 380.35

Richland Apt., WA: AD 343.9

Richmond Int'l. Apt./Byrd Fld., VA: S 266.6 AD 307.2 319.8 371.1 398.2 T 257.8 G 348.6 E 348.6 NG 40.40 122.9 242.4 ANG OP 289.3 ANG 149.325 163.4875 165.0125 165.1375 165.1625 413.175

Richmond, FL: AF 228.8 234.7 238.5 251.0 256.6 263.2 270.4 275.0 278.6 287.8 292.7 298.5 302.4 306.4 325.5 338.4 344.0 356.0 369.0 375.1 386.2 392.8 NORAD CP 364.2

Richmond Muni. Apt., IN: AD 316.7

Richmond, VA: Army Supply Ops 139.375

Rickenbacker ANG Base, Columbus, OH: DI 122.95 372.2 S 132.1 273.5 AD 119.15 123.8 132.3 279.6 392.1 T 120.05 236.6 348.4 G 121.85 275.8 AF Reserve 907th Tactical Air Grp ("Card Call") 252.1 NG 46.80 123.075 160nd NG OP 286.2 166 NG OP 311.3 SAC CP 311.0 321.0 Crew Alerts 413.45 OSI 138.075 138.165 138.175 ANG 32.65 38.65 46.75 49.70 49.85 138.40 139.875 143.825 148.485 148.545 149.15 149.475 149.565 150.165 150.345 163.4625 163.4875 163.5875 164.50 165.0125 165.1375 165.1875 170.375 171.175 173.025 173.4125 173.5625 173.5875 314.2 320.1 338.6 340.8 413.15 413.20 413.30 413.40 Army 49.80

Ridgecrest Naval Weapons Station, CA: USN 463.25

Rio Grande Valley Int'l. Apt., TX: AD 239.0 291.6 T 320.5

Riverbank Army Ammunition Plant, CA: FD 150.55 Pager 173.4625

Riverside Muni Apt., CA: FSS 255.4 AD 295.7 T 257.8

R. J. Bohn Armory Heliport, Bismarck, ND: AD 126.3 T 118.3 257.8 NG 49.80 134.1

Roanoke Regn'l. Apt./Woodrum Fld., VA: FSS 255.4 AD 339.8 353.9 T 353.9 G 257.8 FAA 169.375

Roanoke, VA: USN 36.85

Robert Gray AAF/Ft. Hood, Killeen, TX (1st Cavalry Division; 6th Cavalry Brigade/Air Combat; 2nd Armored Division; 3rd Corps; 13th Support Brigade; Army Armored & Missile Training): DI 38.70 125.05 304.3 S 118.8 AD 118.0 244.0 T 120.75 241.0 265.6 G 126.2 299.8 Flight Following 32.10 143.10 357.9 E 118.6 241.0 WX 41.20 304.4 Ranges 30.45 38.30 Tank Range 173.5125 Railroad 165.1875 MP/Security 165.0875 165.1625 Motor Pool 165.1875 EOD 49.70 49.80 Army 32.65 38.70 40.93 41.50 49.80 138.025 138.10 138.25 138.50 138.65 138.75 138.80 138.85 139.10 139.125 139.20 139.30 139.325 139.40 139.50 139.60 140.05 140.20 140.25 140.30 140.40 140.45 140.50 140.60 140.65 140.75 140.85 140.90 141.10 141.15 141.175 141.20 141.225 141.25 141.275 141.35 141.375 141.40 141.45 141.50 141.65 142.05 142.30 142.40 142.50 142.60 142.80 142.90 143.00 143.025 143.05 143.075 143.125 143.15 143.175 143.20 143.25 143.30 143.325 143.40 148.575 148.60 148.625 148.65 148.675 148.70 148.75 148.80 148.825 148.85 148.875 148.90 148.925 149.57 149.60 149.625 149.65 149.675 149.70 149.725 149.75 149.775 149.85 150.425 150.60 150.65 150.625 150.70 150.725 150.75 150.775 163.375 163.5125 163.5625 164.10 165.0125 165.0375 170.125 160.175 173.4125 173.4625 173.4875 226.3 226.5 226.9 227.3 227.5 227.9 229.4 229.85 230.2 230.8 231.0 231.3 231.6 232.4 233.2 233.35 234.1 234.4 234.8 302.3 321.6 356.3 356.7 365.3 365.5 365.7 365.9 366.1 366.6 366.7 366.9 367.1 367.3 367.5 367.7 367.9 368.1 368.3 368.5 368.7 368.9 370.0 370.2 370.4 373.3 380.6 393.3 393.5 395.4 407.225 407.275 407.325 412.825 412.875 412.90 413.075 413.275 413.475 413.525 413.575 AF 36.85 38.65 46.75 139.70 141.80 142.25 143.975 149.205 163.4625 276.8 293.5 321.2 347.2 387.9 413.15

Robert J. Miller Airpark, Toms River, NJ: AD 259.3

Robert Mueller Muni. Apt., Austin, TX: FSS 255.4 AD 317.6 363.8 370.85 G 348.6 T 355.1 NG 36.80 241.8 AF 150.30

Roberts AAF/Camp Roberts, CA: OP 41.50 126.2 241.0 Range ("Midnight Ops") 38.90 (Also see Camp Roberts listings.)

Roberts Fld., Redmond, OR: FSS 255.4 AD 288.1

Robins AFB, Warner Robins, GA (ACC; 9th AF; 5th Combat Comms Grp.; Air Logistics Center): DI 134.1 372.2 S 118.95 372.5 AD 119.6 124.2 124.8 133.1 279.6 324.3 348.7 388.2 T 126.2 320.1 G 121.9 275.8 CP ("Gaslight") 240.15 AF Reserve CP ("Gunrunner") 252.1 Maintenance ("Eagle Control") 359.2 WX 344.6 Security 148.515 163.4875 FD/Crash 173.5875 Crew Alerts 413.45 OSI 40.17 40.19 138.175 SAC CP 311.0 321.0 AF 46.85 49.75 138.425 138.875 139.65 139.875 143.825 148.065 148.215 148.475 149.325 149.475 149.565 149.895 150.285 163.4625 163.5125 163.5875 164.50 165.0125 165.1375 165.1625 165.1875 166.20 166.225 169.60 171.3875 173.025 173.05 173.075 173.10 173.5375 233.4 258.3 285.4 389.0 393.1 407.375 407.475 412.975 413.025 413.10 413.125 413.15 413.20 413.275 413.30 413.40 413.425 Msc 130.8

Robinson AAF/Camp Robinson, Little Rock, AR: NG 41.50 139.20 241.0

Rochester Muni. Apt., MN: FSS 255.4 AD 307.3 T 257.8

Rochester, NY: Army Reserve 98th Training Division 30.10 34.50 40.90 49.90

Rock Co. Apt., Jonesville, WI: AD 327.0 397.2

Rock Hill Muni. Apt./Bryant Fld., SC: AD 288.15

Rock Island Army Arsenal, IL: Security 165.0875 Army 150.425 164.9875 165.0125 165.1875 166.225 412.875

Rockland, ME: USN 138.55

Rock Springs-Sweetwater Co. Apt., WY: FSS 255.4

Rockwell Int'l. Corp.: Addison, TX 123.35 153.58; Ashtabula, OH 154.625; Albany, GA 123.35; Anaheim, CA 123.075 462.375 462.925 464.075 464.825 472.8375; Arlington, TX 153.38; Bakersfield, CA 462.925; Barberton, OH 153.185 154.625; Beebe River, NH 49.34; Bethany, OH 462.80; Boron, CA 462.925; Canoga Park, CA 123.075 461.40 462.275 462.325; Cedar Rapids, IA (Collins Radio) 31.50 123.35 123.40 123.525 154.54 462.25 462.30 462.40 (HF 2397 2400 4796 4799 6152 6155 6171 6174 9656 9659 11762 11765 15342 15345 15406 15409 kHz); Chatsworth, GA 461.025 462.85 462.975; Chattanooga, TN: 461.025 462.425 462.475; Chicago, IL 462.0625; Des Plaines, IL: 472.0625; Downey, CA 123.075 153.26 462.325 462.925 464.875; Edwards AFB, CA 122.8 123.05 123.35 123.475 123.525 464.875; Fletcher, NC 153.365; Farmington, PA 123.35; Florence, KY 465.00; Galesburg, IL 151.655 451.375 462.20; Greensboro, NC: 153.23; Heath, OH 462.925; Kennedy Space Flight Center 123.475; Kenton, OH 153.23; La Mirada, CA 462.925; Los Angeles, CA: 47.54 123.075 123.35 123.475 123.525 461.525 462.325 462.925 464.875 472.8375; Magic Mtn., CA 462.275; McAlester, OK 157.74; Melbourne, FL 123.475; Montebello, CA 462.325 462.375; New Castle, PA 153.125; Newport Beach, CA 153.26 461.525 462.975; Oakbrook, IL 462.425; Oakland, CA 153.185; Oklahoma City, OK 123.25 123.55; Palmdale, CA 462.925 464.875; Perryville, MO 122.8 123.35 123.525; Pittsburgh, PA 123.35 461.125 464.40; Pontiac, MI 123.35; Richardson, TX 46.02 48.01 153.38 158.31 462.30 462.525 462.90; Seal Beach, CA 123.075 464.875 464.975 472.8375; Santa Ana, CA 462.925; Santa Susana, CA 123.075 461.40 462.275 462.325 472.8375; St. Louis, MO 123.35 123.525; Spartanburg, SC 158.925; Thousand Oaks, CA 123.075 462.925; Troy, MI 462.275; Tulsa, OK 153.11 153.32 462.30 462.525 464.425; Winchester, KY 464.475; Wyomissing, PA 262.30 (Also see specific location listings.)

Rockwood Muni Apt., TN: AD 254.3

Rocky Mount-Wilson Apt., NC: FSS 255.4 AD 285.5

Rocky Mountain Arsenal, Denver, CO: Security 168.575 417.20 419.175 Army 41.50 148.575 148.90 149.115 150.45 150.495 163.5625 165.0375 165.0875 169.225 170.125 173.5625 407.575 410.20 411.20 413.225 413.575 AF 252.22 252.42

Rogers Muni Apt.-Carter Fld., AR: AD 269.0 369.0

Rohnerville Apt., Fortuna, CA: FSS 255.4

Rohn Industries: Brownfield, CA 123.15; Chula Vista, CA 35.92 153.05 153.32 153.365 154.57 158.295 158.31 462.0625 462.25 462.50 462.8125 462.8625 463.2125

463.2625 463.7375 464.175;   Dulzura, CA 462.375 464.175;   Escondido, CA 462.50; Holtville, CA 123.15;   Marino Valley, CA 153.05;   Riverside, CA 31.04 153.05 153.32 153.365 154.60 462.375;   San Jose, CA 151.895

Rolla National Apt., MO: FSS 255.4 AD 323.1

Roosevelt Roads NS/Ofstie Fld, PR (HQ Commander, Naval Forces, Caribbean): S 120.0 280.4   AD 128.6 134.1 277.2 279.6   T 126.2 340.2 360.2   G 120.7 336.4   E 344.3   MAC CP 349.4   WX 344.6   Base OP 349.9   Msc ("Sea Witch") 285.0 323.4 USN 32.25 32.45 36.55 40.15 40.80 41.90 139.50 139.525 139.55 139.725 140.00 140.025 140.075 140.15 140.20 140.225 140.25 140.30 140.35 140.55 140.60 140.625 140.65 140.76 140.775 140.825 140.85 140.88 140.90 140.975 141.00 142.50 142.50 142.55 142.625 142.70 142.825 143.55 143.575 143.60 148.29 148.33 248.40 148.95 149.01 149.35 149.45 150.195 235.4 249.6 254.6 263.6 264.2 265.8 267.4 271.4 273.0 273.8 274.9 276.4 277.1 277.8 278.7 290.1 299.7 301.0 301.9 304.2 305.9 306.1 311.6 315.4 317.0 317.1 320.2 320.5 322.0 324.4 325.0 324.1 328.2 336.2 337.8 341.0 342.6 345.0 350.1 352.4 353.2 360.8 361.0 361.2 362.6 386.9 413.50   (Also see Vieques Island listings.)

Rosamond, CA: AF 141.80 342.4   Rohr Industries 123.15

Roscoe Turner Apt., MS: AD 260.6

Roscommon Co. Apt., Houghton Lake, MI: AD 398.9

Roseau Muni. Apt., MN: AD 256.9

Roseburg Muni. Apt., OR: AD 239.0

Rosecrans Mem'l. Apt., St. Joseph, MO: AD 318.1   T 239.0   G 348.6   Advanced Airlift Tactics Training Center ("Brady Ops") 349.15   ANG CP 349.4   ANG 163.375 163.4625 163.4875 163.5125 163.5875 396.9

Rosemont, MN: USN 143.52

Roslyn ANG Station, NY: Security 163.4875   ANG 41.95 235.5 283.8 301.6 375.5 388.5 394.5 398.8

Ross Co. Apt., Chillicote, OH: AD 267.9

Ross Fld.-Twin Cities Apt., Benton Harbor, MI: AD 257.8 263.1

Rostraver Apt., Monongahela, PA: AD 337.4

Roswell AFS, NM: AD 239.6   T 272.7   SAC CP 311.0 321.0   AF 259.2 305.6 348.7 397.9

Roswell Indust'l. Air Center, NM: AD 239.0 257.6   S 306.2   T 272.2   G 348.6

Rota NS, Spain: S 267.6   AD 120.0 120.8 128.5 271.8 296.4   T 125.4 139.30 236.2 257.8   G 130.7 317.5   MAC 377.8   WX 344.6

Rowan Co. Apt., Salisbury, NC: AD 288.15   NG 49.95

Russellville Muni Apt., AR: AD 348.7

Rutland State Apt., VT: AD 282.2

Ryan Fld., Tucson, AZ: AD 395.9

S-4 Base, NV: OP 297.65 ("Sightings: The UFO Report," a special about UFO's broadcast on the Fox TV Network in 12/91 interviewed an engineer identified as a former employee at this super-secret research facility. It is located in the desert, south of a dry lake bed known as Area 51. He claimed that at S-4 there are at least 9 disc shaped flying objects of extra-terrestrial origin, with at least one of them being operable. These machines were claimed to be fabricated of unknown alloys and propelled by methods not reproducible by known technologies. The discs are being stored and researched at S-4. The government denies these claims, and appears to have made several clumsy attempts to purge the employee's name from government employment files as soon as he began giving out interviews about S-4.)

Sabre AHP/Ft. Campbell, TN: AD 118.1 225.6 T 34.80 143.30 280.9 G 40.85 149.85 267.3 OP 34.80 (Also see Campbell AAF listings.)

Sacramento Exec Apt., CA: FSS 255.4 AD 257.9 285.6 286.6 340.9 363.8 T 257.8

Sacramento Metro Apt., CA: AD 257.9 271.3 285.6 320.1 340.9 381.2 385.5 T 381.6 G 256.7 E 256.7 Cessna Aircraft Co 123.25 123.375

Sacramento Peak Observatory, CA: 163.45 171.175

Sacramento Signal Corps Depot, CA (Army): T 40.95 41.50 Security 165.0625 OP 169.60

Sagami Army Hpt, Honshu, Japan: OP 36.80 122.5 288.8

Saginaw Army Aircraft Plant, TX: 226.4 237.75 249.2 265.5 277.5 299.9 314.6 321.5 356.9 374.4 376.3 386.6

St. Augustine Apt., FL: AD 347.8

St. Charles, MO: AF 225.0 252.0 274.0 300.0 349.6 375.0 420.0

St. Clair Co. Apt., Pell City, AL: AD 381.5

St. Cloud Muni. Apt., MN: AD 323.1

St. Elizabeth Hospital, DC: Pager 165.3125

St. Landry Parish Apt., Opelousas, LA: AD 278.5 338.25

St. Louis, MO: USN 34.14 40.65 CG 165.2625 NG 38.68 38.89 38.91 164.20

St. Louis Downtown-Parks Apt., IL: AD 254.3 T 357.4

St. Louis Regional Apt., IL: AD 338.0 T 239.0

St. Lucie Co. Int'l. Apt., FL: AD 272.75

St. Paul Downtown Apt./Holman Fld., MN: AD 335.5 T 257.8 Army Reserve OP 41.50 139.20 229.1 NG OP 41.40 49.65 126.2 Army 165.50

St. Paul, MN: USN 34.95 38.30 40.80

St. Petersburg-Clearwater Int'l. Apt., FL: FSS 255.4 AD 363.8 T 257.8 G 348.6 CG 121.9 277.8 381.7 381.8 383.9 (HF 5696 kHz) Search/Rescue 282.8

St. Simons Isl., GA: AF 235.5 345.5 396.5

Salem-Leckrone Apt., IL: AD 317.7

Salem, MA: NG 34.70 41.00 42.80

Salem, OR: USN 34.55 36.85

Salina Muni Apt., KS: FSS 255.4 AD 363.2 T 257.7 Beech Aircraft Co 123.2 NG 49.95 304.6

Salinas Muni. Apt., CA: FSS 255.4 AD 302.0 307.0 309.2 T 239.3 G 239.3

Salisbury-Wicomico Co. Regn'l. Apt., MD: FSS 255.4 AD 285.4 314.0

Salt Lake City Int'l. Apt., UT: FSS 255.4 AD 257.2 284.6 322.3 363.8 377.2 G 348.6 T 257.8 E 348.6 Army Reserve 32.90 ANG OP 303.0 SAC CP 311.0 321.0 Lockheed Corp 464.925 ANG 46.85 139.70 140.40 141.70 143.80 149.15 149.325 149.475 149.535 149.565 164.50 253.4 267.8 268.2 293.5 305.7 318.7 391.2

Salt Lake City Muni. Apt #2, UT: AD 322.3 NG 43.20 48.80 49.65 243.8

Salt Springs, FL: USN 289.9

Samuels Fld., Bardstown, KY: AD 327.0 388.2

San Antonio Int'l. Apt., TX: FSS 255.4 AD 252.9 269.1 298.0 307.0 317.5 353.5 392.1 G 348.6 T 257.8 Army 46.70 AF 149.325 Hurricane Hunters 304.8

San Bruno, CA: USN Security 139.50

San Clemente Island NALF/Frederick Sherman Fld., CA: S 268.6 AD ("Beaver") 120.85 266.9 T 126.75 278.8 340.2 G 119.55 352.4 CG 165.3125 415.775 Search/Rescue 282.8 Nuclear Weapons Systems 148.87 149.145 149.25 149.525 149.745 167.85 AF 251.9 USN 32.07 36.57 40.41 40.53 40.79 138.525 138.69 140.20 140.275 140.895 141.00 142.00 142.05 142.075 142.10 142.80 143.715 148.575 148.85 149.07 149.13 149.43 149.49 149.65 150.75 245.0 266.7 268.5 268.6 272.6 273.1 275.7 278.8 301.1 308.1 315.3 342.9 344.1 354.9 358.0 362.0 376.8 385.3 413.20 (HF 3109 6723 kHz) (Also the following two San Clemente listings:)

San Clemente Island/Mt. Thirst Naval Helipad, CA: ("Beaver") 126.65 264.0 326.5

San Clemente Island/Pyramid Head Naval Helipad, CA: ("Observation Post") 277.8 289.9 353.4 359.4

San Diego Int'l. Apt.-Lindbergh Fld., CA: FSS 255.4 AD 157.15 290.4 306.7 323.1 363.1 381.5 T 270.9 CG 157.075 157.15 165.2625 165.3375 171.2375 257.8 381.4 381.7 381.8 383.9 (HF 2182 3123 5696 8984 kHz) Lockheed 464.575 464.9125

San Diego Naval Station, CA (Commander, Surface Force, Pacific Fleet; Fleet Training Center; Naval Supply Center; USMC Recruiting Center): S 282.0 Security 148.35 Naval Intelligence 139.58 140.64 FD 140.46 EOD 140.16 Harbor 139.65 Tugs 140.76 Medics 143.525 413.00 Communications Technicians 150.39 Base Trans-portation 148.29 Power Utilities 149.39 Civil Engineering 138.86 Recruiting 140.15 140.70 148.27 Amphibious Units 36.80 38.60 38.75 Assault Craft ("Alpha") 32.40 ("Bluejay") 32.80 (Administrative 34.50 (Ground OP) 32.60 ("Oarfish") 36.80 ("Bravo") 38.10 Fleet Area Control & Surveillance Facility ("Beaver") 118.65 120.85 226.9 272.6 285.7 289.9 Nuclear Weapons Systems 167.85 168.45 USMC Recruit Depot 140.025 140.15 140.40 141.50 USMC Recruit Depot FD 140.875 Shore Patrol 148.375 Base OP 138.50 140.85 148.35 148.75 Naval Training Ctr 138.775 138.875 NTC FD 140.225 NTC Security 140.04 140.225 Balboa Hosp 143.625 ASW Training Ctr 148.30 ASW OP ("Happy Hunter") 255.3 267.4 284.9 285.8 318.7 USN 30.13 36.53 36.63 36.87 40.83 138.55 138.625 138.75 138.95 138.96 138.98 139.425 139.55 139.725 139.925 139.975 140.075 140.175 140.325 140.45 140.475 140.65 140.675 140.75 140.775 140.70 141.00 142.75 143.625 143.65 148.325 149.055 149.375 150.07 152.25 163.00 163.75 164.50 242.5 245.0 256.5 265.9 272.9 277.1 277.9 283.1 299.4 302.1 304.2 308.5 312.7 313.7 313.8 314.6 315.7 318.5 320.2 323.5 326.5 326.6 328.2 336.2 337.9 340.3 340.5 341.0 342.6 345.1 345.8 346.5 346.6 346.9 353.0 353.1 353.4 354.6 355.0 355.1 357.8 358.1 358.7 359.4 359.6 359.7 360.4 361.0 362.5 363.5 376.9 380.7 380.9 382.2 382.7 382.9 383.5 383.855 384.2 384.5 385.0 385.2 406.375 409.125 416.50

Sand Point Naval Support Facility, Seattle, WA: USN 142.86

Sanford Muni Apt., ME: AD 322.4 381.2

San Francisco CGAS, CA: See San Francisco Int'l. Apt.

San Francisco Int'l. Apt., CA: AD 307.2 323.2 338.2 T 269.1 CG 381.4 381.8 383.9 415.825 (HF 5692 kHz) FAA 41.59 Lockheed Corp 154.54 154.57 464.925

San Francisco Naval Station, CA: Fireboats 36.57   USN 36.53 36.60 36.63 36.87 140.58 148.425 149.40 272.9 292.95 293.05 294.65 294.75 296.35 296.45 297.95 298.05 299.45 299.55 306.35 306.45 307.85 307.95 309.95 309.25 309.35 310.75 310.85 313.7 318.5 323.5 326.5 332.7 340.5 342.6 345.1 345.8 346.6 346.8 353.0 353.1 353.4 354.6 355.0 356.2 357.8 358.1 358.7 359.4 359.7 360.4 361.0 362.6 380.7 380.9 382.5 382.9 383.5 382.4 406.375

San Jose Int'l. Apt., CA: AD 317.6 322.0 346.0 379.1   T 257.6   Lockheed Corp 462.425

San Luis Obispo Co. Apt., CA: AD 269.5 379.9

San Luis Valley Regn'l. Apt., AD 343.7 362.35

San Marcos Muni, Apt., TX: AD 362.3

San Nicolas Island OLF, CA: AD 127.55 128.65 280.7 325.0   T 126.85 127.55 134.1 280.7 311.6 340.2 374.8   USN 138.42 138.68 138.70 139.50 140.525 141.00 142.485 143.70 149.10 150.10 226.7 244.3 248.6 250.7 254.9 256.2 270.5 277.8 278.0

San Patricio Co. Apt., TX: AD 363.1

San Pedro, CA: NORAD 228.9 238.4 254.2 260.8 267.0 270.2 274.4 278.4 281.6 297.7 293.8 309.4 326.3 320.6 324.0 327.9 336.6 341.8 346.2 377.0 387.8 398.0 NORAD CP 364.2

Santa Barbara, CA: USN 32.05 34.95 49.85 138.62 138.70 141.00

Santa Barbara Muni. Apt., CA: FSS 255.4   AD 269.5 321.4 397.9   T 242.4

Santa Cruz, CA: AF 374.53 375.855 395.9

Santa Cruz Island, CA: USN 141.00

Santa Fe Co. Muni. Apt., NM: AD 299.3   T 239.3   NG 34.90

Santa Maria Public Apt, CA: AD 269.5 339.1   T 289.6

Santa Monica Muni. Apt., CA: AD 269.0 360.7 363.2 381.6 385.4   T 257.8

Santa Rosa OLF, Milton, FL: OP 361.1

Santa Ynez Apt., CA: AD 339.1

Santee Cooper Regn'l. Apt, SC: AD 358.3 329.1

Saratoga-Bradenton Apt., FL: AD 258.3 354.0   T 269.7   G 257.8

Saratoga Co. Apt., NY: AD 226.8

Saufley OLF, Pensacola, FL: AD 380.6   OP 321.8   USN 140.05 140.10 149.01 149.025 150.11

Saugus, CA: USN 252.4 264.1 314.6 382.6   Lockheed Corp 153.20 158.295 462.425

Sault Ste Marie AFS, MI: NORAD CP 364.2   DI 372.2   AF 154.0375   NORAD 229.1 233.6 239.4 251.8 254.4 258.0 262.2 273.4 278.2 278.4 284.8 289.0 292.4 297.7 309.5 321.8 318.4 3 348.8 357.2 371.0 379.0 384.0 396.8

Savanna Army Depot, IL: Army 163.5625 165.0625 173.4375 173.4625

Savannah CGAS, GA: See Hunter AAF listings.

Savannah-Hardin Co. Apt., TN: FSS 255.4   AD 239.3

Savannah Int'l. Apt., GA: FSS 255.4   AD 322.5 354.0 387.1 388.8   G 348.6   T 257.8   E 295.7   CP 165th Tactical Air Grp 255.75   ANG Training Site 297.1   SAC CP 311.0 321.0   NORAD CP 364.2   ANG 140.425 141.575 228.8 234.7 238.5 251.0 256.6 263.2 270.4 275.0 275.9 278.6 287.8 292.7 298.5 302.4 306.4 311.3 321.2 325.5 338.4 344.4 356.0 369.0 386.2 392.8

Sawyer AFB, MI: See K.I. Sawyer AFB listings.

Scappoose Indst'l. Apt, OR: AD 360.8

Schenectady Co. Apt., NY: AD 226.8   T 321.1   ANG CP ("Raven Ops") 340.8 ANG Security 163.4875   FD/Crash 173.5875   ANG 173.4125 173.4375 173.5375 225.4 321.1

Schofield Barracks, HI (Army 25th Infantry Division): 38.30 139.075 139.305 141.325 141.475 143.085 165.0875 165.1875

Scholes Fld., Galveston, TX: FSS 255.4   AD 284.0

Schoonover Fld. AAF, Hunter-Liggett, CA: AD 128.7 307.0   Advisories & Range 41.50 126.2 229.5   (Also see Hunter-Liggett & Tusi AHP listings.)

Schuylkill Co. Apt./Joe Zerby Fld., Pottsville, PA: AD 247.2

Schwabisch Hall AAF, Germany: AD 129.85 143.925 275.35 VFR Flight Following 138.25 242.55 T 31.80 37.60 122.1 123.05 142.45 251.05 G 141.30 250.55 OP 33.80 WX 140.30

Scott AFB, Belleville, IL (AMC; 375th Aeromedical Airlift Wing): DI 372.2 S 118.65 273.5 AD 124.7 126.7 259.1 289.1 T 128.85 253.5 G 119.2 275.8 E 121.75 225.4 CP 130.65 172.30 383.2 Army Reserve 40.75 WX 239.8 Security 150.30 Medics 155.16 155.28 Pager 173.5875 MAC Commanders Net 148.525 OSI 138.075 138.165 138.175 AF 46.60 139.65 148.035 148.05 148.475 148.565 149.475 149.535 150.125 150.355 150.775 163.5625 164.9875 165.0125 165.1125 163.1375 165.1625 165.1875 165.3125 173.4375 173.5375 173.5625 271.3 363.6 373.0 375.5 390.8 396.0 413.05 413.15 413.20 413.30 (HF "Hilda" 6750 6838 13201 13214 13244 kHz)

Scotts Bluff Co. Apt., NE: FAA 41.59 41.69

Scottsdale Muni Apt., AZ: FSS 255.4 AD 239.0

Scranton Army Ammunition Plant, PA: 163.5375

Screwworm Eradication Research Lab, McAllen, TX: 168.15

Sculthorpe USAF, UK: AD 131.225 135.275 250.3 264.25 268.2 DI 282.225 T 257.8 378.05 G 277.6 Arrivals 236.4 343.5 343.9 366.7

Seal Beach NWS, CA: Security 142.675 Cargo Handling 138.85 Pagers 138.05 138.675 Base OP 142.50 Security 142.675 USN 34.53 36.53 36.57 36.63 133.74 138.54 138.60 138.78 138.84 138.975 138.98 140.28 140.3256 140.52 140.60 140.90 142.60 142.65 150.15 251.4 259.7 273.0 277.1 277.9 283.4 312.7 313.8 321.8 340.4 361.8 387.4 Msc ("Bullfrog") 138.85 148.835 142.675 AF 244.0 279.0 298.6 336.0 Rockwell Int'l. 123.075 464.875 464.975 472.8375

Seattle ANG Base, WA: SAC CP 311.0 321.0 ANG 46.65 142.275 143.775 148.035 148.065 148.065 148.125 148.185 165.7875 225.05 227.8 235.5 240.0 240.5 252.0 252.5 257.475 257.575 262.5 265.66 266.4 272.475 272.525 287.2 292.1 300.0 315.0 328.3 341.6 343.325 343.35 349.6 355.6 361.5 363.325 363.35 365.0 367.6 369.5 375.5 384.7 388.5 392.5 397.1 398.5 407.85 413.45 415.70

Seattle Naval Base, WA: CG 165.2625 165.375 171.15 USN 32.05 34.95 36.53 36.57 36.63 36.87 46.65 49.85 138.525 138.55 140.10 140.125 140.65 140.70 140.775 141.00 142.50 148.40

Seattle-Tacoma Int'l. Apt., WA: FSS 255.4 AD 263.1 284.7 338.2 385.2 T 239.3 Lockheed Corp 153.05 464.925

Seattle, WA: Army 32.30 408.125

Sebring Regn'l. Apt., FL: AD 349.0

Sedalia Memorial Apt., MO: AD 285.6 AF 148.035 148.515 149.265 173.5375 407.475 407.975

Selfridge ANG Base, Mt. Clemens, MI: DI 134.85 372.2 AD 119.6 126.75 318.2 335.6 395.9 T 120.15 340.7 G 128.3 275.8 E 119.0 259.95 Rescue 123.1 381.0 WX 342.5 927th Tactical Air Grp OP 314.2 127th Tactical Fighter Wing OP ("Demon") 36.45 138.65 292.0 CG ("Detroit Air") 381.8 (HF 5692 kHz) Security 163.4875 173.4375 FD/Crash 173.5875 Army 173.10 ANG 32.65 34.20 36.80 139.70 141.55 141.80 143.55 148.05 148.10 150.225 150.30 163.375 163.4625 163.5125 164.10 165.0125 165.1125 165.1375 165.1625 173.025 173.4125 173.5375 251.9 252.9 259.3 280.5 287.5 293.1 314.4 318.2 358.3 388.2 390.0 391.9 407.375 407.50 413.15 413.20 413.30

Sembach AB, Germany: DI 316.7 AD 129.05 140.90 358.5 378.4 T 122.1 142.90 257.4 257.8 G 233.85 E 233.85 CP 143.80 240.8 WX 141.35 OP ("Vampire") (HF 5705 kHz)

Seneca AAF & Army Depot, Romulus, NY: AD 119.55 120.7 269.6 322.3 Unicom 122.8 OP 126.2 173.4625 241.0 EOD 49.70 49.80 Railroad 163.5625 Pager 143.075 Administrative 165.0875 FD 46.10 46.22 Army 142.90 142.975 143.175 143.275 143.375 149.655 173.4875

Seneca Co. Apt., OH: AD 228.4

Seoul AB, S. Korea: AD 119.1 124.8 363.8 T 126.2 236.6 237.1 G 121.85 275.8 E 124.8 363.8 "Dragon OP" 62.45 CP ("Brickwall") 141.675 291.8 WX 62.45

Seward Muni Apt., NE: AD 270.3

Seymour Johnson AFB, Goldsboro, NC (ACC; 9th AF; 4th Fighter Wing; 68th Bombardment Wing/Heavy): DI 372.2 S 273.5 AD 119.7 123.7 320.1 338.6 T 126.25 236.6 255.6 G 275.8 E 363.8 TAC OP ("Raymond 25") 381.3 TAC Supervisor of Flying ("Lion") 280.5 WX 375.2 Security 148.175 148.545 165.1625 FD/Crash 173.5875 Medics 173.5625 Disaster Preparedness 150.315 SAC CP 311.0 321.0 Crew Alerts 413.45 OSI 138.165 138.175 AF 139.65 148.035 148.065 148.095 148.225 148.50 149.205 149.475 149.505 149.565 150.25 163.4625 163.5125 163.5875 165.40 165.1125 165.1375 175.5375 252.9 276.0 279.7 298.6 316.9 347.2 349.1 363.8 377.85 413.15

Shannon Apt., Fredericksburg, VA: AD 312.2 390.9

Sharpe AAF/Sharpe Army Depot, Lathrop, CA: AD 116.0 123.85 126.85 319.9 FSS 122.05 122.2 122.3 T 40.95 41.50 41.95 126.2 Security & FD 163.1875 173.4125 Base Transportation 163.5375 165.0875 Army 139.30 233.2 241.0

Shaw AFB, Sumter, SC (ACC; HQ 9th AF; 1st, 3rd, 4th, 23rd, 354th, 363rd Fighter Wings; 17th, 19th, 33rd Tactical Fighter Sqdns; 16th Tactical Recon Sqdn; 507th Tactical Control Wing; 31st & 56th Tactical Training Wing; 1st Special Operations Wing; Special Operations School): DI 372.2 S 270.1 AD 118.85 124.7 125.4 133.45 134.1 298.9 306.3 327.3 358.3 T 126.65 348.4 E 121.8 289.4 TAC CP ("Raymond 26") 381.3 WX 342.5 G 126.1 275.8 Maintenance 283.8 OSI 138.075 138.165 138.175 Security 148.545 163.5875 164.50 FD/Crash 173.5875 Emergencies 150.315 Medics 173.5625 AF 32.45 46.85 49.85 49.95 138.15 138.30 139.65 139.70 139.975 143.80 148.095 148.125 148.185 148.455 148.485 149.205 149.265 149.505 150.25 165.1125 170.175 173.7125 236.0 260.4 261.1 276.9 280.5 289.6 294.5 296.2 301.6 311.2 320.7 321.2 335.9 340.8 344.9 349.5 363.8 398.1 407.425 413.15

Sheboygan Co. Mem'l. Apt., WI: AD 387.1

Shelby Co. Apt., Alabaster, AL: AD 385.6

Shelby, MS: AF Range 297.1

Shelbyville Muni. Apt., IN: NG OP 41.50 139.10 241.1

Shell AHP, Ft. Rucker, AL: AD 133.45 133.75 237.5 370.3 T 46.90 139.35 148.90 240.8 241.1 G 141.10 347.7 OP 139.35 148.90 240.8 241.1 (Also see Ft. Rucker listings.)

Shemya AFB, AK: DI 134.80 372.2 AD 119.1 339.8 T 127.2 255.6 AF 118.495 148.065 150.285 163.4875 163.5125 163.5875 165.0125 165.1375 173.5875 258.1 318.3 324.3

Shenandoah Muni. Apt., IA: AD 263.0 281.5 363.8

Shenandoah Valley Apt., VA: AD 284.7

Sheppard AFB/Wichita Falls Muni Apt., KS (3700th Technical Training Wing; School of Health Sciences; 3785th Field Training Wing; 80th Flying Training Wing; Technical Training Center): DI 372.2 S 132.05 269.9 FSS 255.4 AD 118.2 120.4 292.3 308.6 T 119.75 125.5 272.6 G 125.5 289.4 E 121.2 289.0 WX 344.6 SAC CP 311.0 321.0 Crew Alerts 413.45 AF 139.65 148.095 149.235 149.475 163.325 163.4625 163.4875 163.5875 165.1375 172.30 173.025 173.4375 173.5125 173.5375 173.5875 173.6125 261.1 264.8 279.9 283.7 292.9 294.7 318.1 324.5 341.5 349.0 359.3 378.0 383.1 390.9 396.1 413.15

Sheridan Co. Apt., WY: FSS 255.4 AD 351.9

Sherman AAF/Ft. Leavenworth, KS (Army Command & General Staff College; US Disciplinary Barracks; Army Combined Armed Center): DI 139.35 321.7 FSS 255.4 AD 124.7 126.6 318.1 FSS 122.35 255.4 T 41.50 126.2 241.0 Civilian Aero OP 461.225 Security 165.0625 FD 409.125 Engineering 410.10 Base Deliveries 164.10 Army 30.10 30.30 32.10 32.30 32.70 34.10 34.70 38.90 40.90 143.40 150.525 150.675

164.50 164.9625 173.4125 173.4675 173.6125 409.425 412.875 412.90 413.425 413.475

Shingle Point USAF, AK: OP Msc 126.7 364.2

Shorthorn Auxiliary Army Landing Strip, Ft. Hood, TX: T 143.35 237.4 (Also see Hood AAF & Robert Gray AAF listings.)

Shreveport Downtown Apt., LA: AD 327.0 350.2 351.1 363.8 372.9 T 247.6 FSS 255.4

Shreveport Regn'l. Apt., LA: 350.2 351.1 363.8 372.9 T 257.8 G 257.8

Sidney Muni. Apt., NE: AD 269.6

Sidney Muni Apt., OH: AD 316.7

Sierra Army Depot Heliport, Herlong, CA: OP ("Shadow 3") 41.50 126.2 (Also see Amedee AAF listings.)

Sikes Apt., FL: See Bob Sykes.

Sikeston Mem'l. Muni. Apt., MO: AD 362.35

Sikorsky Aircraft Division, United Technologies: Bridgeport, CT 153.805; Stratford Heliport, CT: AD 305.8 T 36.90 41.10 123.2 314.6 359.4 Msc 38.90 49.70 123.15 123.3 123.325 123.35 123.5 123.55 134.1 140.05 153.11 153.38 154.625 233.8 275.2 345.4 380.4 382.6 383.4 462.60; Coyote, CA 462.25; E. Hartford, CT 151.805 153.08 153.32 153.38 (Also see Rentschler Apt. listings.); Farmington, CT 153.38; Manchester, CT 153.38; Middletown, CT 151.805 153.38; North Haven, CT 153.38; Southington, CT 153.38; South Windsor, CT 153.38; Sunnyvale, CA 153.14

Silver Bell NG Hpt, Marana, AZ: OP 41.50 245.1

Silver City-Grant Co. Apt., NM: AD 351.8

Silver City, NM: SAC CP 311.0 321.0 AF 228.9 238.4 254.2 260.8 267.0 270.2 274.4 309.4 316.3 320.6 327.9 341.0 346.2 387.8 398.0

Silver Hill, MD: AF 165.1375 169.60 407.375 Army 411.50 414.825

Silverhill OLF, Robertsdale, AL: OP 345.2

Simmons AAF/Ft. Bragg, NC (18th Airborne Corps; 82nd Airborne Division; 1st Special Operations Command; Golden Knights Army Parachute Team; 5th & 7th Special Forces Grps; JFK Center for Military Assistance; Special Warfare & Airborne Center; 20th Engineer Brigade; 12th Support Brigade; Civil Affairs School): DI 142.35 231.0 S 109.8 AD 133.0 295.0 T 125.9 241.0 G 121.9 229.4 E 121.9 229.4 WX 141.25 265.6 Airspace Control 41.75 Range 30.45 32.50 38.90 41.00 141.075 142.50 246.0 Security 42.20 173.4875 Tactical Maneuvers 41.40 Medics 40.41 150.45 150.50 Pager 163.375 FD 165.0875 Engineers 165.0375 165.1875 Wildlife Control 165.0625 EOD 49.70 49.80 141.075 Rescue 40.50 Army 39.95 40.10 40.60 46.75 138.40 139.00 139.025 139.10 139.20 139.25 139.35 139.40 139.45 139.65 141.025 141.05 141.10 141.175 141.20 141.25 141.30 141.35 141.375 141.40 141.45 141.50 142.25 142.225 142.35 142.375 142.375 142.40 142.45 142.60 142.90 142.975 143.025 143.075 143.15 143.20 143.30 143.40 148.60 148.605 148.675 148.70 148.755 148.815 148.90 149.40 149.575 149.60 149.625 149.675 149.70 149.75 149.85 150.525 150.575 150.625 150.675 150.75 162.225 163.5625 170.125 172.30 173.30 173.025 173.175 173.4125 173.4375 173.4625 173.5125 229.6 229.8 230.1 231.2 231.5 231.7 232.5 232.7 233.0 239.0 265.6 304.4 347.7 356.4 356.6 365.1 366.1 367.0 367.2 367.7 368.1 399.2 407.30 409.075 412.90 413.225 413.50 413.55 AF 260.7 264.8 265.7 276.6 283.7 286.6 317.8 368.8 370.2 389.4 393.3 (Also see Mackall AAF listings.)

Sinep AAF, Turkey: VFR Advisories 66.79 126.3 250.35

Sioux Gateway Apt., IA: S 277.2 AD 269.0 307.0 325.8 G 348.6 T 254.3 AF 32.45 32.85 34.35 36.45 148.175 148.185 148.545 148.55 163.4875 163.5125 163.5875 383.1

Siskyou Co. Apt., Montague, CA: FSS ("Red Bluff Radio") 255.4

Site 5 OLF, Pensacola, FL: OP 251.3

Site 6 OLF, Pensacola, FL: OP 358.8 361.1

Site 8 OLF, Pensacola, FL: OP 251.3 361.1

Sitka Apt, AK: AD 335.6   CG 381.8 (HF 2182 5692 5980 kHz)

Skaggs Island, CA: USN 142.85 365.0   Security & FD 141.85

Skyhaven Apt, NH: AD 322.4 363.8

Sky Manor Apt., Pittstown, NJ: AD 397.9

Slidell Apt., LA: AD 290.3

SMAMA Procurement Office, Sacramento Army Depot, CA: 41.50 150.425 150.585 150.705 164.20 165.0625 169.60 412.835 413.235

Smith & Wesson Ordnance Products, Pittsburgh, PA: 473.275

Smith Reynolds Apt., Winston Salem, NC: AD 233.2   T 257.8

Smyrna Apt., TN: AD 317.45   T 233.1   NG 49.80 120.95 233.8

Snohomish Co. Apt./Payne Fld., Everett, WA: AD 306.9   G 242.1   T 229.4   Army Reserve 34.10 46.70   AF 262.5 287.2 291.8 341.6 349.6 391.7   Boeing Company 123.2 123.225 123.25 123.275 123.325 123.35 123.375 123.425 123.45 123.475 123.525 123.55 151.955 153.26 153.32 462.25 462.45 463.275 467.875 852.4625

Sob Story D.E.W. Line Station, Greenland: AD 122.2 236.6 (HF 5295 kHz)

Soesterberg USAF, Netherlands: AD 122.1 252.3 258.15 362.3   T 122.1 125.05 257.8 290.85   CP ("Wolfhound") 249.45   SOF 297.4   Info 356.55   Dutch Mil 128.35 251.4 279.5

Solar Energy Research Institute, Golden, CO: 164.75 165.4625   Security 417.20 419.175

Solberg-Hunterdon Apt., Readington, NJ: AD 379.9

Solomons, MD: USN 139.50 140.04 142.825 264.1

Somerset Apt, NJ: AD 379.9

Somerset Co. Apt., PA: AD 299.2 307.1

Sondrestrom AB, Greenland: AD 118.8 363.8   FSS 121.3 (HF 2950 5526 10042 kHz) T 126.2 236.6   G 126.2 275.8   CP 130.65 319.4

Sonoma Co. Apt., Santa Rosa, CA: AD 353.5 363.0   T 323.0

Soucek Fld., VA: See Oceana NAS.

South Arkansas Regn'l. Apt, AR: FSS 255.4   AD 269.1

South Bend, IN: USN 30.45

South Caicos Apt., Turks & Caicos Islands: T 118.9   OP 122.8   CG 381.8 282.8

South Pole USN Station, Antarctica: AD 134.1 360.2   Msc (HF 4718 5726 8997 11255 13251 kHz)

Souther Fld., GA: AD 226.4 269.3

Southern IL Apt., Carbondale, IL: AD 269.5   T 322.4

Southern Seaplane Base, Belle Chasse, LA: USN 32.05 40.80 264.2   AF 267.8 358.2

South Jersey Regn'l. Apt., NJ: AD 259.3 363.8

South Portland ANG Station, ME: 230.5 235.5 243.5 252.5 375.5 388.5 394.5 396.5 398.5

South St. Paul Muni. Apt./Fleming Fld., MN: AD 335.5

Southwest FL Regn'l. Apt., FL: AD 306.2 322.5 327.8   T 257.8   G 348.6

Southwest GA Regn'l. Apt., GA: AD 226.8 381.2   T 381.2   G 241.0 348.6

South Weymouth NAS/Shea Fld., MA: AD 120.6 124.1 139.90 263.1 343.6 382.0   T 126.2 340.2 360.2   G 352.4   WX 355.3   Security 140.475   FD/Crash 140.95   Ramp 140.575   USN 32.45 36.55 38.30 40.80 138.72 140.04 140.06 140.58 253.25 254.8 256.25 265.15 273.0 277.2 344.2 355.1 359.5 363.4 363.5 376.8 384.5

Space Center Exec Apt., FL: AD 269.3 340.9 358.3

Spangdahlem AB, Germany: DI 342.7   S 269.9   AD 141.10 257.1 249.4 370.6   T 122.2 257.8 336.9   G 363.8   E 382.9   CP 356.8

Sparrevohn LRRS, AK: T 126.21   NORAD CP 364.2   AF 163.5875 229.1 269.9 288.7 297.6   FSS 122.5

Sparta Community Apt-Hunter Fld., IL: AD 259.1 289.1

Sparta/McCoy AAF, WI: See McCoy AAF.

Spartanburg Downtown Mem'l. Apt., SC: AD 257.9 350.2

Spencer OLF, Pace, FL: OP 358.8

Sperry Corp.: Goodyear, AZ: 123.225 123.45; Phoenix, AZ 463.375; Ronkonkoma, NY 122.9 153.32

Sperry Rand Corp., Belleville, PA: 35.06 153.05

Sperry Univac: Blue Bell, PA: 153.05

Sperry Vickers Corp.: Joplin, MO: 153.08 153.245; Omaha, NE 153.05 462.75; Searcy, AZ 153.215 158.295; Troy, MI 151.745

Spirit of St. Louis Apt., MO: FSS 255.4 AD 254.3 T 348.4

Spokane Int'l. Apt., WA: S 269.9 FSS 255.4 G 348.6 AD 263.0 372.9 384.9 T 257.8 NG Helicopters 38.75 123.05 AF 150.285 235.5 240.5 271.5 362.6 372.5 388.5 390.8 398.5

Springdale Muni. Apt., AR: AD 269.0 369.0

Springfield Beckley Muni. Apt., OH: AD 327.1 G 261.1 T 383.1 ANG 178th Tactical Fighter Grp ("Wolf Cub") 34.15 324.7 AF 34.60 36.80 41.95 148.175 148.475 149.15 149.175 149.475 163.375 163.5375 173.5875 235.5 261.1 345.5 377.5 383.1 390.5 394.5 398.5

Springfield Muni Apt. MN: AD 290.2

Springfield Regn'l. Apt., MO: FSS 255.4 AD 234.2 269.4 T 257.8 NG ("Show Me Zulu") 38.45 41.90 134.95 241.8 242.4

Stallion AAF, Socorro, NM: Range Control ("Cherokee") 126.95 294.6 295.2 (Also see White Sands Missile Range listings.)

Standiford Fld., Louisville, KY: AD 306.2 327.0 343.8 G 348.6 T 257.8 E 257.8 ANG 268.1 AF 163.4625 163.4875 163.5125 163.5875 165.0125 165.1375 268.1 305.7 407.375

Stanford Radio Astronomy Institute, CA: 30.84 33.14 464.475

Stanford Research Institute: Menlo Park, CA 30.66 36.14 36.50 49.80 49.84 154.60 158.43; Palo Alto, CA 43.50 154.49 (HF 3365 5985 kHz)

Stanford University Communications Satellite Planning Center, CA: 44.69

Stapleton Int'l. Apt., Denver, CO: FSS 255.4 AD 269.3 284.0 288.1 351.8 363.0 381.5 T 257.8 E 385.5 VIP CP 253.625 Overflights 307.3 381.5 USN 264.2 363.5 383.6 385.1

Statesboro Muni Apt., GA: AD 363.2 AF 356.8

Stennis Int'l. Apt., MS: AD 287.1 354.1 387.05

Stevens Point Muni Apt, WI: WI: AD 317.7

Stewart Int'l. Apt. & ANG Base, NY (105th Military Airlift Grp; Stewart Annex of USMA West Point): AD 363.1 T 387.15 Army OP 49.75 139.10 321.7 Army Reserve ("Liberty") 38.50 241.0 244.35 ANG 105th MAG ("Polo") 361.4 Transiting NG & Army Reserve OP ("Liberty") 38.20 143.10 244.35 Army 148.925 149.80 321.7

Stillwater Muni. Apt., OK: AD 291.7

Stinson Muni. Apt., San Antonio, TX: AD 353.5 T 379.9 G 379.9

Stockbridge Test Site, NY: AF 139.80 148.10 162.225 257.0 259.2 284.1 291.8 319.6 349.6 379.7 383.0 384.8

Stockton USN Communications Station, CA: Security 142.075 142.75 FD 142.075 142.75 Maintenance 140.975 Base Transportation 142.00 142.625 USN 149.45

Stockton Metro Apt., CA: FSS 255.4 AD 278.3 288.3 319.9 363.2 T 239.0 NG ("Schooner Ops") 34.40 41.80 49.00 139.40 242.4 356.9 USN 249.2 303.4

Strategic Petroleum Reserve Program, LA: 167.825 167.925 406.65 416.60

Sturgeon Bay, WI: USN 233.7 255.1 270.8 301.1 340.7 360.2 385.0

Stuttgart Army, Germany: AD 292.1 361.0 T 249.5 WX 140.3 259.4 DI 31.80 141.65 248.65 G 121.9 Hospital Hpd 30.75 138.60 358.2 Kelly Barracks AHP 31.80 141.65 374.2 Kelly MP ("Sheriff") 39.90 Patch Barracks AHP 31.80 141.65 248.65

Patch MP ("Big Top") 39.70 39.90   Robinson Barracks AHP AD ("Mustang") 39.70 Robinson OP 125.4 248.65

Stuttgart Muni. Apt., AR: AD 353.6

Suffolk Co. Apt., Westhampton Beach, NY: See **The** Frances S. Gabreski Apt.

Sugar Land Muni Apt/Hull Fld, TX: AD 257.7

Suitland, MD: The National Security Agency appears to have a monitoring station here possibly for the purpose of monitoring microwave relays of long distance telephone calls in/out of Washington, DC. The long distance terrestrial microwave station in Suitland operates on 10715 10755 10955 & 10995 MHz.

Sullivans Island, SC: USN 149.025 149.075 380.6

Summerdale OLF, AL: OP 381.9

Summit Airpark, Middletown, DE: AD 323.1

Sumter Muni Apt., SC: AD 327.3

Sunflower Army Depot, DeSoto, KS: Security 173.5125 Army 163.5625

Sunny Point Military Ocean Terminal, Southport, NC: Security 164.9875 FD 165.0875 OP 165.0375 Army 165.1125 165.1875

Surprise Springs USMC VSTOL Facility, CA: T 126.2 340.2   Range ("Bearmeat") 323.5

Sussex Apt., NJ: AD 379.7

Sussex Co. Apt., Georgetown, DE: AD 339.1

Swearingen Aircraft Co., San Antonio, TX: 123.2 123.4

Sylvania/GTE Government Systems: Clam Lake ELF Station, WI 150.92 150.98 154.47125 154.545 154.625; Republic, MI 150.98 154.625; Mtn. View, CA 490.8625; Needham, MA 38.25 153.185; Westborough, MA 153.185; Taunton, MA 153.185

Syracuse Hancock Int'l. Apt./Hancock ANG Base, NY (138th Tactical Fighter Sqdn; 174th Tactical Fighter Wing): FSS 255.4 AD 279.6 398.95 G 348.6 T 239.0 E 398.2 ANG OP ("Carnival") 379.5 NORAD 228.7 360.8 364.2 SAC CP 311.0 321.0 Crew Alerts 413.45 ANG 174th TFW 139.025 Ground Support 138.30 Army Reserve 34.15 38.50 40.10 245.3 339.85 Army 30.10 227.1 OSI 138.075 138.165 138.175 ANG 30.30 32.45 35.10 36.80 40.40 41.40 41.95 46.50 46.85 49.80 51.50 55.60 148.125 148.745 149.20 149.25 149.325 149.475 149.535 150.195 150.20 150.275 150.315 163.5125 163.5875 165.1125 165.1625 173.5375 251.9 254.9 267.8 283.8 301.6 303.0 314.2 321.2 340.8 347.2 369.9

Tacoma Narrows Apt., WA: AD 241.2 290.9

Tacoma, WA: USN 34.95 49.85

Taegu AB, S. Korea: AD 135.9 230.3 346.3 T 126.2 236.6 365.0 G 275.8 WX 346.5 Tran Alert 256.2 CP ("Brickwall") 141.675 291.8

Talladega Muni. Apt., AL: AD 381.5

Tallahassee Com'l. Apt., FL: AD 254.3 343.8

Tallahassee Regn'l. Apt., FL: FSS 255.4 AD 254.3 317.7 343.8 354.1 360.8 G 348.6 T 257.8 E 275.8

Tampa Int'l. Apt., FL: AD 258.3 269.1 279.6 290.3 319.8 363.8 T 269.4 G 269.4

Tarheel Army Ammunition Plant, Burlington, NC: 412.835 413.235

Tatalina LRRS, AK: T 126.1 364.2 AF 122.195 163.5875 229.1 239.7 254.4 269.9 FSS 122.3

Taylor Barracks AHP, Mannheim, Germany: AD 31.80 40.80 122.1 142.65 291.5

Taylor Co. Apt., Medford, WI: AD 317.7

Teledyne Industries: Albany, OR 158.43; Kansas City, MO 461.40; Lima, OH 153.38; Mobile, AL 153.32; Muskegon, MI 123.45 158.43; Neosho, MO 123.45; San Diego, CA: 153.14; South El Monte, CA 461.10; Toledo, OH 153.245

Templehof USAF, Germany: DI 386.9 S 114.1 AD 119.3 120.85 125.3 125.5 125.8 353.8 359.0 362.3 372.0 T 118.1 122.1 337.3 358.0 G 121.9 356.0 Army ("Freedom City") 55.90 122.2

Terminal Island Naval Station, San Pedro, CA: Federal Correctional Institution 409.25 CG 165.3375 381.8 407.975 USN 138.525 148.40

Teterboro Apt., NJ: FSS 255.4 AD 379.9 Goodyear Blimp 132.0 Remington Rand Corp 123.45 154.60

Texarkana, TX: USN 32.45 36.55

Texarkana Regn'l.-Webb Fld, AR: AD 381.4 T 257.8

Texas Instruments: EW Systems, Colorado Springs, CO: 153.335 157.74 464.175; Defense Systems, Dallas, TX 153.095 153.23 154.515 157.74 451.525 462.325 462.45 464.775

Textron Corp.: Arlington, TX 123.2 123.45 FD 154.43; Amarillo, TX 35.10 158.31; East Greenwich, RI 153.23; East Providence, RI 151.865; Ft. Madison, IA 462.35; Ft. Worth, TX 123.3 123.35 123.5 123.55 462.225; Gum Springs, AR 462.225; Hurst, TX 153.35 158.295 462.225 FD 154.43; Meadville, PA 153.095; Muskegon, MI 153.20; Nashville, TN 451.425 462.55; New Britain, CT 462.35; Niagara Falls, NY 461.50; Panama City, FL 156.55 156.985 157.025; Porter, NY 462.20; Pulaski, TN 153.095; Rockford, IL 158.28; Saginaw, TX 123.35 123.55 FD 154.43; Smithfield, RI 153.11; Stratford, CT 153.29; Valencia, CA 151.925; Wheatfield, NY 123.2 123.3 123.4 123.5

Textron-Lycoming Corp.: Greer, SC 461.90 462.425; Williamsport, PA 462.225 462.30 462.35 462.40 463.675

The Dalles Muni. Apt., WA: FSS 255.4

The Francis S. Gabreski Apt., Westhampton Beach, NY: AD 288.1 T 236.6 G 225.4 ANG 106th Aerospace Rescue & Recovery Grp 251.9 282.9 ANG Security 163.4875 165.1125 FD/Crash 163.4875 Emerg 165.1625 ANG 163.4625 163.5125 163.5875 165.0125 165.1375

Theodore F. Green State Apt., Providence/Warwick, RI: AD 269.2 385.6 T 257.8 G 348.6 E 348.6 Security 163.4875 Emergency 149.475 AF 141.80 143.80 148.125 148.50 148.55 149.175 165.1375 283.8 383.3

Thermal Apt., CA: FSS 255.4 AD 285.6

The William B. Hartsfield Atlanta Int'l. Apt., GA: AD 284.7 379.9 T 348.6 G 348.6

Thibodaux Muni. Apt., LA: AD 256.9

Thief River Falls Regn'l. Apt, MN: AD 269.6

Thomas C. Russell Fld., Alexander, AL: AD 369.2 357.6

Thomasville Muni. Apt., GA: AD 259.3 360.8

Thomson-McDuffie Co. Apt., GA: AD 270.3

Three Rivers Muni. Apt./Dr. Haines Fld., MI: AD 263.1 340.9

Thule AB, Greenland: AD 123.1 363.8 T 126.2 255.6 G 275.8 CP 292.1 (HF 6738 8967 11176 13201 17975 kHz)

Tillamook Apt, OR: AD 317.6

Tin City LRRS, AK: T 126.2 364.2 AF 122.195 163.5875 229.1 254.7 269.9

Tinker AFB, Oklahoma City, OK (ACC; 8th AF; Air Logistics Center; 2854th Air Base Grp; 3rd Comb Comms Grp; 552nd Airborne Warning Control Wing): DI 134.975 372.2 S 115.8 270.1 AD 120.45 124.2 124.6 126.65 336.4 385.5 393.1 395.0 T 124.45 289.6 G 121.8 275.8 CP ("Raymond 24") 139.95 141.65 287.45 305.6 381.3 WX 344.6 Logistics Command Flight Test ("Mole Control") 382.6 Air Terminal OP 138.15 TAC 149.20 Security 163.4875 163.5375 Base OP 165.6875 OSI 40.17 40.19 SAC CP 311.0 321.0 Crew Alerts 413.45 Security 163.4875 164.175 FD/Crash 163.5875 164.125 Flightline Maintenance 407.375 407.55 408.05 408.175 408.80 AF 34.10 46.85 138.10 139.85 139.90 141.70 148.20 149.25 149.235 150.175 150.315 163.4625 164.125 164.175 164.20 164.325 164.9625 165.1125 165.1625 165.1875 173.5625 225.3 235.5 236.6 239.9 252.1 266.1 276.8 302.7 311.2 369.5 385.5 388.5 389.0 390.1 394.7 395.0 398.5 407.375 407.45 408.80 413.025 413.10 413.15 413.20 413.30 413.40

Tipton AAF/Ft. Meade, MD (National Security Agency; HQ 1st Army; Army Intelligence Agency; 44th Medical Brigade; 97th Army Reserve Command; Army Signal Air Defense Agency): AD 119.7 231.6 G 121.75 227.1 OP 127.0 241.0 248.2 Security 163.475 163.5375 163.5625 MP 165.375 FD 407.30 FEMA 167.975 Nuclear Regulatory Agcy 411.075 VFR Advisories 127.0 248.2 National Security Agcy 167.825 EOD 49.70 49.80 Msc 32.50 46.79 139.25 140.00 141.025 141.325 142.35 150.425 150.45 150.525 150.575 163.475 163.5625 165.0625 165.5625 173.4125 173.4375 173.4625 173.5125 173.5375 173.5625 407.325 407.475 407.575 412.975 413.525 AF 296.2 301.6 (Also see Suitland, MD & Naval Intelligence Support Center listings.)

Titan II ICBM Missile Silos: AR 140.40 149.31; AZ 143.76; KS 140.40 149.31 (Also see listings for Little Rock AFB.)

Tobyhanna Army Depot, PA: Air OP 126.2 Security 165.0625 FD 33.98 Army 148.575 173.4625 173.6125

Todd Shipyards: Alameda, CA 154.57 154.60 156.60 156.90 158.43 469.4875; San Pedro, CA 35.08 153.26 154.57 154.60 156.60 156.90 469.4875; Brooklyn, NY 158.31; Galveston, TX 153.26 154.60 157.025 464.8875 464.9125 464.9375 464.9625 469.8875; NJ 154.60; New Orleans, LA 462.20; Seattle, WA 158.31 462.225 469.7375

Toledo Express Apt., OH: S 271.3 AD 307.0 321.1 T 392.0 G 348.6 E 348.6 ANG FD/Crash 149.50 ANG Security 163.4875 ANG Maintenance 165.1375 ANG Tactical 34.20 41.15 ANG OP 165.1375 ANG 32.40 32.85 49.75 143.775 143.90 149.525 338.9

Tompkins Co. Apt., Ithaca, NY: AD 257.8 372.0

Tonopah AFS & Range, NV (4450th Tactical Grp): Airspace Control ("Bullseye") 34.60 40.40 Nellis Control 126.95 338.7 AF 134.7 138.20 148.05 149.25 149.31 149.525 150.195 150.225 150.275 150.315 150.325 150.60 163.6125 164.9625 407.275 407.175 407.375 407.475 408.00 408.175 410.00 412.975 413.075 413.175 413.275 413.325 413.375 413.475 416.60 USN 235.0 274.2 311.4 337.0 FEMA 167.975 Nuclear Weapons Systems 139.03 164.3125 167.85 169.60 169.9375 170.01 170.125 171.2625 171.325 171.625 171.8125 172.30 173.9625 230.4 239.4 240.2 248.6 256.2 257.0 259.7 384.4 407.00 (Also see Nellis AFB listings.)

Tonopah Apt., NV: FSS 255.4 AD 397.85

Tooele Army Depot, UT (Chemical-Biological Warfare storage depot): 139.035 141.045 141.135 143.055 163.4125 163.4875 165.0375 165.1875 169.60 173.5125

Topsham, ME: USN 30.15 32.05 34.35

Torrance Muni Apt., CA: AD 269.6 363.2 T 257.8 McDonnell Douglas 49.98 120.0 135.6 153.08 158.28

Torrejon AB, Spain: DI 265.2 AD 119.9 120.9 128.7 225.4 341.4 T 122.1 139.30 275.8 G 118.3 375.0 E 118.3 CP ("Falcon") 306.8 WX 344.6

Torrington Muni Apt, WY: AD 338.2

Towers Fld, FL: See Jacksonville NAS.

Tracor Corp.: Flight Systems, Mojave, CA 123.2 464.975; Aerospace, Austin, TX 462.325 464.925; Shipyard, FL 461.4875

Tracy Defense Depot, CA: Security & FD 165.1875 Base Transportation 163.5375 Helipad ("Schoonover OP") 49.00 Army 141.15 275.4 320.2

Transportation Research Center, East Liberty, OH: Dept. Transportation 40.27 41.17 406.80 416.975 417.975 453.65

Transportation Railroad Test Center, Pueblo, CO: Channel 1 Road/Admin/Police 172.70; Channel 2 Secondary to Channel 1 173.15; Channel 3 Testing 173.05; Channel 4 Testing 172.825; Channel 5 Testing 171.65; Channel 6 Hazardous Materials Training 172.30; Channel 7 Special Test Projects 171.2375; Channel 8 Special Test Projects 173.9125; Telemetry 406.625 406.80 406.95 408.60 416.60 Msc 38.52 38.544 38.568 41.678 41.704 41.73 41.756 41.782 164.30/171.3625 166.025 170.75 173.6375

Trapnell Fld., MD: See Patuxent River NAS.

Travis AFB, Fairfield, CA (AMC; 16th & 60th Military Airlift Wings; 22nd Air Force): Unicom 123.3 DI 376.0 S 116.4 384.9 AD 119.9 126.6 291.0 371.2 395.8 T 120.75 236.6 255.9 G 121.8 289.4 407.525 E 127.55 335.8 MAC CP 130.65 141.90 319.4 349.4 WX 375.2 SAC CP 311.0 321.0 Crew Alerts 413.45 Security 149.475 163.05 163.375 163.4625 FD/Crash 173.025 173.5625 OSI 138.075 138.165 138.075 VIP OP 169.325 Base OP 413.10 413.475 Civil Engineering 149.585 407.325 Motor Pool 138.175 Base Transportation 150.165 413.30 Commanders' Nets 169.325 170.10 170.175 EOD 173.5625 Disaster Preparedness 163.5125 Pagers 149.525 407.50 ALCE 149.15 149.205 165.0125 165.1625 Flightline 149.295 150.135 Maintenance 148.065 148.45 149.565 165.0125 165.0375 165.1375 413.15 413.275 Medics 173.7875 Supply Squadron 163.5875 Cargo 413.075 Ramp 412.575 412.975 413.20 Fueling 413.40 AF 139.90 141.90 148.065 148.10 148.20 148.225 148.485 148.50 149.565 150.345 163.05 164.50 165.4375 173.10 173.5375 236.6 251.9 291.0 294.7 318.1 335.8 339.1 376.0 379.3 385.7 393.8 398.2

Treasure Island Naval Station, CA (HQ 12th USMC District; CG Yerba Buena Island Station): Security 148.30 148.425 148.975 149.65 FD 148.30 Supply Center 138.65 Naval Intelligence 140.075 140.65 140.775 Maintenance 138.65 USN/USMC 36.60 275.4 320.2 CG Base 165.2625 Army 407.45 AF 413.15

Trenton-Robbinsville Apt., NJ: AD 363.8

Tri-Cities Apt., Pasco, WA: AD 243.9 377.2 380.2 T 323.3

Tri-City Apt., Parsons, KS: AD 343.9

Tri-City Apt., Sebring, OH: AD 226.4

Tri-City Int'l. Apt., Saginaw, MI: FSS 255.4 AD 257.7 307.8 T 257.7 307.8

Tri-City Regn'l. Apt., Bristol, TN: AD 317.5 349.0 371.85 T 257.8 G 348.6

Tri Co Apt., FL: AD 370.3

Tri-Co. Apt., Lone Rock, WI: FSS 255.4 AD 380.35

Tripler Army Medical Center, Oahu, HI: 149.55 165.0875 165.1875

Tri-State Apt./Long Fld., Huntington, WV: FSS 255.4 AD 257.8 T 257.8 NG 164.05 165.0625

Troy Muni. Apt., AL: AD 232.5 T 246.5 G 366.2 Army 232.5

Truth or Consequences Muni. Apt., NM: FSS 255.4 AD 285.5

TRW Corp.: Systems Integration Group, Ogden, UT 462.05; Electronics Div., CA 151.715 154.74 464.55; Space Div., US 151.625

TSTC-Waco Apt., TX: AD 269.4 Chrysler Technologies 123.55 257.35 (HF 8822 17964 kHz)

Tucson Int'l. Apt., AZ: S 320.1   FSS 255.4   AD 297.2   318.1 381.1   G 348.6   E 326.2   T 257.8   ANG CP 392.2   ANG 30.45 36.45 36.85 36.95 40.55 41.10 41.70 46.85 49.85 138.925 164.70 165.1125 165.1625 166.225 173.5375 252.1 264.8 275.9 283.7 300.7

Tucumcari Muni. Apt., NM: FSS 255.4

Tulsa Int'l. Apt., OK: S 377.2   FSS 255.4   AD 338.3 351.8   G 348.6   T 257.8 263.0   E 284.7   ANG OP 383.0   NG ("Lunar Ops") 46.90   ANG 32.85 34.20 36.20 36.80 41.45 138.925 163.00 163.4625 163.4875 163.6125 163.5625 173.5875 381.1 392.2

Tulsa, OK: USN 34.15 36.55

Tupelo Muni.-C.D. Lemons Apt., MS: AD 252.7   NG 49.85 241.0

Turkey Point, FL: AF 236.0 251.9 254.7 260.6

Turner Fld., Prospectville, PA: AD 291.7

Turner Fld., VA: See Quantico MCAS.

Turner Fld. Amphibious Base Helipad, Coronado, CA: T 135.1 336.4 340.2   (Also see Coronado Naval Amphibious Base listings.)

Tuscaloosa Muni. Apt., AL: FSS 255.4   AD 257.2   T 256.7   G 256.7

Tuscaloosa, AL: Army 164.20

Tusi AHP, Hunter-Liggett, CA: AD 128.7 307.0   Advisory & Range Control 41.50 126.2 229.5   (Also see Hunter-Liggett & Schoonover Fld. AAF listings.)

Tuskegee Muni. Apt., AL: AD 357.6 388.0

Tustin MCAS(H), CA (Marine Aircraft Grp 16; HMM 163, 164, 268, 363, 462, 465): S 384.3   AD 132.7 380.2   T 41.95 132.1 271.1 340.2 350.1 379.9   G 380.8   E 274.9   WX 344.6   Emergency 41.95

Tweed-New Haven Apt., CT: AD 288.1   Sikorsky OP 123.2 305.8

Twentynine Palms Marine Corps Air Ground Combat Center, CA (7th Marine Amphibious Brigade; USMC Communications-Electronics School; 1st Battalion/4th Marine Regiment): AD ("Bearmeat") 39.80 126.2 323.5   Unicom 122.8   T 126.2 340.2   G 41.70 362.2   WX 308.3   Artillery Range 133.4   Safety OP ("Long Rifle") 49.50 49.85   Police 138.525 138.675   Public Affairs 140.075   Maintenance 138.85   Base OP 139.475 139.55   Medic 138.975   Combat Ctr 140.025   FD/Crash 140.10   Base Commander Net 140.225   USMC 32.80 138.74 140.125 140.34 140.355 140.375 140.875 143.715 150.07 150.10 236.4 250.1 258.9 272.4 281.1 281.7 281.9 291.2 203.7 310.6 336.5 350.5 356.1 362.2 362.9 413.20   AF 276.8

Twin Cities Army Ammunition Plant, Minneapolis, MN: 164.50 164.70 165.0625

Twin Falls Regn'l. Apt./Joslyn Fld., ID: AD 363.0 398.2   T 319.9

Tyler Pounds Fld., TX: FSS 255.4   AD 257.8 265.1   T 257.8

Tyndall AFB, Panama City, FL (ACC; HQ 1st AF; 325th Fighter Wing; Regn'l. Operat. Control Cntr.; Southeastern Air Defense Center; 3625 Technical Training Sqdn): AD 119.75 124.15 294.5 373.0   S 271.8   T 127.82 383.1   G 121.9 255.9   E 118.05 289.4   TAC CP ("Raymond 10") 286.7   WX 344.6   Air Defense Weapons Center CP 286.7   Security 163.4875 164.10   FD/Crash 173.5875   Medic 173.5625 NORAD CP 364.2   AF 140.46 148.05 148.845 149.15 149.235 149.275 149.325 149.505 149.565 150.225 150.30 163.4626 163.5375 163.5875 164.50 164.9875 165.1125 165.1375 171.3875 172.30 173.4375 173.5375 173.6125 228.8 230.4 234.7 235.0 239.2 238.5 238.8 239.1 240.6 250.0 251.9 253.5 256.6 259.4 261.0 261.8 262.0 262.4 263.2 270.4 271.2 274.6 275.0 278.4 278.6 279.9 287.5 287.8 288.7 289.0 290.8 292.7 293.1 298.1 298.5 399.0 301.7 302.2 302.4 306.4 308.9 311.2 325.5 338.4 339.0 340.7 343.4 344.0 344.9 351.2 351.3 356.0 357.5 361.4 363.8 363.9 364.1 369.0 375.1 379.3 383.2 384.7 386.2 390.1 391.9 392.8 394.7 395.9 396.1 399.8 407.45 413.15 413.25 413.30   USN 140.50 143.50 148.29 150.03 274.6 283.4 312.9 321.9   FEMA 162.275

Tysons Corners, VA: Army 32.53 36.99 163.05 164.9625 406.225 414.825   FAA 169.2625   USN 148.41 150.09   State Dept 41.61 408.10 409.70 412.85   Dept Commerce 410.75 410.80 416.625

Ukiah Muni. Apt., CA: FSS 255.4

Umatilla Army Depot, Hermiston, OR (Chemical-Biological Warfare storage depot): 165.0625 165.0875 165.1875 173.5125

Union Co. Apt., Marysville, OH: AD 267.9

Unisys Corp: Salt Lake City, UT 153.11 461.475 462.275 462.30 462.325 462.45 462.50 462.60; Eagan, MN 462.225 462.375 462.475 464.10; San Diego, CA 158.31 461.675; Detroit, MI 461.55; Santa Clara, CA 490.8375; Pasadena, CA 157.74; Sudbury, MA 462.575; Ronkonkoma, NY 153.32; Santa Monica, CA 151.745; Great Neck, NY 153.20 153.32; Lisle, IL 153.05 153.11; Mountain Home, ID 464.175; Reston, VA 151.955 153.095; Dublin, GA 154.515; Bristol, TN 153.245; Waynesboro, GA 154.515; St. Paul, MN 464.10; Brooklyn Center, MN 153.32; Roseville, MN 153.32 462.875; Pueblo, CO 462.40; Hermiston, OR 151.775; Kailua, HI 156.425 156.45

University of IL-Willard Apt., Urbana, IL: AD 285.65 397.9 T 229.4

University of NV Desert Research Institute, Reno, NV: 152.48 153.485

University of OK-Westheimer Airpark, OK: AD 385.5 NG 38.45

University-Oxford Apt., MS: AD 252.7

University Park Apt., State Park, PA: AD 272.7

USS Bainbridge/NJUL (CGN-25): 33.25 50.35

USS Blue Ridge/NQHS (LCC-19): 34.40

USS Constellation (CV-64): 30.15

USS Dahlgren/NJZU (DDG-43): 140.275

USS Enterprise (CVN-65): 32.90

USS Forrestal/NJVF (CV-59): Security 406.75 Msc 410.00

USS Iwo Jima/NXXG (LPH-2): 38.00

USS L.Y. Spear/NASO (AS-36): Duty Frequency 139.525 140.25

USS Nimitz/NMTZ (CVN-68): Shore Patrol 33.80

USS Richard E. Byrd/NHSN (DDG-23): Duty Frequency 139.475

USS Saginaw (LST-1188): 34.35

USS Texas/NTEX (CGN-39): Duty Frequency 140.275

USS Ticonderoga/NTIC (CG-47): 407.40 411.00

USS Yellowstone/NJAG (AD-41): Duty Frequency 139.475

Valdosta Muni Apt., GA: FSS 255.4 AD 259.3 285.6

Valkaria Missile Tracking Station, Malabar, FL: AF 165.0125 (See liistings for Malabar, FL.)

Vallejo CA: USN 149.10 267.5

Vance AFB, Enid, OK (71st Flying Training Wing): S 115.4 271.8 AD 120.525 121.3 291.1 358.3 369.2 T 124.05 348.4 E 225.4 G 124.05 289.4 WX 342.5 AF 139.65 139.85 149.175 150.225 163.5125 164.50 165.0125 173.4125 173.5375 173.5875 258.3 271.3 276.6 286.8 297.2 321.1 326.2 340.9 352.8 359.0 369.2 378.8 379.5 388.2 398.1 413.15

Vandalia Muni. Apt., IL: AD 317.7

Vandenberg AFB, Lompoc, CA (ACC; HQ 20th AF; 1st Strategic Aerospace Division; 1369th Photo Sqdn; Western Space & Missile Center; 394th ICBM Test Maintenance Sqdn; 3901st Strategic Missile Evaluaton Sqdn; 4315th Combat Crew

Training Sqdn; 392nd Communications Grp): DI 123.0 372.2   S 125.7 271.8   AD 118.0 118.35 324.3 339.1 363.8   T 124.95 326.2   G 121.75 275.8   NORAD CP 364.2 SAC CP 311.0 321.0   Crew Alerts 413.45   Range 121.4 296.5 386.6   WX 344.6 Space & Missile Center AD 121.4 386.6   Security 162.6125 163.00 163.4625 163.4875 FD/Crash 173.5875   Ramp 148.515   OSI 138.075 138.165 138.175   Base Engineer 163.5875   Photographic OP 149.175 149.505   Pager 138.325   Base Commanders Net 163.4625 163.5125 164.175   Base Transportation 148.215   Supply Sqdn 148.215 148.425   Medics 173.5875   Communications Technicians 149.205   Missile OP 149.095 149.565 165.0125 165.1125 165.1625 173.4375 173.5625   NASA 164.20 165.6125 Nuclear Weapons Systems 167.85 168.45 239.4 248.6 257.8   Martin Marietta Co 151.965 153.05 153.065   Msc 41.05 384.0   AF 32.45 34.20 34.60 36.80 41.90 49.80 122.9 142.20 142.475 148.035 148.095 148.56 149.15 149.52 149.90 150.00 150.225 150.25 150.275 150.30 150.325 150.35 154.20 164.50 168.625 173.5375 225.0 228.2 228.9 230.4 231.4 234.6 235.0 238.4 243.75 243.89 245.3 254.2 255.6 260.8 267.0 270.2 274.2 274.4 275.4 279.4 280.1 280.8 281.6 286.4 287.2 287.7 290.6 290.9 293.8 320.2 320.6 320.8 324.0 324.3 327.9 336.0 336.6 337.0 341.8 346.2 349.1 349.3 351.3 358.2 358.2 360.6 374.53 375.35 375.85 375.90 376.325 377.0 378.275 384.8 387.8 388.2 393.855 398.0 399.9 406.50 413.15 416.50

Van Nuys Apt., CA: AD 317.5 338.2 360.6 395.9   T 239.0   E 239.0   ANG 303.0 Beechcraft West 123.0 154.515   ITT Gilfillan 123.2 123.225 123.325 123.45 151.655 153.23 462.20   Hughes Aircraft 123.225   General Motors Research 153.26 153.32 158.46 462.475   RCA 123.2   Litton Systems 31.25 32.05 32.15 32.35 32.45 33.25 34.25 35.25 36.25 37.25 38.25 46.50 46.60 46.70 46.80 46.90 47.00 49.65   AF 141.80 148.125 148.225 148.45 148.50 149.265

Van Wert Co. Apt., OH: AD 260.6

Vega Precision Labs, Vienna, VA: 123.375 123.45

Vermillion Co. Apt, IL: AD 291.0 397.9

Vero Beach Muni. Apt., FL: FSS 255.4   AD 370.9   (Also see Piper Aircraft Co. listings.)

Verona Test Site, NY: AF 139.80 142.20 257.0 259.2 281.4 291.8 319.6 349.6 379.7 383.0 384.8

Very Large Array (VLA) Radio Astronomy Observatory, Socorro, NM: Security 162.025   FD 46.63 46.64   Msc 36.55 40.83 46.67 46.70 46.73 46.76 46.79 46.81 46.85 46.88 46.95 46.98 148.985 149.125 237.0 416.4875

Vicksburg MS: Army 34.89 38.98 149.865 150.555

Vicksburg Muni. Apt., MS: AD 259.1

Victoria Regn'l. Apt., TX: AD 353.6

Vidalia Muni Apt., GA: AD 290.4

Vieques Island, PR: USN 138.525 138.55 143.55 143.575 143.725 149.075 149.30 150.075 264.0 269.7 299.3   (Also see Roosevelt Roads NAS listings.)

Vint Hill Farms, Warrenton, VA (Army Electronics Material Readiness Activity; Army Intelligence & Security Command): Security 38.53   FD 40.49 46.85   Army 32.31

Vilsek AHP & AAF, Germany: T 31.80 142.45   Range 30.40 31.10 46.65 139.40 250.35

Virgil I. Grissom Apt., Bedford, IN: AD 269.4

Virginia Tech Apt., VA: AD 317.7 339.8

Volk Fld./Camp Douglas, WI: AD 133.3 380.35   T 127.5 236.6   G 121.9 275.8 Hardwood Range 34.20 132.025 297.1 358.2   Sheboygan Range 260.4   ANG 138.01 138.50 163.4625 163.4875 163.5125 163.5875 165.1375 173.5875 373.1 379.4 389.9 392.0 395.1

Volunteer Army Ammunition Plant, Chattanooga, TN: Security 165.0875   Motor Pool 165.5625   Messengers 165.1875   Army 164.50 164.9625 173.4625

Wabash Muni Apt., IN: AD 363.8

Waco Regn'l. Apt., TX: FSS 255.4 AD 269.4 363.0 T 257.8

Wahaiwa Naval Reservation, HI: USN 143.52 148.425 149.05 149.10 292.95 293.05 294.2 294.65 294.75 296.35 296.45 297.95 298.05 299.45 299.55 302.7 303.4 306.35 306.45 307.95 309.25 309.35 310.75 310.85

Wahoo Muni. Apt., NE: AD 363.8

Wainright AAF/Ft. Wainright, AK (6th Infantry Division/Light; 172nd Infantry Brigade): AD 118.1 126.5 271.3 327.5 363.8 FSS 255.4 G 121.7 261.3 T 40.80 125.0 241.0 WX 344.6 MP's 173.4875 FD 30.85 39.50 173.4125 Transportation Motor Pool 164.70 FE 165.0875 173.5125 CID 172.30 Army 148.515 150.525 162.025 163.5625 164.20 173.125 173.4625 173.5125 173.6375 407.525

Wainright AFS, AK: T 126.2 288.4 FSS 122.5

Wakefield, MA: USN 30.45 38.75

Wakefield Muni Apt., VA: AD 249.9

Wake Island AB, Pacific: FSS 128.0 349.4

Waldron Field NALF, Corpus Christi, TX: T 126.2 264.4

Walker AHP, Ft. Monroe, VA: AD 122.9 Overflights 125.1 253.5 (See Ft. Monroe listings.)

Walker Fld., Grand Jct., CO: FSS 255.4 AD 257.8 T 257.8 G 257.8

Walla Walla Regn'l. Apt., WA: FSS 255.4 AD 343.9 380.2 T 289.4 G 289.4

Wallops Flight Facility, VA: See NASA Wallops listings.

Walnut Ridge Regn·l. Apt., AR: AD 319.3

Walterboro Muni. Apt., SC: AD 319.9

Walter Reed Army Medical Center, DC (Walter Reed Army Institute of Research; Armed Forces Institute of Pathology; Army Institute of Dental Research): Security ("Main" & "Big Brother") 165.0875 Medevac Helipad 41.00 Ambulances 148.80 Pager 148.575 Motor Pool 141.375 Army 32.11 36.22 135.025 139.065 139.125 139.15 139.28 141.475

Waltham, MA: AF 148.50 149.50

Warminster Naval Air Development Center/Johnsville NAF, PA: S 275.6 AD 123.8 291.7 T 126.2 340.2 359.6 Security & FD 140.90 WX 344.6 USN 138.625 148.35 149.01

Warren AFB, WY: See Cheyenne Muni Apt. listings.

Warren Army Tank Plant, MI: Security 165.0625 Army 173.4625 General Dynamics 148.60 148.625 149.625

Warren Co. Apt., Glens Falls, NY: FSS 255.4 AD 307.2

Warren Co. Mem'l. Apt., TN: AD 353.5

Warrensburg, MD: AF 148.145 148.95 149.265 150.10 173.5625 407.525 413.175 418.025

Warsaw Muni. Apt., IN: AD 284.6

Washington Co. Apt., PA: AD 388.0 NG 46.70

Washington Co. Regn'l. Apt., Hagerstown, MD: AD 385.4 T 265.7 Army Reserve 32.30 AF 34.55 138.35 233.4 265.2 309.6 Fairchild Republic Corp 123.2 153.095

Washington, DC: CG 171.3375 409.2375 416.475 418.0125 CG Rescue 282.8 Soldiers & Airmen's Home 164.25 Armed Forces PD 36.71

Washington Dulles Int'l. Apt, DC: See Dulles Int'l. listings.

Washington National Apt., DC: FSS 255.4 AD 269.0 269.5 306.3 322.3 338.2 343.7 396.1 G 257.6 T 257.6 NASA 170.175 Pager 165.2125 Security 165.50 165.6625 166.625 410.25 FD 164.825 Maintenance 166.0875 408.175 Ground Transportation 415.25 416.875 419.025 FAA 165.4125 167.125 169.30

Washington Navy Yard, DC (HQ Washington Naval District): Security 140.125 140.95 150.11 Medics 149.35 FD 148.30 Disaster Control 138.65 Motor Pool 138.96 139.48 Public Works 143.70 USN 138.50 140.14 140.175 140.225 140.25 140.30 140.45 140.46 140.58 140.625 140.65 140.975 141.00 141.025 142.60

Wash-Wilkes Co. Apt., GA: AD 306.9

Waterbury-Oxford Apt., CT: AD 288.1

Waterloo Muni. Apt., IA: AD 257.8 381.2 T 257.8 G 248.2 NG 36.70 40.60 280.8 SAC CP 311.0 321.0

Watertown AFS, NY: NORAD CP 364.2 AF 165.0375 227.1 228.7 235.8 239.2 244.7 254.8 278.4 282.5 288.0 292.8 298.8 303.9 316.2 326.4 338.8 341.1 347.4 351.6 371.8 376.2 389.2 394.8 399.0

Watertown Int'l. Apt., NY: FSS 255.4 AD 377.1

Watertown Muni. Apt., SD FSS 255.4 AD 306.2

Watertown Muni. Apt., WI: AD 380.35 396.0

Watervliet Army Arsenal, NY: Security 165.0625 165.0875 Motor Pool 173.4625 Pager 165.5375

Waterville Robert Lafleur Apt., ME: AD 290.5 299.2 322.4

Watkins-Johnson Corp.: Palo Alto, CA 153.05 153.30; Scotts Valley, CA 462.20; Gaithersburg, MD 464.525

Watsonville Muni. Apt., CA: AD 263.6 307.0

Waukegan Regn'l. Apt., IL: AD 290.2 380.15 T 380.15

Waukesha Co., Apt., WI: AD 307.0 Army Reserve 38.30

Waupaca Muni. Apt., WI: AD 317.7

Wausau Muni. Apt., WI: FSS 255.4 AD 317.7

Waycross-Ware Co. Apt., GA: AD 290.4

Wayland Satellite Ground Station, MA: AF 148.50 149.50 227.05 314.25 315.25 316.25 397.25

Webb AFB, Big Spring, TX: AF 139.85 163.4875 173.4375 173.5875 236.7 341.7 413.15

Weedon Fld., Eufala, AL: AD 278.5 357.6 E 339.8

Webster OLF, St. Ingoes, MD: AD 120.05 281.8 T 126.2 358.0 (Also see Naval Electronics Systems listings.)

Weide AAF, MD: AD 119.0 228.4 OP 126.2 229.4 241.0

Weld Co. Muni Apt., Greeley, CO: AD 287.4 AF 46.85 143.80 314.2 343.0 354.2

Wellsville Muni.-Tarantine Fld., NY: AD 239.35

Wendover AF Auxiliary Fld., UT: OP 122.8 WX 135.075 AF 142.25 226.0 233.4 271.1 287.0

Wertheim AHP, Germany: DI 33.70

West Bend Muni. Apt., WI: AD 307.0 Army 40.80 41.60 241.0

West Branch Community Apt., MI: AD 282.0

Westchester Co. Apt., White Plains, NY: AD 319.8 T 381.2 G 381.2

Westerly State Apt., RI: AD 307.9 380.25

Western Space & Missile Center, Pt. Arguello, CA: AD 121.4 296.5 386.6 (Also see Vandenberg AFB listings.)

Westfield, MA: USN 30.45 38.75

West GA Regn'l. Apt., Carrollton, GA: AD 254.25

West Houston-Lakeside Apt., TX: AD 257.7

Westinghouse Communications: Anne Arundel, MD 275.2 314.6 382.6 490.0625; Baltimore, MD 123.2 123.225 153.185 464.325 495.6625 495.9375 496.0625; Birdville, MD 496.0625; Cheektowaga, NY 153.05; Sharon, PA 153.14 462.325; Compton, CA 461.325; Raleigh 35.06; Pittsburgh, PA 154.54 158.43 462.35 464.30; Horseheads, NY 153.08; Muncie, IN 153.245 153.35 462.50; Escondido, CA 461.975; Running Springs, CA 462.05; Boston, MA 153.05; Braddock Hills, PA 158.46; Charlotte, NC: 153.17 854.8125; Beaver, PA 158.28 451.625; Trafford, PA 153.08 154.54; Jefferson City, MO 153.395 462.20 462.30; Round Rock, TX 35.94 153.065; Madison, PA 153.14 153.35 451.175 462.375; Rochester, PA 463.225; Banning, CA 462.05; Washington, DC 156.255 161.575; Mt. Lukens, CA 462.375; Silver Spring, MD 496.1125; Linthicum, MD 495.6625 496.0375; Mt. Wilson, CA 461.10 461.275; Sunnyvale, CA 154.54 462.20; West Orange, NJ 461.375; Columbia, SC

462.20 462.30; Forest Hills, PA 151.895; Sewickley Twp., PA 151.895; Athens, GA 35.90; Cheswick, PA 153.215; Catonsville, PA 463.65 464.325 495.9375; Cockeysville, MD 495.9375; Hillside, NJ 461.375; San Bernardino, CA 461.05; Elkridge, MD 495.9375; Annapolis, MD 495.6625; Large, PA 462.25; Winter Park, FL 451.175 451.575 854.8125; Orlando, FL 451.675 464.475 854.8125; Lima, OH 451.375; Blairsville, OH 462.45; Ft. Myers, FL 854.7875; Winston-Salem, NC 153.095; Buffalo, NY 462.90; Jonestown, MD 461.30; Byron Center, MI 464.40; Moline, MI 464.40; Dallas, TX 856.0125; Detroit, MI 463.775 865.1125; Oakland, CA 464.45; San Jose, CA 462.025 463.65; So. Boston, VA 153.23; Rural Hill, NC 462.30; Grand Rapids, MI 451.375; Duncan, SC 464.575; Abingdon, VA 464.525; Cary, NC 461.40; Greenwood, SC 153.275

West Memphis Muni. Apt., AR: AD 284.7 291.6

Westmoreland Co. Apt., Latrobe, PA: AD 307.1

Westover Air Reserve Base, Chicopee, MA (439th Tactical Air Wing): DI 123.0 372.2 AD 125.35 325.8 T 114.0 134.85 348.4 G 118.35 275.8 439th TAW OP ("Casino Royale") 252.1 439th TAW CP 319.4 349.4 439th TAW Interplane 138.50 143.80 340.8 SAC CP 311.0 321.0 Crew Alerts 413.45 WX 342.5 NG 38.70 121.65 Security 163.4875 165.1875 FD/Crash 163.4125 173.4125 OSI 40.17 40.19 138.075 138.165 Turner Drop Zone 297.0 Administrative 148.05 148.065 USMC 30.45 Base Commanders Net 149.55 Helicopter OP 38.70 Mobile Units 163.5875 USN 38.75 AF 138.90 149.565 165.0625 173.5375 173.5625 301.4 413.30 413.40

West Point Military Academy & Reservation, NY (USMA; 1st Battalion/1st Infantry): Security ("250") 38.70 MP 141.50 FD ("250-F') 38.85 143.025 Engineering & Maintenance 38.55 38.95 143.35 Motor Pool 38.55 EOD 49.70 49.80 Aviation 49.75 139.10 321.7 Keller Army Hospital 150.70 153.86 Army 40.90 165.0625

West Point Muni. Apt., VA: AD 360.6

West Woodward Apt., OK: AD 379.2

Wharton Muni. Apt., TX: AD 360.8

W.H. Bud Barron Apt., GA: AD 269.3 279.6 388.2

Wheeler AFB, HI (15th Air Base Sqdn; 326th Air Division; Army helicopter training): AD 118.3 119.1 124.8 265.0 269.0 T 126.3 241.0 G 41.50 121.7 237.5 Range 38.30 WX 125.1 344.6 "Pineapple Cntrl." 125.1 Army 242.4 242.6 USN 148.90 268.8 275.4 340.2 AF 139.00 139.20 141.15 141.20 143.00 148.095 155.375 163.4625 163.5125 164.9875 165.0375 165.1625 172.775 173.4125 237.5 349.6 383.0 406.50 416.50

Wheeler-Sack AAF/Ft. Drum, Watertown, NY (10th Mountain Division; Army Materials & Mechanics Research Center; National Guard; Army Reserve): T 49.90 126.2 241.0 G 121.9 229.8 E 229.8 WX 344.6 Base OP 38.30 MP 30.10 139.05 139.15 139.35 141.10 160.65 162.70 Gate Security 38.85 Security 38.00 162.70 Base FD 38.91 139.31 Crash Crews 38.85 NG 40.65 Medevac 41.10 Medics 46.04 49.50 Range 38.10 38.50 46.70 EOD 49.70 49.80 Base Engineers 141.10 142.45 163.075 164.05 Pager 158.70 Safety 38.10 10th MD OP 75.95 10th MD MP 47.60 Army 30.10 46.87 139.025 139.225 139.35 141.475 141.675 142.45 143.075 143.15 AF 40.13 141.55 143.85 143.925 163.5125 165.0375 258.2 379.5

Wheelless Apt., AL: AD 234.4

Wheeling-Ohio Apt., WV: FSS 255.4 AD 388.4 T 257.8

Whidbey Island NAS/Ault Fld., Oak Harbor, WA (HQ for EW Sqdns using EA6B tactical jamming aircraft; Training center for A-6 "Intruder" attack bomber sqdns; USN Reserve; USMC Reserve): DI 134.15 350.0 S 280.3 AD 118.2 120.7 125.1 270.8 286.0 319.2 T 127.9 126.85 127.9 140.10 363.6 340.2 G 121.75 121.9 336.4 E 124.15 135.1 380.8 WX 344.6 Base OP 250.0 Security 138.625 139.525 Medevac 34.15 Search & Rescue 34.15 282.8 Fleet Area Control & Surveillance Facility ("Down Rigger") 125.3 337.1 Helicopters 123.05 244.4 Fueling 139.575 140.75

Pager 149.40   Weapons 138.625   Tactical 281.8 306.0 314.2 318.5 341.2 380.6
Boardman Range 360.2   Maintenance 38.50 355.1   USN 30.45 32.05 32.45 34.95 36.53
36.57 36.63 36.85 36.87 126.05 140.025 140.075 140.10 140.25 140.225 140.30 140.45
140.55 140.60 140.65 140.725 140.775 142.525 142.80 143.715 254.9 258.6 268.7 273.6
300.0 300.6 313.3 319.2 320.2 322.0 325.2 328.4 337.0 339.5 343.6 352.4 355.1 356.2
360.9 361.9 363.6 376.8 384.4 385.0 386.8 406.7625

White Beach Hpt, Okinawa: AD 119.1 126.5 363.8

White Co. Apt, IN: AD 397.9

Whitehouse OLF, FL: AD 120.75 124.9 127.0 284.6 319.9 379.9   T 120.35 268.8
340.2

Whiteman AFB, Knob Noster, MO (ACC; 8th AF; 351st Missile Wing; 351st National
Guard Helicopter Assault Unit): DI 372.2   AD 119.65 285.6 352.0   WX 344.6   T
134.2 255.6   G 165.0125 275.8   CP 165.5375   SAC CP 311.0 321.0   Crew Alerts
413.45   NG ("Hawk OP") 41.00   Security 149.235 149.265 165.0125 165.0375 165.1375
Maintenance 149.265   Civil Engineering 148.245   Pager 163.5375   Personnel 148.95
FD/Crash 173.5875   Minuteman II ICBM Silos 149.175 149.265   AF 34.40 148.05
149.205 149.475 149.565 150.10 150.375 163.5875 164.50 165.1875 173.35 173.6625
226.7 231.4 234.8 234.95 242.0 243.8 260.0 266.2 271.9 308.8 313.3 323.8 335.9 384.7
413.15 413.825

White Sands Missile Range (WSMR), Organ, NM: Security 36.10 36.51 36.91 141.25
"Cherokee Control" 294.6 295.2   Range 34.81 34.85 36.51 36.91   Missile Tracking
412.875   MP 36.10 141.25   Motor Pool 34.09   Land/Air Documentary Photo 30.90
41.43 139.44   Land/Air Optics 34.31 34.85   Land/Air Telemetry 38.45 38.71 38.95
Land/Air Network 38.65   Land/Air Hi Speed Tracking 412.875   Photo Net 30.09
41.43   Video Recording 36.51/36.91   Telemetry 38.45   NASA Optics Loop 34.31
NASA Chase 121.75 126.5   NASA/Northrop Strip T 126.5   NASA/Northrop Strip G
164.10   NASA TV Director 169.075   NASA Public Relations 169.40   Recovery Net
41.10   Cooling Net 168.00   Laser Test 173.5625   Purge Net 162.6125   RCA Drone
(Vega) 164.50   IBM Drone Formation 172.40   Dynalectron Company 463.475
Dynalectron-Ratscat 150.20   Maintenance 34.49   Ground Transportation 30.29 34.09
Flight Test 260.8 264.9   Raytheon Co (trunked system) 861.4875 862.4875 863.4875
864.4875 865.4875   Msc   Chan 1 138.975   Chan 2 139.075   Chan 3 139.225   Chan 4
139.525   Chan 5 148.075/140.025   Chan 6 140.025   Msc 30.49 30.50 32.65 32.89 34.70
38.50 40.10 40.90 41.25 41.34 41.59 41.90 49.93 118.45 119.0 121.8 122.8 123.3
126.95 135.85 135.95 138.20 139.38 139.77 139.80 140.55 140.60 141.35 141.40 141.48
141.68 141.86 142.23 142.35 142.875 142.90 142.975 143.00 143.175 143.275 148.00
148.15 148.45 148.87 148.485 148.605 148.70 148.755 148.815 148.90 149.175 149.85
150.45 150.475 150.525 150.575 150.675 163.325 165.1375 165.5625 165.6125 166.00
167.175 167.85 170.35 170.575 170.94 171.15 171.175 171.23 171.26 171.385 173.4625
173.6625 173.6875 173.8125 173.9125 230.4 230.5 237.4 240.2 243.5 248.6 252.4 256.2
257.0 258.9 259.7 261.3 262.5 265.6 267.3 268.0 275.2 280.8 284.1 287.2 290.6 298.1
292.2 299.1 299.8 304.2 304.3 315.2 319.6 320.7 339.9 341.6 345.4 347.5 349.6 377.5
379.9 383.0 384.0 384.8 386.2 389.5 391.5 395.5 397.1 407.30 409.00 412.975 413.525
416.60

Whiteside Co.-Bittorf Fld, IL: AD 327.0 351.7

Whiting Fld. (North & South) NAS, Milton, FL (Training Air Wing 5; Training
Sqdns 2, 3 & 6; Helicopter Training Sqdns 8 & 18): S 281.2 284.2   AD 126.85
127.35 278.8 286.0 298.9   North T 121.4 344.2   South T 121.4 349.8   North G 341.0
South G 346.8   North E 354.8   WX 317.0   OP 233.7   South Transient Line 253.1
USN 138.60 138.825 138.975 139.475 139.50 139.55 140.10 140.175 140.70 142.85
150.10 264.4 273.0 274.4 279.2 301.0 303.6 304.2 308.2 328.2 340.2 342.8 359.6 356.1
358.0 360.2 361.1 382.8 384.3

Whittaker Corp.: MI 462.1375; Berwick, PA 152.42 153.095 153.335 464.475; Miami, FL 163.185; MN 151.805; Oxnard, CA 154.515; Roxboro, NC 461.125; San Diefo, CA 154.515

Wichita, KS: Army 30.10 40.70 139.20

Wichita-Mid Contn'l. Apt., KS: FSS 255.4   AD 281.5 290.3 325.8 327.1 353.5   G 348.6   T 257.8

Wichita Valley Apt., Wichita Falls, TX: AD 292.3

Wiesbaden AB/AAF, Germany: AD 120.15 120.8 231.25 359.8 367.15   T 30.10 122.1 142.35 369.05   G 138.55 250.55   WX 140.30 253.15   Info 119.15 130.975   Emergency 40.50

Wilbarger Co. Apt., Vernon, TX: AD 259.3

Wildflecken AAF, Germany: Range 38.30 51.30

Wiley Post Apt., Oklahoma City, OK: FSS 255.4   AD 336.4 385.5 393.1 395.0   G 348.6   T 306.9

Wilford Hall USAF Medical Center, Lackland AFB, TX: DI 130.65 372.2   AD 118.05 125.1 125.7 127.1 289.2 307.0 353.5 381.4   T 124.3 320.1   WX 239.8   (See Lackland AFB listings.)

Wilkes-Barre, PA: AF 413.40

Wilkes-Barre/Scranton Int'l. Apt., PA: FSS 255.4   AD 256.7 319.9   T 257.8

Willard Apt., OH: AD 317.7 390.8

William B. Helig Fld., NE: FSS 255.4   AD 338.2

William P. Gwinn Apt., FL: AD 314.6   T 36.90 314.6   G 314.6   United Technologies 38.90 123.275 123.325 123.425 123.45 123.525 153.14 154.57 304.6 464.825

William P. Hobby Apt., Houston, TX: FSS 255.4   AD 257.7 284.0 307.1 379.1 396.0   T 256.9

William R. Fairchild Int'l. Apt., WA: AD 270.8

Williams AFB, Chandler, AZ (82nd Pilot Training Wing): S 271.8   DI 372.2   AD 115.6 119.2 120.4 120.7 124.1 124.9 128.65 269.6 317.5 353.8 379.1 379.8 388.0   T 118.8 126.2 255.6   G 118.8 275.8   E 289.4   WX 344.6   OSI 138.075 138.165 138.175   AF 138.025 139.65 139.85 139.90 148.215 148.225 149.50 149.505 150.285 163.375 163.5125 163.5625 163.5875 163.8375 165.05 165.0375 165.1375 228.4 242.4 254.7 271.8 280.1 286.6 289.4 290.9 296.9 297.4 317.9 337.4 344.9 348.3 371.2 379.5 388.2 391.9 395.9 413.15

Williamsburg Co. Apt., SC: AD 379.1

Williams Co. Apt., Bryan, OH: AD 321.1

Williamson Co. Regn'l. Apt., Marion, IL: AD 269.5

Williamsport-Lycoming Co. Apt., PA: FSS 255.4   T 257.8

Willmar Muni. Apt., MN: FSS 255.4

Willoughby Lost Nation Muni Apt, OH: AD 360.6

Willow Grove NAS, PA (USN Reserve training facility for ASW): S 275.6   AD 123.8 266.8 291.7 325.2   G 121.8 300.8   T 119.6 340.2   E 212.8   WX 344.6   Security 139.50 148.175   Ramp 140.10   ANG OP 46.85 343.0   AF Reserve OP ("Shortstop") 138.90 351.2   Army Reserve 34.55 143.02 226.5   AF MAC CP 349.4   Airborne Refueling 325.2   Base OP 306.8   USN 32.45 36.85 40.15 120.6 124.85 138.55 138.725 139.48 140.85 141.00 141.10 141.80 149.03 283.0 349.9 363.5 380.8 382.8 383.5 385.3   ANG 46.75 46.85 49.75 138.30 138.50 141.80 141.90 143.80 149.175 163.4875 164.9125 165.1375 165.1625 237.2 286.0 391.2 407.40 407.50 413.15 413.20 413.30

Willow Run Muni. Apt., MI: AD 348.3 363.2   T 351.7

Willows Glenn Co. Apt., CA: AD 350.3

Will Rogers World Apt., Oklahoma City, OK: AD 336.4 385.5 393.1 395.0   G 348.6   T 139.90 257.8   ANG CP ("Sooner OP") 319.4   ANG 148.50 149.30 149.475 149.525 150.15 163.4875 165.1125   FAA 162.25 164.05

Wilson Creek, NV: AF Range 124.45 392.1   (Also see Nellis AFB listings.)

Wilson Indust'l. Air Center, NC: FSS 255.4 AD 285.5
Winder Apt., GA: 306.9 NG 44.00
Winchester Regn'l. Apt., VA: FSS 255.4 AD 296.2
Windham Apt., Willamantic, CT: AD 300.4 307.9 327.1
Windom Muni. Apt., MN: FSS 255.4 AD 290.2
Window Rock Apt., AZ: AD 307.2
Wings Fld., Philadelphia, PA: AD 281.3
Winkler Co. Apt., Wink, TX: FSS 255.4 AD 385.6
Winn Army Community Hospital (PJ) Helipad, Ft. Stewart, GA: OP 49.30 126.2
231.8 (Also see Wright AAF listings.)
Winnemucca Muni Apt., NV: AD 269.0
Winona Muni. Apt-Conrad Fld., MN: AD 363.0
Winslow Muni Apt., AZ: FSS 255.4 AD 298.9
Winter Harbor, ME: USN 138.58 139.50 141.00
Wiscasset Apt., ME: AD 263.6
Witham Fld., Stuart, FL: Unicom 122.9 G 121.7 T 126.6 Grumman Aerospace
32.50 34.10 38.90 46.90 49.65 49.70 123.2 123.35 123.45 142.74 143.58 153.56 (HF
3281 3283 kHz)
Wittman Regn'l Fld., Oshkosh, WI: AD 306.3 T 257.6
W. J. McDonald Observatory, U. of Texas, Ft. Davis, TX: 162.20
W. K. Kellogg Regn'l. Apt., Battle Creek, MI (ANG 110th Tactical Air Support
Grp): AD 263.1 340.9 G 348.6 T 239.0 ANG OP 32.35 267.8 ANG Security
163.4875 163.5875 ANG FD/Crash 163.4625 ANG Disaster Preparedness 163.5125
ANG 41.80 41.85 41.95 139.70 385.9 389.0 391.2 Atmy 139.10
Wold Chamberlain Fld., MN: See Minneapolis-St. Paul Int'l. listings.
Wolf OLF, Foley, AL: OP 384.1
Woodbine Muni Apt., NJ: AD 263.6
Woodbridge USAF, UK: DI 315.2 AD 119.0 135.275 232.9 255.8 268.2 T 122.1
257.8 291.35 G 307.4 CP 282.15 WX 259.4 Security 32.20 75.525 78.50 78.525
78.5875 78.725
Wood Co. Apt., Bowling Green, OH: AD 307.0
Wood Co.-Wilson Fld., Parkersburg, WV: FSS 255.4 AD 398.9 T 257.8
Woods Hole Oceanographic Institution, MA: 35.02 151.865 140.00 156.35 156.425
156.45 156.65 156.95 (HF 2098 2163 2398 4141 4163 6212 6245 6970 8263 8329 12422
16566 kHz) CG 41.21 157.05 157.125 157.15 157.175 164.30
Woodward Fld., SC: AD 306.3 327.3
Worcester Muni Apt., MA: FSS 255.4 AD 263.0 327.1
Worms AHP, Germany: MP ("Firefly") 39.90
Worthington Muni Apt, OH: AD 317.4
Wright AAF/Ft. Stewart, Hinesville, GA (Rapid Deployment Force; 1st
Battalion/Ranger, 75th Infantry; 24th Infantry Division): AD 118.4 120.85 125.3
322.5 339.3 354.0 387.1 T 38.50 126.2 231.8 G 121.7 234.4 OP 38.70 Range
("Victory Radio") 41.30 127.35 247.0 Base Railroad 165.1125 Security 163.5375
Military Intelligence 165.0625 165.3375 FD 150.725 173.4875 Motor Pool 163.5625
EOD 49.70 49.80 Army 41.30 40.10 40.15 46.70 46.75 46.95 49.30 49.65 138.10
139.60 141.05 141.30 141.45 141.50 141.80 142.875 143.00 143.10 143.15 143.25
143.325 143.50 143.75 148.60 148.605 148.645 148.675 148.775 148.815 148.885 148.925
149.65 149.70 150.425 150.475 163.4875 164.50 164.9625 165.0375 165.0875 165.1625
165.1875 165.4875 173.4125 173.4625 173.5125 226.3 226.6 227.3 229.6 233.0 248.2
271.1 277.5 300.7 321.6 387.9 407.35 412.90 413.525 AF 142.25 340.6 341.5 342.3
349.3 375.5
Wright-Patterson AFB, Dayton, OH (2750th Air Base Wing; 906th Tactical Fighter
Grp; 4950th Test Wing): DI 122.85 372.2 S 115.2 269.9 AD 118.85 327.1 G 121.8
335.8 T 115.2 126.9 236.6 289.6 CP ("Kittyhawk") 397.0 WX 344.6 OSI 40.17

40.19 1338.075 138.10 138.165 141.525   Security 165.5875 173.4375 173.5375 280.15   FBI 173.4375 173.5375   Air Terminal ("Mobility") 149.50 150.325 164.70   FD/Crash 154.28 166.225 173.5125 173.5625   Base OP 165.1625   Disaster Preparedness 173.6625   AF Museum 413.375   Civil Engineering 163.5125 165.5125   Maintenance 163.5125 164.70 165.1625 165.5875   Supply Expediting 164.70   Motor Pool 413.275   ASD 149.325 302.7 303.7   IBR Materials Lab 46.665   Acoustical Data 46.95   Satcom Project 138.025 138.90   ASD Survival Avionics 251.9 276.8   906th TFG OP 138.125 138.275 138.325 138.375 138.425   Instrumentation 123.25 140.40   AFLC/CC 138.475 142.30 409.90 413.025 413.05   ARIA 139.25   APL Fuels 138.875   Energy Control 139.65   Timing IRIG B 141.70   Medics 148.215   Pager 149.30 407.50   R&D Coordination 407.70   Data Collection 407.425   MAC Radar 413.15   Base FD 163.4625 173.5125   Civil 165.1125   Flight Test 230.4 287.2   AFAL Target Instrumentation 149.225   AFAL Ionospheric Data 408.05 408.125 408.175 413.00 413.05 413.125   AFAPL 413.425   AFAL Team Project 150.195   SAC CP 311.0 321.0   Crew Alerts 413.45   AF 41.10 46.65 148.065 148.425 149.535 150.25 163.6125 225.0 225.8 255.7 257.0 259.2 276.9 294.2 303.4 316.625 316.785 317.9 341.6 349.6 379.7 384.8 397.1 407.40 407.425 407.475   USN 49.95

W. T. Piper Memorial Apt., Lock Haven, PA: Piper Act. Co. 122.8 123.35 123.45 123.525

Wueschheim AS Hpd, Germany: AD 233.6 370.6   T 122.1 139.375 315.55   G 375.0

Wulfsberg Electronics, Overland Park, KS: 126.125 151.875 150.20 163.125 172.345

Wurtsmith AFB, Oscoda, MI (ACC; 9th AF; 379th Bombardment Wing. **Closing date 6/93.**) DI 372.2   AD 132.5 301.5 395.0   T 124.15 236.6 289.6   G 275.8   SAC CP 311.0 321.0   WX 342.5   Base Commanders Net 149.565   MAC CP 130.65   FD/Crash 173.5875   Security 163.05 163.5875 164.05 164.10   Crew Alerts 413.45   Disaster Preparedness 148.095 165.0375   OSI 138.075 138.165 138.175   Medics 173.5675   Civil Engineering 163.4875   Communications Technicians 165.1125   Maintenance 150.195   379th BW Maintenance 163.5125   AF 140.065 163.5625 163.90 164.50 236.6 289.6 290.9 291.1 316.7 363.8 389.8 395.0 413.15

Yakima Air Terminal, WA: FSS 255.4   AD 343.9 393.1   G 348.6   T 257.8   AF 163.5875

Yakima Firing Center, WA: T 40.30 41.50 126.2 241.0   Advisories ("Rattlesnake Radio") 36.70 139.125 393.3   Range 31.30 31.40 31.75 32.40 34.60   Army 143.225 143.275 165.0625 173.4125 173.7125 248.2 412.825   (Also see Gray AAF listings.)

Yeager Apt., Charleston, WV: AD 398.95   T 257.8   G 348.6   ANG 130th Tactical Airlift Grp OP 283.8   Security 163.4875   ANG 139.70 141.80 148.215 150.325 165.1875 301.6   Army 164.05

Yokosuka Hpt, Honshu, Japan: AD 118.3 270.6   T ("Chess Romeo") 135.7 280.2

Yokota AB, Japan: DI 313.6   S 128.4 281.0   AD 118.3 120.7 122.1 123.8 261.4 270.6 363.8 367.0   T 120.3 126.2 315.8   G 133.2 308.6   WX 344.6   5th AF CP 325.8   MAC CP 128.0 349.4   Global HF System 292.1 (HF 4725 6738 8967 8993 13201 15015 17975 kHz)

York Apt., PA: AD 339.3

Yorktown NWS, VA (Naval Mine Warfare Engineering Activity; Naval Opthalmic Support & Training Activity; USMC Security Force Company): Heliports 121.25 140.20 236.2 344.4 Security & FD 140.20 USN 138.84 139.525 139.70 140.80 148.375 149.425 150.40 346.9 Supply Center 140.34 140.48 140.82 141.00 148.95 149.225 149.25 CG 162.125

Youngstown Exec. Apt., OH: AD 306.3 381.4

Youngstown Muni Apt., OH FSS 255.4 AD 306.3 322.3 381.4 393.0 G 275.8 T 263.0 AF Reserve 910th Tactical Airlift Grp CP ("Battle Star") 384.7 Flightline Maintenance ("Victor Control") 384.7 FD/Crash 138.20 173.5875 AF Reserve 149.225 149.235 149.325 150.275 384.7 392.2 407.425 413.20 413.30

Yuba Co. Apt., Marysville, CA: FSS 255.4 AD 327.5

Yucca Airstrip, NV Test Site, NV: AD ("Dreamland") 118.7 126.15 255.8 261.1 (Also see Nevada Test Site listings.)

Yuma Proving Grounds, AZ: See Laguna AAF listings.

Yuma MCAS, AZ (VMFAT-101; VMA-513): FSS 255.4 Unicom 122.5 S 273.2 AD 120.0 124.7 314.0 374.8 T 119.3 126.2 361.2 382.8 G 121.9 340.2 E 118.0 336.4 CP 337.9 Target 337.9 VFR Advisories 124.7 314.0 WX 349.9 USMC 138.975 139.50 139.545 140.055 140.10 140.175 140.25 140.455 140.50 140.65 140.70 140.775 140.895 140.94 141.00 142.50 143.505 143.575 143.715 149.115 149.125 149.15 150.15 165.0375 173.5375 242.2 250.3 258.9 262.6 262.9 268.3 272.3 273.2 279.2 281.3 285.1 299.3 300.45 307.5 310.2 310.3 311.9 315.3 318.5 325.4 342.9 349.9 358.6 360.2 363.4 381.9 384.4 385.1 413.20 Army 407.45 McDonnell Douglas 123.2 123.275 123.3 123.4 123.425 123.45 123.55 153.08 275.0 275.2 314.6 330.8 382.6 (HF 3283 6661 8919 11377 13558 kHz)

Zanesville Muni. Apt., OH: FSS 255.4 AD 370.9

Zaragoza AB, Spain: DI 290.4 AD 119.3 372.6 T 139.30 257.8 G 139.30 375.0 406th TPTW CP ("Vista Cntrl.") 389.9 SAC CP 311.0 321.0 WX 344.6

Z.M. Jack Stell Fld, AR: AD 269.35

Late Additions

Isla Grande Apt., PR: Unicom 122.95 AD 290.2 T 233.8 G 322.3 ANG ("Moro Cntrl.") 40.00 242.4 (HF 9122.5 kHz)

Muniz ANGB, San Juan, PR: Unicom 123.0 S 125.8 FSS 255.4 AD 269.2 290.2 T 257.8 G 348.6 E 284.6 ANG CP 381.3

Prestwick USAF, Scotland: S 127.125 AD 119.45 120.55 248.4 257.8 362.3 385.925 T 118.15 121.8 257.8 362.3 Royal Navy 291.0 (HF 9014 kHz)

Rafael Hernandez Apt., San Juan, PR: AD 134.3 269.0 338.3 CG 122.8 381.8 282.8

Sigonella NAS, Italy: S 297.0 AD 119.25 120.8 122.1 243.4 244.65 344.0 362.3 381.3 T 118.05 122.1 257.8 262.6 G 121.96 315.2 Terminal OP 377.8 WX 344.6 Base OP 344.6 Range 379.0 Air/Air 307.0

Souda USN, Greece: AD 121.0 122.1 T 121.1 122.1 257.8 382.6 WX 379.0 FSS ("Chania Radio") (HF 2989 5637 kHz)

Military Airfields: Middle East Hotspots
Includes Civilian Airports Used as Military Fields
Note: "FSS" indication for listings outside USA indicates a flight service station operated under that nation's equivalent to the FAA.

Chad
Faya Largeau Field: OP 119.7

Egypt
Al Ismailiyah Field: AD 119.1 352.7 T 118.1 118.5 352.7 United Nations Mil OP (HF Primary 6632 9006 11223 13231 13257 kHz; Secondary 3975 4704 5690 6204 6810 6905 kHz)
Aswan Field: T 118.3
Cairo Int'l. Apt.: S 121.7 AD 119.1 119.55 120.7 T 118.1 G 120.1 121.9
Hurghada Field: T 119.6 G 121.9
Luxor Field: AD 124.3 T 119.9 G 121.9
Mersa Matruh Field: T 118.1
New Valley Field: T 118.1

Iran
Badr AFB/Sepha AFB: T 118.1 121.7
Bakhtaran Field: T 122.5 G 121.9
Bandar Abbass Int'l Apt.: AD 353.8 T 313.8 G 121.8 FSS (6547 kHz)
Bushehr Field: AD 310.6 317.5 344.0 385.4 T 121.9 122.5 G 257.8
Chah Bahar Field: T 125.2 261.4 310.6 G 121.7
Dashte-Naz Field: T 121.7 122.55
Dezful Field: AD 131.4 134.1 261.4 344.0 362.3 385.4 T 122.2 124.0 257.8 G 275.8
Doshan Tappeh Field: T 126.0 363.2
Esfahan Int'l. Apt: AD 122.5 122.65 124.6 282.0 313.0 344.0 T 118.3 121.9 261.4 G 121.9 275.8
Ghale Morghi Field: T 122.5
Hamadan Field: AD 117.9 119.1 134.1 344.0 353.8 361.1 385.4 T 123.3 257.8 G 275.8
Khorram-Abbad Field: OP 118.1
Kish Island Field: T 121.9 FSS 121.7 357.8
Mehrabad Int'l. Apt.: AD 134.1 317.5 344.0 362.3 385.4 T 357.8 G 275.8
Shiraz Int'l Apt.: AD 131.4 134.1 317.5 344.0 362.3 385.4 T 257.8 T 275.8 FSS (HF 5658 10018 kHz)
Tabriz Field: AD 263.6 358.0 T 257.8 G 121.7 121.9

Iraq
Basrah Int'l. Apt.: S 112.3 AD 119.4 124.0 128.15 128.7 T 118.7
Saddam Int'l Apt., Baghdad: AD 119.4 120.4 121.0 122.4 122.9 S 112.9 T 118.7 118.9

Israel
Ben Gurion Apt.: S 132.5 AD 119.5 120.5 T 118.3 G 121.8 WX 126.8
J. Hozman Field, Elat: S 132.55 T 118.6 119.0
Ovda Field: T 127.4 129.9
U. Michaeli Field, Haifa: T 123.5 127.4

Jordan
Marka Int'l. Apt., Amman: S 127.6 AD 128.9 T 118.1 G 121.7

Kuwait
Kuwait Int'l. Apt.: AD 121.3 274.6 T 118.3 253.2 G 121.7

Lebanon
Beirut Int'l. Apt.: AD 120.3 120.4 120.6 T 116.1 118.9 G 121.9

Lybia
  Benina Field: AD 118.1 121.3 T 118.1 121.3 G 121.9
  Labraq Field: T 118.1
  Tripoli Int'l. Apt.: AD 124.0 T 118.1 G 120.1
Saudi Arabia
  Al Jouf Field: OP 122.8 Crash Trucks 121.9
  Dhahran Int'l. Apt.: S 112.7 AD 120.3 125.8 360.6 T 118.4 118.7 358.8 G 121.7 362.0 E 126.3 USAF CP 127.9 (HF 9130 11176 kHz) US Mil ("Hotel 1") (HF 9130 11000 kHz)
  King Abdul Aziz Int'l. Apt., Jeddah: S 114.9 AD 118.2 119.1 123.8 124.0 345.6 358.7 T 118.2 124.3 343.7 G 121.6 121.8 362.3 US Mil OP ("Exxon Cntrl.") 321.0
  King Fahd Int'l. Apt, Dhahran: AD 122.9 273.0 T 125.55 297.77 G 118.72 345.6
  King Khalid AB: S 115.9 AD 119.3 124.5 T 118.9 123.7 G 126.2 US Mil OP ("Hotel 3") (HF Primary 9130 kHz; Secondary 7300 12112 kHz)
  King Khalid Int'l. Apt., Riyadh: S 113.3 AD 120.0 238.5 278.0 339.4 T 118.6 118.8 342.2 342.6 G 121.6 121.7 348.6 348.7 E 121.8 335.7
  King Khalid Mil City Field: S 127.6 386.6 T 120.7 237.6 G 118.7 381.4
  Sharurah Field: OP 122.8 Crash Trucks 121.9
  Tabuk/King Fisal AB: S 115.7 AD 125.8 127.7 131.0 T 125.9 G 126.3 E 118.9 US Mil OP ("Hotel 8") (HF Primary 9130 kHz; Secondary 7300 12112 kHz)
Sudan
  Khartoum Field: AD 119.2 120.9 121.9 T 118.1 120.3
Syria
  Damascus Int'l. Apt.: AD 120.0 121.3 T 118.5 G 121.9
  Dier Zzor Field: T 118.1
  Palmyra Field: T 121.9
United Arab Emirates
  Bateen Field, Abu Dhabi: AD 124.4 124.85 125.1 127.5 128.1 129.5 231.4 270.0 290.8 294.0 T 119.9 G 121.9
Yemen
  Hodeidah Field: AD 124.7 T 118.2 G 121.6
  Sanaa Int'l. Apt.: AD 119.0 125.3 T 118.1 118.9 121.6 G 121.6 FSS (HF 8918 11300 kHz)
  Taiz/Ganed Field: T 118.5

Military Airfields Operated by Other Governments:
Central America, Caribbean, Northern South America
Includes Civilian Airports Used as Military Fields

Antigua
  V.C. Bird Int'l, Antigua I.: AD 119.1 T 118.7 G 121.9 USAF 264.8 (USAF HF 10780 20390 kHz)
Bolivia
  Capital Oriel Lea Plaza Field, Tarija: T 118.1
  El Trompillo Field: AD 119.7 T 118.3 G 121.7 FSS 123.7 124.9
  J. F. Kennedy Int'l., La Paz: AD 119.5 T 118.3 G 121.9 FSS (HF 6638 kHz)
  Robore Field: T 118.9 FSS (HF 6638 kHz)
Colombia
  Baracoa Field: T 118.7 OP (HF 3488 6532 kHz)
  Covenas Naval Base: Aero OP 126.2
  El Yopal Field: T 118.3 OP (HF 6553 kHz)
  Ernesto Cortissoz Field, Barranquilla: S 113.7 AD 119.1 T 118.1 G 121.9
  German Olano Field, Palanquerro: T 118.1 126.2 (HF 3023.5 kHz)
  Gomez Nino AB, Villavicencio: AD 119.3 T 126.2

Madrid AB: T 119.7 126.2 OP (HF 3488 kHz)
Marco Fidel Suarez AB, Cali: AD 119.1 T 126.2 OP 126.7 (HF 3488 5556 kHz)
Tres Esquinas Field: T 126.2 OP (HF 5556 5710 kHz)

Cuba
Antonio Maceo Field, Santiago de Cuba: AD 119.4 T 118.1 FSS 126.9 (HF 2811 3407 4451 5562 6708 8876 kHz)
Baracoa Field: AD 119.4 T 122.5 FSS (HF 2811 4451 6708kHz)
Cienfuegos Field: T 118.1 FSS (HF 3407 5562 kHz)
Moa Field: AD 119.4 T 123.4 FSS (HF 2811 4451 6708 kHz)
Nueva Gerona Field: T 118.3 FSS (HF 3407 5562 8876 kHz)
San Julian Field: T 125.0
Santa Clara Field: T 118.1

Dominican Republic
Cibao Int'l Apt.: AD 126.9 T 118.3
San Isidro AB: T 122.3 122.7

Ecuador
General Ulpiano Paez Field, Salinas: AD 123.3 T 122.5 FSS 126.9
Mariscal Sucre Int'l Apt., Quito: AD 119.7 T 118.1 G 121.9 FSS 126.9
Simon Bolivar Int'l. Apt., Guayaquil: AD 119.3 123.9 T 118.3 G 121.9 FSS 126.9 (HF 4669 6535 6649 10024 11360 kHz)

El Salvador
El Salvador Int'l. Apt.: S 117.5 AD 119.9 T 118.0 G 121.7 FSS 126.9
Ilopango Int'l. Apt.: AD 119.5 119.9 T 118.3 G 121.9 FSS 127.1

Guatemala
La Aurora Field: S 126.9 AD 119.3 120.0 120.7 126.5 127.2 T 118.1 118.6 G 121.9 Mil E 120.7
Puerto Barrios Field: T 118.4 120.0 126.2
Retalhuleu Field: T 118.8 120.0 126.2
San Jose Field: T 118.5 120.0 126.2
Santa Elena Field, Flores: AD 121.4 T 118.3 G 121.9 126.9 FSS 120.0

Honduras
Coronel Enrique Soto Cano AB/Palmerola AB: (See listings under US bases.)
Goloson Int'l. Apt.: T 121.9 FSS 127.5
La Mesa Int'l Apt.: AD 119.7 T 118.2 G 121.9 FSS 127.1
Toncontin Int'l. Apt., Tegucigalpa: AD 126.7 T 118.7 G 121.9 Mil OP 122.9

Jamaica
Tinson Pen Field: Msc 121.6

Mexico
Cozumel Int'l. Apt.: AD 120.4 T 118.1
Ensenada Field: T 119.75 FSS 126.2
General Heriberto Jara Int'l. Apt., Vera Cruz: S 127.8 T 118.5
General R. Fierro Villalobos Int'l. Apt., Chihuahua: S 127.9 AD 121.0 T 118.4
Licenciado Benito Juarez Int'l. Apt., Mexico DF: S 127.7 AD 119.7 120.5 121.2 T 118.1 118.7 G 121.0 121.9 E 122.1 FSS 126.9
Licenciado Manuel Crecencio Rejon Int'l., Merida: AD 121.2 T 118.3 FSS 126.9
Tuxtla Gutierrez Field: AD 118.6 T 118.6

Netherlands Antilles
Hato Field, Curacao: AD 119.6 T 118.3

Nicaragua
Puerto Cabezas Field: T (HF 5521.5 kHz) FSS (HF 5521.5 kHz)

Panama
Sherman Field: AD 119.7 121.2 263.0 317.7 DI 261.5 T 121.4 393.8

Peru
Alferez FAP David Figeroa Fernandini Field, Huanuco: FSS 126.9
Capitan Concha Field, Piura: AD 118.4 T 118.4 FSS 126.9
Capitan Montes Field, Talara: AD 119.5 T 118.1 119.5 FSS 126.9 (HF 6649 10024 kHz)
Collique Field: T 126.0
Coronel FAP Alfredo Mendivil Duarte Field, Ayacucho: T 118.1 FSS 126.9
Jorge Chavez Int'l. Apt., Lima: AD 119.7 T 118.1 G 121.9 FSS 126.6 126.9 (HF 6649 10024 10066 kHz)
Las Palmas Field: AD 124.0 T 118.5 G 119.3
Padre Aldamiz Field, Puerto Maldonado: FSS 126.9 (HF 5454 kHz)
Pucallpa Field: AD 118.1 T 118.1 FSS 126.9 (HF 10066 kHz)
Rodriguez Ballon Field, Arequipa: T 118.7 FSS 126.9
San Juan de Marcona Field: FSS 126.9

Venezuela
Barquisimeto Field: S 112.2 AD 119.4 120.7 T 123.5 G 121.9 FSS 132.0 (HF 5695.5 kHz)
Bartolome Salom Field, Puerto Cabello: T 118.5 G 121.9
El Libertador AB: AD 119.3 119.7 120.8 252.0 304.0 320.0 380.0 T 122.5 311.0 G 121.9 FSS (HF 5680 5695.5 kHz) Msc 134.1
General Francisco de Miranda AB: S 127.4 T 118.8 G 121.8 FSS 5695.5 kHz
Jose Antonio Anzoategui Field, Barcelona: S 127.9 AD 119.1 121.1 T 118.7 G 121.9 FSS 130.6 (HF 5695.5 kHz)
Mariscal Sucre Field: S 127.6 T 118.05 311.0 G 121.7 Msc 134.1 322.0
Mayor Buenaventura Vivas Field, Santo Domingo: T 121.9 122.3 (HF 5680 5695.5 kHz) FSS 226.6

Canadian Military/Government Aero Comms

Cadadian CG Heliports Not Shown operate 122.8 and/or 123.2.

Abbotsford, BC: AD 252.5 T 295.0
Alert, NWT: Military 126.7 (HF 5680 6705 11233 kHz)
Amphitrate Point CG Heliport, BC: OP 123.2
Avey Airport, WA (USA): Canadian/US Customs OP 123.2
Bagotville DND Base, QC: S 124.2(E) 125.8(F) 302.5 T 126.2 236.6 337.7 G 121.7 275.8 WX 344.6 Mil Advisories 264.6 Terminal 127.2 227.6 384.5
Banff Apt., AB: Dept of Environment OP 122.8 FSS 126.7
Barrack Green, AB: Military 32.30 45.45
Blissville DND Base, NB: T 126.4
Boat Bluff Light Station CG Heliport, BC: OP 123.2
Bonilla Island Light Station CG Heliport, BC: OP 123.2
Borden CFB, ON: FSS 296.2 Military Aviation 123.5 242.1 Range 49.90 OP 173.67 Rescue 149.44 MP 173.25 FD 149.68 Engineer 173.91 Base Transportation 149.35 173.10 173.34 Military 37.50 37.60 38.40 38.60 38.80 39.10 39.20 40.20 41.10 41.20 42.40 42.80 43.30 44.00 44.30 44.40 44.80 44.90 45.50 45.60 45.70 46.10
Brandon Apt., MAN: AD 285.4 T 248.3
Brantford Apt., ONT: FSS 321.3
Brevoort North Warning System Fld., NWT: FSS 126.7 364.2 Mil 123.55
Brockville Apt., ONT: AD 238.3
Bromont Apt., QC: AD 229.2
Brooks Apt., AB: AD 368.5
Broughton Isl. Apt., NWT: Air Defence Identification Zone 126.7 364.2
Byron Bay North Warning System Apt., NWT: Air Defence Identification Zone 126.7 364.2 Mil 123.55
Calgary Apt., AB: AD 243.5 255.1 265.8 294.9 T 236.6 G 275.8 E 260.2 Apron 260.2 VFR Advisories 374.2 Terminal 243.5
Calgary (All Heliports), AB: T 236.6
Cambridge Bay North Warning System Fld., NWT: Air Defence Identification Zone 126.7 228.9 251.0 270.4 364.2
Campbell River Apt., BC: FSS 296.6
Cape Beale CG Heliport, BC: OP 123.2
Cape Dyer North Warning System Fld., NWT: Air Defence Identification Zone 123.55 126.7 256.6 270.4 274.4 364.2
Cape Hooper North Warning System Fld., NWT: Air Defence Identification Zone 126.7 364.2 Mil 123.55
Cape Mudge CG Heliport, BC: OP 123.2
Cape Parry North Warning System Fld., NWT: Air Defence Identification Zone 126.7 256.6 269.9 270.4 364.2 Mil 123.55
Cape St. James Environment Station CG Heliport, BC: OP 123.2
Cape Scott CG Heliport, BC: OP 123.2
Carmanah Point CG Heliport, BC: OP 123.2
Cartwright Apt., NF: FSS 126.7 364.2
Castlegar Apt., BC: AD 227.3 FSS 295.4 T 286.6
Centralia/Huron Airpark, ONT: FSS 321.3
Charlottetown Apt, PEI: T 236.6 G 275.8
Chatham CFB, NB: AD 346.9 T 126.2 226.4 236.6 G 275.8 WX 344.6 OP 253.6 Security 149.65 FD/Crash 149.14 Military 149.15 149.35 149.80
Chatham Apt, ONT: FSS 321.3
Chatham Point CG Heliport, BC: OP 123.2 FSS 126.7

Chibougamau/Chapais Apt., QC: AD 253.2
Chrome Island CG Heliport, BC: OP 123.2
Churchill Apt., MAN: FSS 327.4 (HF 5680 kHz)
Clinton Point North Warning System Fld., NWT: Air Defence Identification Zone 126.7 364.2 Mil 123.55
Cold Lake CFB, AB: AD 119.4 120.6 124.5 128.2 134.1 248.4 279.8 289.4 294.6 322.8 324.3 336.0 350.5 378.5 S 260.0 T 126.2 226.5 236.6 255.7 G 121.9 275.8 E 124.5 230.6 WX 344.3 Terminal 120.6 322.8 Base OP 340.2 Base Flight OP 308.7
Collingwood Apt., ONT: FSS 296.2
Comox CFB, BC: AD 123.7 128.1 134.1 227.6 289.4 335.9 342.9 378.5 384.5 S 118.6 282.2 T 126.2 358.1 236.6 Terminal 123.7 227.6 442nd Sqdn OP ("Snake OP") 363.0 407th Sqdn VP & VS OP ("Demon Ops") 308.6 VU33 OP ("Anchor Ops") 278.4 Base OP 316.5 WX 344.6
Corner Brook RCMP Heliport, NF: OP 123.2 155.58 155.64 155.67 155.70 155.82 155.88 415.5375
Cranbrook Apt., BC: FSS 262.7
Cree Lake Fld., SASK: Environment Canada OP 122.8
Dauphin Apt., MAN: FSS 297.0
Deer Lake Apt., NF: FSS 239.6
Dewar Lakes North Warning System Fld., NWT: Air Defence Identification Zone 123.55 126.7 256.6 263.2 274.4 364.2
Discovery Island CG Heliport, BC: OP 122.2 126.7
Drummondville Apt., QC: AD 266.0
Earlton Apt., ONT: FSS 296.2
Edmonton Int'l. Apt., AB: AD 363.8 T 381.2 G 275.6
Edmonton Muni. Apt., AB: AD 226.3 T 283.7 Medevac 122.45
Edmonton/Namao CFB, AB: AD 226.3 S 244.5 T 118.0 126.2 236.6 294.7 325.9 G 121.8 275.8 WX 344.6 VFR Advisories 121.1 238.3 Airbase OP 131.4 383.7 (HF 3046 3092 4704 5718 6705 6746 8989 9006 11233 11265 11271 13257 15031 17995 18012 kHz) (WX HF 6753 15035 kHz)
Egg Island Light Station CG Heliport, BC: OP 123.2
Elliot Lake Muni. Apt., ONT: AD 260.9 296.2
Entrance Island CG Heliport, BC: OP 123.2
Esquimalt CFB, BC: MP 149.14 Military 149.345
Estevan Point CG Heliport, BC: OP 132.2
Ethelda Bay Radio Beacon CG Station Heliport, BC: OP 126.7
Florenceville Apt., NB: FSS 295.0
Ft. Frances Muni. Apt., ONT: FSS 327.7
Ft. McMurray Apt, AB: T 236.6
Ft. Nelson Apt., BC: AD 290.6 FSS 295.0 (HF 5860 kHz)
Ft. St. John Apt., BC: AD 285.4 T 295.8
Ft. Simpson Apt., NWT: FSS 296.6
Ft. Smith, NWT: FSS 239.8
Fredericton Apt., NB: AD 270.8 FSS 295.0 T 236.6 G 275.8
Gagetown CFB, NB: Heliport T 126.2 126.4 245.8 321.8 403rd Sqdn OP 34.80 321.8 Security 149.65 FD/Crash 149.14 Military 45.80 46.95 49.90
Gander Int'l. Apt., NF: AD 384.5 T 236.6 G 275.8 Military ("Outcast Ops") 128.85 252.8
Gladman Point North Warning System Fld., NWT: Air Defence Identification Zone 126.7 228.9 251.0 263.2 364.2
Goderich Apt., ONT: AD 266.3 FSS 321.3
Goose Bay/Goose Apt., NF: AD 267.1 FSS 296.2 (HF 5680 kHz) AD 128.1 340.8 T 236.6 G 275.8 E 336.5 Terminal 267.1 CF OP 129.85 350.5 RAF Ranger OP 119.2 129.3 USAF MAC CP 319.4

Grand Forks Apt., BC: FSS 286.6 295.4

Grande Prairie Apt., AB: T 266.8

Greenwood CFB, NS: AD 120.6 335.9 S 244.3 T 119.5 126.2 236.6 324.3 G 133.75 289.4 E 120.6 335.9 Ramp OP 308.6 WX 344.6

Halifax Int'l. Apt., NS: AD 225.2 363.8 S 229.1 T 236.6 G 275.8 RCMP 155.88 410.0125

Halifax/Shearwater CFB, NS: AD 119.2 119.7 120.4 126.2 340.2 360.2 S 271.8 T 119.0 126.2 340.2 360.2 G 121.7 250.1 WX 344.6 OP 308.8 (HF 2660 5703 6708 kHz)

Hall Beach North Warning System Fld., NWT: Air Defence Identification Zone 123.55 126.7 228.9 256.6 263.2 364.2

Hamilton Apt., ONT: AD 290.8 T 308.475 G 398.125

Inuvik Apt., NWT: FSS 262.7

Iqaluit Apt., NWT: FSS 296.2

Ivory Island Light Station CG Heliport, BC: OP 123.2

Jenny Lind Island North Warning System Fld., NWT: Air Defence Identification Zone 126.7 364.2

Kamloops Apt., BC: AD 236.0 254.0 T 297.0

Kelowna Apt., BC: T 292.2

Kenora Apt., ONT: AD 225.2 245.0 FSS 327.7

Killaloe/Bonnechere Apt., ONT: FSS 238.3

Kingston Apt., ONT: AD 238.3

Kingston CFB, ONT: MP 169.56 Military 148.825 149.15 149.80 FSS 238.3

Komakuk Beach North Warning System, YT: Air Defence Identification Zone 126.7 364.2

Lady Franklin Point North Warning System Fld., NWT: Air Defence Identification Zone 123.55 126.7 251.0 256.6 270.4 364.2

La Grande Riviere Apt., QC: AD 282.3

Lahr CFB, Germany: S 360.15 AD 123.3 123.825 284.55 361.7 384.45 T 119.75 122.1 257.8 385.85 G 275.7 E 264.35 "444" OP 38.95 72.80 HF OP 3092 4704 5690 6705 9006 11233 13231 13257 15031 18012 kHz

Lennard Island CG Heliport, BC: OP 123.2

Lester B. Pearson Int'l Apt, Toronto, ON: AD 358.1 363.8 T 236.6 VFR Advisories 253.1

Lethbridge Apt., AB: T 236.6

Lindsay Apt., ONT: FSS 296.2

Lloydminster Apt., AB: AD 340.7

London Apt., ONT: AD 266.3 T 236.6 G 360.2

London CFB, ONT: MP 172.25 Military 169.89 173.20

Longstaff Bluff North Warning System Fld., NWT: Air Defence Identification Zone 126.7 364.2

Lucy Island Light Station CG Heliport, BC: OP 123.2

Mackar Inlet North Warning System Fld., NWT: Air Defence Identification Zone 126.7 364.2

Masset CG Heliport, BC: OP 123.2

McInnes Island Light Station CG Heliport, BC: 123.2

Merry Island CG Heliport, BC: OP 123.2

Moncton Apt., NB: AD 384.8 T 236.6 G 275.8

Mont-Joli Apt., QC: AD 227.2

Montreal/Bell Heliport, QC: OP 130.2 382.6 (HF 5560.4 kHz)

Montreal/Cartiervlle Apt., QC: OP 123.25 123.0 260.0 E 125.6

Montreal/Dorval Int'l. Apt., QC: AD 268.3 287.2 323.2 T 267.1 G 275.8 VFR Advisories 268.3

Montreal/Longueuil Heliport, QC: Environment Canada OP 118.4 126.7

Montreal/Mirabel Int'l. Apt., QC: AD 287.2 323.2   T 282.4   G 246.6   VFR Advisories 350.7

Montreal/St-Hubert Apt., QC: AD 268.3 287.2 352.5   T 352.5   G 283.4   Military 40.90 135.9 322.1

Moose Jaw CFB, SASK: AD 119.0 134.1 135.3 227.6 230.1 234.4 274.5 289.4 308.3 318.8 342.9 374.1 378.5 381.3   S 114.8 257.8   T 126.2 295.6 310.8   G 121.8 275.8 WX 344.6   2nd CFFTS OP 340.1

Mountain View CFB, ONT: AD 268.0

Muskoka Apt., ONT: FSS 351.3

Nanaimo Apt., BC: FSS 291.8

Nicholson Peninsula North Warning System Fld., NWT: Air Defence Identification Zone 126.7 364.2

Nootka CG Heliport, BC: OP 123.2

Norman Wells Apt., NWT: FSS 282.3

North Battleford Apt., SASK: FSS 295.0

North Bay CFB, ONT: AD 127.25 132.375 135.5 136.5 233.4 285.7 325.8 356.3 FSS 115.4 122.5 126.7 296.2   S 124.9 228.2   T 118.3 236.6 257.2   G 121.9 275.8 WX 344.6   Transient OP 308.8   414th Sqdn OP 360.4   Security 149.65   FD/Crash 149.80   Base Transportation 149.35

North Bay/Trans Canada Pipelines Heliport, ONT: FSS 296.2   T 236.6 257.2

Oshawa Apt, ON: T 358.1

Ottawa/Gatineau Apt., ONT: AD 266.8

Ottawa Int'l. Apt/CFB, ONT: AD 252.5 247.0   S 265.6   T 236.6 341.3   G 275.8   E 283.5   WX 344.6   Base OP 131.35 308.7

Ottawa/National Defence Medical Centre, ONT: T 118.8 236.6   Base OP 121.35 308.7

Pachena Point CG Heliport, BC: OP 123.2

Parry Sound/Georgian Bay Apt., ONT: FSS 351.3

Pelly Bay North Warning System Fld., NWT: Air Defence Identification Zone 126.7 364.2

Pembroke Apt., ONT: AD 278.5   FSS 238.3

Penticton Apt., BC: AD 294.0   T 295.4

Petawawa CFB, ONT: AD 235.2 278.5   Unicom 122.8   Air/Ground 45.80 126.4 236.6 250.1   WX 46.95 278.5   Range 49.90   407th Sqdn OP 40.90   Military 163.05

Peterborough Apt., ONT: FSS 296.2

Pine Island CG Heliport, BC: OP 123.2

Porter Island Light Station CG Heliport, BC: 123.2

Portage CFB, MAN: AD 125.2 358.4   S 111.8 120.85 270.5   T 119.2 126.2 236.6 384.2   G 121.7 275.8   WX 344.6   "Viking Ops" 253.6   "Bengal Ops" 123.325 "Ranger Ops" 128.975

Port Hardy Apt., BC: AD 266.3

Powell River Apt., BC: FSS 296.6

Prince Albert Apt., SASK: FSS 262.0

Prince George Apt., BC: AD 231.95   FSS 327.7   T 327.7

Prince George/All Heliports, BC: 327.7

Prince Rupert Apt., BC: AD 284.0

Prince Rupert/Seal Cove Heliports, BC: FSS 122.5

Princeton Apt., BC: AD 351.3

Prophet River Apt., BC: Public Works Canada OP 123.2

Pulteney Point CG Heliport, BC: AD 123.2

Quatsino CG Heliport, BC: AD 123.2

Quebec Apt., Quebec, QC: AD 270.8 322.8   T 236.6   G 236.6

Race Rocks CG Heliport, BC: OP 123.2

Red Deer Indst'l. Apt., AB: AD 239.0

Regina Apt., SASK: AD 266.3 279.8 283.4 FSS 279.8 T 236.6 G 277.3

Riviere-du-Loup Apt., QC: AD 299.6

Rockliffe CFB, ONT: Military 149.35

Saglek North Warning System Fld., NF: FSS 126.7 364.2

St. Anthony Apt., NF: AD 321.9

St. Catherines Apt., ONT: AD 290.8

St. Georges Apt., QC: AD 266.0

St.-Honore, QC: T 237.4

St.-Jean, QC: AD 268.3 287.2 T 356.8

Saint John Apt., NB: AD 270.8 T 236.6 Military 149.11

Saint John's Apt., NF: AD 227.3 230.3 245.0 S 293.6 T 236.6 G 275.8 E 245.0
Security 413.2125 (CFB HF 3092 4704 5718 6705 9006 11233 13257 15031 17995 18012
kHz) (WX HF 6753 15035 kHz)

St. Thomas Apt., ONT: AD 266.3

Sandspit Apt., BC: AD 227.2 FSS 296.2

Sarnia Apt., ONT: AD 254.9

Saskatoon Apt., SASK: AD 239.8 323.0 S 276.8 T 244.7 G 275.8

Saturnia Island/East Point CG Heliport, BC: OP 123.2

Sault Ste Marie Apt., ONT: AD 227.3 344.5 T 236.6

Schefferville Apt., QC: AD 381.4

Sept-Iles Apt., QC: AD 368.5 381.9 T 236.6

Shearwater CFB, NS: See Halifax/Shearwater listings.

Shepherd Bay North Warning System Fld., NWT: Air Defence Identification Zone
123.55 126.7 228.9 251.0 263.2 364.2

Sherbrooke Apt., QC: AD 226.0

Shilo CFB, MAN: Base OP 241.8

Shingle Point North Warning System Fld., NWT: Air Defence Identification Zone
123.55 126.7 256.6 269.9 274.4 364.2

Shirley Bay CFB, ONT: Military 413.4375

Sisters Islets CG Heliport, BC: OP 123.2

Slave Lake Apt., AB: AD 304.2

Smithers Apt., BC: FSS 262.7

Stephenville Apt., NF: AD 228.3 247.0 FSS 279.9 E 247.0

Stirling Apt., ONT: AD 398.4

Stratford Muni. Apt., ONT: FSS 321.3

Sudbury Apt., ONT: T 233.8

Suffield CFB, AB: T 126.2 Range Control 49.90

Summerside CFB, PEI: AD 124.4 384.8 T 120.2 123.85 236.6 294.7 325.9 WX
344.6 OP 308.6

Swift Current Apt., SASK: AD 232.3 FSS 351.3

Sydney Apt., NS: AD 266.3 T 236.6

Terrace Apt., BC: AD 269.1 FSS 239.8

Thompson Apt, MB: FSS 341.3 (HF 5680 kHz) T 341.3

Thunder Bay Apt., ONT: AD 297.6 363.8 S 285.3 T 236.6 G 275.8

Thunder Bay/Pt. Arthur Gen. Hosp. Heliport, ONT: T 236.6

Tillsonburg Apt., ONT: FSS 321.3

Timmons Apt., ONT: AD 226.3 381.4

Tofino Apt., BC: AD 254.9

Tofino Lifeboat Station CG Heliport, BC: OP 123.0

Toronto/Buttonville Apt., ONT: AD 358.1 363.8

Toronto/Downsview Apt., ONT: AD 358.1 363.8 OP 126.2 295.6 G 126.2 295.6
2nd TAW OP 40.90 Security 150.25 Military 34.70 149.14 149.15 149.35 149.65
149.80 150.065 164.52

Toronto Island Apt., ONT: AD 358.1 363.8 T 226.5

Trail Apt., BC: FSS 295.4

Trenton CFB, ONT: AD 128.4 324.3 S 135.45 257.7 G 121.9 275.8 WX 344.6
Base OP 268.0 "Tiger Ops" 232.1 Terminal Cntrl 128.4 275.8 Military 127.75
149.80 (HF 3046 3092 4704 5718 6705 6746 8989 9006 11233 11265 11271 13257 15031
17995 18012 23250 kHz) (HF WX 6753 15035 kHz)

Trois-Rivieres Apt., QC: AD 245.0

Tuktoyaktuk North Warning System Fld., NWT: FSS 122.2 Air Defence
Identification Zone 126.7 364.2

Uplands CFB, ONT: FD 149.35 Military 149.215 149.65 460.20

Valcartier CFB Heliport, QC: T 45.80 126.2 307.6 430th Sqdn OP ("Zero") 34.80

Val-d-Or Apt, QC: AD 308.3 T 236.6

Vancouver Int'l. Apt, BC: AD 352.7 363.8 T 226.5 236.6 G 275.8

Vancouver/Heliports, BC: T 301.1

Vancouver/Point Atkinson CG Heliport, BC: OP 123.2

Victoria Apt., BC: AD 290.8 308.4 T 239.6 G 361.4

Wabush Apt., NF: FSS 296.2

Wainright/Camp Wainright Fld & Fld 21-West, AB: Military 49.90 229.8

Waterloo-Guelph Regn'l. Apt., ONT: AD 268.75

Watson Lake Apt., YT: FSS 287.0

Watson Lake Heliport, YT: AD 298.6

Whitecourt Apt., AB: AD 293.7

Whitehorse Apt., YT: AD 290.6 FSS 286.2 T 236.6

Wiarton, ONT: AD 290.6 FSS 321.3

Williams Lake Apt., BC: AD 381.4

Windsor Apt., ONT: AD 363.2 T 236.6

Winnipeg Apt. & CFB, MAN: AD 356.6 366.5 S 291.4 T 236.6 325.9 G 275.8 E
283.5 VFR Advisories 341.3 CFB OP 131.4 308.8 WX 308.8

Winnipeg/St. Andrews Apt., MAN: T 226.5 G 284.3

Yarmouth Apt., NS: AD 368.5 FSS 295.8

Yellowknife Apt., NWT: FSS 262.0 T 340.8 G 121.9

Yorkton Apt., SASK: FSS 296.6

PILOT TO METRO SERVICE AND WX RADAR FACILITIES

Pilots will make maximum use of PMSV when requesting or reporting enroute weather. When changing to PMSV frequency notify the appropriate ATC unit.

PILOT TO METRO AND WEATHER RADAR FACILITIES

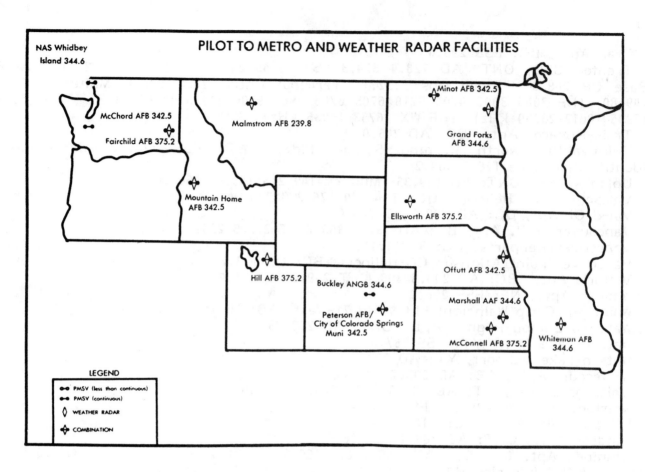

NAS Whidbey Island 344.6

McChord AFB 342.5
Fairchild AFB 375.2
Malmstrom AFB 239.8
Minot AFB 342.5
Grand Forks AFB 344.6
Mountain Home AFB 342.5
Ellsworth AFB 375.2
Hill AFB 375.2
Buckley ANGB 344.6
Offutt AFB 342.5
Peterson AFB/ City of Colorado Springs Muni 342.5
Marshall AAF 344.6
McConnell AFB 375.2
Whiteman AFB 344.6

LEGEND
•—• PMSV (less than continuous)
•—• PMSV (continuous)
◊ WEATHER RADAR
✦ COMBINATION

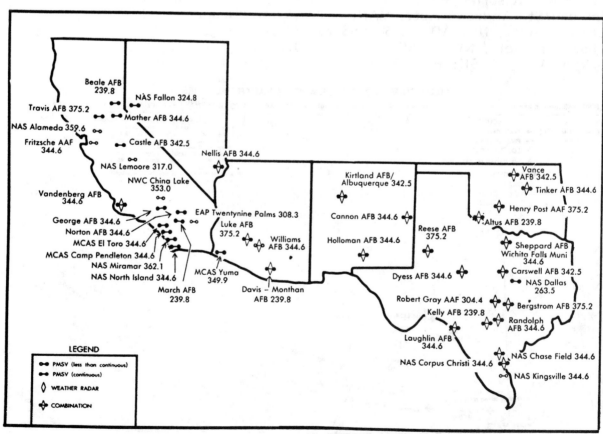

Beale AFB 239.8
NAS Fallon 324.8
Travis AFB 375.2
Mather AFB 344.6
NAS Alameda 359.6
Fritzsche AAF 344.6
Castle AFB 342.5
Nellis AFB 344.6
NAS Lemoore 317.0
NWC China Lake 353.0
Vandenberg AFB 344.6
EAP Twentynine Palms 308.3
George AFB 344.6
Luke AFB 375.2
Norton AFB 344.6
Williams AFB 344.6
MCAS El Toro 344.6
MCAS Camp Pendleton 344.6
NAS Miramar 362.1
NAS North Island 344.6
MCAS Yuma 349.9
March AFB 239.8
Davis – Monthan AFB 239.8
Kirtland AFB/ Albuquerque 342.5
Cannon AFB 344.6
Holloman AFB 344.6
Reese AFB 375.2
Vance AFB 342.5
Tinker AFB 344.6
Henry Post AAF 375.2
Altus AFB 239.8
Sheppard AFB Wichita Falls Muni 344.6
Carswell AFB 342.5
NAS Dallas 263.5
Dyess AFB 344.6
Bergstrom AFB 375.2
Robert Gray AAF 304.4
Randolph AFB 344.6
Kelly AFB 239.8
Laughlin AFB 344.6
NAS Chase Field 344.6
NAS Corpus Christi 344.6
NAS Kingsville 344.6

LEGEND
•—• PMSV (less than continuous)
•—• PMSV (continuous)
◊ WEATHER RADAR
✦ COMBINATION

136

PILOT TO METRO AND WEATHER RADAR FACILITIES

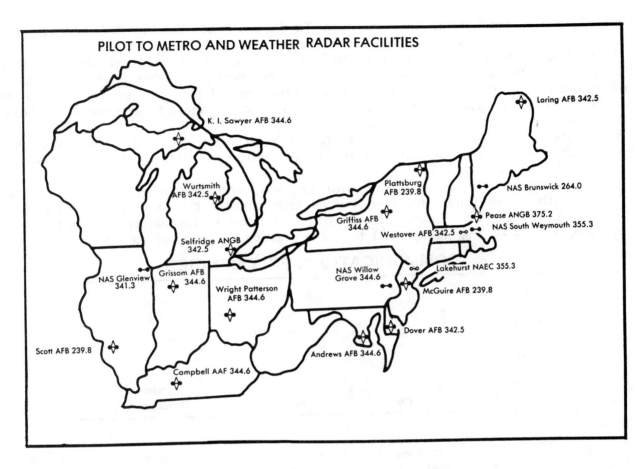

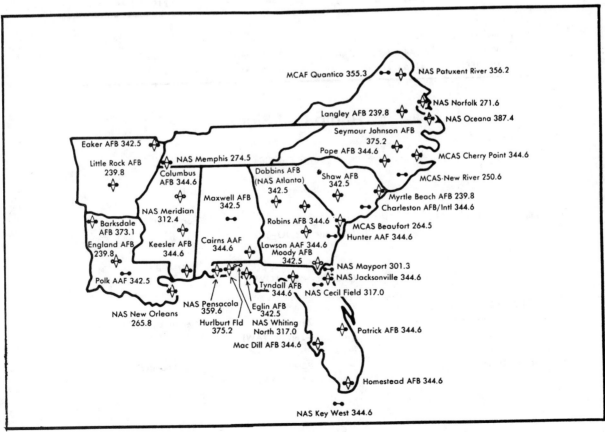

How U.S. & Russian Forces Are Supposed To Communicate During A Confrontation

According to U.S. Department of Defense information current at the time this Registry was published, certain specific communications procedures have been mutually agreed upon by the USA and the Russians. These procedures are to be used "to avoid dangerous military activities and peacefully resolving related incidents."

The agreed upon procedures are to be followed when the armed forces of one nation enter the national territory of the other nation, either unintentionally or as the result of an invasion.

The procedures are broken down into air, sea, and ground related encounters, and specify the communications frequencies that should be used by the opposing military units to inter-communicate in an effort to resolve the matter peacefully.

Here is a copy of the designated frequency and call sign information.

COMMUNICATIONS FREQUENCIES

Operation	Primary Initial Contact	Alternate Frequencies	Sustained Communications
Air–related:			
VHF	121.5 MHz		130.0 MHz
UHF	243.0 MHz		278.0 MHz
HF (USB)	4125.0 kHz	6215.5 kHz	4125.0 kHz
Sea–related:			
VHF	156.8 MHz		156.8 MHz
HF (USB)	2182.0 kHz		2182.0 kHz
Ground–related:			
VHF	44.0 MHz	46.5 MHz	44.0 MHz
HF (USB)	4125.0 kHz	6215.5 kHz	4125.0 kHz

Radio Call Signs

Platform	Call Sign	
	Soviet	US
Ship	"Bugel" (phonetic— BOO–gel)	"Port Mast"
Aircraft	"Sedlo" (phonetic— Sed–LOW)	"Ivory Eagle"
Air Traffic Control or Monitoring Facility	"Zemlya" (phonetic—Zem–le–YAW)	"Electric Light"
Ground Force or Unit	"Polya" (phonetic—Po–le–YAW)	"Post Pounder"

General Accounting Office (GAO)

Washington, DC: 409.40

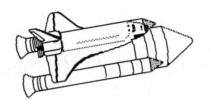

Aeronautics & Space Administration, National (NASA)

Also see additional NASA listings at specific locations shown in the the forward section.

NASA Aircraft & Ships. In addition to any other frequencies listed, aircraft and ships may also be operating on: 117.8 118.4 120.7 126.3 127.8 148.22 148.50 149.10 162.00 163.10 164.80 168.35 231.0 240.4 240.6 240.8 241.0 241.2 241.6 241.8 242.0 256.2 (HF 2625 5190 5696 5810 6693 6893 7464 8891 9043 9125 9131 10780 11205 11407 13170 15015 18200 kHz)

NASA Aircraft Roster: Gulfstream G-159= N2NA N3NA N4NA N5NA;   Gulfstream G-1159= N1NA N650PF N944NA N946NA N947NA;   Beech King 200= N7NA N8NA N9NA N701NA;   Molino 1PK= N38DP;   Lear Jet 25= N266GL N616NA;   Schweitzer SGS= N502NA N7794S;   Cessna 402B= N503NA;   Beech Musketeer 23C= N504NA;   Cessna 310= N505NA;   Beech Queen 80= N506NA;   Cessna 172K= N507NA;   Beech Mentor= N510A N614NA;   Bell 204= N416NA N417NA N418NA N530NA;   Lockheed 188= N428NA N429NA;   Shorts SC7= N430NA;   North American T-39= N431NA;   Northrop T-38= N511NA N821NA N901NA N902NA N904NA N906NA N907NA N908NA N909NA N910NA N912NA N913NA N914NA N915NA N916NA N917NA N918NA N920NS N921NS N923NA N924NA N955NA N956NA;   Bell 301= N703NA;   Lear Jet 24= N705NA;   Lockheed 33= N706NA N709NA;   Convair 880= N710NA;   Lockheed 300= N714NA;   DeHavilland DHC-5= N715NA;   Douglas DC-8= N717NA;   Lockheed 3YO= N718NA;   Sikorsky S-72= N740NA N741NA;   Piper PA-30= N808NA;   Lockheed 104F= N824NA N825NA N826NA;   Boeing 747= N905NA N911NA;   Boeing 377SG= N940NS;   Bell 206A= N950NS

Ames Research Center: See Moffett NAS & Crows Landing NALF
Dryden Research Center: See Edwards AFB
Goddard Space Flight Center, Greenbelt, MD: Security 170.35   FD 170.075 Maintenance 408.15   Pager 163.10 164.175   FEMA 167.6625 167.925   NASA 148.25 148.98 149.52 149.82 154.40 167.825 167.925 170.025 170.40 171.00 171.15 173.6625 173.6875 412.00
Goldstone Space Tracking Facility, CA: NASA 123.0 148.25 148.26 148.98 149.52 154.20 162.025 162.6125 164.20 164.9875 259.7 296.8 314.6 382.6 406.225 410.00 413.825

Jet Propulsion Labs, Pasadena, CA: NASA 122.85 162.025 162.6125 163.00 168.35 170.35 171.00 406.225 410.00

Johnson Space Flight Center, Houston, TX: Maintenance 168.00 NASA 164.00 164.9875 168.45 169.00 169.40 169.60 170.10 171.15 173.6875 314.6 382.6 FAA 164.05

Kennedy Space Center: See listings in front section of directory.

Langley Research Center: See Langley AFB

Lewisburg, TN: 240.0 240.8 241.2 242.0

Lewis Research Center, Cleveland, OH: NASA 122.85 123.3 164.125 164.175 164.225 164.275 170.35 170.40 311.2 314.6 Medics 155.34 155.40

Marshall Space Center: See Redstone AAF

Merritt Island, FL: 148.25 148.56 148.98 149.52 154.20 259.7 296.8

Michaud Plant, LA: NASA 173.7875

National Space Technical Laboratories, Bay St. Louis, MS: NASA 162.0125 164.20 166.625 170.35 170.40 171.00 171.15 173.7375 173.6625 173.6875 173.7875

New Orleans, LA: NASA 162.0125 164.20 164.9725 164.9875 168.45 173.7375 FEMA 167.975

Palestine, TX: NASA 40.82 138.75 406.225 410.00

Rosman Earth Station, NC: NASA 148.25 148.26 148.98 149.52 149.56 149.82 154.20 171.475 172.225

Sandusky, OH: NASA 122.85 123.3 164.125 164.175 164.225 164.275 170.40 314.6 382.6

Washington, DC: NASA 162.025

Also monitor: 40.87 46.73 49.73 49.80 49.83 121.75 122.8 123.175 123.2 123.225 123.375 123.4 123.45 138.54 162.125 163.00 163.025 164.10 164.70 164.975 165.325 165.6125 167.975 169.60 170.125 170.175 170.20 171.3875 171.475 171.50 171.525 171.55 171.575 171.60 172.225 173.025 173.075 173.4125 173.6125 173.6375 173.7375 235.0 240.2 241.4 264.8 279.0 371.1 394.3 395.1 407.175 408.00 408.625 408.80 409.125 409.20 413.825 417.65 418.05 418.575 419.15 (HF 2207.4 2431.4 2541.4 2624 2678 3380 3383.5 3385 3395 4510 4760 4855 5350 6223 6723 6740 6896 6982.5 7675 7723.5 8993 9315 9974 10780 11104 11416 11548 11805 13218 14455 14615 19306 20089 20185 20390 20475 22745 25590 27575 27585 27725 27900 kHz)

Space Shuttle UHF (NFM): Pri-296.8 Sec-259.7 Onboard-279.0

Agriculture, Department of (USDA)

The USDA is an active communication that has gained increasing popularity with monitors ever since the 6th Edition of this registry broke the ice with the first extensive frequency listing for the agency. Our National Forests are crawling with poachers and marijuana growers. Our ports of entry receive arrivals of agricultural items from overseas, including marijuana. Because of this, the USDA plays an important role in the area of inspection and enforcement to protect the public against banned, adulterated, unclean, polluted, contaminated, bug-infested, and spoiled foodstuffs, live animals, and plants. All this, in addition to the agency's activities in the areas of soil conservation, maintaining our nation's forestlands, inspecting domestic agricultural products and their processing, etc., etc. Because the USDA is active in so many urban and rural areas, an on so many levels, it turns out to be a very interesting agency to monitor.

The 229-million acres of forest under the control of the USDA are known to be outfitted with at least eight different types of surveillance systems ranging from telephone taps to closed-circuit TV. Mail interception is also used. Sensors are placed strategically throughout National Forests to keep tabs on human and wildlife activities. Even with these systems, a special force (500-strong) attempts to locate marijuana growers. This force works in close cooperation and coordination with the DEA as well as state and county enforcement agencies.

We list here active USDA in some metro areas, as well as those in National Forests (NF) and National Grasslands (NG), plus other USDA information of use and interest to monitors.

USDA Plum Island Animal Disease Lab, NY: 36.43
USDA Soil Conservation Service: 170.60/172.40 171.075 172.225
USDA Work Centers: 169.925/170.575
USDA Common Repeater Pairs: 164.825/164.125 164.975/? 164.9875/? 166.125/164.625 168.25/168.025 168.625/168.025 168.675/168.075 168.675/168.175 168.70/170.975 168.725/168.125 168.75/168.025 168.75/168.20 168.75/170.50 168.775/172.225 169.125/169.975 169.125/171.075 169.175/169.975 169.875/170.475 169.90/170.50 169.925/169.15 169.925/169.175 169.925/170.525 170.425/? 170.50/168.175 170.55/171.55 170.575/169.95 170.575/171.525 170.975/166.975 171.45/? 171.475/172.225 171.525/170.525 171.525/170.55 171.525/170.575 171.525/172.325 171.575/172.25 172.35/? 172.575/172.375 415.225/411.225 415.25/411.25 415.275/411.275 415.30/411.30 415.325/411.325 415.35/411.35 415.375/411.375 415.40/411.40 415.425/411.425 415.45/411.45 415.475/411.475 415.50/411.50 415.525/411.525 415.55/411.55 415.75/411.75

USDA Forest Fire Fighting Frequencies:
VHF Aero Band: 118,825 118.95 118.975 119.95 119.975 122.75 122.8 122.85 122.9 122.925 123.05 123.075
Air Tactics Ch #1 166.675; Ch #2 169.15; Ch #3 169.20; Ch #4 170.00
Tactical Ch #1 168.05; Ch #2 168.20; Ch #3 168.60
Command Ch #1 168.70/170.975; Ch #2 168.10/170.45; Ch #3 168.075/170.425; Ch #4 168.125/168.725
Logistics Ch #1 414.65/410.775; Ch #2 415.40/411.40; Ch #3 415.50/411.50

USDA Aircraft Roster: Beech Baron 58= N110Z N112Z N120Z N121Z N131Z N133Z N144Z N145Z N150Z N151Z N155Z N156Z N157Z N158Z N159Z N163Z N166Z N185Z N193Z; Beech 99= N140Z; Beech 18= N165ZA N166ZA; Beech Queen 80; 128Z; Beech King 90= N104Z; Beech King 200= N107Z; Rockwell 5008= N7775S; Rockwell 680F= N181Z; Cessna 206= N616 N8604Z N9486G N72306; Cessna 210M= N49RF; Cessna 550= N52RF; Cessna 199C= N2182J; Piper PA-18= N744 N751 N752; Piper PA-23250= N613A; Callair S-182= N734; Hughes 269C= N796 N1099N; Douglas BC-3= N100Z; Bell 212= N46RF; DeHavilland DHC-6= N141Z; Swearingen SA-26T= N187Z; Ayres 52R= N4002Y

USDA in Metro Areas:
AL   Mobile 171.525 415.30
AK   Anchorage 168.025; Juneau 168.025

```
AZ    Tucson 415.325
CA    Los Angeles 164.9125;   Oakland 162.225;   San Francisco 168.625
CO    Boulder 164.9875;   Denver 415.425;   Pueblo 170.45
DC    Washington 169.15
FL    Jacksonville 172.275;   Miami 164.9375 171.525
GA    Atlanta 168.025 168.625 171.525 172.375 415.275
IL    Peoria 164.125
ID    Boise 168.025 412.625 415.40;   Pocatello 168.025
IA    Ames 170.475
LA    New Orleans 169.15 169.90 169.975 170.50 172.25
MA    Boston 171.525; Waltham 171.525
ME    Augusta 171.525;   Bangor 171.525
MD    Baltimore 171.525 415.30
MN    Minneapolis 415.30
MS    Gulfport 171.525
MO    Kansas City 415.30;   Saint Louis 415.30
NE    Omaha 415.30
NV    Reno 169.275
NJ    Elizabeth 171.525 171.575
NY    Brooklyn 171.425 171.525;   Jamaica/JFK 169.1875;   NY City 163.225 171.4125
   171.525 171.575;   Westhampton 171.525
NC    Goldsboro 170.45;   Raleigh 170.45 170.50 171.525;   Wilmington 171.525
OH    Toledo 415.30
OR    Corvallis 169.60;   Portland 168.025 168.775
PA    Philadelphia 171.525 415.30
TN    Knoxville 168.025 168.625
TX    Beaumont 415.30;   Galveston 415.30;   Dallas 169.95;   Houston 166.5625
   415.30;   Lubbock 171.525
UT    Salt Lake City 412.625
VA    Portsmouth 415.30
WA    Seattle 415.30
WI    Madison 164.9375;   Milwaukee 168.625 415.425
PR    San Juan 171.275 171.525 172.325
```

National Forests & National Grasslands

Alabama
Conecuh NF: 168.725 169.325
Talladega NF: 169.725 169.325 415.525
Tuskegee NF: 168.725 169.325
William B. Bankhead NF: 168.725
Alaska
Cugach NF: 168.025 168.625 169.975 169.925 169.975 415.55

Tongass NF: 168.025 168.625 169.125 169.875 169.925 169.975 415.225 415.55
Arizona
Apache-Sitgreaves NF: 169.875 169.95
Coconino NF: 39.18 171.55 172.30 415.35
Coronado NF: 170.55 415.325 415.475 415.525 415.575
Kaibab NF: 169.90 170.50
Prescott NF: 168.175 413.90 415.325 415.475 415.55
Tonto NF: 32.19 164.825 415.275 415.325 415.375 415.40
Arkansas
Ouachita NF: 168.625 169.175 169.90

Ozark NF: 168.625 171.575 172.375 415.475
St. Francis NF: 169.875
California
Angeles NF: 164.125 164.825 168.125 168.20 168.60 169.125 169.175 169.20 169.95
  170.00 171.575 172.375 415.225 415.325 415.35 415.425 415.55
Cleveland NF: 164.125 164.825 166.675 168.05 168.125 168.15 168.20 168.625 168.75
  170.00 415.25 415.275 415.45 415.525 415.55
Eldorado NF: 164.125 166.25 168.025 168.625 168.775 171.525 172.325 415.225 415.325
  415.525 415.575
Inyo NF: 164.9125 166.675 168.125 168.725 170.60 171.40 171.50 172.40 412.40 413.90
  415.25 415.275 415.35 415.475 415.55
Klamath NF: 36.75 38.58 38.75 164.175 164.975 166.5625 166.675 168.025 168.15
  168.625 168.75 170.425 171.50 415.325 415.35 415.375 415.425 415.475 415.525 415.55
Lassen NF: 164.10 164.80 164.9125 166.675 168.625 169.95 171.475 172.225 415.35
  415.525 415.55 415.575
Los Padres NF: 166.675 168.625 169.90 170.475 170.55 171.55 415.25 415.325 415.40
  415.425 415.475 415.525
Mendocino NF: 36.77 164.9375 168.025 168.625 169.15 169.175 169.975 171.55 171.70
  172.40 415.275 415.35 415.425 415.525 415.55
Modoc NF: 164.10 164.80 164.9125 168.15 168.75 169.20 170.175 170.425 415.25
  415.35 415.375 415.475 415.525 415.55
Plumas NF: 164.125 164.825 169.15 169.90 170.55 171.425 172.35 415.225 415.325
  415.35 415.475 415.525
San Bernardino NF: 164.125 164.825 168.65 168.80 169.15 169.875 169.925 170.00
171.475 172.225 172.575 415.525 415.55 415.575
Sequoia NF: 164.825 168.025 168.175 168.625 168.675 168.775 169.15 170.425 170.575
  171.50 412.20 415.225 415.275 415.375 415.45 415.525 417.65
Shasta-Trinity NF: 36.75 38.58 164.10 164.125 164.80 164.825 164.9375 168.025
  168.625 169.10 169.15 169.20 169.875 170.4875 171.575 172.225 172.375 415.225
  415.275 415.375 415.45 415.475 415.55
Sierra NF: 164.15 164.825 164.9125 168.025 168.625 169.20 169.875 170.60 171.40
  171.475 407.175 409.65 409.225 415.325 415.35 415.425 415.475 415.525 415.55
  415.575 419.65
Six Rivers NF: 36.65 38.85 39.67 164.125 164.175 164.825 164.9125 164.975 168.125
  168.625 168.725 169.20 169.625 170.125 407.65 409.15 409.65 410.20 412.40 413.90
  415.225 415.325 415.55
Stanislaus NF: 41.53 168.10 168.15 168.20 168.60 168.75/170.50 170.00 171.10 171.50
  171.525 172.325 415.375
Tahoe NF: 36.41 36.65 38.37 38.55 168.025 168.175 168.775 169.20 169.275 170.575
  171.50 172.40 409.15 409.65 412.40 415.35 415.45 415.475 415.55 419.15 419.65
Colorado
Arapaho NF: 164.10 169.175 169.875 169.975 415.425
Comanche NG: 169.90
Grand Mesa-Uncompahgre NF: 164.125 164.825 166.5875 168.025
Gunnison NF: 164.125 166.5875 168.025 168.625 169.15 415.325 415.525
Pawnee NG: 168.175 169.975
Pike NF: 164.9375 168.125 168.725 169.90 170.475 415.475
Rio Grande NF: 41.53 164.15 164.9125 168.025 168.625 415.525
Roosevelt NF: 164.10 164.9375 164.9875 169.175 169.975 170.475 415.425
Routt NF: 164.825 166.425 168.025 168.625 169.10 169.60 415.525
San Isabel NF: 164.825 168.125 169.90 415.325 415.475
San Juan NF: 41.53 169.925 170.525 415.325
White River NF: 169.925 170.525

Florida
Apalachicola NF: 164.825/164.125 168.675/168.075
Ocala NF: 164.825/164.125 168.675/168.075
Osceola NF: 164.825/164.125 168.675/168.075
Georgia
Chattahoochie NF: 164.825/164.125 168.625 415.275 415.475
Oconee NF: 164.825/164.125 168.625 415.275 415.475
Idaho
Boise NF: 168.025 168.625 169.175 169.95 171.45 172.20 172.25 412.625 415.30 415.40
   415.45 415.475 415.50 415.525 415.55
Caribou NF: 168.025 168.625 171.475 172.225 415.525
Challis NF: 169.875 169.90 414.65 415.525 415.30 415.375 415.55
Clearwater NF: 171.575
Curlew NG: 171.475 172.225
Idaho Panhandle NF: 162.225 169.175 171.425 172.325 412.40 415.25 415.275 415.325
   415.375 415.475 415.525 415.575
Nezperce NF: 169.125 169.95 415.45 415.575
Payette NF: 162.5875 171.55 172.35
Salmon NF: 168.625 171.60 172.40 415.375
Sawtooth NF: 162.025 171.525 415.225 415.275 415.35 415.375
Targhee NF: 169.175 169.95 170.525 410.20 415.225 415.25 415.45 415.475 415.55
Illinois
Golconda Job Corps Camp: 168.775
Shawnee NF: 164.825/164.125 164.825/164.175 170.50 172.225
Indiana
Hoosier NF: 164.825/164.125
Kansas
Cimmaron NG: (info wanted)
Kentucky
Daniel Boone NF: 170.575 171.525 415.225
Louisiana
Kisatchie NF: 164.9375 168.625 169.925/170.525 170.00
Michigan
Hiawatha NF: 164.825/164.125 168.025
Huron NF: 164.925 166.575 169.15 169.175 169.925 170.525
Manistee NF: 169.15 169.175 169.925 170.525
Ottawa NF: 169.125 169.90 169.975 172.25
Minnesota
Chippewa NF: 164.825/164.125
Superior NF: 164.10 169.925 415.30
Mississippi
Bienville NF: 168.075 168.675 170.55
Delta NF: 168.075 168.675 170.55
De Soto NF: 168.175 168.675 168.775 171.475 172.325
Holly Springs NF: 168.175 168.775 169.875
Homochitto NF: 171.425
Tombigee NF: 171.425 172.325
Missouri
Mark Twain NF: 164.9375 166.5625 168.025 168.075 168.10 168.125 168.15 168.65
   168.675 168.70 168.75 170.525 172.25 415.325
Montana
Beaverhead NF: 168.025 168.625 415.45
Bitterroot NF: 168.15 168.625 168.75 170.35 171.00 171.425
Custer NF: 162.225 168.625 169.175 169.975

144

Deerlodge NF: 168.025 168.625 170.35 171.00 415.45
Flathead NF: 163.375 168.675 415.25 415.35 415.575
Gallatin NF: 164.825 168.025 168.625 169.45 171.70 415.375
Kootenai NF: 166.20 171.3875 172.075 415.75
Lewis & Clark NF: 168.025 168.625 168.775 170.50 415.475
Lolo NF: 164.10 164.70 415.35 415.375 415.45
Nebraska
Nebraska NF: 168.625/168.025 169.15
Oglala NF: 168.625/168.025 169.15
Nevada
Humboldt NF: 168.025 168.625 171.475 172.225 415.525
Toiyabe NF: 164.60 165.4125 168.025 168.625 169.875 169.90 169.975 170.55 415.225
  415.275 415.325 415.55
New Hampshire
White Mountains NF: 168.05 170.575 171.525/171.575
New Mexico
Carson NF: 168.625 169.175 169.975 171.55 171.575 172.275 172.30
Cibola NF: 154.755 155.64 170.425 170.45 171.45 172.225 412.625 413.90 415.425
  415.475 415.525
Gila NF: 169.175 169.975 415.275 415.325 415.375 415.475 415.525
Kiowa NG: (Info wanted)
Lincoln NF: 168.05 168.125 169.125 170.425 170.50 172.275 415.25 415.35 415.55
  415.575
Santa Fe NF: 171.55 172.30 415.375 415.425
North Carolina
Croatan NF: 168.125 168.725
Nantahala NF: 164.825 168.025 168.125 168.20 168.625 168.75 168.775 169.125 171.225
  171.475 415.30 415.325 415.575
Pisgah NF: 168.025 168.125 168.625 168.725 169.125 171.475 171.225 415.225 415.30
  415.325 415.575
Uwharrie NF: 168.125 168.725 415.325
North Dakota
Little Missouri NG: 169.175/169.975
Sheyenne NG: 169.175/169.975
Ohio
Wayne NF: 164.825
Oklahoma
Black Kettle NG: (Info wanted)
McClellan Creek NG: (Info wanted)
Oregon
Crooked River NG: 168.025 168.625 415.25 415.325 415.45
Deschutes NF: 169.875 170.475
Fremont NF: 164.125 164.825 168.025 168.625 415.275 415.325 415.425 415.575
Malheur NF: 171.425 172.40 173.025 415.225 415.575
Mount Hood NF: 164.125 158.025 168.625 169.925 169.95 170.50 170.525 415.275
  415.35 415.375 415.425 415.45 415.575
Ochoco NF: 170.50 168.025 168.625 169.175 169.975 172.40 173.025 415.25 415.275
  415.325 415.45
Rogue River NF: 168.025 168.625 169.175 169.975 415.225 415.575
Siskiyou NF: 171.425 172.325 415.275 415.45
Suislaw NF: 162.6125 163.375 168.025 168.625 169.60 415.35
Umatilla NF: 164.125 164.825 168.025 168.625 172.275 415.30 415.325
Umpqua NF: 164.8875 165.5125 415.525

Wallowa-Whitman NF: 36.67 164.15 164.80 168.025 409.15 415.25 415.35 415.375 415.425 415.525

Williamette NF: 164.125 164.825 164.9125 164.9375 164.9625 166.5625 168.025 168.625 415.225 415.525

Winena NF: 168.625 169.925 170.525 415.275 415.325

Pennsylvania

Allegheny NF: 170.525 170.55 170.575 171.525

South Carolina

Francis Marion NF: 164.925 168.075 168.675

Sumter NF: 164.925 168.075 168.675

South Dakota

Black Hills NF: 164.15 164.975 169.60/166.575 166.95/171.475 172.225/170.55 172.275 172.375 415.325 415.475 415.525

Buffalo Gap NG: 164.825/164.125

Cedar River NG: 169.175/169.975

Ft. Pierre NG: (Info wanted)

Grand River NG: 169.175/169.975

Tennessee

Cherokee NF: 168.025 168.075 168.625 168.675 415.525

Texas

Angelina NF: 164.825/164.125 168.75 169.95 170.575 171.475 172.225

Caddo NG: 171.475/172.225

Davy Crockett NF: 164.825/164.025 169.95 170.575 171.475

Lyndon B. Johnson NG: 171.475 172.225

Rita Blanca NG: (Info wanted)

Sabine NF: 169.95 170.575

Sam Houston NF: 164.825 171.475 172.225

Utah

Ashley NF: 168.025 168.625 170.575 415.25 415.525 415.55

Cache NF: 164.125 164.975 168.025 168.675 412.675 415.225 415.30 415.575

Fishlake NF: 168.025 168.825 169.175 169.525 169.975 415.525

Manti-La Sal NF: 168.025 168.625 169.875 171.475 172.225 415.25 415.525

Uinta NF: 168.05 168.625 171.575 172.375 415.30

Wasach NF: 164.975 166.575 168.025 168.625 412.675 415.225 415.30 415.375

Vermont

Green Mountain NF: 166.5625 169.175/169.975

Virginia

George Washington NF: 166.925 171.425 171.525 172.325

Jefferson NF: 171.575/172.25

Washington

Colville NF: 170.125 170.425 170.55 171.475 415.325

Gifford Pinchot NF: 170.125 170.50 171.425 172.225 172.325 415.225 415.25 415.325 415.45 415.475 415.55

Mt. Baker-Snoqualmie NF: 168.025 168.625 169.90 169.925 170.125 170.525 171.475 411.375 411.475 415.225 415.25 415.275 415.30 415.325 415.425 415.375 415.475 415.525 419.50

Okanogan NF: 169.875 170.125 170.475 411.425 415.425 415.475 415.575

Olympic NF: 164.80 164.825/164.125 164.9625 410.625 411.35 411.375 415.225 415.35 415.375 415.575

Wenatchee NF: 164.125 168.025 168.625 171.50 172.25 410.20 415.225 415.25 415.45 415.525

Wisconsin

Chequamegon NF: 164.825/164.125 168.125 172.225 415.325

Nicolet NF: 164.15 164.975 164.9875 168.175 170.425

West Virginia
Monongahela NF: 38.55 38.81 415.325
Wyoming
Bighorn NF: 169.925 170.575 415.325
Bridger-Teton NF: 171.075 415.225 415.25 415.35 415.50 415.575
Medicine Bow NF: 164.875 166.475 166.675 170.425 415.325
Shoshone NF: 168.025 168.625 169.825 170.50 415.35 415.475
Thunder Basin NG: 166.475 415.325

Air Force, U.S. (USAF)

Some basic HF/VHF/UHF frequencies used by USAF air and ground units are shown here. Keep in mind that transmissions in the 118 to 139 and 225 to 400 MHz bands will usually be in AM mode; those between 25 and 75 MHz are likely to be in WFM (wide FM) mode, those from 2 to 25 MHz in SSB (usually USB), while other VHF and UHF will be in NFM (narrow FM). Also note that in 1992 the USAF underwent a major structural reorganization. The USAF components long known as the SAC, TAC, and MAC were reorganized, reshuffled, and revamped to reflect the the nation's defense needs in light of changing world conditions. In a very capsulized view of the new USAF, the three major components are the Air mobility Command (AMC), the Air Combat Command (ACC), and the United States Strategic Command (USSTRATCOM). Generally, you might think of the AMC of a combination of former MAC and SAC elements. Think of the ACC as our air defense and combat ready forces, such as the old TAC, NORAD, Air Guard. Think of USSTRATCOM as being a version of the former SAC. Base, ID, and HF frequency changes have been observed, and are still taking place as this book is being prepared. We have included all known changes. Undoubtedly, monitors will be tracking the changes for some time to come. In the VHF/UHF bands, our listings have usually retained the old SAC, TAC, MAC designations because these frequencies are still in use, and could well continue in use as before by the new USAF elements.

USAF MARS: 49.98 142.125 142.14 142.155 142.455 143.45 143.46 143.64 143.925 143.95
USAF Thunderbirds: 66.90 114.95 120.45 123.4 124.935 140.00 140.40 141.85 235.25 236.55 236.6 250.85 273.5 283.5 295.7 322.0 322.6 382.9 394.0 Ground Crew 413.025 413.075 413.10 413.15 413.275 413.35 413.40
Air Traffic Control: 126.2 134.1 236.6 255.4 257.8 272.7 275.8 285.4 348.6 349.4 363.8
AFB Air/Ground Dispatch: 372.2
Weather ("Metro"): 239.8 342.5 344.6 375.2

AFB Crew Alerts: 413.45

Office of Special Investigation: 40.17 40.19 138.075 138.165 138.175 138.185

Minuteman II ICBM OP: Ch #1 148.455; Ch #2 148.935

UHF Direction Finding: 305.4

"Giant Talk" Network used for ground/air tactical voice comms. Selected HF freqs
3113 3292 3295 3369 4492 4495 4896 5020 5026 5110 5171 5215 5243 5328 5383 5684 5700
5800 5826 5970 5987 6680 6712 6723 6730 6746 6757 6761 6826 6839 6853 6870 6886 6969
7330 7475 7831 7983 8101 9017 9023 9027 9057 9120 9220 9234 9806 10452 11110 11118
11220 11226 11243 11410 11607 12070 13204 13205 13211 13217 13241 13247 13547 13907
14448 14716 14744 14775 14955 15041 15091 17617 17972 17992 18005 18009 18046 18049
18397 18594 18623 20124 20167 20631 20637 20740 20890 21815 23337 23419 23441 27870
kHz

USSTRATCOM: CP (Primary) 311.0 (Secondary (321.0) Other Freqs 321.2 342.2
364.2 375.7 SAC/FEMA OP 266.05 273.8 399.75 SAC/FEMA OP in WFM mode 235.85
246.95

Air Combat Command (ACC): CP 381.3 Other Freqs 140.40 242.2 292.1 280.5
282.5 283.7 292.1 305.6 305.7 306.6 313.6 343.0 349.4 376.2 378.9 382.5 387.9

Air Mobility Command (AMC): 130.65 141.80 297.0 319.4 340.8 349.4 372.8 390.9

Space & Missile Tech Network (SAMTEC): (HF 5700 9029 13218 17428 kHz)

USAF Eastern Test Range: Primary 10780; Secondary 20390

Commando Escort Network: (HF 10452 10510 kHz)

Satellite Downlinks: (NFM mode) 243.945 to 244.21 band

Base Security: 149.175 149.205 163.1875 163.4625 163.4875 163.5125 163.5375
163.5625 165.1125 165.1275 173.4375 173.5125 173.5625 173.5725 173.5875 173.6375
173.6625 173.6875 173.7125 173.7875 (These freqs often, but not always, used as
noted.)

AFB Crash Trucks: 173.5875 (A popular freq for this purpose.)

Global HF System. Air/Ground system for passing command and control
information with aircraft of all Allied Forces military services. Most stations can
operate UHF on 292.2 MHz in addition to HF as noted following--

N.America: 4725 6738 8967 8993 13201 15015 17975 kHz

Europe/Mediterranean: 4725 6738 8967 8993 11176 13201 15015 kHz

Atlantic: 6738 8967 11176 13201 15015 kHz

Caribbean/So. America/Africa: 6738 11176 15015 kHz

Greenland/Arctic: 4725 6738 8967 11176 13201 15015 17975 kHz

Pacific: 6738 8967 8993 11176 13201 15015 17975 kHz

Indian Ocean: 4725 6738 8993 11176 15015 17975 kHz

"Mystic Star" Network. Used for long range air/ground telephone calls from VIP's
aboard mil aircraft, including AF-1, AF-2, and SAM flights. Numerous HF channels
are used, usually with "Foxtrot" channel identifiers. The channel identifiers are
changed from time to time, so they have not been listed. Comms are either USB or
LSB. Also see info under Secret Service for additional listings for calls made during
USA overflights using VHF/UHF frequencies. These are selected HF channels: 2014
3046 3055 4721 4731 4794 5688 5710 5760 5800 5820 6680 6683 6712 6716 6730 6756 6790
6812 6817 6830 6913 6927 6989 6993 7401 7682 7735 7758 7813 7858 7997 8040 8052 8101
8162 8967 8993 9004 9007 9018 9023 9026 9043 9057 9120 9270 9317 9320 9414 9958 9991
10112 10185 10427 10583 11035 11052 11055 11118 11121 11153 11156 11176 11180 11201
11220 11225 11241 11249 11407 11460 11467 11484 11498 11607 11988 12201 13201 13204
13210 13212 13215 13247 13473 13445 13485 13585 13823 13878 14672 14829 15015 15048
15620 16090 16320 17671 17972 17993 18027 18175 18320 18400 18532 18629 18650 19955
20053 20109 20147 20400 20885 22913 22940 23035 23242 23265 23337 23385 23433 23643
23687 23703 24274 24483 25364 25443 25578 26471 29899 kHz

Air/Air Refueling OP: Most Active 235.1 238.9 276.5 283.9 289.7 293.0 295.4 295.8
343.5 344.7; Secondary 260.2 282.7 319.5 319.7 320.9; Also Noted: 228.0 233.5

233.7 236.1 238.4 239.8 242.3 242.5 242.7 243.3 252.1 253.4 254.6 256.6 258.0 259.4
260.8 263.2 263.9 264.7 264.9 266.5 269.9 270.2 271.0 271.1 276.1 276.4 276.7 278.4
279.8 283.8 286.2 286.3 288.8 288.9 291.9 292.3 292.7 297.3 298.3 303.0 308.0 309.4
311.3 314.2 314.5 315.9 318.0 321.2 322.7 322.8 324.2 324.4 325.8 333.1 337.4 339.0
339.2 339.4 341.4 343.0 343.1 352.6 352.7 352.9 358.2 361.4 361.7 363.9 364.1 365.4
366.3 369.2 372.3 375.7 378.2 379.4 384.6 385.6 385.8 388.4 391.0 391.8 394.6 394.9
395.1 396.2 398.5

    Training Freqs (partial listing): 234.8 236.8 238.2 238.6 251.1 252.8 258.2 262.3
264.6 267.9 272.1 279.9 288.3 294.6 295.2 296.7 298.6 298.9 301.7 306.2 313.6 338.7
339.0 346.9 356.8 377.8 381.1 383.2 384.7 385.7 392.1 396.9 398.1

    Other USAF Freqs Used All Areas: 32.35 32.60 32.65 32.85 34.20 34.60 34.75
36.50 36.80 41.45 42.20 46.85 138.975 139.70 139.725 139.80 139.85 139.875 139.90
139.924 141.525 141.55 141.575 141.625 141.65 141.675 141.70 141.725 141.775 141.825
141.875 141.90 141.925 142.15 142.275 142.20 142.25 142.275 143.475 143.75 143.775
143.80 143.825 143.85 143.875 148.00 148.05 148.10 148.125 148.20 148.225 148.45
148.50 148.525 148.545 148.55 149.15 149.225 149.25 149.275 149.30 149.325 149.50
149.475 149.525 149.55 149.925 150.15 150.175 150.195 150.225 150.25 150.275 150.30
150.325 150.35 163.4375 163.5875 165.0125 225.0 225.8 228.4 234.8 238.2 257.2 258.2
266.5 270.1 271.9 276.9 286.9 288.6 289.4 289.5 289.7 289.9 294.2 296.2 300.6 302.7
305.5 316.6275 316.7875 317.1775 317.2775 318.3 322.95 326.3 335.7 335.8 336.1 338.5
340.6 354.2 354.3 356.8 363.9 364.6 368.6 369.1 370.4 378.1 378.8 381.1 394.8 398.5
407.225 407.275 407.35 407.375 407.40 407.425 407.45 407.475 407.50 407.525 407.55
407.575 412.875 412.90 412.925 412.95 412.975 413.00 413.025 413.05 413.075 413.10
413.125 413.15 413.175 413.20 413.225 413.25 413.275 413.30 413.35 413.375 413.40
413.425 413.475 413.50

Some Typical USAF Tactical Identifiers for Aircraft & Ground Stations
(The symbol +# means "followed by numeral(s) to designate individual stations").

Abnormal 10	Vandenberg AFB, CA
Abnormal 20	Wheeler AFB, HI
Afkai (+word) +#	89th Military Air Wing flights
Agar+#	EC-139 aircraft
Airevac+#	Air Evacuation flight
Air Force 1	Presidential Aircraft (President aboard)
Air Force 2	Vice Presidential Aircraft (Vice President aboard)
Air Force Rescue+#	Search and Rescue (SAR) flight
Air Rescue+#	Search and Rescue (SAR) flight
American Eagle	Commando Escort unit flight
April+#	KC-135 tanker aircraft
Arla+#	EC-125N aircraft (4050th Test Wing, Wright-Patterson AFB)
Army 1	Any US Army helo with President of US aboard
Army 2	Any US Army helo with Vice President if US aboard
Arter+#	C-130 Hercules aircraft
Backy+#	KC-10A Extender aircraft
Bake+#	C-130 Hercules aircraft
Belga+#	C-130 Hercules aircraft
Bobcat+#	T-43 trainer aircraft
Bode+#	KC-135 tanker aircraft
Boxer+#	C-21 aircraft
Brickwall	Korean Airlift Control Center
Canforce+#	C-130 Hercules aircraft
Cape Radio	USAF Eastern Test Range, Patrick AFB, FL
Capsule	General call for all AMC aircraft

Chill+#	B-52 Stratofortress aircraft
Cody+#	C-130 Hercules aircraft
Coho+#	KC-135 tanker aircraft
Copter+#	Helicopter flight
Coty+#	C-141 Starlifter aircraft
Cutty+#	T-38 Talon aircraft
Czar+#	B-52 Stratofortress aircraft
Decoy+#	C-130 Hercules aircraft
Demon+#	C-130 Hercules aircraft
Denali	AMC Alaskan Airlift Control Center, Elmendorf AFB, AK
Discard	AMC 22nd AF Operations
Dixie+#	RF-4 aircraft
Dog+#	B-52 Stratofortress aircraft
Doom+#	B-52 Stratofortress aircraft
Dropkick	USSTRATCOM Headquarters
Dude+#	KC-10A Extender aircraft
Dusty+#	C-130 Hercules aircraft
Edgy+#	Aircraft of 552nd AWACS, Tinker AFB, OK
Electric	National Emergency Airborne Control Post
Elite+#	KC-10A Extender aircraft
Ethel+#	KC-135 tanker aircraft
Executive 1	Commercial airliner with President of US aboard
Executive 1-Foxtrot	Commercial airliner with President's family aboard
Executive 2	Commercial airliner with Vice President aboard
Executive 2-Foxtrot	Commercial airliner with Vice President's family aboard
Exxon+#	KC-10A Extender aircraft
Fallon+#	T-37 trainer aircraft
Fame+#	C-21 cargo aircraft
Fireside 1	Langley AFB, VA
Fireside 3	Shaw AFB, SC
Fireside 4	Mountain Home AFB, ID
Fireside 5	Bergstrom AFB, TX
Fist+#	KC-10A Extender aircraft
Fivespot	Commando Escort flight
Fletcher	Commando Escort flight
Flynest	Nuclear & Chemical/Biological Warfare Disaster Team flight
Format	AMC 22nd AF Operations
Furious	AMC South American Airlift Control Center
Gold Coin	Strike Control Command, MacDill AFB, FL
Golden	General call for all ACC ground stations
Griff+#	B-52 Stratofortress aircraft
Gull+#	WC-130 weather recon aircraft, 53rd Weather Recon Sqdn, MS
Gumby+#	B-52 Stratofortress aircraft
Gus+#	KC-135 tanker aircraft
Happy+#	KC-135 tanker aircraft
Havoc+#	B-52 Stratofortress aircraft
Heat+#	FB-111 aircraft
Hi-Fi+#	KC-135 tanker aircraft
Hilda	AMC Command Center
Hobby+#	C-130 Hercules aircraft
Hoist+#	KC-10A Extender aircraft
Hunt+#	C-141 Starlifter aircraft
Impact+#	C-130 Hercules aircraft
Jambo+#	B-52 Stratofortress aircraft

Jolly+#	Search and Rescue helo not on mission
King+#	Search and Rescue C-130 aircraft not on mission
Kiska+#	B-52 Stratofortress aircraft
Lark+#	WC-130 weather recon aircraft, 55th Weather Recon Sqdn, CA
Laser+#	B-52 Stratofortress aircraft
Letterman	Weather Forecaster, Hickam AFB, HI
Looking Glass	USSTRATCOM Airborne CP (EC-185 aircraft)
Luger+#	B-52 Stratofortress aircraft
MAC+#	AMC flight
Mainsail	General call for any GHFS ground station
Marine 1	USMC helo with President of US aboard
Marine 2	USMC helo with Vice Pres of US aboard
May+#	C-130 Hercules aircraft
McCoy+#	F-16 Eagle aircraft
Medevac+#	Evacuation aircraft equipped with medical facilities
Mellow+#	C-130 Hercules aircraft
Minuteman	ANG OP Center, Andrews AFB, MD
Moose+#	KC-135 tanker aircraft
More+#	C-141 Starlifter aircraft
Music+#	C-130 Hercules aircraft
Nighthawk	USMC helo of Marine Sqdn 1, Quantico, VA
Nitro+#	B-52 Stratofortress aircraft
Nomad+#	F-15 Eagle aircraft
Noose+#	C-130 Hercules aircraft
Norse+#	B-1 bomber
Omni+#	C-130 Hercules aircraft
Opec+#	KC-10A Extender aircraft
Pacer+#	C-21 cargo aircraft
Pawn+#	KC-135 tanker aircraft
Peach+#	F-15 Eagle aircraft
Pearl+#	KC-135 tanker aircraft
Pedro+#	Search and Rescue aircraft assigned to a local base
Petro+#	KC-10A Extender aircraft
Phantom	AMC European Theatre Airlift Control Center
Pyote+#	B-52 Stratofortress aircraft
Queen	Air Rescue OP Center, Eglin AFB, FL
Raymond+#	ALC ground station
Razor+#	FB-111 aircraft
Reach+#	AMC aircraft
Rena+#	C-130 Hercules aircraft
Rhett+#	KC-135 tanker aircraft
Rough+#	T-37 trainer aircraft
SAM+#	Special Air Mission VIP flight (Mil or Diplo)
SAM 01	VIP flight with foreign head of state aboard
SAM 26000	AF-2 aircraft, Vice President not aboard
SAM 27000	AF-1 aircraft, President not aboard
SAM 28000	AF-2 aircraft, Vice President aboard
SAM 29000	AF-1 aircraft. President aboard
SAM 31682	Vice Presidential aircraft, Vice President not aboard
SAM 86970	US Secretary of State aircraft, & aboard
SAM 86971	US Secretary of State aircraft, not aboard
SAM 86972	NSA Advisor aircraft, & aboard
SAM 86973	NSA Advisor aircraft, not aboard
SAM 86974	Dept of State aircraft, Secty of State aboard

Save+#	Search and Rescue aircraft assigned to a local base
Sentry+#	E-3 Sentry aircraft, Tinker AFB, OK
Shamu+#	KC-10A Extender aircraft
Shiva+#	B-52 Stratofortress aircraft
Silky+#	KC-135 tanker aircraft
Silo+#	C-130 Hercules aircraft
Skybird	General call to any USSTRATCOM ground station
Skyking	General call to all nuclear forces and support groups
Soda+#	KC-135 tanker aircraft
Sonar+#	B-52 Stratofortress aircraft
Spar+#	VIP aircraft, lower status tham SAM flight
Steel+#	RF-4 aircraft
Super+#	KC-10A Extender aircraft
Swan+#	WC-130 weather recon aircraft, 54th Weather Recon Sqdn, GU
Swift+#	C-12 cargo aircraft
Tame+#	C-5A Galaxy aircraft
Teal+#	WC-130 weather recon aircraft, 815th Weather Recon Sqdn, MS
Tess+#	C-130 Hercules aircraft
Tiger+#	B-52 Stratofortress aircraft
Toma+#	A-7 Corsair II aircraft
Tonight	AMC Pacific Airlift Control Center
Treld+#	KC-135 tanker aircraft
Tribe+#	KC-135 tanker aircraft
Trout+#	C-21 cargo aircraft
Tuff+#	B-52 Stratofortress aircraft
Ursa+#	KC-135 tanker aircraft
US Air Force+#	Flights over foreign territories
Venus+#	SAM aircraft, VIP's not aboard
Wager+#	KC-135 tanker aircraft
Wise+#	C-130 Hercules aircraft
Zeus+#	B-52 Stratofortress aircraft
3-letter word+3#	Student pilot on training mission
3-letter word+4#	Civil Disturbance aircraft
4-letter word+1#	ACC combat crew training mission
3-5 letter word+2#	USSTRATCOM bomber or tanker
6-15 letter word or 2 words	USSTRATCOM ground station

Alcohol, Tobacco & Firearms, Bureau of

CTCSS: 103.5 Hz

Channel 1	165.2875	Tactical
Channel 2	166.5375	Operational
Channel 3	165.2875/166.5375	Primary
Channel 4	166.4625	Treasury Common
Channel 5	165.9125	Tactical
Channel 6	173.8875	Tactical
Channel 7	168.000	Tactical
Channel 8	173.8875/166.5375	Investigations

Surveillance & other frequencies currently being reported: 166.2875 170.4125 407.15 407.85 407.875 409.15/Delta-3

**US Army Corps
of Engineers**

Army Corps of Engineers

Frequencies: 38.69 38.89 142.365 148.925 150.465 150.735 150.75 150.765 156.65 156.70 157.125 162.36 163.00 163.025 163.125 163.4125/164.775 163.4375/163.00 163.4375/164.175 163.4375/164.20 163.4375/165.1875 163.4375 163.5375/163.025 164.05 164.20 164.50 164.9625 165.0125 165.0375 165.0625 165.0875 165.1875 165.4125 168.125 168.325 169.425 169.45 169.525 169.60 170.025 170.225 170.275 170.30 170.325 172.425 173.9875 406.9375/413.2375 407.225/412.975 407.2375/413.5625 407.5625/412.8375 412.8375/407.5625 412.975 413.2375/406.9375 413.5625/707.2375 (HF 2348.5 5011 5015 5327 5346 5400 12267 16077 kHz) Freqs in the 163 MHz band are the ones most often reported by monitors.

Callsigns of base stations begin with the letters "WU" followed by 1 letter and from 1 to 3 numerals. Stations witn 1 numeral are at Division and District HQ's, with those with 2 and 3 numerals are at field offices, dam locks, and various projects. The letter following the "WU" (WUA, WUB, etc.) remains uniform with all stations within each Division and District. Vessels reported have call letters commencing with the letter A.

Army, U.S.

Army Golden Knights: 32.30 123.475 123.4

Army MARS: 40.95 41.59 46.79 49.79 49.93 143.35 143.415 143.90 143.99/148.01 148.65 150.625

Army Aviation Control Towers: 32.10 37.00 38.90 41.50 41.80 46.70 126.2 241.0 229.6

Emergencies: 34.90 139.075

Mobile Convoys: 36.71 36.87

Civil Emergencies: 34.90 149.91

Air Evacuations: 141.375

Nuclear Accident Crews: 30.45 36.30 38.30 38.50

Explosive Ordnance Disposal (EOD): 49.70 49.80 139.00 139.175

Satellite Downlinks (NFM mode): 261.675

Criminal Investigation Division (CID): 141.325 142.325 143.375 150.55 406.9375 407.475 408.425 412.825 412.90 413.025 413.225 413.2375 413.425 413.525

Military Police: 407.25 409.125 409.75

Tactical: 30.09 30.30 34.00 34.10 36.45 38.40 40.55 40.99 139.00

National Guard: 139.10 141.465 142.325 143.05 143.075 143.10 143.125 143.15 143.175 143.20 143.225 143.275 143.30 143.335 143.35 143.40

Missile Test: 139.44

Aero Emergency: 40.50

Post OP: 138.975 139.40

Search and Rescue: 138.75

Command: 143.35

Aero Test: 139.40 141.025 148.025 148.65 148.80 149.86

Army Reserve: 139.20

Security: 149.175 149.205 150.435 150.555

Crash Trucks at Heliports: 30.10

Artillery & Tank Range Control: 30.45 32.70 34.20 34.29 34.30 34.45 34.50 34.70 36.10 36.33 36.75 38.30 38.90 40.45 40.60

National Guard Aviation: 32.30 32.50 34.15 34.40 35.00 36.00 36.10 36.50 36.70 36.80 36.85 38.70 38.85 40.10 40.25 40.30 40.90 41.00 41.60 41.70 41.90 42.00 49.00 49.40 49.70 49.80 49.90 49.95 123.05 126.2 241.0

Art, National Gallery of

Washington, DC: Security 408.00   OP 406.55/411.55

Attorney, U.S.

All Areas: 410.85 410.875 415.85/416.175

Aviation Administration, Federal

Commonly used frequencies:
"Flight Check" air/ground OP to calibrate airport landing systems: 135.85 135.95
Flight Service Stations: 122.2 122.6 123.6 255.4 272.7
Aircraft Emergency: 121.5 243.0
Aviation Weather ("Flight Watch"): 122.0
South FL Hurricane Backup Net: 162.50
Facilities Testing: 165.6375
Maintenance: 165.3375 165.6125 165.7375 169.225
Freqs in wide use: 164.025 166.175 169.35 408.825 410.30 410.90 416.875
Accident Investigation: 165.3375 165.75 166.75

FAA Aircraft Roster: Beech Bonanza 35= N5RB; Beech King 90= N5 N13 N14 N16 N16 N17 N18N19 N20; Beech King 200= N4; Beech King 300= N66 N67 N68 N69 N70 N71 N72 N73 N74 N75 N76 N77 N78 N79 N80 N81 N82 N83 N84; Bell 205A= N37; Boeing 727= N40 N97; Douglas DC-3= N34; Douglas DC-9= N29; Cessna 50= N2 N25; Convair 580= N39 N49 N90 N92; Gulfstream G-159= N3 N48; Israel 1121= N41 N42 N43 N45; Lockheed 1329= N11; Sikorsky S-76= N65; Rockwell 680E= N50; Rockwell Sabre 40= N86 N87 N88 N89; Rockwell 75A= N52 N53 N56 N58 N60 N62 N65

HF OP: 7475 8122 8125 10242 13630 16348 kHz
Numbered FAA Facilities Channels: Ch #1 172.925; Ch #2 172.95; Ch #3 172.975; Ch #4 172.85; Ch #5 172.875; Ch #6 172.90; Ch #7 172.825; Ch #8 172.125; Ch #9 172.15; Ch #10 172.175; Ch #11 166.175
Try the above freqs in all areas, also check out:

Alabama
Anniston (KLE78) 27.625 408.825
Evergreen 408.825
Alaska
Alsek River 169.325
Anchorage (KBX44) 162.275 165.6375
 172.825 172.925 172.95
Bethel (KBB54) 172.825
Bettles (KBE43) 27.625

Big Delta (KBD82) 172.825 172.925
Biorka Isl. (KMA50) 169.325
Byers Creek 172.825 172.925
Cp. Gull 162.275
Cp. Romanzoff 166.10
Cold Bay (KCB22) 172.825
Cordova (KAC26) 172.825 172.925
Craig 169.25
Deadhorse 172.825

Dillingham (KKE47) 172.825 172.925
Duncan Canal 169.325
Ester Dome 162.30 162.35 172.15
Fairbanks (KBF94) 172.825 172.85 172.925
  172.95
Fairwell (KCF31) 182.825 172.925
Finger Mtn. 169.325
Flattop Mtn. 172.15
Giant Mtn. 172.175
Gulkana (KGA25) 172.825
Homer (KCH20) 172.825 172.925
Iliamna 172.825 172.925 410.30
Kake 169.325
Kenai (KBL69) 172.825 172.925 416.875
Ketchikan (KKY21) 172.825 172.925
King Salmon (KCK35) 172.825 172.925
Kodiak (KAK20) 172.825 172.925
Kotzebue (KEJ28) 172.825
Kulu Is. 172.875
Lclrk. Pass 410.30 416.875
Lclark. #3 410.30
McGrath (KCR60) 172.825 172.925
Middleton Isl. (KGB20) 172.825 172.925
Moses Pt. 172.175
Mt. Fanshaw 169.325
Mt. Susinta 172.175 172.70
Murphy Dome (KLH70) 172.175 172.825
  172.925
Newton Pk. 169.25
Nome (KLH70) 172.175 172.825
Northway (KBJ85) 172.825 172.925
Palmer 172.825 172.925
St. Marys 165.6375
Skwenta (KGD33) 167.90
Snntht. Mtn. 169.25
Talkeetna (KAV83) 172.825 172.925
Tatalina 172.825
Tolsona 172.925
Wrangell 410.30 413.60
Yakutat (KKW92) 172.825

Arizona
Ajo 172.125 172.975
Bowie 172.125 172.925
Cochise 172.125 172.825
Douglas 172.125 172.925
Eldon Mtn. 172.925
Flagstaff 172.125 172.925
Globe 172.175 172.975
Heliograph Peak 172.925
Hualph Mtn 172.95
Humboldt Mtn 172.175 172.975
Mt. Lemmon 172.95
Phoenix 172.175 172.975
Pima 172.125 172.925

Pinal Mtn. 172.975
Prescott 172.15 172.95
Safford 172.125 172.925
San Simon 172.125 172.925
Tempe 172.175 172.975
Thatcher 172.125 172.925
Tucson 171.125 172.15 172.925 172.95
Wilcox 172.125 172.975
Yuma 169.35 172.175 172.975

Arkansas
Little Rock 164.05 165.5375 165.6125
  165.7375 165.7625 169.255

California
All Areas 169.225 169.25 169.30 169.325
  169.35
Angels Camp 172.15 172.95
Arcata 172.125 172.925
Bakersfield 172.125 172.925
Bay Pt 172.125 172.925
Beale AFB 172.15 172.95
Blythe 172.15 172.95
Boron 171.175 172.975
China Lake 172.125 172.925
Concord 172.125 172.975
Coyote 172.125 172.925
Crescent City 172.125 172.925
Crystal Peak 172.95
Daggett 172.125 172.975
Edwards AFB 172.175 172.975
El Toro MCAS 172.15
Ferndale 172.925
Foxfield 172.175 172.975
Fremont (KMR96) 172.125 172.175
Fresno 172.125 172.15 172.175
Friant 172.975
Grapevine 172.925
Half Moon Bay 172.175 172.975
Hawthorne (KJK73) 162.275 162.30 165.75
  166.175 169.25 172.10 172.125 172.15
  172.175 172.825 172.90 172.925 172.95
  172.975
Julian 172.975
Lake Tahoe 172.95
Lancaster 172.175 172.975
Long Beach 172.15 192.95
Los Angeles (KOJ77) 165.6375 172.125
  172.825
Marysville 172.125 172.925
Mather AFB 172.15 172.95
McClellan AFB 172.15 172.95
Modesto 172.15 172.95
Montague 172.15 172.95
Mt. Diablo 172.95
Mt. Shasta 172.95

Mt. Soledad 172.175 172.975
Mt. Tamalpais 172.975
Mtn. View 172.125 172.975
Needles 172.15 172.95
Oakland 172.125 172.95
Oxnard 172.15 172.95
Palm Springs 172.15 172.95
Palmdale (KJK77) 172.175
Paso Robles 172.175 172.975
Red Bluff (KKV65) 172.15 172.95
Redwood Peak 172.925
Rand Mtn. 172.925
Riverside 172.15
Sacramento 172.15 172.95
Saddle Peak 172.925
San Diego 172.175 172.975
San Francisco (KSF70) 162.325 172.15
 172.175 172.95 172.975
San Jose 172.175 172.925
San Luis Obispo 172.975
San Pedro Hill 170.20 172.15 172.90
Santa Barbara (KJK75) 172.15 172.95
Santa Maria 172.15 172.95
Santa Rosa 172.175 172.925 172.975
Sausalito 172.125
Snow Peak 172.95
Stockton 172.15 172.95
Tracy 172.125 172.975
Ukiah 172.175 172.975
Upland 172.95
Van Nuys 172.15 172.95
Watsonville 172.125 172.975

Colorado
Akron 165.3365
Alamosa 165.3375
Aurora 166.175
Cheyenne Mtn. 166.175
Colo. Spgs. 165.3375
Denver (WHX46) 165.6875 166.175
Douglas Spgs. 165.3375 166.175
Eagle 165.3375 166.175 172.975
Gr. Jct. (KBA29) 166.175
Grand Mesa 166.175
Gunnison 166.175
Idaho Spgs. 166.175
Kremmling 166.175
LaJunta 165.3375
LaVeta 166.175
Meeker 166.175
Parker 166.175
Thurman 166.175
Trinidad 165.3375

District of Columbia
Dulles 164.825 165.50 165.6375 165.6625

 165.7125 166.0875 408.175 409.30 410.25
 415.125 415.25 416.875 419.025
FAA HQ (KEM80) 162.275 408.825 410.25
 410.90
Wash. Nat'l. (KKW89) 27.625 162.2125
 164.825 165.10 165.4125 165.50 165.6375
 165.6625 408.175 410.25 416.875 419.025

Florida
Avon Park 162.30
Ft. Myers 162.35
Gainesville (KUA21) 27.575 162.05 408.825
Jacksonville (WHX49) 162.05 408.825
Key West (KLD95) 408.825
Melbourne (KXC70) 162.35 165.7125
 408.825
Miami (KMA47) 162.30 162.50 172.10
 408.825
Orlando (KOR82) 162.30 408.825
Tallahassee (KKA36) 408.825
Tampa (KLW57) 162.25
Vero Beach (WHX47) 162.30
W. Palm Bch. (KEH74) 408.825

Georgia
Albany 408.825
Athens 408.825
Atlanta (KDM49) 27.585 27.625 164.60
 165.75 166.175
Augusta 162.325
Fulton Cnty 27.575 27.585 27.625
LaGrange 408.825
Toccoa 408.825
Valdosta (KUR67) 408.825

Hawaii
All Areas 169.225
Diamond Head (KCC97) 27.625 162.6125
 170.15 171.2625
Haleakala NP 172.25
Hilo (KBH49) 169.225 170.15
Honolulu (KGA32) 27.625 162.025 169.225
 170.15 173.075 173.5625 173.8125
Hoolehua 172.15
Kahului Maui (KCU94) 27.625 171.2625
 172.15
Keahole (KLI52) 172.15
Kona 171.2625
Lanai (KLI51) 171.2625
Lihue Kanai (KAL38) 171.2625 172.15
Mauna Kea 408.825
Mauna Loa 170.15 171.2625
Molokai (KLK48) 171.2625
Mt. Kaala (WHX44) 172.15 408.825
Oahu 171.2625
Upolu Point 171.2625

Idaho
Boise (WHX22) 166.175 408.825
Coeur D'Alene 165.4375 166.175
Emmett 165.4375
Idaho Falls 166.175
McCall 166.175
Mullen Pass 165.4375 166.175
Salmon 165.4375 166.175 172.875
Sand Point 165.4375 166.175
Illinois
Chicago (KLE72) 27.625 165.6125 165.61
165.6375 165.7125 165.7375 165.75
169.35 172.175 172.875 172.90 172.975
172.95
Moline (KKZ74) 27.625
Wheeling 171.175 172.925 172.975

Indiana
Indianapolis (KLB48) 27.625 169.35
172.175   172.925   172.975

Iowa
Burlington 27.625 172.125 172.225
172.975
Cedar Rapids 27.625 172.175 172.15
172.925 172.95
Des Moines (WHX57) 27.625 172.15
172.95
Dubuque 27.625
Ft. Dodge 172.975
Mason City 27.625 172.15 172.225 172.95
172.975
Maquoket 172.975
Oelwein 172.975
Ottumwa 27.625 172.975
Sioux City 27.625 172.175 172.225
172.975
Spencer 172.925
Waterloo 27.625 172.225 172.875
Kansas
Chanute 172.975
Dodge City 172.95
Emporia 27.625 172.95
Garden City (KFS50) 27,625 172.175
172.15   172.225   172.925   172.95
Goodland 172.175 172.15 172.225 172.925
172.95 172.975 408.825
Hill City 172.925 408.825
Hutchinson (KLG77) 27.625 172.15
172.95
Larned 172.975
Liberal 172.975
Manhattan 172.975
Oakley 172.95

Olathe (KKA82) 165.6375 172.225 172.925
172.975 408.825 409.825
Pratt 172.975
Salina 27.625 172.125 172.15 172.225
172.975 172.95 172.975
Stilwell 27.625
Topeka (KKY50) 27.625 172.15 172.225
172.95 172.925
Wichita (KKZ68) 27.625 172.125 172.925
Kentucky
Louisville (KUW42) 408.825
Louisiana
New Orleans (WEK71) 39.50 39.62 165.75
166.175
Maine
Augusta (KKU70) 27.625
Bangor (KKU80) 27.625
Houlton (KKH56) 27.625
Portland (KKU54) 27.625
Maryland
Andrews AFB 165.6125 172.95
Hagerstown (KLM94) 27.625
Massachusetts
Boston 41.59 164.05 165.6375 165.6875
Burlington (WHX45) 165.6125
Cambridge 27,575 27.585 41.39 165.6375
170.40 171.00
Worcester 169.325
Michigan
Detroit (KLE80) 27.625 169.35 172.175
172.875 172.925
Gr. Rapids (KLD27) 27.625
Lansing (KAE21) 27.625
Minnesota
Minneapolis (KLD73) 27.625 165.6375
169.35 172.175 172.975
St. Paul (KGJ42) 27.625
Mississippi
Greenville 162.275
Greenwood (KKY54) 27.625 165.75 166.175
Gulfport (KEG95) 408.825
McComb (KLAS23) 27.625
Missouri
Butler 172.925
Cp. Girardeau 172.125 172.15 172.225
172.925 172.95 172.975
Chesterfield 165.75 166.175 172.15 172.95
Chillicothe 172.975
Columbia (WHX58) 27.625 172.15 172.225
172.95 172.975 408.825
Crocker 172.95
Farmington 172.975
Grant City 172.95

Joplin 27.625 165.7125 172.15 172.225
  172.95 172.975 408.825
Kansas City (KKU40) 27.625 164.05
  165.6125 165.7125 165.75 166.175 172.125
  172.15 172.925 172.95 409.45 410.30
Macon 172.95
Molden 172.95
St. Joseph (KLF29) 27.625 172.125
  172.225 172.925 172.975
St. Louis ((KKY51) 27.625 165.75 166.75
  172.125 172.925 409.45 410.30
Vichy 27.625 408.825
Warrensburg 172.95
Wontzville 172.95
Willow Springs 172.925
Montana
Bozeman 165.3375 166.175
Butte (KKV33) 165.3375 166.175
Dillon 165.3375
Drummond 166.175
Glasgow 166.175
Helena 166.175
Judith Mn. 166.175
Lewistown 165.3375
Livingston 165.3375
Miles City (KKX667) 166.175
University Mtn. 166.175
Nebraska
Ainsworth 172.925
Beatrice 172.975
Broken Bow 172.95
Chadron 192.95
Columbus 172.925
Gr. Island 41.59 41.69 172.125 172.15
  172.225 172.925 172.95 172.975
Hayes Cntr 408.825
Lincoln 27.625 172.125 172.15 172.175
  172.225 172.925 172.95 172.975
McCook 27.625 41.59 41.69 172.975
N. Platte (KCA20) 27.625 41.59 41.69
  172.125 172.15 172.225 172.925 172.95
  172.975 408.825
Omaha (KKY44) 27.625 172.15 172.225
  172.95 172.975
O'Neill 41.59 41.69 172.975
Scottsbluff (KLF74) 27.625 41.59 41.69
  172.125 172.15 172.225 172.925 172.95
  172.975 408.825
Sidney 172.975
Superior 172.95
Wayne 172.95
Nevada
Angel Peak 172.925
Las Vegas (KKV20) 172.125 172.925

Lovelock 172.15 172.95
Mt. Wilson 172.975
Peavine 172.975
Peaquop Mtn. 172.975
Reno (KKU87) 172.15 172.175 172.95
  172.975
Tonopah (KLW71) 172.15 172.95
Wells 172.175 172.975
Winnemucca 172.15 172.95
New Hampshire
Candia 167.175
Lebanon 172.175
Nashua (KJK81) 27.575
New Jersey
Atlantic City (KLN80) 165.75 166.10
  166.175 172.125 172.1875 172.725
  172.85 172.9125 172.95
Newark (KLC46) 27.625
New Mexico
Abiquiu 169.225
Albuquerque (KGH23) 165.5375 165.7375
  166.175
Carlsbad 164.05 165.3375 165.6125
  165.7375 165.7625 166.175 169.225
Farmington (KGA46) 166.175
Sandia Mtn. 165.5375
T. or C. 166.175
Tucumcari (KAB34) 166.175
Zuni (KEA82) 165.5375 166.175
New York
Albany (KKY71) 27.625
Buffalo (KKZ75) 27.625
Douglaston 164.05 165.75 166.175
Dunkirk 172.95 173.9875
Elmira 164.05 166.175
Hamburg 172.95 173.9875
Islip (KCD73) 164.05 166.175 419.025
Ithaca 164.05 166.175
Jamaica/JFK (KEK41) 164.05 166.175
  407.175 408.825 410.30 410.90
Jamestown 172.95 173.9875
Malone 172.875 173.9875
Massena 172.90 173.9875
Niagara Falls 172.95 173.9875
Ogdensburg 172.90 173.9875
Plattsburgh 172.875 173.9875
Potsdam 172.90 173.9875
Rochester 166.175 172.95 173.9875
Sayville (WSY70) 162.80
Syracuse 172.95 173.9875
Watertown 172.95 173.9875
North Carolina
Asheville (KKW51) 27.625
Charlotte 27.625

Cofield (KBH85) 408.825
Fayetteville (KLJ61) 27.625
Hickory 408.825
New Bern (KUR66) 408.825
Wilmington (KDQ21) 408.825

North Dakota
Bismarck (KKU50) 166.175
Dickinson 165.3375 166.175
Fargo (KDM46) 166.175
Gr. Forks 165.3375 166.175
Jamestown 165.3375 166.175
Minot (KGC28) 165.3375 166.175
Watford City 166.175
Woodworth 166.175

Ohio
Cleveland (KLD69) 27.625 169.35 172.175
 172.875 172.925 172.975
Columbus (KLB79) 27.625
Dayton 164.025
N. Canton (KLF21) 27.625
Vandalia (KLA21) 27.625

Oklahoma
Okla. City (KIA21) 27.585 27.625 162.25
 162.35 164.05 165.5375 165.6125 165.6375
 165.6875 165.7375 165.75 166.175 169.125
 169.2125 169.225 169.25 169.3125

Oregon
All Areas 166.25
Eugene (WHX25) 165.4375
Hillsboro 166.175 408.825 409.025
Horton 166.175
Kimberley 166.175 172.875
King Mtn. 166.175
Klamath Falls 165.4375 166.175
Lakeview 165.4375 166.175
Laurelton 166.175
Medford (WHX26) 165.4375
Monroe 165.4375
Newburg 166.175
No. Bend 165.4375
Pendleton 166.175 408.825
Portland (WHX40) 166.175 408.825 409.025
Redmond (WHX27) 165.4375 166.175
 172.875
Sheridan 166.175
The Dalles 165.4375 166.175

Pennsylvania
Bradford 165.05 166.175
Erie 172.95 173.9875
Philadelphia 164.05 166.175 408.825 419.90
Pittsburgh (KKW22) 27.625 164.05 166.175
 408.825 410.90 416.875
Williamsport (KQF21) 27.625

South Carolina
Anderson 408.825
Charleston (KUR64) 408.825
Columbia 408.825
Florence (KUS79) 408.825
Greenville 408.825
Greer (KBZ80) 408.825
Myrtle Beach (KUR65) 408.825

South Dakota
Aberdeen 166.175
Huron (KBR27) 166.175
Pierre (KKU51) 165.3375 166.175
Rapid City (KCE24) 165.3375 166.175
Sioux Falls (KBC28) 165.3375 166.175
Turkey Ridge 166.175
Yankton 165.3375

Tennessee
Bristol (KKW23) 27.625 41.04
Crossville (KKX70) 27.625
Erin 164.025
Jackson 408.825
Knoxville (KFC87) 27.625 408.825
Memphis (KDM52) 166.175
Nashville (KUV70) 27.625 408.825

Texas
Beaumont (KED67) 164.05 166.175
Dallas/DFW (KLJ26) 166.175
Dyess AFB 172.975
Guadelupe Pass 166.175
Houston (KIC30) 164.05 165.5375
 165.7375 166.175 169.225 413.60
Lubbock 165.3375 165.7625 166.175
Mt. Franklin 166.175
San Antonio (KIA48) 164.025 166.175
Waco 165.3375 166.175

Utah
Bryce Canyon 166.175
Cedar City (KAX36) 165.3375 166.175
Delle 165.3375
Fairfield 165.3375
Monticello 166.175 172.975
Ogden 165.3375 166.175
Provo 165.3375
St. Frances Peak 166.175
Salt Lk. City (KDC20) 165.3375

Virginia
Bedford (KKZ27) 166.175
Charlottesville 164.05
Linden (KLM93) 27.625
Newport News 166.175
Norfolk (KLD46) 27.625 164.05
Richmond 164.05 166.175
Roanoke (KLD57) 27.625 164.05
Tysons Corners 169.2625

Vermont
Burlington (KKZ69) 27.625
Washington
All Areas: 166.125 166.25
Auburn (KCJ70) 408.825
Bellingham 165.4375 166.125 413.60
Ellensburg 166.175
Everett 165.4375 166.175 172.175
Ft. Lawton 165.4375
Grass Mtn. 166.175
Larch Mtn. 166.175
Mica Peak 166.175
Miller Peak 166.125
Moses Lk. 166.125
Mt. Constitution 410.25
Olympia (WHX30) 165.4375 166.175
Omak 165.4375 166.175
Pt. Angeles 165.4375 166.125
Seattle (WHX20) 164.05 165.4375
 408.825
Spokane (WHX42) 165.4375 166.175
Stampede Pass 166.175
Tatoosh Is. 165.4375 166.175
Walla Walla 166.175
Wisconsin
Green Bay (KEB24) 27.625
Milwaukee (KKY53) 27.625
Oshkosh 172.125
West Virginia
Clarksburg 164.05 166.175

Wyoming
Boysen Peak 166.175
Boysen Reservoir 166.175
Casper (KAI82) 165.3375 166.175
Cheyenne 165.3375
Douglas 166.175
Evanston 166.175
Laramie 166.175
Lovell 166.175
Lusk 166.175
Rock Sprgs (KKW90) 165.3375 166.175
Sheridan 165.3375 166.175
Worland 165.3375 166.175
American Samoa
Pago Pago (KDM48) 27.625 171.2625
Tafuna 27.625
Puerto Rico
San Juan (KDM45) 172.95 408.825
Virgin Islands
St. Croix (KUU97) 408.825
Bahamas Islands
Bimini (KUV50) 148.125 162.30 172.10
 408.825
All Areas: 27.575 27.585 27.625 27.665
 164.025 165.6375 165.75 165.7625 166.175
 172.175 172.15 172.175 172.825 172.875
 172.925 172.95 172.975 408.825

ARTCC Centers & Remote Sites UHF Frequencies

Albuquerque (NM) Center

Alamogordo	257.6
Albuquerque	363.2
Amarillo	261.5 351.7 239.25
Animas	281.5 341.7 351.8
Carlabad	343.6
Childs Peak	288.3 307.3 350.2 371.9
Clines Corners	284.6 299.3
El Paso	270.3 285.5 343.6
Ft. Stockton	274.4 274.6 278.3
Globe	258.3 260.6 269.3 290.3 306.2 290.3 338.3 339.8 350.3 353.9
Guadalupe	274.6 278.3
Humboldt Mtn.	267.9

Mesa Rica	360.8
Mount Dora	319.9 351.7
Prescott	298.9 312.0 370.9
Raton	299.3
Roswell	257.6 259.2 353.6
Sandia Mtn.	299.3
Tesque Peak	299.3
Truth/Consequences	285.5
Tucson	273.6 281.5 351.8 398.9
Tucumcari	251.1 267.9 279.6 319.2
West Mesa	284.6 307.2 363.2
Winslow	298.9 312.0
Zuni	287.9 307.2

Anchorage (AK) Center

Adak	254.3
Anchorage	269.0 306.2 379.1
Annette Island	284.6

Barrow	385.6		
Bethel	372.0		
Bettles	352.0		
Big Delta	322.5		
Big Lake	279.6		
Biorka Island	335.5		
Cape Newenham	273.6		
Cold Bay	278.3		
Deadhorse	370.9		
Fort Yukon	284.7	370.1	
Galena	290.2		
Gulkana	317.5	360.8	
Gustavus	357.6		
Homer	270.3	316.1	
Kenai	269.0	273.45	
379.1			
King Salmon	354.0		
Kodiak	281.4		
Kotzebue	263.0		
McGrath	353.8		
Middleton Island	269.4		
Murphy Dome	285.4	319.2	
Nome	290.4		
Northway	323.0		
Point Lay	282.2		
Port Heiden	288.3		
St. Paul Island	338.3		
Shemya	339.8	346.3	
Sparrevohn	387.1		
Talkeetna	279.6		
Yakutat	263.1		

Atlanta (GA) Center

Albemarle	251.1		
Anniston	306.2		
Athens	256.9	306.9	
327.15			
Atlanta	264.2	273.6	279.2
306.2 317.7 327.8 343.9			
Augusta	323.0		
Birmingham	261.5	316.1	
Black Jack Mtn.	370.9		
Chattanooga	270.6	299.2	353.8
363.1			
Columbus	239.35	357.6	
Crossville	236.7	254.3	279.5
Foothills	380.35		
Gadsden	353.7		
Glade Springs	371.85		
Greensboro	343.8	379.2	
Hampton	343.9	371.95	
380.15			

Hickory	263.0	290.2	
307.35			
Huntsville	354.05		
Jonesville	257.9	291.75	
Macon	273.6	335.65	
343.75 360.75			
Millen	352.4		
Monroeville	267.9		
Montgomery	270.25	280.1	
290.5 308.6 319.1			
Mt. Oglethorpe	290.8	307.9	377.05
Newport	236.5	269.5	
Owing	269.1	322.4	327.0
Pine Level	290.5	335.6	
Tri City	301.4	319.9	
Uniontown	252.9	297.4	339.1
351.9 352.8			

Boston (MA) Center

Augusta	307.0		
Barnstable	269.3	290.3	307.3
321.3 370.9 387.1			
Berlin	282.2		
Bucks Harbor	269.3	290.5	
Calverton	379.85		
Cambridge	360.6		
Concord	338.2	381.4	
Cummington	379.1		
Gardner	338.2		
Houlton	319.1	346.4	
Hugenot	387.0		
Islip	259.1	346.3	
Kingston	256.9		
Lake George	348.7	354.1	393.3
Lebanon	348.7	381.4	
Melrose	281.5	353.7	370.9
Millinocket	319.1		
Mt. Mansfield	282.2	380.3	
Pawling	279.5	388.8	
Saint Albans	290.5	319.1	321.3
346.4			
Shelton	306.3	317.7	343.8
351.7			
South Acton	285.4	322.4	
Turin	279.5	321.3	323.0
377.1 380.3			
Utica	332.4		
Woodstock	269.2	277.4	307.9
360.6 398.9			

Chicago (IL) Center

Aurora	354.0		

Bradford	353.5 398.9		
Burlington	316.1		
Cedar Rapids	261.5		
Chicago Heights	272.7		
Crown Point	387.05		
Danville	353.95		
Dells	380.35 307.1		
Des Moines	319.8		
Des Plaines	298.9 317.4 360.8		
Downers Grove	338.3 363.2 364.8		
Dubuque	281.4 285.5 343.6		
Fort Wayne	269.1 362.3		
Goshen	263.1 317.6		
Grand Rapids	287.9 319.1		
Hampshire	348.7 381.4		
Horicon	263.0 327.8 343.9		
Jones	254.3 343.7		
360.75			
Milford	284.7 353.8 377.2		
397.9			
Milwaukee	291.7 323.1 360.6		
364.8			
Moline	351.7 385.65		
Monee	360.75		
Muskegon	285.4		
Oshkosh	319.25 387.1		
Ottumwa	354.1		
Pullman	269.6		
Rockford	379.2 381.6		
Rossville	350.35 370.85		
South Bend	273.6		
Volk Field	269.65		
Washington	239.3 297.4 385.6		

Cleveland (OH) Center

Algonac	269.2 354.0 380.6		
Belmont	281.5 291.6 379.1		
Blue Knob	299.2 307.1 327.1		
353.8			
Bradford	338.3		
Carleton	269.5 354.1		
Chardon	306.3		
Detroit	319.9		
Dunkirk	263.1		
Findlay	269.3 288.3		
Flint	335.6		
Holland	306.9		
Litchfield	277.4 343.8 360.7		
Mansfield	317.7 350.2		
Moon Twp.	227.8 236.1 319.2		
385.5			
Morgantown	239.3		
Mt. Hope	307.2		

Paris	348.7		
Saginaw	307.8 351.9		
Sandusky	261.5 327.0		
371.95			
Warren	267.3 316.1 317.4		
389.7			
Waterford	323.2		
Waterville	379.2		
Wayland	239.35 371.85		
381.6			

Denver (CO) Center

Alamosa	354.15 362.35		
377.05			
Aspen	306.9 327.8		
Brush	319.2		
Casper	239.0 322.5		
Cheyenne	281.5 284.7 307.1		
350.3			
Colby	306.3 379.9		
Cortez	363.05		
Crawford	257.9 338.2		
Denver	256.9 272.7 282.2		
285.5 290.2 306.9 322.3			
Durango	363.05		
Eastonville	380.15		
Farmington	290.4 291.7 307.8		
319.0 352.0 363.05 386.8			
Goodland	353.7		
Grand Island	269.6		
Grand Mesa	269.1 275.3 307.9		
327.0 327.8			
Gunnison	307.9 319.0		
Hanksville	271.2		
Hayden	257.6 327.8		
Hayes Center	335.6		
La Junta	343.8 354.15		
380.15			
Lusk	239.0		
Medicine Bow	281.5 285.5 350.3		
Natoma	307.8 322.4 353.7		
No. Platte	269.6		
Ogalalla	240.3 269.6		
O'Neill	257.9 269.6 385.5		
Pueblo	323.05 362.35		
377.05			
Rapid City	322.5 338.2		
Rock Springs	327.8 346.4		
Sterling	272.7		
Sundance	239.0		
Tuba	296.7 363.05		
386.8			
Walton Peak	285.5		

Fort Worth (TX) Center

Abilene	269.4	282.2	317.7
Ardmore	270.0	322.4	
Big Spring	350.2		
Blue Ridge	254.3	377.1	397.9
Brownwood	269.4		
Clinton-Sherman	290.2	363.1	
Dublin	289.8	351.9	353.7
387.0			
El Dorado	269.1	272.75	
Ft. Worth	377.1	380.3	
Frankston	227.4	265.1	
Hobbs	385.6		
Keller	289.9	323.2	360.6
380.2			
Lubbock	327.1	362.3	
Marshall	269.2	327.8	
McAlester	250.4	278.3	
Midland	291.65	385.6	
Monroe	271.2		
Oklahoma City	298.9	363.1	
Paducah	231.3	316.1	319.8
348.65 354.0 389.6			
Paris	348.7		
Plainview	316.1		
San Angelo	322.55		
Scurry	287.9	347.0	363.2
Shreveport	271.2	307.9	
Texarkana	284.6	357.6	381.4
Waco	269.5		
Wichita Falls	278.5	319.8	
348.65 360.7 389.6			

Honolulu (HI) Center

Hamakua	284.6		
Mt. Haleakala	278.3	291.6	307.1
317.5			
Mt. Kaala	269.4		
Kokee	306.9		
Mauna Kapu	269.4	327.1	
Waimanalo	278.3	291.6	307.1
317.5			

Houston (TX) Center

US Arrivals/Departures 263.1 269.0			
269.5 281.5 306.3 307.2 385.5			
Alexandria	269.2	278.55	
317.5 319.9 343.9 381.5			
Austin	290.5	353.8	
Brownsville	263.1		

College Station	272.7	282.3	371.9
Fredericksburg	307.3	385.4	
Galveston	306.3	351.8	370.9
Grand Isle	269.5	360.8	
Hattiesburg	281.5	285.6	
Kingsville	281.5	291.6	
Lacombe	327.05	380.2	
Lafayette	263.1	338.25	
Lake Charles	353.9	381.6	
Laredo	307.2	319.1	323.1
Lometa	343.9		
Lufkin	269.6	343.6	
Mobile	288.15	387.05	
322.4			
Natchez	291.7		
New Orleans	380.2	385.5	
Newton	225.1	343.9	
Palacios	279.6	306.9	
Rockport	281.9	319.8	322.5
353.6 360.7			
Rock Springs	346.4	380.2	
San Antonio	285.4	291.7	299.2
322.5 335.6 343.7 385.55			
Sealy	279.6		
Uvalde	285.4	327.0	

Indianapolis (IN) Center

Brookville	282.3	307.9	351.8
Charleston	381.6		
Evansville	284.65	379.9	
Henryville	269.45	278.5	
352.0			
Indianapolis	251.1	290.3	319.8
385.4			
Livingston	319.15	323.2	
London	246.0	253.5	290.5
346.3 380.2			
Marietta	398.9		
Marmet	269.6	307.3	385.6
Merwyn	239.25	281.4	
Muncie	319.8		
New Hope	353.65	394.1	
Portsmouth	290.4	363.2	
Rosewood	269.0		
Rossville	319.2		
Terre Haute	270.3	307.1	
Tri City	335.6		
Winchester	263.05	317.75	
343.65 387.0			
Zanesville	288.1	343.6	353.5
370.9			

164

Jacksonville (FL) Center

US Arrivals/Departures 251.1 317.4 381.4

Albany	226.8 359.0 381.55
Alma	282.3 290.4 346.3
Brooksville	343.9 377.2
Charleston	370.95 379.1 399.1
Columbia	298.9 319.2 335.5
Crestview	338.3 346.4 350.2 371.9
Daytona Beach	357.1
Dothan	288.3 353.5
Florence	306.3 321.4
Gainesville	291.7 360.7 385.6
Glenco	277.4
Jacksonville	327.1
Millen	363.2
Myrtle Beach	317.4 343.6 381.4
Orlando/Eustis	360.6
Panama City	251.1
Perry Foley	352.0
St. Augustine	236.7 288.1 307.25 346.25
Savannah	285.65 322.5 380.05
Tallahassee	307.2 343.8 360.8 364.8
Valdosta	348.3 363.0 379.2 399.6

Kansas City (KS) Center

Anthony	257.0 263.1 344.8
Butler	327.0
Chillicothe	381.5
Columbia	279.6 299.2 350.2
Decatur	335.6
Edna	343.9 369.9
Effingham	290.4 346.4
Emporia	269.2 285.4 323.2
Farmington	291.7 307.8 319.0
Gage	324.1 379.2
Garden City	269.4 281.4 387.1
Hutchinson	269.5 273.6 337.4 353.9
Jacksonville	327.5
Kansas City	352.0
Kirksville	269.3 369.9 370.9
Liberal	290.8
Manhattan	388.8
Marion	269.5

Mt. Vernon	317.7
Natoma	307.8 322.4
Oklahoma City	291.7
Olathe	352.0
Ponca City	317.6 319.1
Quincy	290.7 319.9
Richland	317.5 353.7
St. Charles	269.6 323.1 327.1
St. Joseph	251.1
St. Louis	351.9 369.9 380.2
Salina	363.2
Sedalia	285.6
Springfield	269.4 277.4 290.5
Topeka	279.5 290.2 343.7 369.9
Tulsa	288.15
Vandalia	338.2

Los Angeles (CA) Center

US Arrivals/Departures 269.5 285.5 285.6 291.7 307.8 322.4 327.1 338.3 343.7 348.7 350.3 354.1

Bakersfield	263.0 317.7 372.0
Baldwin Hills	277.4 322.4 351.7
Barstow	279.6 284.7 290.2 314.2 317.4 351.9
Blythe	285.6
Boron	283.6
Cedar City	271.2
Julian	261.5 277.4 285.6 291.7 307.8 346.4 354.1
Keeler	283.6 377.1
Los Angeles	284.7 351.7
Mt. Potosi	283.6 377.1
Nelson	314.2 319.2 343.6
Ontario	346.4
Riverside	290.2
Saddle Peak	285.5 351.8
San Luis Obispo	269.5 307.0 327.8
Santa Barbara	269.5 327.1 338.3 346.3
Santa Catalina	354.1
Seligman	282.3 319.2 323.2
Tonopah	291.7 319.8 322.5 377.1
29 Palms	282.3 285.6
Yuma	278.5

Memphis (TN) Center

Brinkley	276.3 286.6 309.7
Columbus	269.4 275.4 320.4 363.2 387.1

Fayetteville	269.0	353.8	
Ft. Smith	398.9		
Graham	285.5	296.7	
379.25			
Greenville	269.3	282.25	
322.35			
Greenwood	259.1	298.95	
Harrison	286.6		
Huntsville	307.0		
Jackson	285.2	259.1	
Louisville	263.0	282.1	362.6
Malden	350.3		
McKellar	239.3	317.4	354.0
Memphis	239.3	306.9	322.3
360.8			
Meridian	263.0	285.4	299.6
323.0 377.2			
Nashville	263.1	306.3	317.6
327.8			
Paducah	397.9		
Pine Bluff	269.35	281.4	
Russellville	307.1	343.8	348.7
Shelbyville	353.5		
So. Fulton	362.35		
Tupelo	252.7	259.2	260.6
Walnut Ridge	257.6	319.3	

Miami (FL) Center

US Arrivals/Departures 298.9 306.9
307.2 307.9 319.1 323.0 363.2 379.25
381.45

Avon Park	256.7	257.7	285.5
349.0			
Brooksville	323.2		
Ft. Myers	322.5	335.5	
Gr. Bahama Island	282.2		
Gr. Turk Island	307.2		
Key West	306.9	323.1	
Melbourne	269.3	343.7	348.7
379.25			
Miami	269.05	281.5	
319.1 323.0 359.3 363.2 381.45			
Nassau	298.9	307.9	
Pahokee	307.1		
Sarasota	307.3	377.1	
Vero Beach	319.0	370.9	398.9
W. Palm Beach	263.1	278.5	363.6

Minneapolis (MN) Center

Aberdeen	371.9	
Alexandria	269.2	319.9
Alpena	279.6	

Bemidji	251.1		
Brainerd	239.0		
Darwin	323.1		
Des Moines	288.1	343.8	372.0
Dickinson	263.0	321.3	380.3
Duluth	284.6	290.5	321.3
Dupree	363.0		
Eau Claire	335.6	353.9	
Fairmont	257.7		
Fargo	278.3		
Farmington	307.9	352.0	
Ft. Dodge	288.3		
Grand Forks	269.6	321.3	
Green Bay	307.9		
Hayward	278.5		
Houghton	269.0	321.3	379.1
Huron	339.8		
Int'l. Falls	377.1		
Iron Mtn.	322.5	387.0	
Jamestown	270.3	281.5	
LaCrosse	321.3	363.0	
Mankato	306.9		
Marysville	282.3	317.7	
Mason City	263.1	380.2	
Minneapolis	319.2	353.7	
Minot	279.6	319.1	
Omaha	290.4	321.3	
O'Neill	385.5		
Pellston	321.3	323.0	327.1
Pierre	228.5	269.1	317.5
Redwood Falls	269.5	290.2	321.3
Rhinelander	281.5		
Rochester	307.3		
Roseau	256.9		
Saginaw	282.5		
Sioux City	269.0	363.1	
Sioux Falls	291.7	317.4	
Traverse City	398.9		
Watertown	306.2		
White Cloud	299.2	353.6	

New York (NY) Center

Barnstable	269.3	290.3	307.3
321.3 370.9 387.1			
Barnegat	354.0		
Big Flat	306.2	322.4	
Douglaston	285.5	381.6	
Elk Mtn.	290.4	298.9	350.3
363.2			
Flint Hill	278.3	290.2	339.8
Joliet	322.5	380.2	
Matawan	282.3	350.3	
North Mtn.	269.1	273.6	319.9
Philipsburg	272.7	306.2	343.9

Sayre	352.0	372.0	
Ship Bottom	254.3	335.6	353.5

Oakland (CA) Center

Angels Camp	281.5	284.6	290.4	
316.1 319.9				
Bishop	319.8			
Fallon	269.3	285.5		
Ferndale	387.1			
Fresno	281.5	285.4	319.1	
343.8 353.8				
Half Moon	274.6	307.3	357.6	
387.1				
Hollister	357.6			
Mina	307.9	319.8		
Mt. Tamalpais	323.0	353.5		
Priest	285.4	290.5	307.0	
319.1 343.8				
Red Bluff	269.1	290.3	350.3	
Reno	269.3	285.5		
Sacramento	269.1	316.1		
San Luis Obispo	307.0			
Tonopah	307.9	319.8		
Ukiah	281.4	306.2	353.5	
379.2				

Salt Lake City (UT) Center

Ashton	338.3	381.6	
Baker	387.15		
Battle Mtn.	269.0	352.0	
363.15			
Big Piney	381.6		
Billings	351.9		
Blackfoot	381.6		
Bliss	363.0	397.9	
Boise	272.7		
Bozeman	338.3		
Burley	363.0		
Butte	285.4	338.3	
Cascade	399.0		
Cedar City	299.2	343.6	346.3
381.45 398.9			
Delle	385.55		
Delta	370.85	381.45	
Elko	269.0	363.15	
Ely	397.85		
Fairfield	370.55		
Francis Peak	257.7	377.15	
387.05			
Glasgow	272.75		
Great Falls	285.4	319.0	
Green River	291.6	353.5	

Hanksville	271.2		
Jackson	259.1	285.2	285.6
Judith Mtn.	272.75	285.4	
Lakeside	285.4		
Lovell	285.6		
Malad City	379.25		
Miles City	272.75		
Missoula	285.4		
Myton	275.7	377.15	
Rome	387.15		
Salmon	338.3		
Sheridan	343.7		
Squaw Butte	387.15	399.0	
Sunnyside	370.85	380.35	
381.45			
Thermopolis	285.6	353.5	
Tonopah	291.7	319.8	
397.85			
Watford City	272.7		
Wilson Creek	278.1	380.35	
397.85			
Winnemucca	363.15	380.05	

San Juan (PR) Center

Borinquen	338.3		
El Yunque	269.0	279.6	285.5
299.2 307.0			
Pico del Este	269.0	279.6	285.5
299.2 307.0			
San Juan	269.0	307.0	338.3

Seattle (WA) Center

Beacon Hill	273.6	353.9	
Cottonwood	251.1	335.2	
Ferndale	306.3	360.7	
Horton	239.0	279.6	291.7
Klamath Falls	306.3	351.7	
Lakeview	327.1	351.7	
Larch Mtn.	269.0	278.3	343.6
Marlin	291.6		
Medford	239.0	306.3	360.7
Mohler	307.8		
Neah Bay	319.2		
Mullan Pass	307.8		
Pendleton	281.4	321.3	343.9
Redmond	281.4	288.1	
Scappoose	288.1	317.6	
Seattle	306.2	343.6	
Spokane	251.1	282.3	335.5
Stampede Pass	270.3		
The Dalles	257.6		

Whidbey Island 319.2
Yakima 251.1 273.6 343.9
353.9

Washington (DC) Center

US Arrivals/Departures 272.7 279.6
284.7 285.5 323.0 352.0 377.1 380.2
Bucks Elbow 263.1 282.2 284.7
371.9
Buena Vista 317.7 319.0 353.9
377.2
Cape Charles 275.7
Cedar Lake 362.3
Clinton 327.0
Elkins 387.1
Falls Church 351.8 357.6 381.5
Grantsville 381.5
Green Bay 269.4 351.9 377.1
380.3
Hagerstown 385.4
Johnsonville 322.45 348.25
Kenton 277.4
Linden 319.1
Lynchburg 270.35
Martinsburg 269.65
Millville 363.0
Modena 287.9
New Bern 272.75 360.65
Patuxent River 353.6
Roanoke 317.7
Rocky Mount 285.5 354.1 377.1
Sampson 288.05
Sea Isle 285.4
Ship Bottom 254.3
So. Boston 307.0
Westminster 385.4
Whaleyville 258.1 327.8
387.05 398.85
Wilmington 290.5

Canadian Centres & Remote Sites Operated by Transport Canada UHF Frequencies

Edmonton (Alberta) Centre

Brooks 368.5
Calgary 243.5 265.6
Edmonton 240.9 248.2 294.5
Ft. Nelson 290.6
Ft. St. John 285.4
Lloydminster 340.7
Red Deer 239.0

Slave Lake 304.2
Whitecourt 293.7
Whitehorse 290.6

Gander (Newfoundland) Centre

Gander 289.4 294.5 342.9
384.5
St. Anthony 321.9
St. John's (NF) 227.3 230.3 245.0
Stephenville 228.3 247.0

Moncton (New Brunswick) Centre

Chatham 346.9
Fredericton 270.8
Goose 294.5
Hopedale 381.4
Moncton 290.6 294.5
St. John 270.8
Schefferville 381.4
Sept-Iles 368.5
Sydney 266.3
Yarmouth 368.5

Montreal (Quebec) Centre

Chibougamau 253.2
Gatineau 266.8
Mont-Joli 227.2
Montreal 229.2 245.0 294.0
Quebec 270.9
Riviere-du-Loup 299.6
Sept-Iles 381.9
Sherbrooke 226.0
Val-d'Or 308.3

Toronto (Ontario) Centre

Brockville 231.95
Elliot Lake 260.9
Hamilton 290.8
London 266.3
North Bay 356.3
Sarnia 254.9
Sault Ste Marie 227.3 344.5
Stirling 398.4
Timmins 381.4
Toronto 236.8 294.5 354.3
374.5
Waterloo 268.75
Wawa 298.6
Wiarton 290.6

Vancouver (BC) Centre

Castlegar	227.3
Enderby	381.9
Kamloops	236.0 294.0
Port Hardy	266.3
Prince George	231.95
Prince Rupert	284.0
Princeton	351.3
Puntzi	315.7
Sandspit	227.2
Terrace	269.1
Tofino	254.9

Vancouver	245.0 294.5 350.7
Victoria	308.4
Williams Lake	381.4

Winnipeg (Manitoba) Centre

Brandon	285.4
Kenora	225.2
Regina	266.3 283.4
Saskatoon	239.8
Swift Current	232.3
Thunder Bay	297.6
Winnipeg	294.5 349.6

Banks, Federal Reserve

All Locations: 409.525 413.875 413.925 415.10

Bonneville Power Administration

Operations: 172.525/168.325   Emergencies 172.50/168.30
Other freqs: 151.625 167.075 168.225 169.50 169.825 170.075 171.825 172.55 172.575 407.025 408.025 408.475 408.525 408.55 411.65 411.675 412.125 412.20 412.25 412.35 415.15 416.025 416.675 417.375 417.525 417.65 417.725 417.825 417.85 417.95 417.975 419.85

Boundary & Water Commission, International (US/Mexico)

Frequencies: 27.575 27.585 162.025 162.125 164.175 164.475 169.525 170.325 172.40
172.475 173.175 173.9625 412.125 417.725 (HF 3238.5 5326 6783.5 6976 9946 kHz)

HF Net:

KKP24	El Paso, TX	KKP26	Armistad Dam, TX
KKP25	Falcon Dam, TX	KKP27	Harlingen, TX

Most active VHF stations reported:

KAN893	El Paso, TX	172.475	412.125
KAN894	Caballo, NM	173.175	
KAN895	Borrego, TX	173.175	
KAP833	Anzaludas Dam, TX	162.125	
KCT286	Zapata, TX	162.175	173.975
KCT287	Amistad Dam, TX	162.025	164.175
KCT288	Amistad Dam, TX	164.175	
KCT289	Comstock, TX	162.025	
KCT290	Yuma, AZ	164.475	
KDE601	El Paso, TX	417.725	
KDE602	Canutillo, TX	172.475	
KDE603	Harlingen, TX	169.525	
KDE604	Anzaludas Dam, TX	170.325	
KDE605	Rio Grande City, TX	169.525	
KDE606	Roma, TX	169.525	
KDE607	Presidio, TX	173.175	
KDE608	Las Cruces, NM	172.475	
KDE609	Hatch, NM	172.475	
KDE610	Los Ebanos, TX	169.525	
KDE611	Hayner, NM	172.475	
KDE612	Leasburg, NM	172.475	
KDE613	Ft. Hancock, TX	172.475	
KDE614	Amistad Dam, TX	164.175	
KKE912	Falcon Dam, TX	162.025	172.40
KKI871	Harlingen, TX	162.025	172.40
	Lower Rio Grande Valley, TX	164.175	

Bugs, Body Mikes, & Other Surveillance

Monitors suggest that wireless microphones, room transmitters, and body mikes ("wires") are reported on the following frequencies: 48.60 49.50 149.00 149.35 165.9125 166.3375 167.3375 167.3425 167.4875 168.0115 169.20 169.225 169.445 169.505 170.245 170.305 171.045 171.105 171.45 171.845 171.85 171.90 171.905 172.00 172.20 173.3375 172.375 174.60 177.60 181.60 183.60 186.60 190.60 192.60 195.60 196.60 199.60 457.5625 467.7875. Units may be found operating almost anywhere between 169 and 215 MHz, NFM or WFM mode. Also check between 49.67 and 50 MHz, also the 88 to 108 MHz FM broadcasing band for low-cost units. Note that many FM wireless intercoms and "baby monitors" operate between 49.67 and 50.00 MHz. Baby monitors are often left running all the time, day and night, and tend to pick up conversations and other domestic sounds from several rooms of a house, or an entire apartment. As such, they qualify as "inadvertant" electronic surveillance equipment. Search the entire band, especially checking 49.67 49.77 49.83 49.845 49.86 49.875 49.89 49.93 49.97 49.99 MHz for these signals. Some "baby monitor" signals can be picked up from a mile or more away.

Cordless telephone surveillance is conducted beteen 46.61 and 46.97 MHz. Search the entire band, especially checking 46.61 46.63 46.67 46.71 46.73 46.77 46.83 46.87 46.93 and 46.97 MHz (and midway points between these) for signals. Some newer cordless phones operate in the 902 to 928 MHz band, some claiming to use voice scrambling techniques. A scanner with a good outside antenna, mounted up high, might be able to pick up cordless phones from several miles away.

Monitoring of analog cellular phone conversations (869.04 to 893.97 MHz band) is common, although a violation of the Electronic Communications Privacy Act (Public Law 99–508 of October 21, 1986). Cellular channels are allocated with 30 kHz separation between each.

Civil Air Patrol (USAF Auxiliary)

National Simplex: 148.125 148.15 MHz   National Emergency: HF 4585 kHz
VHF Aero Band OP: 122.9 123.1
VHF FM OP: 148.15/143.75 148.15/143.90 Packet 143.75 149.925
HF SSB OP: 2371 2372.5 2374 4464.5 4467.5 4507.5 4582 4585 4599.5 4602.5 4627 4630 7635 7920 14902 20873 26618.5 26620 kHz

State Organization (Wings) Tactical Identifiers

AL	Goldenrod		MI	Father
AK	Sourdough		NE	Wigwam
AZ	Thunderbird		NV	North Wind
AR	Dogwood		NH	Profile
CA	Whitebear		NJ	Zigzag
CO	Pikes Peak		NM	Pueblo
CT	Nutmeg		NY	Empire
DE	Gabby		NC	Red Dog
DC	Aero		ND	Blackfoot
FL	Sparrow		OH	Black Hawk
GA	Red Star		OK	Sooner
HI	Firebrand		OR	Beaver Fox
ID	Magpie		PA	Keystone
IL	Red Fox		PR	Pineapple
IN	Red Fire		RI	Rhody
IA	Corn State		SC	Crescent
KS	Jayhawk		SD	Dacotah
KY	Middleground		TN	Blue Chip
LA	Magnolia		TX	Eagle Nest
ME	Pinetree		UT	Uncle Willie
MD	Plat		VT	Pico
MA	Freedom		VA	Blue Flight
MI	Red Robin		WA	Fir
MN	Star Fish		WV	Lowland
MS	Mockingbird		WI	Badger
MO	Blue Bird		WY	King

Individual units add numerals to the above tactical identifiers.

Coast Guard, U.S. (USCG)

Most often reported frequencies shown. HF duplex pairs shown as shore/vessel frequencies:
  Distress: 27.065 156.80 157.10 (HF 2182 kHz)
  Search & Rescue: 123.1 156.30 282.8 (HF 3023 5680 kHz)
  Comms with civilian vessels: 27.065 156.30 156.55 156.60 156.70 156.80 157.10 (HF 2182 2670 4125 4426/4134 6215 6501/6200 8281 8764/8340 12990 13049/12242 16420 17314/16432 kHz)
  Tactical & Drug Enforcement: 34.30 34.45 34.85 41.80 51.15 65.60 163.175 164.4125 164.55 165.3375 165.5625 254.2 282.425 353.9 381.8 (HF 3130 4302 4376 5063 5320 5451 5463 5469 5508 5514 5523 5715 5785 6222 6266 6277 6465.5 6512 6812 6954 7527 7643 7916 8245 8768.5 8500 8566 8611 kHz + Customs Service freqs) In the Gulf of Mexico area anti-smuggler OP on 37.00 MHz ("Deathdealer Base") may be a USCG activity.
  USCG Intelligence Service: 165.0125 165.3125 165.3375
  CG Base Security: 409.825 415.925 416,85 417.125 419.125 419.625 419.925
  USCG Auxiliary: Primary 157.175; Secondary 143.28 143.80 143.875 148.305 148.825 157.05 157.075 157.10 157.15 (HF 2230 2670 kHz) (Note: Opns on 143.28 in at least some areas use 136.5 Hz CTCSS tone.)
  USCG Reserve: 27.89 30.36 30.38 30.41 157.50 157.65
  Marine Broadcasts: 157.10 (HF 2003 2638 2670 kHz)
  VHF Packet Comms: 171.155 (1200 baud)
  Environmental Matters: 36.25 41.71 156.75 157.125 165.3125 168.50 163.175
  USCG Aero OP: 126.4 164.30 237.9 240.6 275.1 277.8 285.0 342.2 381.7 381.8 383.9 (HF usually on shared basis with USN, especially noted on 2261 3120 3123 4143.6 4335 5692 5696 6381 8648 8980 8984 11195 11198 11201 12887.5 15081 15084 kHz) Freq 126.4 reported in use between Cutters and helos for landing & takeoff comms.
  Intership HF: 2003 2082.5 2093 2203 2638 2830 4143.6 kHz
  Coordination with Army Corps of Engineers: (HF 2350 4850 kHz)
  Emergency OP: 156.80 157.10
  Ports & Harbors: 156.05 156.175 156.25 156.60 156.70 (HF 2716 2836 kHz)
  General OP All Areas: 38.27 156.30 156.55 156.60 156.70 157.05 157.075 157.15 157.175 171.2375 171.3125 171.3375 171.3625 407.625 407.975 409.00 (HF 2103.5 2638 2659 2662 2667 2670 2675 2678 2683 2686 2691 2694 2699 2702 2738 2748 2830 3421 3253 3382 4143.6 4419.4 4575 4850 5320 5422.5 6218.6 6221.6 6521.9 8291.1 8294 12429.2 12435.2 16581.7 16591.3 22127.1 22133.3 kHz)

Commerce, U.S. Dept. of

Also see listings under specific divisions of Dept. of Commerce.
National Marine Fisheries Service: 163.225/162.05 163.225/162.10
Dept. of Commerce: 27.405 27.565 27.575 27.585 27.610 30.05 30.06 30.07 30.18 34.98 36.22 38.22 40.27 40.29 41.07 41.34 122.9 123.05 123.3 162.025 162.05 162.075 162.10 162.125 162.15 162.20 162.3625 162.3675 162.375 163.225 163.275 163.30 163.325 164.025 164.075 165.4375 165.4625 165.4875 165.5125 165.5375 165.5625 165.5875 165.6125 166.025 166.05 166.075 166.10 166.125 166.15 166.175 166.225 169.025 169.075 169.375 169.425 169.45 169.50 170.20 171.675 172.025 172.055 172.065 172.10 173.025 173.10 173.125 173.5875 173.975 410.075 410.10 410.425 410.50 410.575 410.75 410.80 410.825 410.975 412.90 414.625 415.85 415.90 416.375 416.95 416.975

Interstate Commerce Commission (ICC)

All Areas: 409.20

Federal Communications Commission (FCC)

The FCC is most often noted by scanner monitors in all areas on 167.05/172.80 MHz, a frequency pair that was first revealed to monitors in an earlier edition of this Registry. In published statements, FCC personnel have hinted that other VHF or UHF FCC two-way channels are also used, although none have thusfar been reported by reliable monitoring sources. The fact is that FCC monitoring vans are equipped to operate on just about any communications frequency, including CB channels. In order to check the proper operation of licensed public safety, maritime, aero, industrial, transportation or other licensed systems, FCC units sometimes find it necessary to communicate with these stations on their respective frequencies.

Still, monitors have continued inquiring about the possibilities of the FCC mobile units using 41.06 MHz, but nobody has yet reported actually monitoring anything on that frequency. Other unconfirmed FCC communications facilities are supposedly in Long Beach, CA on 127.125 MHz; Washington, DC on 37.50 and 153.185 MHz; Laurel, MD on 168.35 MHz. Other unconfirmed but rumored frequencies include 408.00 and 418.00 MHz. We have yet to hear from any monitor reporting activity on any of these frequencies and wonder if there is any real reason to continue to give them any consideration at this point.

On the HF bands, an earlier edition of this Registry was also first to publish information of those frequencies and their channel designator numbers. It does appear that these frequencies are used by FCC monitoring facilities running RTTY (425/45 and 425/75N has been reported) using "bit inversion" privacy mode. The "bit inversion" key is changed once per month. Channels reported especially active include 3, 3A, 5, and 5D. A while back, monitors used to also report SSB and CW, but only RTTY has been reported in recent years.

Channel Numbers: Ch #1 2220 kHz; Ch #1A 2295 kHz; Ch #2 4483 kHz; Ch #2A 5133 kHz; Ch #2B 5373 kHz; Ch #3 7790 kHz; Ch #3A 7604 kHz; Ch #4 10655 kHz; Ch #4A 10902 kHz; Ch #5 13830 kHz; Ch #5A 13493 kHz; Ch #5B 13990 kHz; Ch #5C 13992 kHz; Ch #5D 14971 kHz; Ch #6 10850 kHz; Ch #6A 19230 kHz; Ch #7 22964 kHz; Ch #7A 23035 kHz; Ch #8 41.06 MHz; Ch #9 167.05/172.80; Ch #? 172.05/172.80

Tactical ID's (& Callsigns) for VHF

BR3		Linden Hall
C2	KAA459	Kansas City, MO
CN3		Ambrose, TX
CY1		Sunland
D7		Anchorage Office, AK
F1	KEE468	Buffalo, NY

F7	KIA691	Norfolk, VA
FK7		Anchorage Monitoring Station, AK
G3	KMA485	Los Angeles, CA
G5	KSA489	Chicago, IL
GC2		Livermore, CA
H3		Beaumont, TX
JD3		Fairbanks, AK
JG8		Kingsville, TX
K4		Santa Ana, CA
KN5	KRD998	Washington, DC
L4	KAA533	St. Paul, MN
L6	KKA919	Dallas, TX
L8	KGA363	Philadelphia, PA
LS8		Douglas, AZ
M2	KGA362	Baltimore, MD
M4	KIA869	Miami, FL
MC1		Mobile, AL
MJ4		Canandaigua, NY
N1	KMA487	San Francisco, CA
N9	KUA209	Honolulu, HI
NF1		Ft. Lauderdale, FL
OL1		Allegan, MI
P5	KIA697	Tampa, FL
PA1		Portland, ME
PH2		Laurel, MD
R5	KKA922	New Orleans, LA
R8	KQA488	Detroit, MI
R9	KOA487	Portland, OR
RA5	KUA209	Honolulu, HI
RU4		Charlotte Amalie, VI
S1	KKA921	Houston, TX
S3	KCA404	Boston, MA
TY3	KOA489	Seattle, WA
U6		Television (East)
U7		Television (Central)
U8		Television (West)
U9		San Diego, CA
V2	KIA695	Savannah, GA
V7	KAA530	Denver, CO
VM7		Chillicothe, OH
W2		Spokane, WA
W6	KEA469	New York, NY
XB8		Temporary (Emergency) Locations
Y3	KMA485	Los Angeles, CA
Y4		San Pedro, CA
YO6		Powder Springs, GA

RTTY Callsigns, Tactical ID's & Locations

KAA60	GI	Grand Island, NE
KCA35	BE	Belfast, ME
KCA38		Canandaigua, NY
KCA39		Ambrose, TX
KGA91	LR	Laurel, MD

KGA93	WA	Washington, DC
KIA83		Lexington, KY
KIA84	PS	Powder Springs, GA
KIA85	FL	Ft. Lauderdale
KIP71		Long Beach, CA
KKA59	DS	Douglas, AZ
KKA60	KA	Kingsville, TX
KKA61		Muskogee, OK
KKW38		Seattle, WA
KMB26		Santa Ana, CA
KMB27	LV	Livermore, CA
KOA54		Twin Falls, ID
KOA55		Spokane, WA
KOA56	FE	Ferndale, WA (?)
KOT72		San Diego, CA
KQA62	AL	Allegan, MI
KQG56		Chillicothe, OH
KUN70	WP	Waipahu, HI
KWC41	AN	Anchorage, AK
KWO66		Fairbanks, AK
KWX44	AN	Anchorage, AK
KWX45	AN	Anchorage, AK
KWX47	AN	Anchorage, AK
KWX48	AN	Anchorage, AK
WWQ20	SS	Sabana Seca, PR

Congress, Library of

Landover, MD	KLA421	408.125	411.40
Washington, DC	KLW571	408.125	411.40

Congress, U.S.

Democratic Pager	170.375
Republican Pager	169.575

Consumer Product Safety Commission (CPSC)

Bethesda, MD   KWM952   168.00

Court, Superior

Washington, DC (Security)   163.275

Court, U.S. Supreme

Washington, DC (Security)   163.10

Court, U.S. Tax

Washington, DC   409.40

Courts, Administrative Office of (AUSC)

Stations in North Carolina at Asheville, Bryson City, Charlotte, Shelby, & Statesville. All believed to operate on 164.20 MHz.

Customs Service, US

Leading the way in the international war against smuggling, the Customs Service turns up in news headlines and TV footage on a weekly basis. This has always kept the agency high on the list of activities high on the "want to monitor" list of most people who own scanners and communications receivers, for the agency uses frequences spread out across HF, VHF and UHF.

The primary supply routes into the US for contraband are from the south, although things are always changing to a certain extent. South Florida continues as a popular spot, although Puerto Rico and the Virgin Islands are popular, as are Bimini and other Bahamas locations as offshore staging areas on the trip from South America. From these areas, ships and aircraft can bring illicit drugs directly to areas all along Gulf coasts, and well northwards along the Atlantic and Pacific Coasts. The aircraft are bold enough to land on rural roads of such poor quality that you'd think twice about driving your car there. A popular western entry route is through Mexico, into Santa Cruz and Cochise Counties ("Cocaine Alley") of Arizona. The US Customs Service, often in concert with a myriad of other federal agencies (including the USCG, USN, DEA, FBI, CIA, FCC, State Dept., FEMA, ATF, Dept. of Commerce, HHS, Dept. of the Interior, INS, NOAA, DEA, Dept. Agriculture, selected CAP units) as well as state and local agencies, is dedicated to cutting off the flow of drugs prior to their arrival within the nation's borders. This requires vessels and aircraft, and the communications that monitors invariably find to be fascinating.

It's the hunt and chase, the pursuit, the attempts at evading the blockade against smugglers that is taking place in the Caribbean, the Gulf of Mexico, in Cocaine Alley, and now in many other coastal and interior areas. Much of the communications can be monitored, and monitors generally seem to be under the impression that all Customs Service communications are "in the clear." This isn't true, the agency does have secure circuits. Customs Service aircraft carry a small plaque that reads "Non-secure radios will not be used when using any secure radio or the intercom for classified communications."

Nerve centers for Customs operations are scattered. Joint Task Force 4 (JTF-4) operates from the navy base at Key West, FL, The West Coast counterpart is JTF-5, out of Oakland, CA. Both are under the command of USCG officers, reporting directly to the US Atlantic and Pacific commands. There's also a Customs National Aviation Center. Its task is to control the deployment of interdiction aircraft as well as the coordination national surveillance data. This facility provides intelligence information to enforcement units in the field.

There are two Customs Service command, control, and communications and intelligence (C3I) centers, one for the East Coast, one for the West Coast. The East Coast center is in Miami, the other is at March AFB, CA. An administrative facility is in Oklahoma City, OK. The two C3I centers have radar consoles that provide information on all aircraft flying along the Atlantic, Pacific, and Gulf coasts, as well as along the US/Mexican border. The radar inputs come from FAA, military (including NORAD) sources.

179

Customs also collects radar data from units installed in aerostats. These are helium-filled blimp-like platforms for radars. Tethered to the ground by strong cables, they are raised to altitudes of 15,000 to 20,000 ft. and are very useful in detecting low flying aircraft. Present/proposed Customs aerostats are in southern PR, Morgan City, LA; Matagorda, TX; Alabama Port, AL; Venice, FL; Horseshoe Beach, FL; Rio Grande City, TX; Marfa, TX; Eagle Pass, TX; Ft. Huachuca, AZ; Deming, NM; and in the Bahamas at Great Inagua, Grand Bahama, and George Town. USAF aerostats are at Venice, FL and Cudjoe Key, FL.

Customs vessels and aircraft are also radar equipped, as are the units of other agencies (USCG, USN, etc.) that are on anti-smuggler patrol in coordination with Customs. Also, intelligence coming into the C3I centers is radioed to vessels and aircraft.

Customs operates UHF air/air and air/ground radios for short-distance comms. These are 225 to 400 MHz-band sets in the clear and with encryption. There are also Customs Service VHF-FM comms taking place, These units can operate with voice privacy but have no encryption at this time, At some point, it is planned for the VHF systems to be encrypted.

On HF, Customs comms are via a scrambler-capable Rockwell (Collins) computer driven SSB system. Monitors have noted that this system has a data burst on one frequency followed by a series of data bursts on other frequencies. What this represents is the equipment autoscanning 10 primary comms frequencies in an effort to contact a specific other station. The data burst is a selective calling signal intended to break the squelch of that specific station when the autoscanning reaches that station's guard channel. Recently the 10 autoscan channels were noted as being: ZB YC VE VF VG ZE VC YG YH and YI. The high powered ("Atlas") base station transmitter site is Cedar Rapids, IA, with remote outlets in Newport Beach, CA, and near Richardson, TX.

Over the years, monitors have noted that a large number of HF frequencies have been used. Some have been in continuous use for a long time, others have been phased out and replaced by new ones. Some that were on hiatus have been returned to service. At least one frequency was seemingly shut down after it was ruined by what sounded to observers like deliberate jamming. In general, HF frequencies are referred to by code letters, such as "Yankee Delta" (YD), or "Sierra India" (SI).

Our HF listing shows all Customs Service SSB frequencies (and identifiers) that had been reported up to the time this edition was compiled.

The Customs Service aircraft roster is as complete as possible, but some of the agency's aircraft have "unlisted" tail numbers.

Tactical ID's shown include some guesses, and are subject to change.

Customs Service Aircraft: Lockheed P3= N91LC N96LW N145CS N146CS; Sikorsky Black Hawk= "23670"; Lockheed 1PV Ventura= N15390 N16295 N16370 N18314; Douglas DC-6= N1125J; Grumman FM-2= N15941 N17115; Bellanca 17-30A= N6641V; Rockwell 680= N6218D; Nomad= N3225F N6313P; Piper Cheyenne= N9085U N9091J N9116Q N9159Y N9233T N9279A; Cessna 206F= N60838; Cessna 210= N732HJ N732XE; Cessna 337= N25892; Cessna 550= N435A N586RE N753CC N797CW N2531K N2663Y N2734K N6001L N26494 N26496 N26621

VHF/UHF: CTCSS 100.0 Hz
Operational Repeaters: 165.2375/166.4375 169.45/171.05

Tactical Repeaters: 162.05/164.575 163.125/164.325 165.4375/163.30 165.5125/166.275 165.7625/166.5875

Organized Crime-Drug Enforcement Task Force Repeaters 165.925/167.6375

Simplex-
Operational: 165.2375 169.45

Aeronautical: 123.075 165.7375 235.3 240.2 254.2 281.4 282.425 353.9 381.8

Organized Crime-Drug Enforcement Task Force: 167.6375

Tactical: 162.05 163.125 164.10 164.775 165.4375 165.4625 165.5125 165.7625 165.8625 166.5875 166.8625

HF Identifiers/Frequencies: (kHz)
A-5277 B-5841 C-7300 D-9497 E-10076 F-7657.5 G-14690 H-18666 I-23675 L-14350 P-14686 R-23042.5
S01-26600 S02-25410 S03-24120 S05-21990 S07-19050 S08-17301 S13-15443 S24-12215 SI-18171 SJ-19131
TA-10242 TC-20890 TD-23214 TE-25350 TH-23343
VA-27870 VB-20631 VC-18594 VD-17475 VE-10242 VF-11494 VG-13907 VK-3369
XA-2808.5 XB-4991 XC-5058.5 XD-7778.5 XE-9238.5 XF-11073.5 XG-15953.5 XH-17601 XI-19131
YA-3428 YB-5571 YC-8912 YD-11288 YE-13312 YF-17912 YG-20890 YH-23214 YI-25350
ZA-4500 ZB-7527 ZC-9802 ZD-12222 ZE-15867
Additional frequencies reported: 4055 5527 5860 6870 7475 7582 8125 11246 11288 11408 12138.5 13312 13630 14443 15964 16141 16348 17443 18283 20852 kHz

Some ID's Monitored on Customs Service channels, with possible locations. Those indicated as +# have numerals following to designate individual units. If a numeral is monitored before the tactical ID of a portable or mobile unit, it indicates the Customs Service District number. Locations and facilities not indicated otherwise are operated by U.S. Customs:

Almighty	USN, Guantanamo Bay, Cuba
Alpha+#	Individual Customs Service agent
Ambush	Possibly a surveillance blimp
Atlas	Customs HQ (remote to transmitters in CA & IA)
Ballyhoo+#	Possibly small intercept craft (have high #'s)
Bat	Turks & Caicos Base
Billfish	Bahamas vessel base.
Black Sheep	Houston, Texas
Broadway	New York, NY
Camelback	Phoenix, Arizona
Charlie 3	FAA, Miami, Fla.
Charlie 20	FAA. Houston, Tex.
Clambake	Boston, Mass.
Comm-4-Alpha	
Condor 800	Sometimes operates from suitcase transceiver with ID of Condor 800M
Cothen+#	Comms Technicians
Crown City	San Diego, Calif.

Crownpoint	
Delta 06	Possibly an AWACS aircraft
Desert Base	Tucson, Ariz.
Domino	Tyndall AFB, Fla.
Edsel	Aircraft
Empire Base	Riverside, Calif.
Fat Albert+#	Aerostats
Flint Base	DEA, Dallas, Texas
Flint+#	DEA aircraft
Freemason	
Fried Chicken	New Orleans, La.
Gangster	
Ghost Rider	FAA, Albuquerque, New Mexico
Hammer	Customs C3I, March AFB, Calif.
Happy Hour	"Blue Lightning" OP Center, Gulfport, Miss.
Homeplate	Homestead AFB, Fla. (status?)
Jackpot	Jacksonville, Fla.
India+#	Individual Customs Service Inspector
Kilo+#	FBI unit
Lima+#	Customs Service aircraft
Lone Star	Houston, Texas
Longhorn	Austin, Texas
Marlin 350	El Paso (TX) Intelligence Center (EPIC)
Marlin 395	El Paso (TX) Intelligence Center (EPIC)
Mike+#	Customs Service patrol vessel.
Mushroom	Tampa, Fla.
Oceanside 300	"Blue Lightning" OP Center, Miami, Fla,
Omaha+#	Customs Service aircraft
Opbat	DEA, Turks & Caicos OP
Oscar+#	Local/County/State Police unit
Overlord	Command Center, Oklahoma City, Okla.
Panhandle	Pensacola, Fla.
Panther	DEA, US Embassy, Bahamas
Papa+#	Customs service patrol vehicle
Paradise	San Juan, Puerto Rico
Ping Pong	Border Patrol, Corpus Christi, Texas
Pit Stop	A ground radar unit.
Pyramid	
Quest	
Rainbow	A radar unit, Virgin Islands.
Ranch House	Radar unit, Turks & Caicos Islands.
Razorback	San Juan, Puerto Rico
River City	San Antonio, Texas
Roadrunner	Albuquerque, New Mexico
Rockfish+#	Patrol vessels.
Roadstat	A radar unit.
Rosebud	
Seabass	
Sea Breeze	Possible USN vessel.
Serpent	
Shark+#	USCG Cutters (numerals correspond to vessels' hull numbers)
Shrimp Boat	New Orleans, Louisiana
Sierra+#	Customs Service Internal Affairs unit

Slingshot	Customs Service C3I East, Miami, FL
Slingshot Alpha	Alternate site for Slingshot.
Spruce Goose	Los Angeles, Calif.
Starfish+#	Patrol vessels.
Stingray+#	Patrol vessels.
Storm Cloud	Miami. Fla., vessel repair facility
Sundance	Lima, Peru
Sunshine	Miami, Fla.
Swordfish	USCG aircraft.
Tango+#	Customs Tactical Enforcement Support Team (TEST)
Tide Walker	Customs vessel
Tigershark 351	
Tropic Air	Opa Locka Airport, Fla.
Vulture+#	Aircraft
Waverunner	
White Lake	El Paso, Texas
Winter Wonderland	Chicago, Ill.

While standard callsign formats have not been monitored, it is thought that the following formal callsigns are (or once were) assigned as indicated:

KAE310	New York, NY
KAE311	Boston, MA
KAE312	Miami, FL
KAE313	San Juan, PR
KAE314	San Francisco, CA
KAE315	Honolulu, HI
KAE316	Ketchikan, AK
KAE317	Seattle, WA
KAE318	San Diego, CA
KAE319	Chicago, IL
WCW901	Houston, TX

Drug Enforcement Administration (DEA)

Frequencies between 163 and 174 MHz usually belong to other agencies and are for coordination with Customs Service, ATF, etc. Examples include 165.2875 and 166.4625 MHz. Check listings for those agencies operating in coordination with DEA for frequencies between 163 and 174 MHz. Also note, however, that Joint Task Force (JTF) operations consisting of DEA personnel as well as other federal, state, county, and local enforcement officers have also been noted on some DEA UHF channels (as indicated here). The CTCSS tone on DEA frequencies is 156.7 Hz.

DEA Academy, VA: 170.90 171.45 172.20

DEA Aircraft: Cessna 206= N9413Z N9944R N9959R; Swearingen SA-227AT= N2709Z; MBB 80-105LS= N5321S (Also see listings for Dept. of Justice aircraft.) Some aircraft with "unlisted" tail numbers may possibly be in use, in addition to those shown. DEA aircraft in Colombia & Panama reported on 40.00; Cali area on 126.7 (HF 3448 5556 kHz); Medellin area 126.9 (HF 3488 5508 kHz)

Frequencies Reported:

120.375	Aircraft
120.775	Aircraft
173.00	To FBI(?)
281.4	Aircraft
414.525	Channel 11 Strike Force - Tactical
416.05	Tactical
417.025	Joint Task Force (JTF)
417.175/414.125	JTF
417.40	JTF
417.45	JTF
417.50	JTF
417.55/414.425	JTF
418.05	Interagency
418.175	Channel 8 Strike Forcce - Tactical
418.50	Air/Ground
418.575	To USCG
418.625/416.05	Channel 1 Strike Force
418.675	Channel 4 Strike Force - Tactical
418.70	Tactical
418.725	JTF
418.75/415.60	Channel 3 Strike Force - Tactical
418.775	JTF
418.80	Tactical
418.825/415.60	Channel 5 Strike Force
418.875	JTF
418.90/416.325	Channel 2 Strike Force
418.95/416.20	Channel 6 Strike Force
418.975/417.025	Channel 7 Strike Force
419.00/417.40	JTF
419.25	Channel 9 Strike Force - Tactical
419.375	Channel 12 Strike Force - Tactical
419.95	JTF

DEA 10-Codes

10-1	Cannot copy your transmissions
10-2	Your transmissions received clearly
10-4	Your transmission is acknowledged
10-5	Relay my message
10-6	Stand by
10-7	Out of service at _____
10-8	In service
10-9	Repeat your information
10-10	Prisoner present at (time)
10-15	Residence
10-16	Change radio channel
10-19	Return to _____
10-20	Location
10-21	Call _____ by landline
10-22	Disregard
10-25	Report in person to meet _____
10-28	Vehicle registration information
10-30	Subscriber information
10-33	Emergency traffic
10-99	Emergency: Agent Needs Assistance
10-100	Tactical operation

DEA Primary Operations Channels

Transmitter Site	Area Served	Chan	Control Point
Region I (Boston HQ)			
CT Brigeport	Bridgeport/New Haven	2	Hartford/KLR706
CT Glastonbury	Hartford	2	Hartford/KLR706
MA Boston	Boston	1 3 4	Boston/KLR705
MA New Bedford	New Bedf./Providence	1	Boston/KLR705
MA Mt. Wachusetts	Cent. MA/W. Boston	2	Boston/KLR705
Region II (NY City HQ)			
NJ Alpine	N. NJ/Upper NYC	3	NYC/KLR710
NJ Atlantic City	Atlantic City	6	local/KLR707 & NYC/KLR710
NJ Somerville	N. Cent. NJ	5	NYC/KLR710
NY Buffalo	Buffalo area	2	local/KLR711 & NYC/KLR710
NY Manorville	E. Long Island	4	NYC/KLR710
NY Melville	Cent. Long Island	5	NYC/KLR710
NY NY City	NY City	3 4	NYC/KLR710
NY Empire St Bldg	NY City/Newark NJ	1 6	NYC/KLR710
NY Burlington House	NY City	5	NYC/KLR710
NY Rochester	Rochester	1	LEAA Task Force
Region III (Philadelphia HQ)			
DE Wilmington	Wilmington	5	Wilmington/KLR717
PA Chapel Oaks	Valley Forge	2	Phila/KLR715
PA Donora	Pittsburgh	1	Pittsb/KLR716
PA Eddystone	So. Philadelphia	3	Phila/KLR715
PA New Castle	Pittsburgh	1	Pittsb/KLR716
PA Penndel	N.E. Philadelphia	4	Phila/KLR715

PA Philadelphia	Philadelphia	2		Phila/KLR715
PA Pittsburgh	Pittsburgh	2 3		Pittsb/KLR716
DC Washington	Metro DC/VA/MD	2 3 4		Wash/KLR724
MD Baltimore	Baltimore Metro	1 3 4		Balto/KLR720
MD Frederick	Balto Metro/W. MD	6		Balto/KLR720
NC Charlotte	Charlotte	6		Greensbro/KLR721
NC Wilmington	Wilmington	1		Wilm/KLR723
NC Greensboro	Greensboro	1 3		Greensbro/KLR721
WV Charleston	Chstn to Huntington	2		Chrlstn/KLR725
VA Norfolk	Norfolk	1		Norfolk, KLR722
VA Richmond	Richmond	1		Norfolk, KLR722

Region IV (Not domestic, no information available.)

Region V (Miami HQ)

FL Cape Canaveral	Cape Canaveral	2		Orlando/KLR728
FL Ft. Lauderdale	Ft. Lauderdale	2		Miami/KLR730
FL Homestead	Homestead to Key West	6		Miami/KLR730
FL Jacksonville	Jacksonville	2		Jax/KLR733
FL Orlando	Orlando	6		Orlando/KLR728
FL Miami	Miami	1 3 4		Miami/KLR730
FL Tampa	Tampa	3 5		Tampa/KLR734
FL W. Palm Beach	W. Palm Beach	6		W. Palm Bch/KLR750 & Miami/KLR730
GA Atlanta	Atlanta	1 6		Atlanta/KLR731
GA Brunswick	Brunswick	1		Savannah/KLR708
GA Savannah	Savannah	6		Savannah/KLR708
SC Beaufort	Hilton Hd/Beaufort	2		Savannah/KLR708
PR El Yunque	San Juan	6		San Juan/KLR790
PR Maricao	Mayaguez	2		San Juan/KLR790
PR Maravillas	Ponce	3		San Juan/KLR790
SC Charleston	Charleston	1		Chrlstn/KLR729
SC Columbia	Columbia	2		Columbia/KLR732
SC Georgetown	Georgetown	6		Chrlstn/KLR729
SC Myrtle Bch	Myrtle Bch	2		Chrlstn/KLR729

Region VI (Detroit HQ)

KY Louisville	Louisville	1		Louisv/KLR749
MI Ann Arbor	Ann Arbor	3		Detroit/KLR745
MI Charlotte	Lansing/Charlotte	1		Detroit/KLR745
MI Detroit	Detroit	3 6		Detroit/KLR745
MI Flint	Flint	2		Detroit/KLR745
MI Grand Rapids	Grand Rapids	2		Detroit/KLR745 & local/KVS720
OH Akron	Akron	2		Clevel/KLR747
OH Cincinnati	Cincinnati	2		Cincinn/KLR746
OH Gahanna	Columbus	1		Columbus/KLR748
OH Shaker Hts	Cleveland	1		Clevel/KLR747
OH Toledo	Toledo	1		Detroit/KLR745

Region VII (Chicago HQ)

IL Arlington Hts	N & NW Chicago	4		Chicago/KLR755
IL Chicago	S/SE/SW Chic/Hammond	1		Hammond/KLR758 & Chicago/KLR755
IL Chicago	N/NW/W Chicago	2		Chicago/KLR755
IL Chicago	Chicago Metro	3		Chicago/KLR755
IL Springfield	Springfield	6		Sprfld/KLR792
IN Indianapolis	Indianapolis	2		Indpls/KLR756
WI Milwaukee	Milwaukee	1		Chicago/KLR755 &

Milw/KLR761

Region VIII (New Orleans HQ)

AL Birmingham	Birmingham	2		Birm/KLR736
AL Mobile	Mobile	2		Mobile/KLR741
AR Little Rock	Little Rock	2		Litt Rock/KLR738
LA Baton Rouge	Baton Rouge	2		Batn Rge/KLR742
LA Lafayette	Lafayette	1		New Orleans/KLR735
LA Lake Charles	Lake Charles	2		New Orleans/KLR735
LA New Orleans	New Orleans	1	3 4	New Orleans/KLR735
LA Shreveport	Shreveport	2		Shrevpt/KLR791
MS Jackson	Jackson	2		Jackson/KLR737
MS Wiggins	Biloxi/Gulfport	2		New Orleans/KLR735
TN Memphis	Memphis	2		Memphis/KLR740
TN Nashville	Nashville	2		Nashville/KLR739

Region IX (Not domestic, no information available.)

Region X (Kansas City HQ)

IA Des Moines	Des Moines	1	Des Moines/KLR766
KS Wichita	Wichita	2	Wichita/KVS703
MN Duluth	Duluth	1	Duluth/KVS704
MN Minneapolis	Minneapolis/St. Paul	2	Mpls/KLR760
MO Kansas City	Kansas City	1 2	Kans City/KLR765
MO St. Louis	St. Louis	2	St. Louis/KLR768
NE Omaha	Omaha	2	Omaha/KLR767
SD Sioux Falls	Sioux Falls	1	Sioux Falls/KVS721

Region XI (Dallas HQ)

TX Edinburg	McAllen	6	Dallas/KLR770 & local/KLR777
TX El Paso	El Paso	6	Dallas/KLR770 & local/KLR775
TX Falcon Hts.	Falcon Hts.	6	Dallas/KLR770
TX Ft. Worth	Ft. Worth	6	Dallas/KLR770
TX Freer	Freer	6	Dallas/KLR770
TX Houston	Houston	1	Dallas/KLR770 & local/KLR771
TX Laredo	Laredo	1	Dallas/KLR770 & local/KLR776
TX Los Fresnos	Brownsville	1	Dallas/KLR770 local/KLR751
TX Lubbock	Lubbock	6	Dallas/KLR770 & local/KLR752
TX Austin	Austin	6	Dallas/KLR770 & local/KLR778
TX Carrizo Sprgs.	Carizzo Sprgs.	2	Dallas/KLR770
TX Corpus Christi	Corpus Christi	2	Dallas/KLR770 & local/KLR779
TX Cotulla	Cotulla	2	Dallas/KLR770
TX Dallas	Dallas	1	Dallas/KLR770
TX Del Rio	Del Rio	1	Dallas/KLR770 & local/KLR759
TX Eagle Pass	Eagle Pass	2	Dallas/KLR770 & local/KLR754
TX Odessa	Odessa	1	Dallas/KLR770 & Midland/KLR753

TX Pettus	Pettus	6		Dallas/KLR770
TX San Antonio	San Antonio	1		Dallas/KLR770 & local/KLR773
TX Sarita	Sarita	6		Dallas/KLR770
TX Uvalde	Uvalde	2		Dallas/KLR770
TX Zapata	Zapata	6		Dallas/KLR770
OK Oklahoma City	Oklahoma City	2		Dallas/KLR770 & local/KLR772
OK Tulsa	Tulsa	1		Dallas/KLR770 & local/KLR774

Region XII (Denver HQ)

AZ Douglas	Douglas	6		Douglas/KLR745
AZ Mt. Lemmon	Tucson	2		Tucson/KLR784
AZ Nogales	Nogales	1		Nogales/KLR794
AZ Phoenix	Phoenix	1		Phoenix/KLR782
AZ Yuma/San Luis	Yuma/San Luis	1	3	San Luis/KLR764
CO Boulder	Boulder	2		Denver/KLR780
CO Colo Sprgs	Colo Sprgs	2		Denver/KLR780
CO Denver	Denver	1		Denver/KLR780
NM Albuquerque	Albuquerque	1		Albuquerque/KLR781
NM Caballo Mt.	Las Cruces	2		Las Cruces/KLR763
NM Jacks Peak	AZ/Deming/Silver Cy/Border	1		Las Cruces/KLR763
UT Salt Lk City	Salt Lk City	1		SLC/KLR783
WY Cheyenne	Cheyenne	1	3	Cheyenne/KLR744

Region XII (Seattle HQ)

AK Anchorage	Anchorage	2	3		Anchorage/KLR796
ID Boise	Boise	1	3		Boise/KLR799
MT Great Falls	Great Falls	2			Gt. Falls/KVS719
OR Portland	Portland	1	2	3	Seattle/KLR795 & local/KLR797
OR Eugene	Eugene	2			Eugene/KIY950
WA Seattle	Seattle	2			Seattle/KLR795
WA Seattle	N. Seattle	3			Seattle/KLR795
WA Seattle	S. Seattle	4			Seattle/KLR795
WA Seattle	Seattle/Blaine	1			Blaine/KVS700 & Seattle/KLR795
WA Spokane	Spokane	1			Seattle/KLR795 & local/KLR796

Region XIV (Los Angeles HQ)

Note: In addition to operating on the channel shown, all repeaters in Region XIX can also operate on Channels 3 & 4 <u>only</u> from the LARO Center.

CA Bakersfield	San Joaq Vly/Bakersfield	6	LARO/KLR785
CA Calexico	Calexico/S Imprl Vly	5	LARO/KLR785 & local/KLR793
CA Fresno	San Joaq Vly/Fresno	2	LARO/KLR785 & local/KVS713
CA Imperial Vly	Calexico/Imperial Vly	6	LARO/KLR785 & Calexico/KLR793
CA Indio	Indio/Salton Sea/Palm Spgs	5	LARO/KLR785
CA Los Angeles	L.A. & Orange County	2	LARO/KLR785
CA Lucerne Vly	Lucerne Vly/29 Palms	2	LARO/KLR785
CA Mill Valley	SF Bay/Mill Vly/Marin Co.	5	LARO/KLR785 & SF/KLR788
CA Mojave	Mojave Desert/Lanc/Palmdale	5	LARO/KLR785
CA Orange Co.	Orange & LA Co's.	5	LARO/KLR785

CA Palm Springs	Palm Spr, S to Salton/Banning	1	LARO/KLR785
CA Palomar	N San Diego Co/Mission Vly	1	LARO/KLR785 & San Diego/KLR787
CA Sacramento	Sacramento	2	LARO/KLR785 & local/KVS701
CA San Bernardino	Rivrside/Perris Vly/San Berndno	6	LARO/KLR785
CA San Diego	San Diego	2	LARO/KLR785 & local/KLR787
CA San Francisco	San Francisco	2	LARO/KLR785 & local/KLR788
CA Santa Barbara	SL Obispo/Sta Barbara	1	LARO.KLR785
CA Santa Cruz	Sta Cruz/San Jose/Montrey Bay	1	LARO/KLR785
CA San Ysidro	San Diego Co.	5	LARO/KLR785 San Diego/KLR787
CA South Bay	Los Angeles Metro	1	LARO/KLR785
CA Tecate	Tecate	2	LARO/KLR785 local/KVS702
CA Tracy	Modesto/Tracy/Stockton	5	LARO/KLR785
CA Vacaville	Sacto. Delta/Vacav/San Pablo Bay	1	LARO/KLR785
CA Ventura	Ventura Co.	5	LARO/KLR785
CA Walnut Creek	Contra Costa/Sacto Co's	6	LARO/KLR785 & SF/KLR788
HI Honolulu	W Oahu Isl/Honolulu	6	Honolulu/KLR786
HI Kaneohe	E Oahu Isl/Kaneohe	2	Honolulu/KLR786
HI Maui	Maui Island	5	Honolulu/KLR786
NV Las Vegas	Las Vegas	2	LARO/KLR785 & local/KLR789
NV Reno	Reno	2	LARO/KLR785 & local/KIY960

Federal Emergency Management Agency (FEMA)

FEMA/AF Coordination: 266.05 273.8 399.75; WFM mode 305.55 322.75 336.8 382.35 397.05

VHF channels reported: 27.650 27.850 27.90 138.225 138.575 139.10 139.825 139.45 139.225 139.95 140.025 140.90 141.725 141.875 141.95 142.025 142.23 142.35 142.375 142.40 142.425 142.925 142.95 142.975 143.00 143.05 143.25 143.60 143.625 163.10 164.8625 165.6625 166.225 167.925 167.975 168.35 169.25 169.60 169.875 170.20 173.1875 409.125

HF channels (shown in kHz): 2321.5 2361.5 2378.5 2446.5 2659.5 3342.5 3380.5 3389.5 4781.5 5212.5 5 5403.5 5822.5 5962.5 6050.5 6107.5 6109.5 6152.5 6177.5 6180.5 7349.5 9463.5 10195.5 10494.5 10589.5 11711.5 11802.5 11958.5 12010.5 12217.5 14451.5 14777.5 14837.5 14886 14900.5 14909.5 16202.5 16431.5 17520.5 17650.5 18745.5 19758.5 19970.5 20028.5 24555 Calling/Emergency 10494.5 (day); 5212.5 (night); 17650.5 (backup)

VHF stations reported:

KCI609	Rockville, MD	167.975
KCI611	Ft. Meade, MD	167.975
KCI612	Ft. Belvoir, VA	167.975
KCI614	Fairfax, VA	167.975
KCI615	Arlington, VA	167.975
KCI616	Alexandria, VA	167.975
KCI617	Hyattsville	167.975
KCI618	Washington, DC	167.975
KCI621	Falls Church, VA	167.975
KCI624	Lorton, VA	167.975
KCI625	Washington, DC	167.975
KCI626	Andrews AFB, MD	167.975
KCI627	Fairfax, VA	167.975
KCI629	Washington, DC	167.975
KFW624	(portable), UT	167.975
KGB641	Washington, DC	27.850
KGB643	Olney, MD	27.850 173.1875
KGD204	Olney. MD	167.975
KNW95	Agana, GU	142.35 142.375 142.975 143.00
KPS301	Maynard, MA	140.025 143.00 143.60
KPS302	New York, NY	139.825 139.925 142.95 143.00
KPS310	Bothell, WA	142.375 143.05
KPS311	Boston, MA	140.90 143.00 143.60
WGY901	Maynard, MA	169.875
WGY906	Denton, TX	169.875
WGY989	Nat'l Emerg Training Ctr, Emmitsburg, MD	
		163.10 166.225 168.35 169.60
	Cumberland, MD	27.650 27.900
	Greenbelt, MD	167.975
	Hickory, MD	27.650 27.900
	(portables), AZ	142.35 142.375 142.425 142.935 143.00
	(portables), CA & NV	142.35 142.375 142.425 142.975 143.00
	(portables), US	164.8625 165.6625

Energy, Department of (DoE)

HF networks (shown in kHz): 2446.5 2610.5 2625.5 3389.5 4480.5 4598.5 4604.5 4776.5 4946.5 5212.5 5377.5 5379.5 6804.5 6930.5 7349.5 7359.5 7429.5 7465.5 7690.5 7723.5 7767.5 8054.5 9359.5 10494.5 10555.5 10871.5 11126.5 12020.5 12233.5 13803.5 14400.5 15454.5 16065.5 18417.5 19791.5 20405.5 23533.5 25432.5

HF air/ground OP (shown in kHz): 2287.5 2622.5 4480.5 4669.5 6646.5 6982.5 7840.5 8963.5 9115.5 11126.5 11397.5 13261.5 13803.5 16065.5 17902.5

VHF air band OP: NV 118.7; WA 121.3; NM 122.75 122.8 122.85 122.9; OH 122.8; ME 122.9; MN 122.9; SC 122.9; TX 122.9; UT 122.9; US 123.05

UHF air band: US 239.4 257.0 259.7 292.1; Pacific 225.7 228.2 230.4 235.0 240.2 248.6 255.2 370.0

DoE aircraft roster: Bell 206= 8PN N612 N618DE N5015H N5015K N5015T N16912 N16913 N16916; Bell 222= N222DE N444DE; DeHavilland DHC-6= N35062 N72348; Aerospatiale 350D= N510HP N520HP; Fairchild 27= N7806M; MBB BK= N1165R N1175R; Douglas DC-9= N29AF; Beech King 100= N20EG; Beech King 200= N2451D N2748X N6733R N7233R N63791; Convair 580= N30EG; Cessna 180= N755W; Cessna 182= N6722E; Cessna 305= N3302T

DoE frequencies available in all areas: 30.37 34.03 34.86 36.33 36.39 41.31 138.35 139.77 141.68 142.23 148.47 163.775 164.225 164.275 164.30 164.325 164.35 164.375 164.40 164.75 165.85 167.825 167.85 167.875 167.925 167.975 168.45 170.40 171.20 171.2625 171.95 173.00 410.35 410.80 411.025 411.075 411.60 412.375 416.25 416.30 416.35 416.40 416.45 417.975 418.05 418.575

DoE facilities (also see listings in front section of book at specific mil bases):

Argonne Research & Development Labs, Lemont, IL: Security 155.475   FD 154.25 154.265   Medics 155.34   Msc 27.575 27.585 27.595 27.615 27.625 27.635 27.645 32.02 40.47 42.50 154.68 164.30 164.325 164.375 164.75 411.20 418.075 (HF 3336.5 kHz)

Brookhaven National Labs, Upton, NY: Security 168.45   FD 46.40 46.46 164.225 Medics 155.28 155.325   Msc 164.275 164.325 164.375 167.825 167.85 167.975 171.20 171.95 411.60 413.85 (HF 3335.5 kHz)

Fermi National Accelerator Lab, Batavia, IL: FD 154.07   Msc 154.10 164.30 164.325 164.35 164.725 167.925 168.45 159.60 408.60 410.80

Fernald Plant, OH (Weapons Materials): 27.275 164.275 164.375 167.825 171.95

Germantown, MD DoE Command Center: Security 164.225   Mobile Phones 162.225 Msc 40.47 162.05 164.375 170.075 170.75 236.6 410.35

Hanford Reservation, Richland, WA (Weapons Materials): Security 164.275   Pager 164.325   Maintenance 164.375   Msc 27.700 164.00 164.40 165.80 167.825 168.45 170.575 171.20 172.50 173.025 173.10 406.225 407.175 410.35 411.15 411.20 413.825 413.95 416.075 416.40 416.50 (HF 11556.5 kHz)

Idaho National Engineering Lab, Idaho Falls, ID (Weapons Materials): 40.47 162.225 163.175 163.325 163.4625 163.75 163.8375 164.175 164.25 164.325 164.375 164.40 164.525 164.575 164.70 164.770 164.9625 165.7125 166.225 166.325 167.825 167.85 167.925 167.975 171.20 171.2625 171.425 171.95 406.225 406.275 406.85 406.825 410.35 411.20 413.80 413.85 413.95 (HF 3336.5 5309.5 5752.5 5948.5 7701.5 8015.5 9919.5 11556.5 14657 17398.5 kHz)

Kansas City Plant, Kansas City, MO (Weapons Products): 41.67 164.225 164.375 167.85 168.45 171.95 410.35 411.20 413.85 416.30 416.40 (HF 3336.5 5309.5 5752.5 5948.5 7701.5 8015 9919.5 11556.5 14657 17398.5 kHz)

Knolls Atomic Power Lab, Schenectady, NY: 164.225 164.275 164.75 167.825 171.95 409.20 409.30 409.50 409.75; Kesselring Site 164.225 164.275 164.75 167.825

Lawrence Labs (Weapons Design):
   Berkeley, CA: Security 164.325   FD 164.375   Msc 164.225 164.275
   Livermore, CA: Security 164.475   FD 164.325   Pager 164.975   Msc 41.67 154.845 155.40 162.225 163.375 164.225 164.275 164.375 164.70 168.00 170.025 171.20 171.925 173.00 410.35 410.80 411.15 411.60 416.40 416.45 416.60 416.65 (HF 11557 kHz)

Los Alamos Science Lab, NM (Weapons Design): 27.575 32.02 34.14 40.47 122.75 122.8 139.77 140.68 142.23 148.47 162.6125 163.375 164.10 164.225 164.275 164.325 164.35 164.375 164.40 164.425 164.45 164.50 165.2625 166.25 166.235 166.825 167.825 167.85 167.875 167.975 168.45 170.725 171.20 171.2625 171.325 171.3875 171.525 171.625 172.30 257.0 315.1 406.225 406.375 406.75 407.175 408.125 408.175 416.05 (HF 3336.5 5752.5 7701.5 11556.5 kHz)

Mound Laboratory, Miamisburg, OH (Weapons Production): 40.47 164.225 164.325 167.875 171.20 171.95 410.35 411.20 413.80 416.40 416.35 467.45 (HF 3336.5 11556.6 kHz)

Naval Nuclear Power Training Unit, Ballston Spa, NY: 162.225

Nevada Test Site: See listings elsewhere in this Registry.

Paducah Plant, Paducah, KY (Weapons Materials): 27.275 27.585 44.62 164.225 164.25 164.325 164.375 164.75 166.275 167.825 407.05 (HF 6803 kHz)

Pantex Plant, Amarillo, TX (Nuclear Weapons Assembly): 30.37 40.47 41.61 41.67 46.61 164.225 164.275 164.35 164.40 164.375 167.825 167.85 168.45 171.20 171.95 409.20 411.025 416.30 (HF 3336.5 5752.5 7701.5 11556.5 kHz)

Pinellas Plant, St. Petersburg, FL (Weapons Production): 40.47 164.225 164.35 461.75 466.50 466.75 (HF 3336.5 kHz)

Rocky Flats Plant, Estes Park, CO (Weapons Production): 27.575 40.47 43.18 154.905 164.225 164.235 164.40 167.825 167.85 167.875 167.925 168.45 171.20 171.95 409.20 409.30 410.35 411.025 412.825 416.30 417.20 419.175 464.625 (HF 11556.5 kHz)

Sandia Labs, Albuquerque, NM (Weapons Design): Security 167.925 Maintenance 170.025 Msc 27.575 27.585 27.675 122.75 122.8 122.85 138.61 139.03 139.77 140.6125 141.42 141.68 141.70 142.23 143.41 143.91 162.5965 162.805 163.00 163.7905 164.00 164.125 164.25 164.30 164.35 164.375 164.425 164.725 164.9375 164.9625 164.975 164.9875 165.0125 165.2625 165.325 165.80 166.125 166.20 166.225 167.175 167.975 170.075 170.125 171.20 171.215 171.225 171.40 171.95 173.05 173.19 173.195 257.0 292.1 351.1 370.0 384.0 384.8 409.20 409.30 410.35 410.80 411.025 411.20 412.70 412.75 (HF 3336.6 5309.5 5752.5 5948.5 7701.5 8015 9919.5 11556.5 14657 17398.5 kHz)

Savannah River Plant, SC (Weapons Production): Railroad 164.275 Msc 27.565 27.575 27.585 27.605 27.635 27.655 40.47 122.9 123.05 159.45 163.605 163.61 163.75 163.79 163.795 163.80 163.82 163.84 163.8625 163.8875 163.90 163.92 163.94 163.9625 163.9875 164.005 164.225 164.325 164.375 164.75 165.2625 167.825 167.85 167.875 167.925 167.975 168.45 168.65 169.60 169.975 171.20 171.405 171.95 (HF 3336.5 5309.5 5752.5 5948.5 7701.5 8015 9919.5 11556.5 14657 17398.5 kHz)

Y-12/X-10/K-25/K-33 Plants, Oak Ridge, TN (Weapons Production): Medics 155.34 27.545 27.555 27.565 27.595 27.675 40.47 41.61 41.67 49.87 163.175 163.925 164.10 164.225 164.325 164.375 164.40 164.525 164.55 164.675 164.775 165.2625 166.575 166.655 167.025 167.125 167.825 167.845 168.45 170.075 171.20 171.50 171.625 172.20 172.30 172.725 173.6125 173.7125 173.7875 407.175 409.30 409.50 409.725 410.35 410.80 411.025 411.20 411.35 412.125 412.725 412.75 416.20 416.40 417.65 417.725 417.875 419.125 419.15 419.875 (HF 3336.5 6803 kHz)

Washington, DC DoE HQ: 162.025 162.05 162.125 162.225 164.75 170.125 171.20 171.95 409.025 (HF 3336.5 5309.5 5752.5 5948.5 7701.5 8015 9919.5 11556.5 14657 17398.5 kHz)

Engraving & Printing, Bureau of

All locations: 171.3875 172.275

Environmental Protection Agency

EPA oil spill containment & cleanup: 36.25 41.71 122.925 156.75 157.125 164.45 (Monitor for industrial & other fed agency OP for oil spill containment & cleanup on 25.040 25.080 150.98 154.585 158.445 159.48 163.175 165.3125 168.50 454.00 459.00; also monitor state, county, local agency frequencies.)

EPA stations known:

AL	Montgomery	KQT3311	164.45
CA	(mobiles)	KK3355	40.97
FL	Panama City	KEY798	164.45
FL	Pensacola	KEY798	164.45
	(vessels)	KT5521	156.65 156.70 157.10
MI	Ann Arbor	KT5533	408.00
MN	Duluth	KT5520	408.00
NV	Las Vegas	KTQ317	164.45 173.9125
NV	Mt. Potosi	KQT317	164.125/164.45
NJ	Edison	KTQ312	164.45
NY	Rochester	KTQ320	164.45
NC	Rsctgl. Pk.	KTQ315	164.10 164.45
OH	Cincinnati	KEY798	170.125 172.30
	(mobiles)	KT5526	41.39 41.47 122.925 164.45 408.00
OH	Fairfield	KEY798	172.30
OH	Sandusky	KTQ319	164.45
OR	Corvallis	KTQ314	38.74
PA	Philadelphia	KEC320	165.4125/164.45
RI	Narragansett	KEC322	165.4125/164.45
TX	Houston	KTQ318	164.45
US	All areas		122.925 156.75 157.125 163.4375
			164.45 165.4125 173.8625

**Department of the Interior
U.S. Fish and Wildlife Service**

Fish & Wildlife Service (FWS)

FWS enforcement operations are on 408.675/410.625. FWS undercover agents also use handheld transceivers operating on 168.25 and 168.40 MHz. This agency oversees more than 90-million acres and requires, in addition to enforcement personnel, a number of surveillance systems. Systems believed to be in use include vehicle tracking devices, miniature transmitters, satellites, telephone taps, and telephone pen-registers that make a written record of all numbers dialed from telephones equipped with such devices. When skip propagation conditions are right, monitors can copy FWS stations from great distances on the 34 MHz FWS channels (especially busy 34.85 MHz, which is a primary operational frequency of this agency).

VHF aero band OP: 117.975 121.9375 121.9625 132.0125

VHF/UHF band: 34.25 34.41 34.81 34.83 34.85/34.43 40.39 162.6125 163.075/168.375 163.10 163.125 163.15 164.25 164.625 164.775 164.80/164.10 166.325 166.75 166.925/166.075 166.925/166.325 168.25 168.225 168.40 168.525 168.575/169.50 169.025 169.40/168.525 169.55/168.575 169.65 169.925 170.05 170.075 170.10 170.60/170.00 170.60/170.025 171.65 171.675 171.75/172.45 172.65/171.625 172.65/171.65 172.675 173.7625 408.675/410.625 408.525 408.675/410.625 408.75 410.625 412.275 414.825/408.425 414.925/408.525 415.015/408.625 415.125/408.725 417.775 417.95 419.975

HF nets: AK & HI 3215 5907.5 kHz

FWS aircraft: Cessna 185= N60984 (Also see Dept. of Interior roster.)

FWS vessels:

KWZE	Black Bear	WZ2002	Speedboat #11
WTDB	Brant	WZ2003	Murre II
WTDC	Crane	WZ2007	Patrol Boat
WTDE	Teal	WZ2008	Patrol Boat
		WZ2010	Grizzly Bear
WTDG	John R. Manning	WZ2011	Coot
WTDH	Pribilof	WZ2013	Heron
WTDI	Hugh M. Smith	WZ2016	Speedboat #10
WTDQ	Pregon II	WZ2017	Rorqual
WTDT	Theodore N. Gill	WZ2019	Geo. M. Bowers
WTFA	Auklet	WZ2024	Alaska
WTFD	Merganser	WZ2027	FWS-905
WTFE	Murre	WZ2028	FWS-1451
WTFG	Shearwater	WZ2029	FWS-19
WTFH	Widgeon	WZ2030	FWS-1450
WTFJ	Pelican	WZ2031	FWS-20
WTFX	Phalarope II	WZ2032	Canvasback
WXT5893	G.B. Heron	WZ2056	Ranger III

General Services Administration (GSA)

This Registry series pioneered information on the GSA. A large percentage of the GSA's 18,000 employees are in the agency's Public Buildings Service (PBS) or the GSA's Law Enforcement Branch. The PBS the group responsible for the design, construction or leasing, appraisal, operation, maintenance and protection of most of the federally controlled buildings in the nation. This covers 284-million square feet of space, including the parking areas, of about 8,500 federally owned and leased buildings. In addition to hundreds of millions of dollars worth of construction projects now underway, Building Protection, which is a major component of the PBS, utilizes intrusion alarm systems, entry control devices, physical barriers, and a uniformed and armed security force. Uniformed personnel operate at fixed posts, on roving patrols, or are assigned to mobile response units and special tactical squads. In addition to preventing or deterring traditional property crimes, such as theft and vandalism, PBS must provide protection directed against persons and incidents disruptive to the normal conduct of government business. These include real or threatened bombings, unruly demonstrations, and depredation of property. The Law Enforcement Branch provides security for government officials and other personnel against terrorist attacks, demonstrations, and other threats to their safety while they are discharging their duties.

Public Buildings Service: 415.20/413.95
Law Enforcement: 412.40 417.20 417.20/419.175 417.425
Other GSA Frequencies Reported: 40.35 162.125 163.025 163.075 163.125 163.175 164.275 164.70 165.2625 166.225 166.35 166.95 168.525 168.675 411.275 413.875 414.475 416.025 417.65 419.875

GSA known callsigns & facilities:		
KGC253	Lorton, VA	163.075
	163.175 168.575	
KGD286	Farmville, VA	163.075
KHA214	Casa. Depot, IN	419.875
KLH424	Washington, DC	168.80
KPA500	Waltham, MA	
KPA501	Hingham, MA	
KPA502	Cambridge, MA	
KPA503	New Haven, CT	
KPA504	Fitchburg, MA	
KPA505	Springfield, MA	
KPA506	Bridgeport, CT	
KPA507	Boston, MA	
KPA509	Manchester, NH	
KPA510	Providence, RI	
KPA511	Providence, RI	
KPA512	Montpelier, VT	
KPA513	Bangor, ME	
KPA514	Rutland, VT	
KPA516	Augusta, ME	
KPA517	New Bedford, MA	
KPA518	Pittsfield, MA	
KPA519	Hartford, CT	
KPA520	Lowell, MA	
KPA521	Worcester, MA	
KPA522	Burlington, VT	
KPA523	Concord, MA	
KPA564	New York, NY	
KPA565	Newark, NJ	
KPA566	Albany/Scotia, NY	
KPA567	New York, NY	
KPA568	Bellemeade, NJ	40.35
KPA569	Scotia, NY	40.35
KPA570	Binghamton, NY	40.35
KPA571	El Yunque, PR	
KPA572	Crown Mountain, VI	
KPA573	Hato Rey, PR	
KPA574	Syracuse, NY	
KPA575	Crown Mountain, VI	

KPA576	Buffalo, NY		
KPA577	Trenton, NJ		
KPA578	Trenton, NJ		
KPA578	Rochester, NY		
KPA612	Washington, DC	163.075	
	163.175 168.575		
KPA613	Washington, DC	163.075	
	163.175 168.575		
KPA614	Baltimore, MD	163.075	
KPA615	Curtis Bay, MD	163.075	
KPA616	Middle River, MD	163.075	
KOA617	Curtis Bay, MD	163.175	
KPA618	Washington, DC	163.675	
KPA619	Pittsburgh, PA		
KPA620	Washington, DC		
KPA621	Washington, DC		
KPA622	Washington, DC		
KPA623	Washington, DC		
KPA624	Arlington, VA		
KPA625	Suitland, MD		
KPA640	Philadelphia, PA		
KPA641	Norfolk, VA		
KPA642	Richmond, VA		
KPA643	Baltimore, MD		
KPA644	Harrisburg, PA		
KPA645	Woodlawn, MD		
KPA646	Columbia, SC		
KPA648	Washington, DC	411.275	
	414.475 416.025		
KPA649	Baltimore, MD	163.175	
KPA650	Washington, DC		
KPA651	Washington, DC		
KPA652	Washington, DC		
KPA658	St. Petersburg, FL		
KPA659	Miami, FL		
KPA660	Jacksonville, FL		
KPA661	Tampa, FL		
KPA662	Birmingham, AL		
KPA663	Mobile, AL		
KPA664	Atlanta, GA		
KPA665	Marietta, GA		
KPA666	Jackson, MS		
KPA667	Raleigh, NC		
KPA668	Greensboro, NC		
KPA669	Asheville, NC		
KPA670	Columbia, SC		
KPA671	Nashville, TN		
KPA672	Montgomery, AL		
KPA673	Charleston, SC		
KPA673	Huntsville, AL		
KPA674	Huntsville, AL		
KPA675	Miami, FL		
KPA676	Orlando, FL		
KPA677	Louisville, FL		
KPA678	Memphis, TN		
KPA679	Glynco, GA		
KPA706	Cleveland, OH		
KPA707	Cleveland, OH		
KPA708	Toledo, OH		
KPA709	Columbus, OH		
KPA710	Dayton, OH		
KPA711	Cincinnati, OH		
KPA712	Jeffersonville, IN		
KPA713	N. Haven, IN		
KAP714	E. St. Louis, IL		
KPA715	Flint, MI		
KPA716	Grand Rapids, MI		
KPA717	Detroit, MI		
KPA718	Indianapolis, IN		
KPA719	Duluth, MN		
KPA720	Milwaukee, WI		
KPA721	Battle Creek, MI		
KPA722	Hammond, IN		
KPA723	Springfield, IL		
KPA724	Chicago, IL		
KPA725	Chicago, IL		
KPA726	Akron, OH		
KPA727	Ft. Snelling, MN		
KPA728	Ft. Snelling, MN		
KPA729	Akron, OH		
KPA761	Kansas City, MO		
KPA762	Kansas City, MO		
KPA763	Kansas City, MO		
KPA764	Kansas City, MO		
KPA765	St. Louis, MO		
KPA766	St. Louis, MO		
KPA767	St. Louis, MO		
KPA768	St. Louis, MO		
KPA769	St. Louis, MO		
KPA770	St. Louis, MO		
KPA771	Omaha, NE		
KPA805	Ft. Worth, TX	162.125	
KPA806	Ft. Worth, TX	164.70	
KPA807	Ft. Worth, TX	164.70	
KPA808	Ft. Worth, TX	164.70	
KPA809	Austin, TX	164.175	
KPA810	Austin, TX		
KPA811	Austin, TX		
KPA812	Austin, TX		
KPA813	Dallas, TX		
KPA816	Baton Rouge, LA		
KPA817	Houston, TX		
KPA820	New Orleans, LA	162.125	
KPA821	Albuquerque, NM		
KPA822	Albuquerque, NM		
KPA823	Albuquerque, NM		
KPA824	Santa Fe, NM		
KPA825	San Antonio, TX		

KPA826	Oklahoma City, OK		KPA915	Richmond, CA	
KPA827	Sandia Crest, NM		KPA916	Sacramento, CA	
KPA828	El Paso, TX		KPA917	San Diego, CA	
KPA829	Lubbock, TX		KPA918	San Diego, CA	
KPA830	Laredo, TX		KPA919	W. Los Angeles, CA	
KPA863	Colo. Spgs., CO	162.225	KPA920	Honolulu, HI	
KPA864	Denver, CO	162.225	KPA921	Mt. Diablo, CA	
KPA865	Denver, CO		KPA922	Tucson, AZ	
KPA868	Lakewood, CO		KPA923	So. Mountain, AZ	
KPA869	Clearfield, UT	166.225	KPA924	San Francisco, CA	
KPA870	Golden, CO		KPA925	San Francisco, CA	
KPA872	Fargo, ND		KPA926	San Pedro, CA	
KPA873	Salt Lk. City, UT		KPA929	Laguna Niguel, CA	
KPA876	Shpdcr. Pk.		KPA959	Auburn, WA	163.025
KPA877	Lakewood, CO		KPA960	Anchorage, AK	
KPA878	Ogden, UT	166.225	KPA962	Boise, ID	
KPA879	Salt Lk. City, UT	166.225	KPA963	Portland, OR	
KPA881	Lakewood, CO	165.2625	KPA964	Auburn, WA	163.025
KPA882	Lakewood, CO		KPA965	Chehallis, WA	
KPA883	Lakewood, CO		KPA966	Seattle/Auburn, WA	
KPA884	Salt Lk. City, UT		KPA967	Seattle, WA	
KPA885	Ogden, UT		KPA968	Spokane, WA	
KPA886	Bismarck, ND		KPA969	Fairbanks, AK	168.80
KPA887	Billings, MT			Hyde Park, NY	166.95
KPA888	Helena, MT			417.20	
KPA890	Missoula, MT			Moses Lk., WA	32.87
KPA909	Bell, CA	164.275		Scotia, NY	46.22
KPA910	San Francisco, CA	168.80		Washington, DC	27.575
KPA911	Bell, CA			163.175 163.70 163.875	
KPA912	Fresno, CA			165.0625 168.80	
KPA913	Los Angeles, CA			All Areas	40.35 168.80
KPA914	Oakland, CA				

Geological Survey & Bureau of Mines

Surface mining OP: 168.50/166.80
Exell Helium Plant, Exell, TX: 167.125 415.15
Other freqs: 30.03 34.87 36.17 40.59 41.13 46.43 164.10 164.525 164.675/169.825 164.80/164.10 166.275 166.375/166.975 166.80 166.875 166.95/166.35 166.975 167.075 167.125 167.95 168.50/166.95 168.55 169.575 169.625 169.825/164.675 172.425 172.675 172.725 407.425 407.525 407.575 408.075 408.50 410.575 411.625 411.675 412.175 412.375 412.825 412.875 412.975 412.95 412.975 414.824 412.70 417.40 417.575 419.875 419.95

Ground Wave Emergency Network (GWEN)

A nationwide military low-frequency communications system developed to assure continuity to contact with US strategic forces in the absence of satellite, landline, and HF comms due to electromagnetic pulse (EMP) or other result of enemy attack. Operation is via packet mode (1200 baud, 600 Hz shift), with pulses lasting 2 seconds. Although some components of the system utilize UHF or microwave links, the GWEN system is basically operational on twenty LF channels. These are:
Ch #1 150.625 kHz; Ch #2 151.875 kHz; Ch #3 153.125 kHz; Ch #4 154.375 kHz; Ch #5 155.625 kHz; Ch #6 156.875 kHz; Ch #7 158.125 kHz; Ch #8 159.375 kHz; Ch #9 160.625 kHz; Ch #10 161.875 kHz; Ch #11 163.125; Ch #12 164.375 kHz; Ch #13 165.625 kHz; Ch #14 166.875 kHz; Ch #15 158.125 kHz; Ch #16 169.375 kHz; Ch #17 170.625; Ch #18 171.875 kHz; Ch #19 173.125; Ch #20 174.375 kHz. Note that these listings are **kHz**, not MHz. These frequencies cannot be received only on a communications recveiver, not on a scanner.

Health & Human Services, Dept. of (HHS)

HHS operates aeronautical Unicom stations on 122.85 throughout AZ & MT, also at some locations in MS NV NM NC ND & SD. These are in addition to listings below.

Alabama
Birmingham   171.2375
Alaska
All Areas   27.575 27.585
Anchorage   KRS615   164.30
               KUP682   172.2375
Barrow   KIK733   27.575 27.585
Bethel   KIK732   27.575 164.30
Kanakank   KIK734   27.575 17585
Kotzebue   KIK735   27.575 27.585
Mt Edgecombe   164.80 165.2625
St Geo. Isl.   KDW901   27.575 27.585
               KDW902   27.575 27.585
St Paul Isl.   KDW901   27.575 27.585
Tanana   KIK731   27.575 27.585
                                        164.30

Arizona
All Areas   27.575 27.585
                                        41.83
Chinle   KUU611   164.30
Cichn Butte   KUU611   164.30 165.3125
Dilkon   KUU611   164.30 165.3125
Kaibeto   KUU611   164.30 165.3125
Kitt Peak   KRS617   168.525
Leupp   KUU611   165.3125
Lr. Greaswd   KUU611   164.30 165.3125

Lukiachk.   KUU611   164.30
Mt Eden   165.3125
Nahatems   165.3125
Navajo Mtn   165.3125
Piney Hill   164.30
Pinon   KUU611   164.30 165.3125
Roof Butte   165.3125
San Xavier   KRS614   163.075 163.175
Sells   KEY795   163.175
Showto   KUU611   165.3125
Teech Spgs   KUU611   165.3125
Tuba City   KUU611   164.30
White River   165.2625
Winslow   KUU611   164.30
Arkansas
Jefferson   KUP861   171.00 171.2375
                                        171.3625
California
All Areas   27.575 27.585
Richmond   171.2375
San Francisco   164.30
Colorado
Ignacio   "Ute 102"   172.675
District of Columbia
Washington   KBF362   36.22 164.30
    165.2625 165.3125 166.825 166.85 166.85

198

407.70 408.05 413.425 419.60

Georgia

Atlanta	KIK740	30.34 32.14
32.22 40.38 40.97		
	KMM714	171.2375
Lawrenceville	KIK739	171.2375

Idaho

All Areas	27.575 27.585

Illinois

Chicago	KFQ70	171.2375 409.00
		415.625

Kansas

Holton	165.3375

Louisiana

Carrville	164.30 165.3125
New Orleans	164.30

Maryland

Baltimore		171.3375 407.97
		415.625
Bethesda	KID470	36.22 36.75
41.83 171.2375 409.00 411.45 415.825		
415.925 419.60 419.80		
Ft Dietrick	KEY798	419.60
Frederick	KUU614	165.0625 165.33
Poolesville	KBJ334	36.35
Rockville	KGB633	408.05 409.00
Silver Sprg		409.025
Woodlawn	KEY799	419.60

Massachusetts

All Areas	27.575 27.585
Boston	171.3625

Missouri

Kansas City	171.2375

Montana

Blackfoot Resvtn		36.18
Crow Resv		36.18
Harlem	KUU616	171.2375
St Ignatius		164.30

Nevada

All Areas	27.575 27.585

New Mexico

Crown Pt	KUU611	164.30
Dezz. Bluff		165.3125
Gallup	KUU611	164.30
Mescalero	KO7572	172.675
Mt. Taylor		165.3125 419.60
San Fidel		415.625 419.60
Sandia Crest		419.60
Sanostee	KUU611	164.30 165.3125
Santa Fe		27.575 27.585
Shiprock	KUU611	164.30
Taos	KUP864	171.3375
Zuni		40.37

New York

Flushing	171.2375
Staten Island	171.2375

North Carolina

Durham	164.30

Ohio

Cincinnati	30.42

Oklahoma

Ada	164.30 166.10
Anandarka	165.3375 166.10
Antlers	165.3375
Ardmore	165.3375
Blair	165.3375
Bunch	165.3375
Claremore	164.30 165.3375
	166.10
Clinton	164.30
Enid	165.3375
Eufaula	166.10
Hugo	166.10
Lawton	164.30 165.3375
	166.10
Miami	166.10
Muse	165.3375
Muskogee	165.3375 166.10
Oilton	165.3375
Oklahoma City	165.3375 166.10
Pawnee	166.10
Ponca City	165.3375 166.10
Poteau	165.3375
Purcell	165.3375
Shawnee	166.10
Stillwater	166.10
Talequah	164.30 166.10
Talihina	164.30 166.10
Tishomingo	165.3375 166.10
Wewoka	165.3375
Wright	165.3375

Oregon

All Areas	27.575 27.585

Pennsylvania

Philadelphia	27.275 27.585
	171.2375

South Dakota

Nassauby	KUU615	164.30
Pine Ridge		169.625
Rapid City		164.30
Rosebud	KUU617	164.30
Winner		171.2375

Texas

Dallas	409.00

Utah

All Areas	41.83

Virginia
Norfolk   KRR402   164.30
Orange   WZ2725   419.15
Washington
All Areas   27.575 27.585
All USA
27.575 27.585 30.42 30.43 32.14 36.22
36.25 36.27 38.22 41.39 41.43 41.47
164.30 171.2375 409.00 413.425 419.60

Home Loan Bank Board, Federal

Washington, DC   409.40

Housing & Urban Development, Dept. of (HUD)

All Areas: 164.50 164.8625 165.6625 168.00 169.10
Stations reported:

DC	Washington	KGU70	168.00
GA	Forest Park		165.6625
TX	Palo Pinto		164.50
VA	Richmond		164.50
WA	Seattle		164.50

Immigration & Naturalization Service (INS) & Border Patrol (BP)

Repeaters:
163.625/162.825	BP	CTCSS 100.0 123.0 151.4 Hz
163.625/162.85	INS	CTCSS 151.4 Hz
163.625/162.875	BP	CTCSS 151.4 Hz
163.625/162.90	BP	CTCSS 206.6 Hz
163.625/162.925	BP	CTCSS 100.0 Hz

163.625/162.975	BP	CTCSS 151.4 Hz
163.65/162.85	INS	CTCSS 100.0 Hz
163.65/162.95	INS	CTCSS 100.0 Hz
163.675/162.825	BP	CTCSS 123.0 Hz
163.675/162.875	BP	CTCSS 206.6 Hz
163.675/162.925	BP	CTCSS 123.0 Hz
163.675/162.975	BP	CTCSS 206.6 Hz
163.70/162.90	BP/INS	Tactical CTCSS 107.2
163.725/162.825	BP	CTCSS 151.4 Hz
163.725/162.85	BP	CTCSS 151.4 Hz
163.725/162.875	BP	CTCSS 100,0 Hz
163.725/162.925	BP	CTCSS 151.4 Hz
163.725/162.975	BP	CTCSS 100.0 Hz
163.75/162.85	INS	CTCSS 123.0 Hz
163.75/162.95	INS	CTCSS 123.0 206.0 Hz
163.775/162.825	BP	CTCSS 206.6 Hz
163.775/162.875	BP	CTCSS 123.0 Hz
163.775/162.90	BP	CTCSS 100.0 Hz
163.775/162.925	BP	CTCSS 206.6 Hz
163.775/162.975	BP	CTCSS 123.0 Hz
165.875/168.975	Anti-Smuggler	CTCSS 103.5 Hz
165.925/167.6375	Org Crime/Drug Task Force	CTCSS 100,0 Hz
168.8625/165.925	BP	CTCSS 100.0 Hz

Border Intrusion Alarms: 170.625 170.65 170.70 170.775

Simplex Frequencies
 Border Patrol 162.625 163.375 163.625 163.675 163.725 163.775 165.8625 165.925
 Immigration & Naturalization Svc 162.85 163.65 163.75 168.825
 Tactical 162.90 163.05 163.70 163.9625 165.2375 168.35
 Org Crime/Drug Task Force 167.6375
 Anti-Smuggling 165.875 168.975
 Surveillance 170.625 170.675 170.725 170.75 170.825

 UHF Frequencies: 408.20 408.225 408.25 408.225 408.30 408.35 408.375 408.40 413.55 413.60 413.625 413.65 413.625 413.675 413.70 413.725 413.75 413.775 414.625 417.025 417.05 417.125 417.15 417.125 418.85 418.95 418.975

Aircraft roster: Hughes 369= N67BP N97BP N3973A N37929; Pitts S-1= N28970 N29009; Cessna 182= N1260M N1324M N4869N N4885N N6229F; Cessna 206= N732ZQ; Piper PA-18 Cub= N2320P N2357Z N8991Y N9724P N14327 N63946 N63946 Also see aircraft roster for Dept. of Justice.
 In some areas, mobile units with a "Zero" prefix are transport vehicles operated by a "D.O" (Detention Officer). An "A Number" is the serial number on the upper right hand corner of immigration papers; it is used as a "Control Number." The "Control Name" refers to the surname of the subject in question.
 Along the US side of the US/Mexican border there are seismic detectors. Each one is numbered, and auxiliary detectors attached to the main ones are also numbered. The auxiliary detectors ("Ports") indicate the direction of travel. All readings are sent to EPIC (El Paso Intelligence Center) by radio telemetry and come up on computer screens as well as hard copy. Some patrol vehicles have on-board equipment for local control, if necessary. A radio report of "Hit on 1250 Port 2" indicates that sensor #1250 has picked up a subject; the Port number indicates the direction of travel.

Some remote farms, homes, and ranches that don't landline telephones are equipped with "panic buttons" that register at EPIC when they are pressed. A radio report such as "Sensor 1277" or "Sensor "1451" refers to a signal having been received from one of these devices. That dispatches a patrol car.

Other BP terminology encountered includes: "FOS"= Field Operations Supervisor; "ASU"= Anti-Smuggling Unit; "VR"= Voluntary Return aliens being returned; "OTM"= Alien, other than Mexican; "EWI"= Entered Without Inspection; "PIO"= Patrol Intelligence Officer; and "PO"= Patrol Officer. Along the border, "ZX-5" is a roadblock on I-25, north of Truth or Consequences, NM; "ZX-7" is a roadblock on I-10 at milepost #121, NM. It should be noted that BP units, at times, are often the first units on the scenes of trafic accidents and other civil emergencies, and aid work with local, county, and state public safety agencies at such times.

Station Callsign Roster

KAD200	Washington, DC		
KAD210	Richmond, VA	KAD662	Massena, NY
KAD213	Philadelphia, PA	KAD663	Chateaguay, NY
KAD214	Philadelphia, PA	KAD667	Watertown, NY
KAD215	Boston, MA	KAD668	Ft. Covington, NY
KAD220	Miami, FL	KAD670	Ogdensburg, NY
KAD236	Miami, FL (Krome Ave.)	KAD673	Churbusco, NY (?)
KAD252	St. John, VI	KAD678	Cannons Corners, NY
KAD254	Christianstad, VI	KAD680	Buffalo, NY
KAD256	Playa Ponce, PR	KAD687	Albany, NY
KAD258	San Juan, PR	KAD690	Niagara Falls, NY
KAD259	Charlotte Amalie, VI	KAD694	Rouses Point, NY
KAD260	New Orleans, LA	KAD696	Beecher Falls, VT
KAD261	Mobile, AL	KAD698	Derby Line, VT
KAD262	Pensacola, FL	KAD699	Derby Line (Interstate), VT
KAD263	Lake Charles, LA	KAK700	Detroit, MI
KAD264	Baton Rouge, LA	KAK701	Trenton, MI
KAD265	Gulfport, MS	KAK702	Port Huron, MI
KAD600	New York, NY	KAK703	Sault Ste Marie, MI
KAD607	Portland, ME	KAK705	Port Huron, MI
KAD616	Van Buren, ME	KAK720	Grand Forks, ND
KAD620	Houlton, ME (Sector HQ)	KAK721	International Falls, MN
KAD622	Calais, ME	KAK722	Pembina, ND
KAD624	Van Buren, ME	KAK723	Portal, ND
KAD626	Jackman, ME	KAK724	Pine Creek, MN
KAD627	Coburn Gore, ME	KAK725	Noyes, MN
KAD640	Swanton, VT (Sector HQ)	KAK730	St. Paul, MN
KAD642	Highgate Spgs., VT	KAK739	Chicago, IL
KAD644	Derby Line, VT	KAK740	Havre, MT
KAD646	Pittsburg, NH	KAK741	Sweetgrass, MT
KAD647	Champlain, NY	KAK742	Opheim, MT
KAD650	Morses Line, VT	KAK751	Wolf Point, MN
KAD651	Norton, VT	KAK760	Spokane, WA
KAD652	Alburg, VT	KAK761	Bonners Ferry, ID
KAD653	Alburg Spgs., VT	KAK762	Kettle Falls, WA
KAD654	E. Richford, VT	KAK780	Blaine, WA
KAD655	W. Berkshire, VT	KAK782	Seattle, WA
KAD659	Overtons Corners, NY	KAK783	Lynden, WA
KAD660	Malone, NY	KAK786	Lynden, WA
KAD661	Thousand Islands, NY	KAK880	Livermore, CA

KAK820	Chula Vista, CA		KAK885	Columbus, NM

KAK820   Chula Vista, CA
KAK821   Los Angeles, CA
KAK822   San Clemente, CA
KAK823   Temecula, CA
KAK827   Imperial Beach, CA
KAK830   San Pedro, CA
KAK832   Oxnard, CA
KAK840   El Centro, CA
KAK841   Calexico, CA
KAK841   Indio, CA
KAK847   Riverside, CA
KAK850   Yuma, AZ
KAK860   Tucson, AZ
KAK865   Nogales, AZ
KAK866   Douglas, AZ
KAK872   Lochiel, AZ
KAK880   El Paso, TX
KAK883   Lordsburg, NM

KAK885   Columbus, NM
KAK886   Antelope Wells, NM
KAK888   Las Cruces, NM
KAK892   Deming, NM
KAK894   Truth or Consequenses, NM
KAK896   El Paso (EPIC), TX
KAK899   El Paso, TX
KAK900   Marfa, TX
KAK904   Presidio, TX
KAK920   Del Rio, TX
KAK922   Sonora, TX
KAK940   Laredo, TX
KAK941   San Antonio, TX
KAK960   McAllen, TX
KAK961   Rio Grande, TX
KAK964   Mercedes, TX
KAK980   Brownsville, TX

Bureau of Indian Affairs (BIA)

BIA Police: 164.8625 419.625
Indian Schools: 40 MHz channels; BIA Fire Departments 166.6125 168.40
Common BIA repeater pairs: 170.075/172.775 171.75/172.625 171.75/172.675
172.425/171.70 172.675/172.025

Stations:
Alaska
Anchorage   KWA597   164.25
Metlakatla   KWA599   168.55
Mt Edgecombe   KWA596   164.80
Arizona
Ashaydn.   KOJ514   171.75 172.625
Black Mesa   KOP564   164.775 164.80
                          417.675
Black Peak   KOJ509   171.65 172.525
Black Pncl.   KOJ584   171.65 172.525
Chediski   KOJ552/556 172.675
Chinle Agcy.   KOJ572   40.31 165.6875
                KOP511   40.01
Cichn, Butte   KOP506   40.01 40.31
Chuck Box   KOJ533   172.075
  172.675 406.475 408.075
Cibecue   KOJ538   see KOJ533
Coolidge   KOJ510   163.125 171.75
                KOJ513/517 see KOJ510
Cottonwood Schl. KOP511   40.01 40.31
Cove School   KOP512   40.03 40.33
Deer Springs   KOJ554   172.675
Defiance Mtn.   KOJ560   40.33
  166.8625 165.6875 169.70 169.725
  172.425 412.275 419.65
Demnehatso   KOP584   40.01 40.31

Devilshead   KOP562   164.8625
                KOP567   164.80
  164.8625 165.6875 165.7125
Dilkon School   KOP514   40.01 40.31
Dry Lake   KOJ541   172.425
Flagstaff (FBI) KEX705   164.80
  164.8625 165.7125
Fluted Rock   KOJ580   171.525 171.65
Foghat Ridge   KOJ555   172.675
Ft. Apache   KOD598   406.475
408.075
                KOJ532   171.70
  172.675 406.475 408.075
                KOJ545   172.10 172.70
Ft. Defiance   KOJ562   172.525
                KOJ570   40.03 40.33
  164.8625 165.6875 171.65 411.625
Ft. Mc Dowell   KOJ528   414.875
Goat Mtn.   KOJ526   166.875
Greasewood   KOP539   40.01 40.31
Hayden   KOJ512   171.75
Headgate   KOJ508   171.775
  172.425
Hilltop   KOJ521/594 171.70
  172.425
Hotevilla   KOJ547   166.975
  168.375

203

Hunters Point	KOP543	40.03 40.33
Kaibito	KOP554	40.03 40.33
Kayenta	KOJ574	40.01 40.31
Keams Canyon	KOJ546	166.975
	KOP560	164.80
164.8625 165.6875 165.7125 168.375		
Kinliche	KOP541	40.03 40.33
Kinney	KOJ557	172.025
172.675		
Kitt Peak	KOP527	168.375
Leupp	KOP527	40.01 40.03
40.31 40.33		
Limestone	KOJ537/553	172.675
406.475 408.075		
Long Mesa	KOJ504	168.325
171.775		
Lwr Greaswood	KOP569	40.31 164.30
Lwr Mtn School	KOP537	40.01 40.31
Mammoth	KOJ515	172.625
Many Farms	KOP502	40.01 40.31
	KOJ593	164.825
165.6875 412.375		
Maverick	KOJ535	172.025
172.675 406.475 408.075		
	KOJ559	172.675
	KOJ577	171.70 172.425
McKays Peak	KOJ554	406.475
419.475		
	KOJ551	172.675
Monzntpt.	KOJ561	166.875
Mt Lemmon	KOJ511	171.75
Mt Turnbull	KOP576	167.025
172.425		
No Ah Tee	KOP565	40.31 164.80
168.375 411.85		
Nazlini	KOP568	40.31
Oakridge	KOJ582	172.525
Odart	KOJ543/558	172.675
Old Summit	KOP578	172.425
Oracle Jct	KOJ534	171.75
Papago Farms	KOJ590	163.075
Parker	KOJ556/588	171.775
172.425		
Peach Sprgs	KOJ501/539	168.325
Phoenix	KOP575	164.8625
154.6875		
	KOP597	406.475
Pinal Peak	KOJ516	167.025 171.75
Piney Hill	KOJ581	171.65
	KOJ563	172.525
Pinon	KOP571	164.80
165.7125		
	KOP583	40.01 40.31
Pipe Sprgs	KOP540	40.03 40.33
Point of Pines	KOJ522	171.70 172.425
Poston	KOJ517/519	171.775
172.425		
Preston Mesa	KOJ593	40.33 164.80
164.8625 172.425 411.65		
Quajote Mtn	KOP500	168.375
Red Lake	KOP572	164.80
165.7125		
school	KOP504	40.03 40.33

Rocky Ridge	KOP523	40.03 40.33
Roof Butte	KOP586	171.65
	KOJ598	40.33
164.8625 172.525 408.725 411.65 412.35		
Sacaton	KOJ529	163.125
Sacaton Mtn	KOJ536	169.40 171.75
San Carlos	KOJ500	166.375
167.025 172.40 172.425		
Scottsdale	KOJ527	408.725
412.725		
Sebada Lake	KOP547	40.01 40.31
Sells Agcy	KOJ530	163.075
Shonto Schl	KOP503	40.03 40.33
Supai	KOJ503	172.425
Tale Pt	KOP531	167.025
Teec Nos Pos	KOJ564	40.03
Thornton	KOJ502	168.325
Toyei	KOP542	40.01 40.31
408.525		
Tuba Cy Agcy	KOJ561	40.03 40.33
164.8625 165.6875		
Valentine	KOJ505	168.325
Vicks Hill	KOJ524	412.225
White Cone	KOP573	164.80
165.7125		
Whiteriver	KOJ550	172.025
406.475 408.075 414.875		
Wide Ruins	KOP546	40.01 40.31
Willow Mtn	KOJ523	171.40
172.425		
Window Rock	KOJ565	32.94 40.02
40.03 40.33 163.125 164.8625 165.6875		
407.725 411.625		
Winslow	KOP530	40.01
Yalepoint	KOP531	40.31 164.80

California

Big Hill	KMC501	172.775
Hoopa	KMC500	171.725
172.775		
Hrmtsbnc.	KMC507	173.7625
Klamath	KMC505	see KMC500
Palm Cancon	KMC506	173.7625
Riverside	KOP580	406.475

Colorado

Herman Peak	KAC502	171.75
Ignacio	KAC500	171.75
Pk. Pt.	KAC507	171.75
Sandylms	KAC505	171.75
Spring Crk	KAC508	171.75
Towaoc	KAC501	171.75

Florida

Big Cyprus	KIE511	167.125
Brighton	KIE512	163.025
167.125		
	KIE514	166.325
167.125		

Idaho

Bannock Creek	KOD538	171.775
172.45		
Blackfoot	KOD536/539	see KOD538
Ferry Butte	KOD533	see KOD538
Ft Hall	KOD535	see KOD538
Gibson	KOD534	see KOD538

Portneuf Rsvr	KOD537	see KOD538

Kansas

Lawrence	KKF560	162.025

Minnesota

Bemidji	KAC560	172.425
414.825		
Big Meadows	KAC556	171.725
172.425		
Bolsfort	KAC567	see KAC556
Cass Lake	KAC562	see KAC556
FBI		see KAC556
Gr Portage	KAC550	see KAC556
Heritage	KAC566	see KAC556
Marshal	KAC568	see KAC556
Mt Maude	KAC551/553	see KAC556
Mt Sophie	KAC552	see KAC556
Naytahwaush	KAC557	see KAC556
Nett Lake	KAC564	see KAC556
	KAC565	172.425
414.825		
Northome	KAC563	408.525
Ponemah	KAC558	see KAC556
Red Lake	KAC555	see KAC565
Ridge Tower	KAC559	see KAC556

Montana

Anton Butte	KOD547	166.325
Babb	KOC516	36.18
Busby	KOD546	36.18
Cody Butte	KOD580	36.18
Contint'l Butte	KOD543	166.275
Crow Agcy	KOD515	408.725
	KA9360	36.18
Cut Bank	KOC518	36.18
Divide	KOC517	36.18 166.925
Dixon	KOC595	166.325
166.925		
Ferry Basin	KOC594	see KOC595
Fisher	KOC514	36.18
Fisher Butte	KOD548	36.18
173.7625 412.275		
Harlem	KOD540	36.18
166.325 167.075 167.125		
Hot Sprgs	KOC590	166.325
166.925 172.425 172.675		
Irvine	KOC588	see KOC595
Jocko	KOC586	see KOC595
Kicking Horse	KOC584	see KOC595
Lame Deer	KOD545	164.625
167.075 408.725		
Oliver Pt	KOC587	166.925
172.425		
Pistol Creek	KOC593	see KOC595
Polson	KOC596	see KOC595
	KOC597	172.425
172.675		
Poplar	KOD504	166.325
167.075		
Rocky Boys	KOD541	166.275
167.075 167.125		
Ronan	KOC583	see KOC595
	KOC599	166.725
St Ignatius	KOC598	see KOC597
Seville	KOC519	36.18

Swift Current	KOC518	36.18
Wolf Pt	KOD505	see KOD504
	KOD506	166.325

Nebraska

Statewide FBI		38.98
Winnebago Tribe	KAC585	38.98

Nevada

Cnspr. Mtn.	KOJ591	172.45
Owyhee	KOJ540	171.775
172.45		

New Mexico

Alamo	KOP528	40.31
Albuquerque	KKF530/540	166.30
	KOP566	164.8625
165.6875		
	KOP582	406.475
Baca	KOP535	40.01 40.31
Bclbt. School	KOP508	40.03 40.33
Bdspr. School	KOP548	40.03 40.33
Black Rock	KKF520	171.75
Borrego Pass	KOP509	40.01 40.31
Canon City	KOP516	40.01 40.31
Carizozo Canyon	KKF505	171.75
Cebollito Pk	KKF537	166.30
Cedar Sprgs	KKF503	171.75
Clingt. Mtn	KKF506	171.75
Clark Pk	KKF533	166.30
Colgate Schl	KOP532	40.03 40.33
Crown Pt	KOJ571	40.01 40.31
164.8625 165.6875		
Crystal School	KOP513	40.03 40.33
Dulce	KKF500	171.75 411.85
Dzlthdtl.	KOJ576	40.31
Eagle Creek	KKF516	171.75
Farmington	KOJ589	40.03 40.33
	KOJ596/597	40.03 40.33
Five Canyon	KKF508	171.75
Ft Wingate	KOJ568	40.03 40.33
163.125 167.125 408.575		
	KOP596	412.375
Gallup	KOJ575	32.94 40.02
40.03 163.125 408.725		
Gamerco	KOJ577	163.125
167.125		
Harley Mtn	KKF512/519	171.75
Huerfano	KOP533	40.31
Isleta	KKF538	166.30
Jnsnc. School	KOP519	40.03 40.33
Lake Valley	KOP520	40.01 40.31
Lamosca	KOJ592	40.31 164.775
411.85 417.95		
Magdalena	KOP525	40.01 40.31
Mariano Lake	KOP521	40.01 40.31
Marley Mtn.	KKF512	172.675
Mescalero	KKF510	171.75
Mt Powell	KOP545	172.575
Mt Taylor	KKF535	166.30
Muerfano	KOP533	40.01
Nhznd. School	KOP351	40.03 40.33
Ojito	KKF501	171.75 411.85
Ojo Encinitas	KOP549	40.01 40.31
Osborne	KKF504	171.75
Pajarito Mtn	KKF513/514	171.75

Pojo Aque	KKF529	166.30
408.775 411.775		
Pueblo Pintado	KOP526	40.01 40.31
Puycliffs	KKF536	166.30
Ramah	KKF521	40.37
Red Rock Schl	KOP522	40.03 40.33
Sanostee Schl	KOP524	40.01 40.03
40.31 40.33		
Santa Clara Tribe	KKF532	166.30
Santa Fe	KKF531	406.475
	KKF534	166.30
Shiprock	KOJ566	40.03 40.33
164.8625 168.685		
	KPP587	412.375
Silver	KKF517	171.75
Silver Canyon	KKF507	171.75
Stong	KKF528	166.30 411.775
Taos	KKF541	166.30 411.775
Thoreau	KOP538	40.01 40.31
Toadlena Schl	KOP552	40.01 40.03
40.31 40.33		
Tohatchi	KOJ583	172.525
	KOP507	40.01 40.31
	KOP592	412.375
Tohnitso	KOJ585	172.525
Torreon	KOP534	40.01 40.31
Washington	KOJ578	172.525
	KOJ579	172.525
172.575 172.725		
Wingate	KOJ569	40.01 40.31
Wofford	KKF511	171.75
Zuni	KKF524/526	171.75
Zuni Top	KKF522	40.37
	KKF523	171.75

New York

Hogansburg		42.72

North Carolina

Burnett Knob	KIE501	164.625
Cherokee	KIE500	164.675
165.3375		
Mt Noble	KIE502	see KIE500

North Dakota

Statewide FBI		38.98
Belcourt	KAC590	38.98 164.625
Dunseith	KAC591	38.98 164.625
Ft Totten	KAC595	38.98 164.625
Ft Yates	KAC530	38.98
Mandaree	KAC512	38.98 41.14
New Town	KAC510	41.14
Parshall	KAC506	38.98
Twin Buttes		41.14
Whitshield	KAC514	38.89 41.14

Oklahoma

Brushy Mtn	KKF581	168.30
Khilocco	KIE530	163.025
Kiamichi Mtn	KKE571	168.30
Talequah	KKF580	167.15 169.775
Talihina	KKF570	168.30

Oregon

(portable)	KOC567	166.6126
168.40		

Bear Sprgs	KOC566	171.775
172.425		
Chemawa	KOD563	172.30
Clear Lake	KOC561	see KOC566
Deadman Sprgs	KOD592	172.425
Eagle Butte	KOC564	see KOC566
Formans Pt	KOC562	172.425
Green Ridge	KOC557	see KOC566
Kahneeta Hot Spgs	KOC565	see KOC566
Mission	KOD590	see KOC556
Pendleton	KOD590	see KOC556
Redmond	KOD563	172.425
Sdwltr. Butte	KOC563	see KOC566
Shtk. Butte	KOC554	see KOC566
Warm Springs	KOC555	see KOC566

South Dakota

Statewide BIA	KAC538	166.475
FBI X1 to X36R; 2X3 to 2X32 38.98		
39.10 39.28 39.32		
Aberdeen	3-7	39.10 39.16
39.24 39.32		
Allen	KAC521	169.625
Bridger	KAC541	38.98
Bullhead	KAC532	38.98
Cherry Creek	KAC536	38.98
Dupree	24-7Q	39.10 39.16
39.28 39.32		
Eagle Butte	KAC535	38.98
	24-7D	see 24-7Q
Flandreau	KK7480	38.98
Ft Thompson	KAC576	38.98 414.825
	14-7A	see 24-7Q
Ft Yates	20-7	see 24-7Q
Goodwill	KAC517	414.825
Ideal	67-71	see 24-7Q
Kyle	KAC523	169.625
	KAC529	169.625
169.775		
Lake Andes	KAC584	414.825
Little Eagle	KAC531	38.98
	20-7K	see 24-7Q
Loneman	KAC528	169.625
	KAC515	169.775
Lwr Brule	KAC577	38.98 414.825
	45-7	see 24-7Q
Manderson	KAC522	169.625
McLaughlin	20-7P	see 24-7Q
Mission	KAC581	38.98
	67-7K	see 24-7Q
Mobridge	KAC533	38.98
24-7B & 24-7M		see 24-7Q
Mt Coolidge	KAC526	164.625
O'Kreek	67-7O	see 24-7Q
Pickstown	KAC586	38.98 408.525
Pine Ridge Rsvn	KAC520	169.625
169.775		
Porcupine	KAC516/524	see KAC529
Porcupine Rdg	KAC527	38.98 164.625
164.675		
Promise	KAC539	38.98
Reliance	45-7G	see 24-7Q
Rdscffld.	KAC537	38.98

Rosebud	KAC580	38.98
	67-7	see 24-7Q
St Francis	67-7S	38.98 39.10
39.16 39.28 39.32		
Sisseton	KAC519	414.825
	55-7T	see 24-7Q
Stephan	KAC578	38.98 414.925
Swiftbird	KAC542	38.98
Wagner	KAC587	414.825
Wakpala	20-7W	see 67-7S
Wanblee	KAC525/534	169.625
169.776		
White Horse	KAC540	38.98
Whitstnl.	KAC518	38.98 414.925

Utah

Brigham City	KOD530	406.475
408.475 412.275		
Ft Duchesne	KOJ595	411.625
La Mink	KOJ599	41.14 416.025
Little Mtn	KOD531	406.475
Navajo Mtn	KOP501	40.33

Washington

Portable (FD)	KOC568	166.6125
168.40		
Anthnm. Rdg	KOC569	163.175
Boundary Butte	KOD569	172.30 172.775
Buoyville	KOC577	170.075
Cape Chapparal	KOC533	40.37 40.85
Capital Peak	KOC544	166.6375
Cody Butte	KOD580	see KOD569
Cook Creek	KOC551	166.6375
168.375		
Cougar Creek	KOC528	40.85
Crown Pt	KOC542	166.6375
Desautel	KOD562	172.30 172.775
Everett	KOC548	see KOC551
Ft Simcoe	KOC531	40.37 40.85
Glenwood	KOC523	40.37 40.85
Gold Mtn	KOC550	166.6375
	KOD579	36.18 172.30
172.775		
Granger	KOC576	170.075
Grt Broken Mtn	KOC531	40.85
Harrah	KOC572/573	170.075
Hoquaim	KOC543	36.18
	KOC545	see KOC551
Site "I"	KOC579	170.075

Inchelim	KOD572	see KOD579
Johnny Gg. Mtn	KOD578	see KOD569
Kalispell	KOD564	172.425
Keller	KOD577	see KOD579
Mill Creek	KOC522	40.95
Mitchell Pt	KOD568	see KOD569
Monumental	KOD586	36.18
Moon Mtn	KOD581	36.18
Moses Mtn	KOD574/589	see KOD579
Mt Constitution	KOC549	166.6375
Neah Bay	KOC546	see KOC551
	KOC548	36.18
Neilton	KOC543	36.18 166.6375
Nespelem	KOD570	see KOD579
Okanagan	KOD573	see KOD569
Omak Mtn		36.18
Quartz Mtn	KOD584	36.18
Satus Pt	KOC529	40.37 40.85
164.575 406.475		
Signal Peak	KOC526/527	40.37 40.85
Snsgr. Mtn	KOD588	172.30
Sopelia	KOC532	40.85
Toppenish	KOC525	40.37 40.85
168.375		
Toppenish Crk	KOC575	170.075
Wapato	KOC571	170.075
Wellpinit	KOD571	172.425
Wellpinit Mtn	KOD569	172.425
Whitemore	KOD576	see KOD579
White Swan	KOC524	40.37 40.85
White Swan Rdg	KOD585	see KOD569
Whitestone		36.18
Yakima	KOC574	170.075

Wisconsin

Ashland	KAC569	414.825
Battlefield	KAC572	172.425
Hayward	KAC573	172.425
Mellen	KAC570	172.425
408.825		
Rat Lake	KAC575	172.425
Squirrel Hill	KAC571	172.425
Washburn	KAC574	414.825

Wyoming

Black Mtn	KOC507	36.18
Ft Washakie	KOC500	167.075
Wind River	KOC506	166.725
Winkleman Dam	KOC505	36.18 166.325

Central Intelligence Agency (CIA)

HQ Langley, VA: "Base Victor" 149.565   Mobile units 165.825

Monitors also report 165.3875 MHz and shared use of some frequencies assigned to State Department during visits to US of foreign dignitaries.

Also monitor: 406.25 406.85 408.45 408.55 408.70 408.80 408.90

See listings for Camp Peary, Williamsburg, VA.

Interior, Department of the

The following information applies to all branches of the Dept. of the Interior, including those listed separately in this Registry (q.v.), and adds to those listings.

Aero OP: 117.975 121.9375 121.9625 122.8 122.9 122.925 123.025 123.05 132.0125 166.675 167.95 168.025 168.55 168.625 169.15 169.20 172.60
Emergencies:
    Logistics– 41.27 41.55 46.63 46.81 46.99 414.65 415.40
    Command–   168.70/170.975   168.10/170.45   168.075/170.425   411.75/417.30 411.925/417.35 412.15/417.50 412.20/417.80
    Tactical– 166.775 166.935 167.10/169.75 167.25/166.725 168.05 168.20 168.25 168.40/166.6125 168.475 169.35
    Fire Fighting: 168.40/166.6125

Aircraft Roster: Callair S182= N68AT N78AT;   Bell 206= N19UD N22PP N612BR N2113Z;   Hughes 269A= N8134Y N81342 N82249;   Rockwell 690= N611 N618 N81470; DeHavilland DHC-2= N9260Z;   DeHavilland DHC-6= N490AS;   Grumman G-21- N644R N778 N789;   McKinnon G-21= N780;   Bell 47G= N256SW;   Fairchild 6= N5308F; Partvena P68= N701;   MBB BO= N617;   Beech Baron 55= N18363;   Cessna 180= N702 N704 N708 N721 N727 N729 N757 N757X N763 N767 N61053;   Cessna 185= N714 N714KH N725 N735EA N735HB N740 N761 N783 N1055F N1217F N2171F N9395N N9987N N24164 N87144;   Cessna 206= 32PA N70Y N736 N9178G N9304R N9497R N9623R N9625R N9798G;   Cessna 414= N3183M;   Piper PA-23250= N613A;   Piper PA-18= N720 N724 N784 N785 N2387S N2520S N3685Z N4479Z N4500W N24798 N90978 N91240 N91251 N91260

Federal Bureau of Investigation (FBI)

The FBI retains it's crown as the world's unqualified high-profile intelligence and enforcement super-agency. The mail from this book's readers clearly indicates that it continues its reign as the highest-interest federal activity. Scanner monitors are fascinated. This us undoubtedly because the FBI is in national headlines regularly, being closely associated with the investigation of terrorist activities, domestic espionage, bank robberies, aircraft hijackers, kidnapings, organized crime, corruption of public officials, national security matters, and other similar activities that have made the FBI the world's most well-known and highly respected investigative agency. While such investigations are part of the day-to-day work of the agency's staff of 24,000 men and women, to most of scanner owners, the activities of the agencies are more than fascinating to hear.

Not that this is the easiest federal agency to monitor. Not by a mile, and it's intentional, I can assure you. While some transmissions are sent "in the clear," others are exchanged with a very effective digital voice scrambling system that cannot be copied by unauthorized listeners (so far as I am aware). To the scanner user, such scrambled transmissions sound like a hiss, or "white noise."

Although there does appear to be a bank of frequencies the agency generally uses, specific frequencies do seem to be added and dropped with some regularity at various agency offices. Moreover, repeater output/input frequency pairs vary widely across the country, as do the ID's used to refer to channels. In some of the earlier editions of this Registry, we had attempted to match specific frequencies with particular areas, only to find that (on a national level) such a listing became outdated quite rapidly.

Presently, 163.5375, 163.8625, and (car/car simplex) 167.5625 are in national use. Local vehicles and offices also use other frequencies in addition to these. Some monitors report hearing 160 MHz transmissions being simulcast over their UHF link frequencies.

In general, the FBI uses one group of frequencies between 162.6375 and 164.525. These are the most often noted repeater output frequencies. Most of the activity seems to be between 163.8375 and 163.9875 MHz. Repeater input frequencies and most simplex channels are in a band that runs between 167.2125 and 167.7875. Some FBI activity has also been reported on several 165 MHz frequencies, including 165.925/167.6375 (participation in Organized Crime/Drug Enforcement Task Force). The UHF band appears thusfar to be used for links and relays. These frequencies are generally found in the frequency ranges of 412.30 to 412.90, 414.00 to 414.50, and 419.15 to 419.60 MHz. Frequencies in the 121.6 to 121.925 MHz portion of the VHF aero band have been reported in use when the agency communicates with a skyjacked aircraft on the ground at an airport. Best bet is to regularly search/scan these bands for currently active frequencies in your local monitoring area.

Note that at the present time, the digital voice scrambling system in use apparently reduces mesaage intelligibility to some degree and some messages attempted in scrambled ("Papa") mode can't be understood and have to tried with the "bubble machine" (scrambler) shut off, or via landline.

FBI stations all have formal callsigns, although there are plenty of tactical ID's to be monitored such as "Bronco Base," "Bulldog 7," "Lucky 2," "Roadrunner 9," "Ranger 7" and the like. These may designate members of different squads. These are rather tentative and therefore no attempt has been made to index them here.

There are still occasional reports of SSB and RTTY activity on the listed HF frequencies. Most likely these circuits are maintained for backup or standy purposes in case of the failure of landline or other circuits. They do not appear to in routine full-time use, but may possibly be tested on a scheduled basis.

We have compiled a listing of what we believe are the frequencies most likely to produce this agency's communications. Putting a scanner into "search" mode near these frequencies may let you discover additional frequencies. We also list agents' lingo and buzzwords that might be monitored, as well as the callsigns known to have been assigned. All information also shown under the listings for the Dept. of Justice applies to the FBI.

HF frequencies: 2332 2810 4040 4618 5060 5390 5913 6594 7905 9015 9195 9240 10500 10915 11028 11075 11210 11490 13660 14460 14495 14534 15955 16376 17405 17603 18173 18668 23675 23875 kHz

VHF/UHF frequencies reported: (CTCSS 167.9 Hz) 32.75 36.07 40.22 40.86 41.97 122.9 156.39 156.57 156.69 162.6375 162.65 162.6625 162.675 162.6875 162.70 162.7125 162.725 162.7375 162.75 162.7625 162.775 162.7875 163.8375 163.85 163.8625 163.875 163.8875 163.90 163.9125 163.925 163.9375 163.95 163.9625 163.975 163.9875 164.1625 164.175 164.1875 164.20 164.2125 164.225 164.2375 164.25 164.35 164.3625 164.375 164.3875 164.4125 164.425 164.525 165.65 165.925/167.6375 167.2125 167.225 167.2375 167.25 167.2625 167.275 167.2875 167.30 167.3125 167.325 167.3375 167.35 167.3625 167.375 167.3875 167.40 167.4125 167.425 167.4375 167.45 167.4625 167.475 167.4875 167.50 167.5125 167.525 167.5375 167.55 167.5625 167.575 167.5875 167.60 167.6125 167.625 167.6375 167.65 167.6625 167.675 167.875 167.70 167.7125 167.725 167.7375 167.75 167.7625 167.775 167.7875 170.00 170.70 170.80 170.825 170.85 170.90 171.35
UHF Link Frequencies: 412.35 412.425 412.45 412.475 412.50 412.55 412.575 412.675 414.00 414.025 414.05 414.075 414.0875 414.10 414.125 414.15 414.175 414.20 414.225 414.25 414.275 414.30 414.325 414.35 414.375 414.40 414.425 414.475 414.50 414.55 414.575 414.75 419.075 419.175 419.20 419.225 419.275 419.30 419.325 419.35 419.40 419.425 419.45 419.475 419.50 419.525 419.55 419.575 419.60 467.95

Aircraft: Bell 206= N3202D; Cessna 172= N91398 (Also see Dept. of Justice.)

VHF/UHF Callsigns:

KAC920	Minneapolis, MN	KEC258	Burlington, VT
KAC921	St. Paul, MN	KEC259	Plattsburgh, NY
KAC924	Pierre, SD	KEC261	Glenns Falls, NY
KAC925	Duluth, MN	KEC270	New York, NY
KAC926	Sioux Falls, SD	KEC271	New York, NY
KAC929	Grand Forks, ND	KEC272	Garden City, NY
KAC930	Rapid City, SD	KEC277	Jamaica, NY
KAC932	Minot, ND	KEC278	Poughkeepsie, NY
KAC933	Bemidji, MN	KEC280	Staten Island, NY
KCB800	Boston, MA	KEC281	Richmond Hills, NY
KCB801	Providence, RI	KEC283	New Rochelle, NY
KEC220	Charlotte, NC	KEV220	Charlotte, NC
KEC225	Greensboro, NC	KEV232	Raleigh, NC
KEC232	Winston-Salem, NC	KEV300	Miami, FL
KEC254	Watertown, NY	KEV301	Ft. Lauderdale, FL
KEC255	Syracuse, NY	KEV302	W. Palm Beach, FL
KEC256	Syracuse, NY	KEV303	Ft. Pierce, FL

KEV304	Homestead, FL	KEX749	Canton, OH
KEV305	Key West, FL	KEX750	Sandusky, OH
KEV320	Tampa, FL	KEX760	Detroit, MI
KEV340	Norfolk, VA	KEX762	Flint, MI
KEV341	Newport News, VA	KEX763	Monroe, MI
KEV360	Richmond, VA	KEX764	Bay City, MI
KEV380	Savannah, GA	KEX767	Marquette, MI
KEX500	Kansas City, MO	KEX768	S. Ste Marie, MI
KEX510	Kansas City, MO	KEX770	S. Ste Marie, MI
KEX570	Kansas City. MO	KEX772	Traverse City, MI
KEX571	Wichita, KS	KEX780	Indianapolis, IN
KEX590	Buffalo, NY	KEX800	Springfield, IL
KEX591	Rochester, NY	KEX820	Columbia, SC
KEX592	Geneva, NY	KEX821	Charleston, SC
KEX593	Jamestown, NY	KEX823	Florence, SC
KEX595	Niagara Falls, NY	KEX840	San Antonio, TX
KEX600	New Haven, CT	KEX844	Del Rio, TX
KEX620	Newark, NJ	KEX845	Laredo, TX
KEX621	Paterson, NJ	KEX846	McAllen, TX
KEX622	Piscataway, NJ	KEX847	Brownsville, TX
KEX623	Trenton, NJ	KEX860	Cape Girardeau, MO
KEX624	Camden, NJ	KEX880	Springfield, IL
KEX625	Sea Girt, NJ	KEX958	Vermont, IL
KEX626	Red Bank, NJ	KFC990	San Francisco, CA
KEX628	Hackensack, NJ	KFP901	Sacramento, CA
KEX640	Philadelphia, PA	KFP950	Dallas, TX
KEX641	Harrisburg, PA	KFP959	San Angelo, TX
KEX643	Scranton, PA	KFP970	San Francisco, CA
KEX644	Wilkes-Barre, PA	KFP990	Sacramento, CA
KEX645	Allentown, PA	KFQ200	Little Rock, AR
KEX648	Lansdale, PA	KFQ240	Alexandria, VA
KEX650	Newtown Square, PA	KGB715	Hyattsville, MD
KEX651	Williamsport, PA	KGB747	Baltimore, MD
KEX652	State College, PA	KGB750	Baltimore, MD
KEX660	Pittsburgh, PA	KGB793	Washington, DC
KEX680	San Diego, CA	KIA320	Louisville, KY
KEX690	San Diego, CA	KIE320	Lexington, KY
KEX693	Oceanside, CA	KKF905	Las Cruces, NM
KEX694	El Centro, CA	KKF909	Alamogordo, NM
KEX700	Phoenix, AZ	KKF910	Deming, NM
KEX701	Tucson, AZ	KKF920	El Paso, TX
KEX702	Safford, AZ	KKF925	Houston, TX
KEX703	Nogales, AZ	KKF940	New Orleans, LA
KEX705	Flagstaff, AZ	KKF943	Alexandria, LA
KEX706	Yuma, AZ	KKF944	Baton Rouge, LA
KEX720	Portland, OR	KKF945	Lafayette, LA
KEX740	Cleveland, OH	KMC250	Los Angeles, CA
KEX741	Akron, OH	KMC251	Riverside, CA
KEX742	Toledo, OH	KMC253	Santa Ana, CA
KEX743	Youngstown, OH	KMC254	Long Beach, CA
KEX744	Painesville, OH	KMC255	Van Nuys, CA
KEX745	Mentor, OH	KMC256	Covina, CA
KEX747	Baltimore, MD	KMC268	Palm Springs, CA
KEX748	Mansfield, OH	KMC270	Indio, CA

KOD200	Butte, MT
KOD207	Great Falls, MT
KOD208	Coeur d'Alene, ID
KOD209	Glasgow, MT
KOD210	Kalispell, MT
KOD220	Seattle, WA
KOD222	Bremerton, WA
KOD223	Bellingham, WA
KOD232	Wenatchee, WA
KQC390	Cincinnati, OH
KQC391	Dayton, OH
KQC392	Columbus, OH
KQC397	Portsmouth, OH
KSC210	Chicago, IL
KSC214	Rockford, IL
KSC215	Joliet, IL
KSC216	Aurora, IL
KSC217	Chicago Hts., IL
KSC220	Milwaukee, WI
KSC221	Superior, WI
KSO970	San Francisco, CA
KUA270	Honolulu, HI
KUZ220	Charlotte, NC
KUZ225	Greensboro, NC
KUZ228	Winston-Salem, NC
KUZ232	Raleigh, NC
KUZ336	Wilmington, NC
KWA291	Anchorage, AK
WWA290	San Juan, PR
WWA291	Charlotte Amalie, VI
WWA292	Fajardo, PR
WWA293	Ponce, PR
WWA294	Aguadilla, PR

HF Callsigns
KAG69	Denver, CO
KAG81	Minneapolis, MN
KAG88	Omaha, NE
KAG98	Omaha, NE
KCC61	Boston, MA
KCC76	New Haven, CT
KEC67	Albany, NY
KEC71	Buffalo, NY
KEC96	New York, NY
KGC77	Cleveland, OH
KGC87	Cincinnati, OH
KGD83	Baltimore, MD
KGE23-to-93	Washington, DC
KGG64	Philadelphia, PA
KGG76	Pittsburgh, PA
KIG67	Atlanta, GA
KIG73	Birmingham, AL
KIG81	Charlotte, NC
KIG91	Knoxville, TN

KIH67	Louisville, KY
KIH73	Memphis, TN
KIH78	Mobile, AL
KII74	Richmond, VA
KII83	Savannah, GA
KIJ23-to-39	Miami, FL
KIJ44	Tampa, FL
KKI68	Dallas, TX
KKI88	Houston, TX
KKI99	San Antonio, TX
KKJ22-to-41	San Francisco, CA
KKJ67	Albuquerque, NM
KKJ78	Little Rock, AR
KKJ88	New Orleans, LA
KKJ98	Oklahoma City, OK
KMG23-to-48	San Diego, CA
KMI66	Los Angeles, CA
KOG69	Butte, MT
KOG71	Phoenix, AZ
KOG73	Portland, OR
KOG93	Salt Lake City, UT
KOH23-to-41	Seattle, WA
KSC63	Indianapolis, IN
KSC71	Milwaukee, WI
KSC81	Springfield, IL
KSD81	Chicago, IL
KUR25-to-56	Honolulu, HI
KWX27-to-42	Anchorage, AK
WWR25-to-82	San Juan, PR

(Other VHF & HF calls believed to b
in use in addition to these.)

Some buzzwords, lingo, and slang used by agents:

A.I.C.	Agent in charge
A.R.O	Agent's regional office
Big Guy	Primary suspect
Big One	Major street
Big Ribbon	Major highway or Interstate
Bird Dog	Surveillance aircraft
Boat	Car
Box	Van
Break Off	Terminate surveillance
Bubble Machine	Voice scambler
Cave	Surveillance command post
Charlie	Clear (unscrambled) communications
C.I.	Case Informant; Confidential Informant
C.P.	Command post
The D	Aircraft departure time (ETD)
Diaper Change	Replacing batteries in portable equipment
Double L	Telephone call
E.C.C.	Mobile repeater
Eyeball	Visual surveillance
Eyes	Binoculars or infrared night vision scopes
Flicks	Surveillance videotape or other photographic material
Foxtrot Garage	Federal garage
Half Signal	Agent's spouse
Homefront	Agent's office
The I	An Interstate highway
In The Clear	Unscrambled voice comms
Kennel	Agent's office
A Leg	An agent on surveillance in the street
The Locals	Local law enforcement officers
A Louie	A left turn
Main Interest	Primary subject under surveillance
Mickey D's	McDonald's restaurant
Nest	Suspect's residence or office
Noisemaker	A "bumper beeper" surveillance transmitter for vehicle tailing
The O	Suspect's office
Our Boy	Primary person under surveillance
Our Friend	Primary person under surveillance
Our Guy	Primary person under surveillance
Our Interest	Primary person under surveillance
Our Main Interest	Primary person under surveillance
Outside Agency	The news media
Package	Subject in custody
Papa	Scrambled comms
Plank	A bridge
Port	A motel or hotel
Primary	Primary person under surveillance
The R	The suspect's home
R.A.	Resident Agent
Rabbit	Person under surveillance
Rabbit Making Tracks	Subject on the move
Redballed	Agent stopped at red light, subject still moving
The Rezz	The subject's residence

Signal ##	Reference to a particular agent
Soap Bubbles	Voice scrambler
Special	A tactical operation
S.W.	Search warrant
Subject	Primary person under surveillance
Tango Juliet ##	Highway exit number
Target	Primary person under surveillance
That Thing	A "bumper beeper" surveillance transmitter
U.C.	Undercover agent or operation
U-ie	A U-turn
Uniform	Route of travel straight ahead
Victor	Driving in the right lane
Walker	An agent on foot surveillance in the street
Walking The Dog	Subject or agent on foot
Wire	Hidden body transmitter or recorder
Wired	Wearing a hidden body transmitter or recorder

FBI 10-Codes seem to be the same as shown for DEA. Also make reference to "600" (Subject Vehicle) and to "601" (Subject Residence).

Justice, U.S. Dept. of Justice

Information is not available on which divisions of the Dept. of Justice utilize the following facilities, and some are apparently used to coordinate with other enforcement or invesigative services or agencies. Therefore, the following information applies to the Bureau of Prisons, the FBI, the DEA, the INS, the Border Patrol, and the U.S. Marshals Service.

Aircraft: Casa C-212= N104CA N119CA; Convair 580= N5804; Swearingen= N5805; Beech Queen 65= N2402C; Beech Queen 80= N2437A; Beech Mentor T-34= N771NS; Aerospatiale 350= N840BP N841BP N842BP N844BP; Hughes 369= N5062Q N5473X N5475A N6602M N6602N N8388F; Pitts S-1= N2912X N2920E N2923B N2923W N2927R N2928H N2941Q N9591C N29712; Cessna 210L= N8617X; Piper PA-18= N4349Z N4664Z N6590L N6609L N9047Y N54010 N82325 N83325 N91187 N91202 N91203 N91212 N91244

Stations:

CA	Vandenberg AFB, CA		137.075 138.165
DC	Washington	KFQ372	165.90
FL	National Parks		171.725 172.525
MD	Andrews AFB		163.4875
NM	Los Alamos		167.925
OH	Wright Patterson AFB		163.4875
OK	Tinker AFB		163.4875

TX	Ft. Bliss	172.825 173.4875 413.425
TX	Franklin Mtn.	170.025
VA	Quantico MCAF (FBI Academy)	149.37 184.00
US	All Areas	36.07 411.025

Labor, U.S. Department of

Keep in mind that this agency usually functions as a unit of Organized Crime Task Force operations on 165.925/167.6375. The agency has still been paid scant attention by monitors.

Stations believed to be operating:

Arizona

Phoenix		164.70 406.20

Arkansas

Little Rock	KCB691	162.225 164.70

California

Long Beach		406.20
Los Angeles	KIY879	172.30 406.20
Sacramento	KCB672	172.30
San Bernardino	KCB671	172.30
San Francisco		406.20/414.775 411.35 412.40
San Diego	KCB674	407.125 408.025
San Jose		408.025

Colorado

Denver		406.20

District of Columbia

Washington		162.90 163.75 408.475 409.125

Florida

Gainesville	KCB682	166.20
Jacksonville	KCB673	406.20 408.025
Miami		406.20
Tampa		406.20

Georgia

Atlanta		406.20
Brunswick	KCB676	408.025

Illinois

Chicago		406.20
Wilmington		409.025 415.45

Indiana

Edinburgh	KGU557	164.175 409.025

Kentucky

Morganfield	KFZ930	164.70
	KSQ962	162.225 164.175
Prestonburg	KCB690	164.70

Louisiana

New Orleans		406.20
Shreveport	KCB675	408.025 413.025

Massachusetts

Boston		406.20

Maine

Bangor	KCB684	162.225

Maryland

Baltimore		163.75
Port Deposit		173.75

Michigan

Detroit	KCB689	406.20 408.025
Gr Rapids		408.025

Mississippi

Crystal Sprgs	KIY879	164.175
Gulfport	KCB683	172.30

Missouri

Excelsior Sprgs	KCB686	165.6125 166.25
Kansas City		406.20
St. Louis	KCB685	406.20 408.025

Nevada

Las Vegas		406.20
Reno	KCB673	162.025 408.025

New Mexico

Albuquerque		408.025

New York

Bronx	KCB687	162.025
Buffalo		406.20
Calicoon	KCB677	406.225

Cassadaga	KCB670	406.225	**Texas**		
Liberty	KCB677	409.025	Dallas		406.20
NY City		406.20	McKinney	KRV677	163.00
North Carolina			San Marcos	KFU446	164.70
Kittrell	KCB680	164.70	**Utah**		
Ohio			Clearfield	KGY343	164.70
Cincinnati	KP8018	173.6125	**Washington**		
Cleveland		406.20	Meglr. Hill		162.225
Oregon			**West Virginia**		
Astoria		162.225 162.85	Triadelphia		168.35
Pennsylvania			**Puerto Rico**		
Philadelphia		406.20	San Juan		406.20
Tennessee			**All Areas**		
Knoxville		164.70	Portables		406.20

Land Management, Bureau of

Also refer to all information shown for Department of the Interior.

Frequencies reported: 36.01 41.27 41.55 46.63 46.81 46.99 49.73 49.77 49.91
123.5875 163.025 163.05 163.085 168.375 163.125 163.15 163.175 163.75 163.8375
163.8625 163.9125 164.10 164.20 164.525 164.55 164.725 164.775 165.975 166.00 166.20
166.225 166.325 166.35 166.375/166.975 166.4875/167.075 166.6125 166.75/168.30
166.775 166.80 166.85 166.875 166.90/166.30 166.925/166.325 166.95/166.35
166.975/166.375 167.00 167.025 167.075 167.10/169.75 167.15 167.825 167.90 167.95
168.25 168.225 168.275 168.30 168.30 168.35 168.375 168.40/166.125 168.425 168.475
168.50 168.525 168.55 168.575 168.85 169.00 169.025 169.075 169.175 169.225 169.325
169.35 169.40/168.375 169.40/168.525 169.55 169.575 169.65 169.775/168.55 169.875
170.025 171.725 171.775 172.60 172.775 406.275 408.425 408.525 408.575 408.625
408.775 411.625/408.425 411.675 411.75/417.30 411.825 411.875 411.925/417.35 412.025
412.05 412.10 412.125 412.15/417.50 412.20/417.80 412.225 412.25/417.85 412.275
412.375/408.525 414.575 414.825 414,875 414.925 414.975 415.025/408.425
415.075/408.625 415.15/408.775 416.075 416.125 417.225 417.275/408.575 417.35
417.375/408.475 417.45 417.525 417.625 417.725 417.80 417.825 417.85/412.25 417.875
417.925 417.975 418.325 419.00 419.125 419.15 419.625 419.65 419.675/408.575 419.775
419.825 419.85 419.875/412.225 419.925 419.975

Federal Law Enforcement Training Center (FLETC)

Loccation: Brunswick NAS, GA   Callsign: KAE356
Security: 170.975
Maintenance: 170.10
Tactical Frequencies: TAC-1 415.30;   TAC-2 417.20;   TAC-3 419.175
Surveillance Repeater: 172.20
Driver Training: 169.55 169.60 170.00 170.325 170.425 170.60 173.025 173.075
  173.125
Criminal Investigator Training: F-1 173.125;   F-2 171.50;   F-3 171.50;
        F-4 173.875;   F-5 170.825
Other Frequencies: 170.825 170.925 172.30 173.125 173.175 173.7375 173.7875

Maritime Administration, Federal

Frequencies: 166.15/169.075 165.5875
  Base Stations: New York, NY;   Beaumont, TX (KAM575);   New Orleans, LA;
Miami, FL;   Washington, DC;   San Francisco, CA;   San Pedro, CA;   Hato Rey, PR;
Chicago, IL
  Mobiles/Ships: Call letters KF7620

Marshal Service, U.S.

U.S. Marshals serve federal warrants, arrest those sought under federal warrants, transport federal prisoners to/from and between federal courts and correctional facilities. The fleet of aircraft used by the agency to transport federal prisoner is known by its unwilling passengers as the world's most exclusive private airline. The Marshal's service also operates the federal witness program.

Since the federal witness protection program began in 1969, well over 5,000 witnesses have entered the program. There are presently 600+ witnesses in the program. More than 30 witnesses have been murdered after voluntarily leaving the program. In each case, the released witness apparently failed to follow security guidelines outlined to them by the government.

Aircraft roster: Beech King 90= N12AB; Beech Queen 80= N5583V; Learjet 24= N100RA; Rockwell 680W= N11CT; Mitsubishi MU-2B= N115J; Beech Bonanza 33= N535T; Boeing C-97= N1175K; Boeing 727= N2777; Douglas DC-6= N7041U; Rockwell Sabre 75A= N127MS N128MS N129MS N131MS N132MS N223LP (Also refer to information under Department of Justice listings.)

Marshal's Service Frequencies: (CTCSS 127.3 Hz)
162.7875/170.85	City Repeaters
163.20/163.8125	Administrative & Operational Repeaters
164.60/163.8125	Border Area Repeaters

Simplex: 162.7875 163.20 164.60

Federal Courts: (CTCSS 203.5 Hz)
162.7125/170.85	Operational Repeaters

Simplex: 170.75 170.85

Stations are located in all areas, but only the following callsigns are known:

Callsign	Location	Callsign	Location
KFQ384	Cleveland, OH	KRD249	San Francisco, CA
KFQ386	Phoenix, AZ	KRD617	Pittsburgh, PA
KLP207	Bridgeport, CT	KRD667	Erie, PA
KOW694	Seattle, WA	KRD671	Cincinnati/Dayton, OH
KRD217	Chicago, IL	KRD675	Philadelphia, PA
KRD221	Indianapolis, IN	KRD676	Scranton, PA ("Base 212")
KRD225	Louisville, KY	KRD684	Dallas/Ft Worth, TX
KRD232	Detroit, MI	KRD686	Houston, TX
KRD245	Rome, NY	KRD696	Charleston, WV
KRD247	New York, NY		

Mint, Bureau of The

Reported to be operating on 150.11 171.3875 172.275 407.925 411.675 415.00 419.65, presumably at Denver, CO; Philadephia, PA; San Francisco, CA; & West Point, NY.

Navy, U.S. (USN) & Marine Corps, US (USMC)

Popularly reported frequencies:
USN MARS: 40.10 138.90 142.155 143.46 148.075 148.375 148.41 148.95 148.975 149.05 150.09 150.125 150.375 150.39 150.40
Naval Investigative Svc,: 138.65 139.525 140.025 140.075 140.65 140.775 162.375
Base Security: 140.575 140.82 148.83
Recruiting: 148.40
NAS Crash Trucks: 140.10 140.22
Pacific Missile Range vessels: 32.45
USN/USMC Air Traffic Control: 41.95 126.2 340.2 360.2
Blue Angels Team: 121.9 123.4 134.1 141.56 142.00 142.025/142.625 143.00 143.60 241.4 250.8 251.6 275.35 307.7 360.4 384.4 391.9 395.9
Air/Ground HF:
    All areas: 3050 3109 4014 4711 6723 9032 9037 11190 11255 kHz
    Atlantic/Caribbean: 6697 7535 8972 11267 15522 23287 kHz
    Pacific: 4040 4416 4813.5 8778 12761 13181 18009 kHz
    Indian Ocean: 12215 23315
    USMC: 5446 kHz
    Also see listings under US Air Force for Global HF System.
Ports/Harbors: 385.0 (HF 2150 2434 2716 2838 kHz)
Fleet Common Aero: 277.8
Air-to-Air: 300.6 385.25
Ships, Aircraft & Shore Facilities All Areas: 138.575 138.58 138.62 140.28 141.55 148.975 163.75 165.25 165.625 166.375 167.50 167.875 170.125 168.25 170.125 171.25 171.625 225.0 235.0 240.6 251.6 264.2 270.6 275.1 275.35 277.0 285.0 289.8 301.0 306.35 307.85 307.95 309.25 309.35 310.75 310.85 320.2 345.8 355.0 357.9 358.9 359.4 380.55 387.4
Ships, Aircraft & Shore Facilities Atlantic/Caribbean: 140.10 140.22 150.39 162.25 163.375 164.125 164.50 166.75 170.50 172.375 173.125 177.00 244.3 246.3 246.8 248.6 250.7 252.4 255.2 256.7 292.95 294.75 296.35 296.45 297.95 298.05 299.55 306.35 306.45 307.4 393.85

Ships, Aircraft & Shore Facilities Pacific: 138.725 140.025 140.15 140.225 140.55 141.00 163.00 164.50 169.00 169.375 173.50 236.4 253.2 277.7 280.2 293.15 294.85 296.35 296.55 297.95 298.15 299.45 299.65 306.35 306.55 308.05 309.45

Satellite Downlink reported (NFM mode): 257.55; (NFM mode): 250.45 250.55 251.95 to 269.95 band

North American Aerospace Defense Command (NORAD)

National HQ: Space Defense Operations Center (SPADOC), Cheyenne Mountain, Colorado Springs, CO

Air Intercept Control Channel (AICC), All Stations (NORAD CP): 364.2

Reported Air/Ground & Air/Air OP in the various NORAD Sectors-- other frequencies are also in use:

24th Air Division: Northeast Air Defense Sector, Griffiss AFB, NY; Callsign: Huntress; also Tyndall AFB, FL, **Southeast Air Defense Sector.**
Frequencies reported: 128.975 228.7 233.5 233.6 235.8 238.7 239.2 239.4 251.8 252.0 254.8 258.0 265.4 270.1 273.4 278.4 282.5 283.8 288.0 282.8 303.9 312.8 316.2 318.4 326.4 338.1 338.8 342.1 346.9 347.4 351.6 357.2 371.8 376.2 382.0 389.2 394.8 399.0

22nd NR: Regional Control Center, North Bay. Ontario, Canada
Frequencies reported: 123.55 126.7 228.9 251.0 256.6 263.6 270.4 274.4

23rd Air Division: Northwest Air Defense Sector, McChord AFB, WA
Frequencies reported: 228.6 235.8 235.9 238.2 238.6 238.7 239.1 239.7 240.0 252.0 260.9 261.4 265.4 271.0 276.4 277.6 278.4 279.4 282.6 287.7 288.4 293.6 293.8 328.0 348.2 351.5 355.2 359.8 374.0 374.2 386.0 390.2 394.2 394.4 397.8

26th Air Division: Southwest Air Defense Sector, March AFB, CA;
Frequencies reported: 228.6 228.9 234.6 235.9 238.4 238.6 239.7 254.2 260.8 260.9 261.4 267.0 271.0 272.0 273.4 274.4 282.6 278.4 278.7 287.7 288.4 293.6 293.8 299.0 309.4 316.3 320.6 324.0 327.9 336.6 341.8 346.2 346.9 348.2 351.5 355.2 359.4 359.8 374.0 377.0 386.0 387.8 390.2 397.8 398.0

Alaskan NR: Elmendorf AFB, Anchorage, AK; Callsign: Top Rocc
Frequencies reported (DEW Line): 236.6 288.4 359.9 (HF 5295 kHz)

Hawaiian NR: Wheeler AFS, HI; Callsign: Golden Monarch

UHF ground transmitting facilities are located at various remote sites distant from the Regional Control Centers.

NORAD HF OP: 4827 5297 6708 9023 9793 11441 14894 20885 kHz

Callsigns containing the words "Bandsaw" and "Dragnet" (such as Bandsaw Juliet, Dragnet Tango, etc.) are E-3A AWACS electronic surveillance aircraft.

Nuclear Emergency Search Team (NEST)

HQ: Las Vegas, NV
Stations: KCl785 169.60; KCl798 167.95; KEL223 172.30; KFP881 167.85;
KGF260 172.30; KGI304 410.80; KIJ551 164.775; KOG821 164.10; KOG222 164.225
166.225; KOK222 167.825; KOK225 164.025; KOK229 150.45; callsigns not known
on 149.22 163.00 164.2375 169.675

Nuclear Regulatory Commission (NRC)

In addition to frequencies indicated here, the NRC is believed to have the
capability to operate on frequencies of the Department of Energy at that agency's
facilities. During the Three Mile Island nuclear emergency, NRC ops were monitored
on frequencies assigned for Interagency National Emergency Fire Cache (INEFC)
use. In the event of any similar problem in the future, INEFC frequencies would
almost certainly be used during the critical stages.

HF Frequencies: Daytime calling/emergency is 10494.5 kHz; Night
calling/emergency frequency is 5212.5 kHz. Backup is 17650 kHz. Frequency
20028.5 kHz is common to all NRC facilities. Other HF frequencies include 2378.5
2446.5 2659.5 3342.5 3380.5 3389.5 5692.5 6050 6107.5 6152.5 6177.5 7349.5 11722.5
11802.5 11958.5 12217.5 14477.5 14837.5 14886 14900.5 14909.5 17650.5 kHz.

INEFC Frequencies:
    Air Tactical 166.675 169.15 169,20
    Command 168.70/170.975 168.10/170.45 168.075/170.425
    Logistics 414.65 415.40
    Tactical 168.05 168.20 168.60
Stations reported:

Arlington, MD	KYE281	167.875 168.45 411.20 416.40
Bethesda, MD	KYE280	167.875
	KYE281	164.275
Ft. Meade, MD		411.075
Harrisburg, PA (TMI)		162.80 168.05 168.60 168.225 170.00
Shoreham, NY		167.875
Washington, DC	KYE280	167.875
Handhelds (all areas)	KK7785	27.575 27.585 169.10 172.75

Office of The Administration (OA)

Washington, DC   162.275

U.S. DEPARTMENT OF COMMERCE
National Oceanic and Atmospheric Administration

National Oceanic & Atmospheric Administration (NOAA)

In addition to facilities & information listed elsewhere in this Registry:

Weather Broadcasts Ch #1 162.55; Ch #2 162.40; Ch #3 162.475; Ch #4 162.475; Ch #5 162.45; Ch #6 162.50; Ch #7 162.525

In most instances, transmitters are connected to control points by landlines. In some areas, however, the transmitters are at isolated locations where the only practical means of feeding them their programming is by microwave, VHF, or UHF. In such installations, VHF and UHF control links and relays are usually established on frequencies from within the following group: 173.025 410.075 410.10 410.575 415.90 416.35 416.375 MHz.

NOAA HF backup communications networks: 2776 3363 5925 6977.5 9947.5 14792 kHz

NOAA VHF aircraft frequencies: 122.9 122.925 123.05 123.075

NOAA Hurricane Hunters: 304.8 (HF "Miami Monitor" 3407 4428 5562 6673 6824 8876 8918 8993 10015 11176 11246 11296 11398 13267 13354 13354 14325 17901 18019 21937 kHz; 13354 is primary day freq; 6673 primary night

NOAA aircraft roster: DeHavilland DHC-5= N13689; DeHavilland DHC-6= N48RF; Rockwell 500S= N51RF N67RF; Rockwell 690A= N53RF; Lockheed 3D= N42RF; Hughes 369= N59RF; Bell 212= N60RF; Beech King 90= N46RF; Cessna 50= N52RF; Schweizer SGS-2= N9929J

NOAA ships: 34.98 36.22 38.22 41.71 157.075 157.125 164.025 164.075 170.20 171.80 172.025 (Also operate on standard HF maritime frequencies.)

NOAA ship roster (general call to all NOAA ships: WGCS)
KJLM   Murre II (S-663), National Marine Fisheries Service
KNBD   Delaware II (R-445), National Ocean Survey
WTDF   Townsend Cromwell (R-443) National Marine Fisheries (also WQ4000) (WZ2593 WZ2594, mobiles KD7994 KD7995)
WTDK   David S. Jordan (R-444), National Marine Fisheries Service
WTDM   Miller Freeman (R-223), National Ocean Survey
WTDO   Oregon II (R-332), National Ocean Survey
WTEA   Discoverer (R-102), National Ocean Survey (WZ2608 WZ2609 WZ2611 WZ2612 WZ2613 WZ2614 WZ2615 WZ2616 WZ2617 WZ2618 WZ2619)
WTEB   Fairweather (S-220), National Ocean Survey (WZ2521 WZ2522 WZ2523 WZ2524 WZ2525 WZ2526 WZ2527 WZ2528 WZ2529 WZ2643 WZ2644 WZ2645 WZ2646 WZ2647 WZ2648 WZ2649)
WTED   Chapman (R-446), National Ocean Survey
WTEF   Rainier (S-221), National Ocean Survey (WZ2516 WZ2517 WZ2555 WZ2556 WZ2557 WZ2571 WZ2575 WZ2576 WZ2577)
WTEG   Mt. Mitchell (S-222), National Ocean Survey (WZ3015 WZ3016 WZ3017 WZ3018 WZ3019 WZ3020 WZ3021 WZ3022 WZ3033 WZ3034 WZ3035 WZ3036 WZ3037 WZ3038 WZ3039)

WTEJ   McArthur (S330), National Ocean Survey   (WZ3030 WZ3031 WZ3032 WZ3033
        WZ3034 WZ3035 WZ3036 WZ3037 WZ3038)
WTEK   Davidson (S-331), National Ocean Survey (WZ3039 WZ3040 WZ3041 WZ3042
        WZ3043 WZ3044 WZ3044 WZ3045 WZ3046 WZ3047 WZ3048 WZ3049)
WTEP   Oceanographer (R-101), National Ocean Survey (WZ2633 WZ2634 WZ2635
        WZ2636 WZ2637 WZ2638 WZ2639 WZ2640 WZ2641 WZ2642)
WTEQ   Pierce (S-221), National Ocean Survey (WZ2598 WZ2599 WZ2600 WZ2601
        WZ2602)
WTER   Researcher (R-103), National Ocean Survey (WZ2540 WZ2541 WZ2542 WZ2543
        WZ2544 WZ2545 WZ2546 WZ2547 WZ2548 WZ2549)
WTES   Surveyor (S-132), National Ocean Survey (WZ2560 WZ2561 WZ2562 WZ2563
        WZ2564 WZ2565 WZ2566 WZ2567 WZ2568 WZ2569)
WTET   Rude (S-590). National Ocean Survey (WZ2625 WZ2626 WZ2627)
WTEW   Whiting (S-329), National Ocean Survey (WZ2603 WZ2607)
WTEY   Heck (S-591), National Ocean Survey (WZ2620 WZ2621 WZ2622)
WTEZ   Ferrel (S-492) National Ocean Survey (WZ2628 WZ2629 WZ2630)
WA9337 Polaris
WZ2101 George Callio
WZ2102 Watres
WZ2103 Don J. Miller
WZ2109 unnamed craft, Los Angeles, CA area
WZ2513-16   unnamed craft, Boston, MA area
WZ2517-19   unnamed craft, New York, NY area
WZ2520   unnamed craft, Valdez, AK area
WZ2531-34   unnamed craft, photogrammetry operations
WZ2535-37   unnamed craft, Field Unit #742
WZ2538-39   unnamed craft, New Orleans, LA area
WZ2550-52   unnamed craft, Los Angeles, CA area
WZ2553-59   unnamed craft, San Francisco, CA area
WZ2629   Sea Hawk
WZ3050-50   unnamed craft, Atlantic Marine Center
WZ3060-70   unnamed craft, Pacific Marine Center
WZ3392   unnamed craft, Fisher Island, FL area

Other calls with KA, KD, KE, & KF prefixes followed by 4 numerals are mobile
units and handhelds.

National Park Service (NPS)

All information shown for Department of the Interior applies to NPS.

Enforcement activities within the 79-million acres under the supervision of the
NPS includes the use of miniature transmitters, vehicle tracking devices, hidden
sensors, satellites, and even scanner receivers.

Aircraft: Bell 206L= N33PP

Common repeater pairs (out/in): 163.15/162.6125 164.175/164.725 164.475/165.4375
164.575/? 164.725/166.275 164.725/169.15 164.75/164.25 164.80/164.10 166.075/168.30
166.30/166.90   166.325/166.925   166.35/166.95   166.375/166.975   166.725/166.975
166.7875/166.30   166.90/166.30   166.925/165.925   166.925/166.075   166.95/166.35
166.95/168.325   166.975/166.375   167.075/168.30   167.15/166.35   167.175/166.375

168.325/167.075   168.425/169.125   168.425/169.40   168.475/169.175   168.50/166.80
168.55/167.95   168.575/169.55   169.55/168.575   169.65/169.15   169.675/170.35
169.775/168.30   169.925/170.525   170.05/169.40   170.05/169.55   170.075/169.725
170.10/169.55   171.2625/172.525   171.625/172.40   171.625/172.475   171/675/172.425
171.675/172.675   171.725/172.525   171.75/172.625   171.75/172.75   171.775/172.45
171.775/172.475   172.40/171.70   172.425/171.625   172.425/171.725   172.45/171.75
172.475/171.675   172.525/171.65   172.525/171.725   172.575/171.675   172.65/171.625
172.675/171.675   411.625/409.55   411.70/417.925   411.725/409.65   411.825/409.75
411.925/409.85 415.15/408.55 419.825/414.825

National Parks

Acadia, ME	164.175/164.725
Arches, UT	166.325/166.925
Badlands, SD	170.05/169.40 170.10
Big Bend, TX	162.975 173.725 166.375/166.975
Biscayne, FL	171.675/172.675
Bryce Canyon, UT	168.575/169.55
Canyonlands, UT	166.325/166.925
Capitol Reef, UT	168.575/169.55
Carlsbad Caverns, NM	164.425 164.9875 (FM: 52.5 73.5 94.5 115.5 **kHz**)
Channel Islands, CA	171.675 172.40/171.70
Denali, AK	166.30 166.35 166.90 411.825 417.825
Everglades, FL	171.725/172.525 172.45
Glacier, MT	39.82 163.075 164.375 166.375/166.975 167.025 170.025 170.10 408.425 414.925
Glacier Bay, AK	166.95
Grand Canyon, AZ	41.77 171.75/172.45 172.425
Grand Teton, WY	171.675/172.425
Grt. Smokey Mtns/. NC/TN	167.15/166.35 415.125/408.725
Guadalupe Mtns., TX	164.625
Haleakla, HI	169.55 170.10 411.625/409.55
Hawaii Volcanoes, HI	168.425/169.40 168.55/167.95
Hot Springs, AR	166.325/166.925
Isle Royale, MI	168.525 169.675/170.35
Katmai, AK	164.425 164.9875
Kings Canyon, CA	164.75/164.25 165.1625 166.875 168.35 171.75/172.45 172.50 173.7875 417.975
Lassen Volcanic, CA	169.725 170.075
Mammoth Cave, KY	169.55/170.10
Mesa Verde, CO	170.05/169.40
Mt. Rainier, WA	163.075 163.2375 163.39 164.475 164.9875 166.875 167.125 167.15 171.775/172.45 172.625 406.25
No. Cascades, WA	164.9875 166.75 408.725
Olympic, WA	164.9875 168.525 169.55 406.25 411.625/409.55 419.625
Petrified Forest, AZ	170.05/169.40
Redwood, CA	164.425 165.1625 165.3125 166.35 166.95 408.625 417.725 417.975
Rocky Mtn., CO	166.35 166.95 408.625 411.825/409.75 417.825
Sequoia, CA	164.75/164.25 165.1625 166.875 171.75/172.45 172.50 173.7875 417.975
Shenandoah, VA	166.30 166.60 166.90 411.85
Theo. Roosevelt, ND	166.375/166.975 170.60/170.025
Virgin Islands, VI	171.725 172.625

Voyaguers, MN	166.30 166.90 411.625/409.55 417.725
Wind Cave, SD	170.05
Yellowstone, MT/ID/WY	152.42 164.80 166.375/166.975 167.15 411.675 411.775
	417.375 417.475 417.575 463.45
Yosemite, CA	168.30 171.65 171.775 171.80 172.025 172.65 172.675
	172.775
Zion, UT	166.325/166.925

National Historical Parks

Appomatox Ct. Hse., VA	166.35 166.95
Boston, MA	166.35 166.95
Chalmette, LA	163.15 168.375 169.675
C & O Canal, DC/MD/WV	166.95/166.35 168.30 168.425/169.175 409.05 417.975
Colonial, VA	167.15 168.425/169.125 170.05/169.40
Cumberland Gap, KY/TN/VA	166.30 166.90 166.7875/166.30
Harpers Ferry, MD/WV	168.425/169.175
Independence, PA	163.15 164.425 164.475 164.725 166.7875/166.30 168.25
	168.25 168.45 172.40
Jean LaFitte, LA	163.15 169.675/168.375
Klondike Gold Rush, AK	166.95
Lowell, MA	166.95
Lyndon B. Johnson, TX	170.075 411.625/409.55
Minute Man, MA	164.425
Morristown, NJ	164.475 165.4375
San Antonio Missions, TX	172.40/171.70
Valley Forge, PA	164.475 165.4375

National Battlefields

Antietam, VA	166.35 166.95
Cowpens, SC	171.775/172.475
Ft. Necessity, PA	171.65 172.40
Monocacy, MD	166.35 166.95 417.975
Petersburg, VA	163.125
Stones River, TN	172.775
Tupelo, MS	171.675 172.675
Wilson's Creek, MO	173.7625

National Battlefield Parks

Kennesaw Mtn., GA	166.30 166.90 171.775/172.475
Manassas, VA	163.125
Richmond, VA	166.35 166.95 168.325/167.075

National Military Parks

Chickamuga/Chattanooga, GA/TN	168.325/167.075
Ft. Donelson, TN	167.15/166.35
Fredericksburg/Spotsylvania Co., VA	166.35 166.95
Gettysburg, PA	164.725/166.275
Guilford CH, NC	164.625
Horseshoe Bend, AL	171.75/172.45
Kings Mtn., SC	171.775/172.475
Pea Ridge, AR	168.325/167.075
Shiloh, TN	164.425
Vicksburg, MS	166.30 166.90

National Memorials

Arkansas Post, AR	166.325/166.925
Arlington House, VA	171.675 172.75 414.825/408.425
Chamizal, TX	166.425

Coronado, AZ	171.725/172.525
DeSoto, FL	171.775
Ft. Caroline, FL	170.05
JFK Center, DC	409.05 411.825/409.75
Johnstown Flood, PA	171.675 172.40
Lincoln Boyhood, IN	168.35
Mt. Rushmore, SD	170.05
Theo. Roosevelt I., DC	171.675 172.75 414.825/408.425
Wright Brothers, NC	164.20 164.725 169.65

National Historic Sites

Allegheny Portage RR, PA	171.65 172.40
Andersonville, GA	408.475
Bent's Old Fort, CO	166.35 166.95
Carl Sandburg Home, NC	171.775
Chimney Rock, NE	32.73
Christiansted, VI	171.725 172.675
Edison, NJ	164.475/165.4375
Eisenhower, PA	164.725/166.275
Eleanor Roosevelt, NY	166.35 166.95
Ft. Davis, TX	166.425
Ft. Laramie, WY	173.7625
Ft. Raleigh, NC	164.20 164.725 169.65
Ft. Smith, AR	164.75/164.25
Ft. Union Trading Post, ND	166.375/166.975
Ft. Vancouver, WA	41.13 408.575
Friendship Hill, PA	172.40/171.70
Golden Spike, UT	171.675
Grant-Kohrs Ranch, MT	168.35
Herbert Hoover, IA	169.65/169.15
Home of FDR, NY	166.35 166.95
Hopewell Vlg., PA	171.675 172.40
Jefferson Nat'l. Expansion, MO	171.625 172.475
Knife River Ind. Vlgs., ND	166.375/166.975
Martin VanBuren, NY	166.35 166.95
Saint-Gaudens, NH	173.7625
San Jose Mission, TX	172.40/171.70
Vanderbilt Mansion, NY	166.35 166.95

National Monuments

Agate Fossil Beds, NE	32.73
Alibates Flint, NM/TX	166.30 166.90 411.825/409.75
Bandelier, NM	164.425 165.4125
Black Canyon of the Gunnison, CO	166.35 166.95 419.625
Booker T. Washington, VA	166.35 166.95
Buck I. Reef, VI	171.725 172.625
Cabrillo, CA	171.75/172.45
Canyon de Chelly, AZ	166.35 166.95
Capulin Mountain, NM	164.425 165.4125
Castillo de San Marcos, FL	170.05
Cedar Breaks, UT	166.325/166.925
Chiricahua, UT	171.725/172.525
Colorado. CO	166.30 166.90
Craters of The Moon, ID	171.675
Custer Battlefield, MT	36.18 167.15/166.35
Death Valley, CA/NV	169.55/170.10

Devils Tower, WY	170.05/169.40
Dinosaur, CO/UT	166.375/166.975 167.075
Effigy Mounds, IA	169.65/169.15
El Morro, NM	166.35 166.95 168.525 169.40
Florissant Fossil Beds, CO	167.025
Ft. Jefferson, FL	167.625 171.725
Ft. Matanzas, FL	170.05
Ft. McHenry, MD	166.35 166.95
Ft. Pulaski, GA	164.80/164.10
Ft. Sumter, SC	170.05
Fossil Butte, WY	171.675
G. Washington BP, VA	163.125
G. Washington Carver, MO	168.35
Gran Quivira, NM	164.425
Grand Portage, MN	166.325/166.925
Gt. Sand Dunes, CO	166.35 166.95 173.7625
Homestead, CO/UT	169.65/169.15
Hovensweep, CO/UT	170.05/169.40
Iwo Jima, DC	38.00
Jewel Cave, SD	170.05
John Day Fossil Beds, OR	164.475 164.9875
Joshua Tree, CA	171.675/172.675
Lava Beds, CA	171.675 171.75 172.45 172.675
Lehman Caves, NV	163.15/162.6125
Montezuma Castle, AZ	168.35
Mount St. Helens, WA	172.225
Muir Woods, CA	164.80/164.10
Natural Bridges, UT	166.325/166.925
Navajo, AZ	166.35 166.95 172.575/171.675
Ocmulgee, GA	171.775
Oregon Caves, OR	164.425
Organ Pipe Cactus, AZ	164.425
Pinnacles, CA	170.05/169.40
Pipe Spring, AZ	166.325/166.925
Rainbow Bridge, UT	171.625/172.40 172.475
Saguaro, AZ	166.35 166.95 167.15
St. Croix I., ME	164.175/164.725
Scotts Bluff, NE	32.73
Statue of Liberty, NY/NJ	34.79 417.85 417.925
Ellis Island, NY/NJ	34.79 414.825/408.425 414.925/408.525 417.85 417.925
Sunset Crater, AZ	166.35 166.95
Timpanogos Cave, UT	166.15
Walnut Canyon, AZ	166.30 166.90
White Sands, NM	166.6375
Wupatki, AZ	166.35 166.95
Yucca House, CO	170.05/169.40

National Preserves

Big Cypress, FL	172.425/171.625 172.745
Big Thickett, TX	166.30 166.90 417.225 417.725
Denali, AK	166.30 166.35 166.90 166.95 411.825/409.75 417.825

National Seashores

Assateague Isl., MD/VA	166.30 166.35 166.375/166.975 166.90 167.15/166.35 167.275/166.375 167.275 411.70/417.925
Canaveral, FL	164.75/164.25

Cape Cod, MA   171.725/172.575   FD 33.70
Cape Hatteras, NC   162.40 164.725 169.65
Cape Lookout, NC   169.65/169.15
Cumberland I., GA   171.725/172.525 411.825/409.75
Fire Island, NY   166.90/166.30
Gulf Isls., FL   171,725/172.525
Padre I., TX   164.10 166.30 166.90
Point Reyes, CA   170.05/169.40
National Parkways
Blue Ridge, NC/VA   166.30 166.375 166.90 166.975 167.15/166.35
                                       167.175 171.675 411.70/417.925
J.D. Rockefeller, WY   166.375/166.975 167.075 171.675 172.425
Natchez Trace, AL/MS/TN   171.675/172.675 171.775 411.85
National Lakeshores
Apostle I., WI   164.175/164.80
Indiana Dunes, IN   166.275 166.975
Pictured Rocks, MI   166.30 166.90
Sleeping Bear Dunes, MI   166.375/166.975
National Rivers
Big So, Fork, KY/TN   163.075 166.75 168.375
Buffalo, AR   164.25 164.475 164.75
New River Gorge, WV   166.35 166.95
National Scenic Rivers & Riverways
Delaware, NY/NJ/PA   164.575 166.35 166.775 166.95 168.55/167.95
Lwr. St. Croix, MN/WI   164.75/164.25 711.725/409.65 411.825/409.75
Ozark, MO   171.625/172.475 411.625/409.55 411.65 411.70/417.925
                                       417.775 411.825/408.425 414.925/498.525
St. Croix, MN/WI   164.75/164.25   408.675   411.725/409.65   411.825/409.75
Upper Delaware, NY/NJ   164.575 168.55/167.95
Parks
Cacotin Mtn., MD   171.725/172/525
Ft. Benton, MT   166.35 166.95 173.7625
Greenbelt, MD   165.925
Perry's Victory, OH   170.10/169.55
Pr. Wm. Forest, VA   168.425 168.475/169.175
Rock Creek, DC   171.675 172.475
Wash. DC area (incl memorials, parks, parkways, etc.) 150.425 164.325 165.925
                                       165.975 166.325 166.375 166.725 166.775 166.85
                                       166.925 166.975 167.075 167.175 168.30 168.425
                                       172.475 172.75 406.475 409.55 409.65 409.75 409.85
                                       411.625 411.725 411.825 417.975
Nat'l. Visitors' Cntr, DC   411.925 416.125 417.725
National Recreation Areas
Arapaho, CO   166.35 166.95
Bighorn Canyon, MT/WY   166.30 166.325/166.925 166.90
Chattahoochee River, GA   166.30 166.90
Chickasaw, OK   168.425/169.40
Coulee Dam, WA   166.375/166.975 414.825/419.825 415.125/408.725
Curecanti, CO   166.30 166.90 419.625
Cuyahoga Vly, OH   39.84 39.86 166.375/166.975
Delaware Water Gap, NJ/PA   164.575 166.775 166.90 166.95/166.35 168.55/167.95
                                       412.125 417.725 417.975
Gateway, NY/NJ   34.79 166.325/166.925 166.775 166.925 167.075 167.95
                                       168.55 417.25 417.825 417.975

Gavley River, WV	166.35 166.95
Glen Canyon, AZ/UT	171.65 172.475 172.625/172.40
Golden Gate, CA	163.15/162.6125 164.00 164.80/164.10 164.525 412.35
	416.025 417.575 417.725 417.975
Lake Chelan, WA	165.975 166.75 419.825/414.825
Lake Mead, AZ/NV	166.30 166.90 168.35 411.70/417.925 412.025 417.375
	417.625
Lake Meredith, TX	166.30 166.90 411.825
Mt. Rogers, VA	166.375 166.975 167.175
Ross Lake, WA	164.9875 408.725
Santa Monica Mtns., CA	171.725 172.525 172.575
Whiskeytown, CA	164.425 165.3125 170.075

All Areas

Park transportation	40.07 40.21
Portable base	408.675

Postal Service, U.S. (USPS)

Postal Inspectors & Security (nationwide): (CTCSS 91.5 Hz) 169.00 169.375 169.60
169.65 169.85 413.60/414.825 414.75/407.775 415.05/407.725 416.075 416.225 418.30

Alaska
Anchorage	162.225

Alabama
Mobile	164.70

Arizona
Phoenix	163.7875 410.20
Tucson	163.375 168.00

California
Flint Peak	164.9875
Los Angeles	162.225 163.375 164.9625 170.125 410.325 410.35
	414.725 416.775 418.30
Oakland	164.175 170.125 173.6125 418.10
Pasadena	163.375 406.225 410.20
Richmond	164.175 164.9875 173.7125 173.7375
Sacramento	164.9875 410.20 418.10
San Bernardino	410.325
San Bruno	163.125 409.275 409.45
San Diego	164.9875
San Francisco	38.33 164.9625 169.375 170.125 407.725 407.775 408.05
	409.275 409.45 413.60 414.75 416.775 418.10
San Jose	164.9625

Colorado
Colo. Springs	162.225
Denver	162.225 164.175 168.00 171.2625 172.30

Connecticut
Hartford	164.9625 415.05
Waterbury	164.9625

District of Columbia
Dulles	163.375
Washington	163.00 163.375

Florida
Jacksonville	164.50 409.10 409.525 409.90 410.20
Miami	162.225 164.50 164.9125 166.225 407.725 407.775 414.75
St. Petersburg	162.225
Tampa	162.225 406.375 410.20
W. Palm Beach	164.50

Georgia
Atlanta	162.225 163.00 163.375 164.175 164.20 164.70 168.525 409.275 410.20 410.325

Iowa
Davenport	410.325
Des Moines	164.20 164.50 164.70 406.375 410.20

Illinois
Chicago	27.275 162.225 163.375 164.9625 164.9875 166.225 170.125 408.025 410.00 410.10 410.20 410.325 414.75 416.975
Des Plaines	406.325
Forest Park	171.625 172.30

Indiana
Indianapolis	171.3875 412.20

Kansas
Kansas City	163.00

Kentucky
Covington	164.9625
Lexington	419.125
Louisville	164.9875

Louisiana
New Orleans	164.175 169.00 410.325

Massachusetts
Boston	164.9875 166.20 166.375 168.225 169.1125 170.10 170.125 416.30
Springfield	162.225 166.20 170.125 171.2625 172.30

Maryland
Baltimore	162.225 169.00 172.30
Bethesda	168.525
Largo	164.50 166.220 167.125 172.30
Rockville	173.373 417.65

Maine
Portland	166.20

Michigan
Allen Park	409.10 409.525 409.90
Detroit	164.9625 171.2625

Minnesota
Duluth	416.975
Minneapolis	163.00 163.375 164.10 164.175 164.20 164.9875 166.225

St. Paul	163.00 163.375 164.10 164.175 164.20
Missouri	
Kansas City	164.70 164.9875 169.60
St. Louis	164.70 166.225 169.60 171.2625 406.375 410.20
North Carolina	
Charlotte	163.375 171.2625
Greensboro	162.225 166.225 171.2625 171.3875
Nebraska	
Omaha	164.70 169.00 406.325
New Jersey	
Bellmawr	172.30
Jersey City	167.125 168.325
Kearney	162.225 164.20 164.9625
Newark	172.30
Secaucus	164.9875 170.125 170.775 171.175 171.2625 172.30
New York	
Albany	410.20
Bronx	173.6125
Buffalo	410.325
Hicksville	169.60 173.6375
Jamaica/JFK	173.6125 408.00 408.675 409.025 409.275 409.825 410.20 410.325
Long Island City	169.1125 173.6875 414.75
Menands	172.30
NY City	163.375 166.375 406.325 409.275 410.325 416.225
Smithtown	169.1125
Ohio	
Cincinnati	162.225 163.375 164.9625 171.2625 171.3875
Cleveland	27.275 162.225 164.9125 169.00 173.7375
Columbus	164.20
Dayton	164.9875
Lima	27.575 27.585
Oklahoma	
Norman	406.375 410.20
Oklahoma City	410.20
Tulsa	162.225
Oregon	
Portland	164.70 168.50
Pennsylvania	
Bedford	27.575
Harrisburg	164.70
King of Prussia	409.275
Lancaster	170.125
Philadelphia	164.20 164.50 164.70 166.275 169.60
Pittsburgh	163.375 164.10 164.50 164.70 164.9625 169.60 409.275
Warrensburg	164.70
South Carolina	
Columbia	166.20
Tennessee	
Chattanooga	162.5875
Knoxville	163.00
Memphis	163.375 164.10 164.175 164.70 164.9125 166.20 171.2625
Nashville	162.225 171.2625

Texas
Dallas   162.225 164.175 171.3875 406.225 406.325 406.40
        407.775 409.175 409.225 409.275 409.35 409.45
        410.325 414.725
Fort Worth   406.225 406.375 409.225 409.35 410.10
Houston   406.375 410.20 410.325
San Antonio   409.45
Utah
Salt Lake City   163.00 406.40
Virginia
Fairfax   172.30
Norfolk   162.225
Portsmouth   163.375
Richmond   166.20 167.125 410.325
Washington   167.125
Washington
Masdison   166.225
Milwaukee   166.225 408.825 416.775
Puerto Rico
San Juan   164.10
All Areas
169.00 169.375 169.65 169.85 170.175 406.325 406.375 409.175 409.275 409.45 410.20
410.325 413.60 414.725 414.75 415.05 416.225 418.10 418.30 418.575

Government Printing Office (GPO)

Washington, DC   Security 410.20 410.45 411.20 415.30 415.45

Prisons, Bureau of

Channel 1 (Primary/Administrative/Operations): 170.875
Channel 2 (Riots/Escapes): 170.925
Channel 3 (Emergency): 170.65
Channel 4 (Emergency): 170.825
Channel 5 (Emergency): 170.90
Handheld units reported on 409.25; Beepers on 413.6625

All Federal Correctional Institutions have callsigns, those known are:

KBL311	Lexington, KY	KOE957	La Tuna, TX
KLV312	Chicago, IL	KOE965	Petersburg, VA
KOE950	McNeil I., WA*	KOE971	Terre Haute, IN
KOE951	Morgantown, WV	KOE975	Sandstone, MI
KOE952	Memphis, TN	KOE979	Milan, MI
KOE955	Heliograph, AZ		

*Also operates on 155.835.

Reclamation, Bureau of

All information listed for Department of The Interior applies.

Aircraft roster: Bell 206= N626;   Cessna 414A= N3183M;   Rockwell 690A= N615

Frequencies: 34.78 40.57 41.02 48.26 122.925 123.5875 162.25 163.025 163.05
163.075/168.375 163.175 163.8375 163.8875 164.20 164.25 164.425 164.475 164.525
164.5375 164.55 164.575 164.725/164.20 164.75 164.775 164.80 164.9875 165.4125
165.4625 165.5125 166.00 166.20 166.30/166.90 166.35 166.375 166.6375/166.975
166.6375/167.15 166.725 166.75 166.80 166.825 166.85 166.875 166.90/166.30
166.925/163.025 166.925/166.325 166.95/166.35 166.975/166.375 167.025 167.125
167.15/166.6375 167.175/166.35 167.805 167.825 168.275/167.125 168.325 168.425
168.475 168.50 168.575 169.00 169.10 169.425 169.55/168.575 169.55/170.10 169.625
169.675 169.725 169.775 170.00 170.025 170.375 170.60 171.175 171.625 171.75 171.775
171.825 172.425/167.15 172.425/171.775 172.525 172.625 172.65 172.725 172.775
406.175 406.225 406.475 408.425 408.525 408.55 408.575 408.625 409.60/416.675 409.90
410.20 410.70/418.55 411.625 411.825/415.125 412.025 412.225 412.25 412.30 412.35
412.375 412.775 414.825 414.925 414.975/419.775 415.025 415.075 415.125 415.175
416.125 417.225 417.40 417.425 417.45 417.625 417.675/412.375 417.725/419.625
417.825 417.925 417.975 419.625 419.775 419.825/417.975 419.85 419,875/415.075

Internal Revenue Service (IRS)

Frequencies reported: (CTCSS 123.0 Hz)
Criminal Investigation Division (CID) Repeaters & Duplex: 165.95/167.00
418.175/414.70 418.225/414.70 418.225/415.00 418.225/415.725 417.725/415.725
CID Simplex: 165.95 166.4625 167.00 418.175 418.20 418.225
Internal Affairs: 166.00 166.00/167.10 167.10

National Science Foundation (NSF)

Aircraft roster: Beech King 200= N312D; Beech Queen 80= N306D; Lockheed
188C= N308D; Rockwell Sabre 60= N307D
Stations:

AZ	Kitt Peak Observatory	KHZ812	164.35 164.50 409.20
AZ	Tucson	KZH811	164.35 164.50
CA	Livermore	KFW623	164.70
CO	Boulder	KGT327	164.20 165.6625 409.825
CO	Broomfield	KJZ4	122.9
		KGT326	164.05 164.50
CO	Erie	WKQ74	409.825
CO	Grover	KEO205	164.05
		KGT323	164.05 164.20 164.50 164.70
		KGT324	122.9
		KZH819	164.35
CO	Roberts Mills	KGT325	164.05 165.50 164.70
CO	Roseville	KLW571	165.6625
HI	Hilo	KIY881	168.725/168.125
HI	Mauna Loa Volcano	KJ8211	167.95 168.55
		KIY880	168.125/168.725
NM	Augustine	KZH813	162.025/164.35
NM	Sacramento Peak Observatory	KJ8212	162.025/164.35
TX	Palestine	KJD2	122.9 138.75
WY	Laramie	KGT328	408.00
WY	Sherman Hill		164.05 408.00
PR	Arecibo Radio Astronomy Obsvtry.	WDR71	148.515
		KEO208/KZH815	165.1125
		KJ8203	150.195 163.4875
		KES49	162.175/166.725
PR	Dominqut.	KZH817	165.1125

PR	El Coto	KZH816	165.1125
PR	Islote	KES50	166.725/162.175
		KES51	166.85
PR	Los Canos	KEO206	165.1125
PR	Rio Blanco	KGT330	165.1125
US	portables	KEO249	138.54 165.6625 166.05

Secret Service, U.S.

The most active frequencies before/during a visit by the President, the Vice President (and/or their immediate families) are Baker, Charlie, Mike, and Tango, also channels shown designated for use by the White House Communications Agency (WHCA).

(CTCSS 103.5 Hz)

Alpha	32.23	WHCA vans, possible base in DC area
Baker	165.7875	Pres/VP/VIP Security
Charlie	165.375	Nationwide Primary, Command Post coordination
Delta	169.925	WHCA vans
Echo	407.85	Air Force 1 phone patch ground uplink (paired 415.70)
Foxtrot	415.70	Air Force 1 phone patch aircraft downlink (paired 407.85)
Golf	165.7625	Input to 165.375 repeaters
Hotel	166.2125	President/VP Security
India	407.925	Treasury Security Force (Pres./VP Security)
Juliet	170.00	Camp David pager
Kilo	167.825	White House Communications Agcy (WHCA)
Lima	168.7875	WHCA (voice scramblers)
Mike	165.2125	VIP & Former Pres. Security, & Counterfeit Division
November	166.70	WHCA
Oscar	164.8875	WHCA
Papa	164.40	Input to 165.2125 repeaters
Romeo	166.40	Input to 165.7875 repeaters
Sierra	166.5125	WHCA
Tango	164.65	Presidential/VP Security
Victor	164.10	Presidential/VP Security
Whiskey	167.025	WHCA Pager
X-Ray	166.4625	Treasury Dept. common frequency
Yankee	162.6875	Air Force 1 phone patch uplink (paired 171.2875)
Zulu	171.2875	Air Force 1 phone patch downlink (paired 162.6875)

"Color" Channels of Uniformed Treasury Security Force

Black	415.10	Training Division
Brown	414.85	Foreign Missions
Gray	418.35	
Orange	418.775	White House Uniformed Division
Red	415.975	Foreign Missions
Silver	415.65	
Violet	415.80	Training Division
White	407.675	
Yellow	414.675 415.95	WHCA ("Boardwalk")

USMC Helicopters: 46.70 46.75 46.80 122.85 375.0

UHF Air/Ground circuits from AF-1 & AF-2 in addition to those noted for Secret Service-- (AM mode) 265.8 361.6 375.0; (WFM mode) 305.55 322.75 336.8 382.35 397.05

Press aircraft accompanying AF-1 & AF-2: 129.525

Additional WHCA frequencies: 418.125 418.175 418.65 (Frequency hopping radios reported to operate on freqs every 25 kHz between 408.625 and 409.00.)

Other Secret Service & related channels reported: 34.07 34.35 162.375 162.6875 163.00 163.3625 163.40 163.775 163.8125 163.9125 164.75 164.80/165.85 165.0875/166.2125 165.0875/166.20 165.2875 165.3375 165.5125/166.4875 165.65/166.6375 165.675 165.6875/166.2125 165.7875 165.8625 165.90 165.9125 166.375 166.4875 166.6375 167.90 168.225 168.40 168.45 168.575 406.425 407.825 407.85 407.875 407.925 407.95 415.725 417.75 419.725 (Frequencies in 407 MHz band used for agents' body radios with "wristwatch" microphones.)

Note that channel pairs Echo/Foxtrot & Yankee/Zulu are extensively used for phone patches by Air Force 1 and 2, and also for some Special Air Mission VIP aircraft. Some SAM aircraft on Echo/Foxtrot include SAM-12492, SAM-31683, SAM-41682, SAM-60200, and SAM-60202. Most patches are directed to "Crown" (White House Communications Center). Ground stations for the (NFM mode) Echo/Foxtrot system are on 407.85 are located throughout the nation and are remoted directly to/from Washington so that communications are possible on Echo/Foxtrot while aircraft are on the ground or are flying over or within about 250 miles of the nation's borders. Monitors on the ground beyond the range of any ground stations should be able to copy the aircraft on 415.70 MHz (NFM). The Air Force 1 & 2 Yankee/Zulu system appears primarily in use for localized staff or Secret Service operational phone patches while the aircraft is preparing to land, while it is on the ground, and with calls placed from motorcade limos.

The following Secret Service code name list covers from the 1960's to the present, which means that many of the names are no longer used. Some persons show up more than once, indicating that they had been reassigned new code names once or more by the White House Communications Agency. Some of these code names have appeared in the national media, others have never been identified, and we must assume that some identifications here are incorrect.

Acrobat	Andrews AFB, MD	Ballfield	
Andy	Andrews AFB, MD		
Angel	Air Force 1	Bamboo	Presidential motorcade
Apollo		Bandbox	SS Uniformed Division
Backhoe			White House unit
Backseat	SS Uniformed Division motorscooter unit	Barefoot	
		Baseball	SS Training Div.
Bagpipe	SS Uniformed Division liason unit	Beehive	SS Tech Developm Div
		Bellhop 1	SS Elipse motorscooters

Bellhop 2	SS WH motorscooters	Clothes Brush	
Bigtop	SS Treasury Secur Div	Cloudburst	WHCA, Anacostia NAS
Birdseye	Dept. of State	Cloverleaf	VP Residence (Carter)
Buscuit		Coach House	Dulles Airport, DC
Blackboard	SS Protective Intell Div	Cobweb	VP office, DC
Blacktop	SS Uniformed Division ·foreign mission unit	Companion	Blair House, DC
		Coppertone	Rose Kennedy
Blowtorch	SS Uniformed Division Exec Protec CP	Corkscrew	
		Cowpuncher	AF-1
Blueprint	SS Tech Security Div	Crossbow	WHCA OP's Desk
Boardwalk	SS Foreign Mission Div	Crown	WH Comms Center
Bookstore	WH Comms Center	Crystal	Chassiah Begin Milo
Brimstone	Reagan Ranch, CA	Curbside	Wash Nat'l Airport
Broadside	NYC VIP protec CP	Daily	Prince Charles
Buckeye	Camp David, MD	Dancer	Rosalynn Carter
Buckshot	NYC Spec Coordiation Center	Dasher	Jimmy Carter
		Deacon	Jimmy Carter
Bulldog	DC VIP protec CP	Deckhand	Jeff Carter
Bullpen		Derby	Jack Carter
Bungalow	SS Uniformed Division foreign msn substation	Diamond	Chip Carter
		Digger	James Carter IV
Bunker		Dog Pound	Press aircraft (Carter)
Cableboy	Advance Team (Carter)	Dragon	Walter Mondale
Cactus	Camp David, MD	Driftwood	Carter home, GA
Caliber	Portable comms package	Duchess	Sarah R. Carter
Calico	Eleanor Mondale	Dusty	Jason Carter
Cameo	Joan Mondale	Dynamo	Amy Carter
Candlestick	VIP portable comms CP	Eagle	Bill Clinton
Cannonball	RADM J.A. Chaney	Electric	Nat'l Emergency Command Aircraft
Caravan	VP follow car (Carter)		
Carbine	CCT Anacostia NAS, DC	Elm	Camp David, MD
Carbine 1	Portable comms package	Evergreen	Hillary Clinton
Carbon		Fable	
Cargo	Mrs. Mondale car	Fadeaway	Secretary of State
Carnation	CCT, Ft Ritchie, MD	Falcon	Pres. air cover aircraft
Carousel	AF-2 (Carter years)	Fan Jet	John Block
Carpet	Army garage, WH	Fencing Master	Sec. of Treasury
Cartwheel	NSA, Ft. Meade, MD	Fiddler	
Castle		Finley	Sec. of Defense
Cavalier	Walter Mondale	Fireplug	Sec. of Labor
Cedar	Menachem Begin	Fireside	Sec. of State residence
Cement Mixer	WH Situation Room	Fire Truck	James Edward
Centurion	Theodore Mondale	Fistfight	Sec. of HEW
Challenger	Presidential nightwatch	Flag Day	Spkr., Hse of Rep.
Champion		Flivver	Wm. French Smith
Chandelier	Dept. of State	Flotus	First Lady of US
Chariot	VP Mondale vehicle	Flying Fish	Sec. of Interior
Checkerboard	Advance Team (Carter)	Fog Horn	State Dept. Secur Div
Checkmate	Advance Team (Carter)	Footprint	Sen. Strom Thurmond
Chessman	Wm Mondale	Forefinger	Jan Pierce
Christopher	Bebe Rebozo (Nixon)	Foreward Look	Neil Baldrigger
Citadel		Foxcraft	Terrell Bell
Clam Chowder	Ron Nessen (Ford)	Fraction	
Claw Hammer	Gen. A. Haig (Nixon)	Fullback	State Dept Secur van

Gimlet		Rawhide	Ronald Reagan
Gladiola		Redfern	HRH Queen Elizabeth II
Goffer		Redwood	Gary Hart
Halfback	Pres. follow vehicle	Register	
Halo	Pope John Paul II	Reliant	Ronald P. Reagan
Handshake	SS office	Rhyme	Maureen Reagan
Hawkeye	Z. Brzezinski (Carter)	Ribbon	Patti Reagan Davis
Headlight	SS garage, DC	Riddler	Michael Reagan
Hedgehog	Fire truck	Ridgeline	Reagan residence, CA
Hercules+#	Counter-sniper response	Ringside	Madison Sq Gdn., NY
	team member	Roadhouse	Waldorf-Astoria, NY
Hill Top	Treas. Dept.	Roadrunner	WHCA comms van
Hobnail		Rob Roy	
Holly	Army Helo	Rosebud	Maureen Reagan
Horsehide	Ambulance	Rosebush	
Horsepower	WH Pres Protec Div	Sandbox	
Hotshot	Duty Officer. WHCA	Sandstone	Reagan residence, CA
Hudson	Nixon office, NY	Saturn	Vice Pres Aircraft
Huntsman	NYC surveill 'copter	Sawhorse	
Instructor	Eugene McCarthy	Scarlet	Kele Anderson
Kiley		Scorecard	Dan Quayle
Kittyhawk	HRH Queen Elizabeth II	Searchlight	Richard M. Nixon
Kneecap	Emerg escape aircraft	Shadow	
Lancer	John F. Kennedy	Sheepskin	George Bush
Lightfoot	Madison Hotel, DC	Shotgun	NY City Cmd Post
Lizard	Sec Serv Mobile CP	Signature	Pres. 'copter
Lock Master	Jimmy Carter	Skymaster	CP, Andrews AFB, MD
Lotus Petal	Rosalynn Carter	Smelter	
Magic	Helo coordination CP	Snapshot	Howard Baker
Marine 1	Pres. 'copter	Snowbank	Barbara Bush
Marine 2	VP 'copter	Snowstowm	George Bush
Miracle	John Anderson	Softpack	A shotgun
Mustang		Spectator	
Napoleon	Frank Sinatra (Reagan)	Springtime	Mamie Eisenhower
Nighthawk	Pres. 'copter	Stagecoach	Pres. limousene
Pacemaker	VP staff	Staircase	1st Family Detail Off.
Pass Key	Gerald R. Ford	Starburst	John Anderson
Patroller	VP 'copter	Stardust	John Anderson
Pavillion	VP office	Starlight	Pat Nixon
Peninsula	New Sen Off. Bldg, DC	Store Room	Truman Library, MO
Peso	Susan Ford	Storm King	Nixon residence, NY/NJ
Pinafore	Betty Ford	Strawberry	Rosemary Woods (Nixon)
Pincushon	Rayburn Off. Bldg, DC	Stutter	
Pivot	Medevac, Bethesda, MD	Sunburn	Ted Kennedy
Playground	Helo pad, Pentagon, DC	Sundance	Ethel Kennedy
Pork Chop	Old Sen Off Bldg, DC	Sugarfoot	
Potus	President of The US	Sunshine	Mrs. Marilyn Quayle
Principal	Prince Charles	Supervisor	Dan Quayle
Professor	Longworth Bldg, DC	Swordfish	Phillip Crane
Punch Bowl	Capitol Bldg, DC	Tailor	
Pushbutton		Templer	
Radiant	Doria P. Reagan	Thunder	Rev. Jesse Jackson
Rainbow	Nancy Reagan	Tiller	Dorothy Bush
Rainbow Trail		Timberwolf	George Bush

Tinkerbell		Unicorn	Prince Charles
Tool Room	VP office, DC	Victoria	Ladybird Johnson
Tower	Andrews AFB, MD	Volcano	LBJ Ranch, TX
Tracer	VP lead vehicle	Volunteer	Lyndon B. Johnson
Tracker	VP follow vehicle	Walnut	
Traffic		Warehouse	Sheraton Center, NY
Trail Breaker	VP official limo	Welcome	J.R. Haldeman (Nixon)
Tranquility	Barbara Bush	Whaleboat	Ron Ziegler (Nixon)
Transit		Wheels Down	Pres. a/c has landed
Trapline	Neil Bush	Wheels Up	Pres. a/c taken off
Treasure Ship	AF-2	Windstone	Reagan residence, CA
Tripper	J. Bush	Wisdom	J. Ehrlichman (Nixon)
Tumbler	George Bush, Jr.	Woodcutter	H. Kissinger (Nixon)
Tuner	Marvin Bush		

National Security Agency (NSA)

Fort Meade, MD   167.825 reported

   NSA is believed to monitor terrestrial microwave long distance telephone circuits from facilities in Suitland, MD. A major NSA monitoring facility is operated by the Naval Security Group atop Brother Ridge, at Sugar Grove, WV. This facility includes four large satellite dishes and a Wullenweber HF antenna. This is a high security restricted area. Among the circuits presumably monitored are those containing international phone and data traffic going through Intelsat satellites from the Comsat earth station 70 miles away in Etam, WV and also other earth stations at Roaring Creek, PA and Jamesburg, CA. Most of the international calls going in and out of the US are handled through these earth stations.

Also see listings for Tipton AAF in front section of this directory.

Senate, U.S.

Republican pager   171.975
Democratic pager   171.175

Smithsonian Institution

Washington, DC   KFX752   Security F1 169.20; F2 169.0375
                                         Motor Pool 169.05
                                         Washington Zoo 169.725
                                         National Gallery of Art 406.55

Standards & Technology, National Institute of
(Formerly National Bureau of Standards)

CO	Boulder	KMB805	40.47
		KID389	41.34
		KGK26	165.4375 165.6125
		KJY92	165.5625
		KMB806	166.075
		KMB807	166.15
		KGB544	412.90 416.975
			164.025 164.575 166.025 41.75 410.90
CO	Sunset	KJY92	165.5625
		KJY93	166.025
DC	Washington		164.025 166.125 166.15 166.225
MD	Gaithersburg	KGB548	Security 166.15; Msc 163.225 163.30 164.025
			165.5625 166.175 169.025 410.15 410.825
VA	Sterling		171.90 171.925
US	All areas & coastal waters		40.27 164.025 166.15 166.175 169.025 410.15
			416.95

State, U.S. Department of

Standard repeater pair (out/in) is 409.625/407.20. In addition to frequencies listed here, activity also reported on 164.70 169.05 169.10 169.6125 169.7125.

Aircraft roster: Ayres Thrush S2R-T34= N 3090M N3094M N3096B N3100E N3100N N3100T N3100U N3100V N3101D N3101F N30906; Cessna 305= N32FL; Fairchild 123K= N8168T N8190B N97033; Bell 212= N2765R N2767X N7964J N16985 N16995 N50094; Bell 205A= N8146H N8146M N8147G N8147Q N8148C N8149H N8149P N8151G N8152G N8152J N8152K N8152Q N8159C N8159Z N81463 N81464 N81473 N81477 N81499 N81500 N81518 N81522 N81523 N81526 N81568 N81569

California

Los Angeles		169.80
Mt. Lukens	KHA205	409.625/407.20
San Bernardino Mtn.	KHA204	409.625/407.20
San Francisco	KHA204	409.625/407.20

District of Columbia

Washington	KHA202	409.625/407.20
	KIY871	409.70/408.10
	KIY872	166.6125
	KV4314	163.15
	KXU700	168.225
		164.125 169.625 169.80 170.45 407.60 408.60
		409.165

Florida

Miami	KHA207	409.625/407.20

Illinois
Chicago   KHA203   170.45 409.625/407.20
Massachusetts
Boston   KHA206   411.15/407.20
New York
New York City   KHA202   409.625/407.20
                         KIY870   409.70/408.10
                         KXJ780   409.70/408.10
                                     170.575
Whiteface Mtn.   409.625/407.20 407.60 408.60
Pennsylvania
Philadelphia   KHA208   409.625/407.20
Tennessee
Oak Ridge   41.61 46.97
Texas
Dallas   409.625/407.20
Virginia
Arlington   KXU701   27.575 168.225
Quantico   168.35
Tysons Corners   KIY870   409.70/408.10 41.61
All Areas
Portables/Mobiles   KU6500   27.575
                         KHA200   407.60 408.60 409.625/407.20
   Other frequencies: 32.25 165.6165 165.7125 166.10 169.05 169.615 408.60 409.7025
418.60

Dept. of State facility in Baja Mexico reported on 163.575

Technology Assessment, Office of (OTA)

Washington, DC   409.10

Tennessee Valley Authority (TVA)

   Aircraft roster: Bell 47G= N48221 N62231 N99620; Bell 204- N1525T N46968; Bell
206B= N10CT N655WW N16706;   Hughes 369= N45777;   Cessna 210N= N6479Y N6930N;
DeHavilland DHC-2= N30NR

   Aero band: 121.9625   Railroad: 166.275
   Construction Division HF Ch #1 2094.4; Ch #2 4195; Ch #3 6223; Ch #4 8295.6;
Ch #6 12433.7 kHz;   Other HF frequencies 2783.4 3296.4 4089.2 4117.1 4145 4411.5
6210.7 6520.2 8738.9 kHz

VHF/UHF: 26.900 27.575 27.585 38.97 38.98 38.99 40.01 40.03 40.50 40.57 40.61 40.62 40.73 40.74 40.75 40.85 162.025 163.05 163.125 163.15 163.175 163.375 164.25 164.805 166.225 166.25 166.325 166.375 166.655 166.825 166.875 167.025 167.075 167.10 167.125 167.15 167.175 168.225 168.325 169.40 169.425 169.45 169.475 169.50 169.525 170.025 170.05 170.075 170.15 170.225 170.275 171.3875 171.65 171.70 171.825 171.85 171.875 171.90 171.925 172.025 172.40 172.425 172.625 172.725 172.75 172.825 173.05 173.7625 406.125 406.175 408.425 408.575 409.45 409.55 409.725 411.35 411.45 411.55 411.625 411.70 411.775 411.825 411.875 412.00 412.125 412.25 412.375 412.625 412.675 412.725 412.775 415.075 415.175 415.45 416.475 417.30 417.35 417.65 417.725 417.775 417.80 417.825 417.975 418.35 419.15 419.875 419.95

Transportation, Department of (DoT)

This information relates to all divisions of the DoT, whether or not listed separately in this Registry. This includes Federal Highway Administration, Maritime Administration, National Transportation Safety Board (NTSB), Federal Railroad Administration, Railroad Transportation Test Center (Pueblo, CO), St. Lawrence Seaway Development Corp., National Highway Traffic Safety Admin., Urban Mass Transportation Admin., & the FAA.

Aircraft roster: Cessna 180G= N713 (See FAA roster)

Federal RR Admin: 165.75 166.025
National Highway Safety Admin: 36.15 40.26 40.97
National Transportation Safety Board (NTSB): 165.7625/166.175 166.025 418.20

CO Pueblo, RR Test Center 38.52 38.544 38.568 41.678 41.704 41.73 41.756 41.782
      164.30/171.3625 166.025 171.2375 171.65 172.30 172.70 172.825 173.05 173.15
      173.9125
DC Washington 166.025 170.55 171.3125 171.3625 419.125 419.975
ME Pittsfield 169.225
MS Dennis 165.2625
MS Tupelo 166.025/165.2625 172.675
NC Lineville 166.025/165.2625
NY Massena, St. Lawrence Seaway 46.06 164.9625 165.3125 415.775 415.925
OH E. Liberty, Transp. Research Ctr., Nat'l. Hwy. Tfc Safety Admin 40.27 41.17
      416.975 417.975 453.65
TN Columbia 166.025/165.2625
TX San Angelo, Nat'l Hwy Safety Admin., Uniform Tire Quality Grading Test
      Facility 171.3625
VA Langley, Federal Highway Admin. Research Sta. 416.225
VA Roanoke 171.3625 171.725

Other DoT activities: 27.575 27.585 32.13 32.21 34.05 36.25 38.52 40.39 41.21 41.37 41.41 41.73 160.20 163.10 164.30 164.625 164.9625 164.9875 165.2625 165.3375 165.7625 166.025 166.375 169.225 170.55 170.75 171.2375 171.3125 171.3635 171.65 172.725 172.30 172.675 172.70 172.825 173.15 173.6375 173.9125 415.775 415.925

416.225 416.925 419.125 419.875 419.975 (HF 2119.4 2383.4 2431.4 2513.4 3242.4 4056.5 4145 4420.8 5321.5 73.75 7476.5 8126.5 8292.5 8295.6 9076 11029.5 11722.5 12430.6 kHz)

Treasury, Dept. of The

These operations not yet identified with any specific division of the Treasury Department. Divisions of the Treasury Dept. include Bureau of Alcohol Tobacco & Firearms; Customs Service; White House Communications Agency; Bureau of Engraving & Printing; IRS; Federal Law Enforcement Training Center; Bureau of the Mint; and Secret Service. The common frequency for all Treasury Dept. divisions is 166.4625 MHz.

Frequencies (all areas): 27.575 27.585 165.205 165.215 165.4875 166.20 166.4375 166.625 166.875 169.55 407.7875 414.80 414.90

Callsigns:

KDF221	Washington, DC	KSJ935	Providence, RI
KSJ905	Providence, RI	KSJ987	Washington, DC
KSJ912	New York, NY		

Codes (All Divisions)

10-1	Unable to Copy - Change loc	10-29	Check for wanted
10-2	Signal good	10-33	Emergency
10-3	Stop Transmitting	10-38	Stopping suspicious vehicle
10-4	OK, Acknowledged	10-34	Riot
10-5	Relay message	10-42	Ending duty tour
10-6	Busy (unless urgent)	10-43	Information
10-7	Out of service	10-63	Make written copy
10-8	In service	10-67	Clear for net message
10-9	Repeat message	10-75	In contact with subject
10-13	Weather/road report	10-76	Enroute to:
10-17	Meet subject	10-77	E.T.A.
10-19	Return to:	10-78	Need assistance
10-20	Location	10-80	Chase in progress
10-21	Call by landline	10-85	Delayed
10-22	Disregard	10-88	Telephone # is:
10-23	Arrived at home	10-91	Pick up subject
10-24	Assignment completed	10-95	Subject in custody
10-25	Report in person to:	10-97	Radio test
10-26	Detaining subject, expedite	10-99	Wanted indicated
10-28	Vehicle registration check	10-101	Pick up papers at:
		10-102	Switch to channel:

United Nations

New York, NY: 165.6125 165.7125 165.95 166.10 407.60 408.10/409.70 408.60 409.625 412.00

Vehicle Tracking/Surveillance Frequencies

In addition to the exclusive federal bands listed in this book's Introduction, the following frequencies are authorized for vehicle tracking transmitter use. The following frequencies may be used by all investigative and law enforcement agencies, federal, state, county, and municipal. Transmitters for vehicle tracking surveillance use non-voice modulation (P0 mode), run no more than 30 mW, and must automatically shut down after ten days of operation.

Frequencies ±1 kHz: 30.86 30.90 30.94 30.98 31.02 31.06 31.10 31.14 31.18 31.22 31.26 31.30 31.34 31.38 31.42 31.46 31.50 31.54 31.58 31.62 31.66 31.70 31.74 31.78 31.82 31.86 31.90 31.94 33.06 45.94 45.98 46.02

Frequencies ±2.5 kHz: 31.985 33.015 33.425

Bands: 37.00-37.43 37.89-38.00 39.00-40.00 42.00-42.91 46.05-46.60 47.00-47.41 150.995-151.49 153.74-154.445 154.635-155.195 155.415-156.25 158.715-159.465 453.0125-453.9875 458.0125-458.9875 460.0125-460.5125 460.5625-460.6375 462.9375-462.9875 465.5625-465.6375 467.9375-467.9875

Stolen Vehicle Recovery Systems (LoJack, etc.) use 173.075. Mobile tramsmitters use 2.5 watts, bases 300 watts ERP max. Mobiles may transmit a 200 millisecond signal every 10 seconds, but when they are being actively tracked the signal may be transmitted every second. Base stations may not transmit for more than 1 second per minute.

Veterans Administration

Veterans Administration (VA)

Abbreviatons used here: AM= Ambulances; CL= Clinic; DO= Domicilliary; EM= Emergency; FD= Fire Dept; MC= Med Center; NC= Nat'l. Cemetery; NH= Nursing Home' OP= Operations; PA= Pager; PD= Security.

Alabama
Birmingham MC	AM 15534 OP 163.00 163.375 171.3875
Montgomery MC	AM 155.28 155.34
Tuscaloosa MC/NH	AM 155.28 155.34 OP 163.00 163.375 168.00
Tuskegee	AM 155.34 PD 155.01 OP 154.98 162.225 163.375 173.7125

Arizona
Phoenix MC	OP 164.175
Prescott MC/DO	OP 164.10 169.00
Tucson MC/NH	OP 164.175 169.00

Arkansas
Fayetteville MC	AM 155.28 155.34 OP 163.00
Little Rock MC/NH	AM 155.28 155.34 OP 164.175

California
Fresno MC	AM 155.34 PD 163.00 PA 168.00
Livermore MC	AM 155.40 PA 164.00 168.525 OP 164.50
Loma Linda MC	AM 155.34 155.40 PD 168.525 168.575 PA 171.3875 OP 163.00
Long Beach MC/NH	AM 155.34 PD 168.525 168.575 PA 171.3875 OP 170.40
Los Angeles MC/DO	AM 155.34 PD 168.525 168.575 PA 171.3875 OP 164.175 167.825 419.45
NC	OP 419.15
Martinez MC	AM 155.40 PD 163.00 PA 169.30
Menlo Park	PD 164.50
Palo Alto MC/NH	PD 164.50 PA 168.525
Riverside NC	OP 164.175
San Bruno NC	OP 170.00
San Diego MC	AM 155.175 155.325 155.385 PD 168.525 PA 163.00
NC	OP 171.3875
Sepulveda MC	AM 155.34 PD 168.525 168.575 PA 171.3875 OP 166.825 169.275 170.175
Statewide	EM 406.325 409.325 413.825 417.60

Colorado
Denver MC	OP 166.20 169.00
Ft. Lyon MC/NC	PD 154.77 154.905 154.935 OP 164.50 164.70 166.20
Grand Junction MC/NH	AM 155.34 155.40 PD 155.01 155.37 OP 162.225 164.175 168.00

Connecticut
Newington MC	AM 155.34 PA 166.225 168.525 OP 40.45 167.825

Florida
Bay Pines MC/DO/NH/NC	PD 163.375 PA 164.175 168.525 OP 164.20
Gainesville MC/NH	OP 163.375 164.175 168.525
Lake City MC/NH	OP 163.375 164.10 164.175 168.00 168.525
Miami MC/NH	AM 155.295 OP 163.375 164.20 164.175 164.70 168.525
Riviera Beach CL	OP 163.375

Tampa MC	AM 155.325 PD 163.375 164.20 PA 168.525 169.60 OP 164.175 164.20
Georgia	
Atlanta	PD 166.20/167.1125 OP 164.50 170.175
Augusta MC/NH	OP 164.175 168.00 168.525
Dublin MC/DO/NH	OP 163.375 168.525
Hawaii	
Honolulu NC	OP 168.525
Idaho	
Boise MC	AM 155.28 155.34 OP 168.00
Illinois	
Chicago MC	AM 155.28 155.34 PD 164.70 PA 164.175 409.30 OP 165.6875 166.20 166.825 171.3875
Danville MC/NH	OP 164.50 166.20 168.00 168.525
Downey	AM 155.28 OP 30.37 166.20
Hines MC	AM 155.28 155.34 155.40 PA 408.425 OP 40.45 169.20
Lakeside	AM 155.28 OP 409.30
Marion MC	OP 409.30
N, Chicago MC/NH	PA 409.30
Indiana	
Ft. Wayne MC/NH	AM 155.28 155.34 OP 166.20 173.025
Indianapolis MC/NH	AM 155.28 155.34 OP 164.20 168.00 169.60
Marion MC/NH/NC	AM 155.34 OP 164.20 166.20 168.00
Iowa	
Des Moines MC	OP 163.00 168.525
Iowa City MC	PA 166.20
Knoxville MC/NH	PA 155.19 155.61 155.85 168.00 PA 162.225
Kansas	
Leavenworth MC/NH/NC	OP 166.20 168.00 168.525
Topeka MC/NH	PD 166.20 OP 164.175 168.00 168.525 171.3875
Wadsworth	OP 164.175 167.975
Wichita MC	OP 36.16 164.175 168.525
Kentucky	
Lexington MC/NH/MC	FD 153.77 154.37 OP 162.225 168.525
Louisville MC/NC	OP 164.50 168.525
Louisiana	
Alexandria MC/NH/NC	PD 168.525 PA 171.3875 OP 153.98
New Orleans MC	AM 155.28 155.34 PD 166.20 PA 163.00 OP 409.325
Shreveport MC	PD 168.525 171.3875
Maine	
Togus MC/NH	AM 155.34 OP 163.00 168.525
Maryland	
Baltimore MC/CL/NC	OP 40.45 163.05 164.9875 409.325
Ft. Howard HO/NH	FD 46.28 46.46 OP 46.56 162.5875 164.50 164.9875
Perry Point MC/NH	PD 164.35 FD 46.18 46.54 164.35 OP 164.9875 173.6375
Massachusetts	
Bedford MC/NH	AM 155.34 PD 162.225 PA 168.5375 OP 168.525
Boston MC/CL	PA 164.50 170.175
Brockton MC/NH	AM 155.34 PA 164.20 169.60 OP 163.00 163.375
Jamaica Plain	PD 163.375 171.15
Northampton MC/NH	PA 167.85 OP 173.7125
W. Roxbury MC	AM 155.16 155.28 155.34 PA 164.175
Michigan	
Allen Park MC	OP 168.00 168.525 408.425 409.30

Ann Arbor MC	AM 155.34 OP 164.20 168.525
Battle Creek	AM 155.28 155.34 PD 168.525 OP 162.225 162.5875 164.175 168.00
Iron Mtn. MC/NH	OP 163.375 168.00
Saginaw MC	OP 162.225 164.175 168.00 168.525

Minnesota

Chicago Lakes	PA 163.25
Minneapolis MC/NC	OP 30.17 162.125 162.225
St. Cloud MC/NH	OP 30.19 164.70 168.525

Mississippi

Biloxi MC/DO/NH/NC	AM 155.28 155.34 OP 168.525
Gulfport	OP 168.00 168.525
Jackson MC/NH	OP 162.225 174.70 168.525

Mississippi

Columbia MC/NH	AM 155.265 155.34 PD 155.475 155.73 OP 163.00 169.60
Kansas City MC	AM 155.34 OP 162.225 168.575
Poplar Bluff MC/NH	OP 163.00 164.9625
St. Louis MC/NH/NC	PD 419.15 OP 163.375 168.00 168.525

Montana

Ft. Harrison MC	AM 155.28 PD 39.82 OP 164.175 169.00
Miles City MC/NH	PD 39.82 OP 164.9625 168.00

Nebraska

Grand Island MC/NH	PD 39.82 OP 163.00 166.20 168.00
Lincoln MC	OP 162.225 166.20 168.00
Omaha MC	OP 158.76 163.375 166.20

Nevada

Reno MC/NH	OP 170.175

New Hampshire

Manchester MC/NH	PD 162.275 OP 30.19 166.20

New Jersey

E. Orange MC/NH	AM 155.34 OP 164.175 169.00
Lyons MC/NH	OP 30.35 38.99
Somerville	OP 30.18

New Mexico

Albuquerque MC/NH	OP 162.225 168.00
Santa Fe NC	OP 162.225

New York

Albany MC/NC	AM 155.28 155.34 155.40 PD 169.60 PA 163.25 164.175 OP 168.00
Batavia MC	AM 155.175 155.34 PA 162.225 408.425 OP 171.2625
Bath MC/NC	AM 155.28 155.34 155.40 PD 39.14 39.46 PA 162.225 OP 164.70
Bronx MC	PD 166.675 PA 170.35 OP 165.5625
Brooklyn MC/NC	PD 164.9375 OP 409.30
Buffalo MC/NH	AM 155.34 PD 168.00 PA 164.175 166.675
Calverton NC	OP 165.1875
Canandaigua MC/NH	AM 155.28 155.34 PD 169.00 FD 46.42 PA 163.375 OP 168.00
Castle Point MC/NH	PD 155.475 166.225 PA 164.50
Farmingdale NC	OP 165.1875
Montrose MC NH	PA 168.525 OP 164.175
New York MC	PA 164.70 OP 168.525
Northport MC	PA 164.175 OP 166.675 168.525 168.875

St. Albans MC	OP 164.9375
	PA 168.00
Syracuse MC/NH	OP 163.00 168.525

North Carolina

Asheville MC/NH	OP 164.175 164.70
Durham	AM 155.28 155.34 OP 169.60 173.7375
Fayetteville MC/NH	AM 155.28 155.34 OP 164.175 168.525
Salisbury MC/NH/NC	OP 164.175 168.00

North Dakota

Fargo MC/NH	AM 155.34 155.40 OP 163.00 171.3875

Ohio

Brecksville MC/NH	AM 155.34 OP 164.20 173.6125
Chillicothe MC/NH	AM 155.22 155.28 155.34 PD 39.38 39.72 39.78
	FD 154.13 154.445 OP 168.00 168.525
Cincinnati MC/NH	AM 155.28 FD 154.385 OP 166.20 168.525 409.325
Cleveland MC	AM 155.28 OP 164.20 173.6125
Dayton MC/DO/NH/NC	OP 164.175 164.70 166.20 169.275 169.60

Oklahoma

Muskogee MC	AM 155.34 OP 168.525 171.2625 171.3875
Oklahoma City MC	AM 155.34 OP 163.375

Oregon

Portland MC	AM 155.34 PA 164.10 OP 168.00 168.525
Roseburg MC/NH/NC	PD 155.70 OP 166.225 168.525
White City DO	PD 155.61 158.91 FD 154.13 OP 166.225 168.525
	169.1125
Wilamette NC (Portland)	OP 407.475

Pennsylvania

Altoona MC/NH	OP 163.00 168.525
Butler MC/NH	FD 33.82 33.88 OP 163.00 168.525
Coatesville MC/NH	OP 164.175 168.525
Erie MC/NH	OP 163.00 164.20
Lebanon MC/NH	AM 155.34 PD 37.24 37.26 OP 164.175 168.00
Philadelphia MC/NC	PA 163.05 164.9625 169.85 OP 170.475
Pittsburgh MC/NH	OP 164.70 166.225 168.00
Wilkes-Barre MC	AM 155.16 155.22 OP 164.9625 168.525

Puerto Rico

San Juan MC	OP 162.225 168.525

Rhode Island

Providence MC	AM 155.28 155.34 PD 171.3875 PA 164.20

South Carolina

Charleston MC	OP 164.175 168.525
Columbia MC/NH	OP 156.015 164.175 168.525

South Dakota

Ft. Meade MC/NC	OP 164.125 168.00
Hot Springs MC/DO/NC	PD 39.10 OP 162.225 164.175 168.00
Sioux Falls MC/NH	OP 153.815 163.00 168.00

Tennessee

Chattanooga CL/NC	OP 168.525
Memphis MC/NH/NC	AM 155.28 155.295 155.34 OP 163.00 168.525 PD 410.00
Mountain Home MC/DO/NC	AM 155.28 155.34 OP 166.225 169.00
Murfreesboro MC/NH	AM 155.28 155.34 PD 37.26 OP 164.175 168.525
Nashville MC/NC	AM 155.28 155.34 OP 163.375 168.00

Texas

Amarillo MC	AM 155.28 155.34 OP 163.00 168.525

Austin   OP 164.175
Big Spring MC/NH   PD 37.18   OP 163.375 168.00
Bonham MC/DO/NH   PD 168.00   PA 163.375
Dallas MC   AM 155.325   OP 167.975 168.525
Ft. Sam Houston NC   OP 164.10
Houston   AM 155.28 155.34   OP 163.375 164.10 164.175 168.00
                                   171.3875
Kerrville MC/NH/NC   AM 155.34   PD 37.18 168.00   OP 162.225
Marlin MC   OP 166.20 169.025 169.125
San Antonio MC   AM 155.28 155.34   PD 168.00   FD 168.525   PA 163.375
Temple MC/DO   AM 155.28 155.34   PA 164.20   OP 168.525 169.125
                                   171.2625
Waco MC/NH   OP 40.45 164.20 169.025 169.125

Utah
Salt Lake City MC/NH   AM 155.16 155.28   OP 155.985 169.00

Vermont
Wht. River Jct MC/NH   AM 155.28 155.34   FD 46.38   OP 164.20 168.525

Virginia
Hampton MC/DO/NH   PD 168.425   OP 163.0375 164.9625 168.525
Richmond MC/NC   AM 155.34   OP 164.10 164.9375 166.20 409.325 409.40
Salem MC/NH   OP 164.10 168.00 168.525

Washington
Seattle MC   AM 155.34   OP 162.225 164.10 166.225
Spokane MC   AM 155.28 155.34   OP 164.175 166.20
Tacoma MC/NH   AM 155.34   PD 156.09   OP 166.225 168.00
Vancouver MC   AM 155.34   PA 164.9875   OP 169.60
Walla Walla MC   AM 155.28 155.34   OP 164.50 169.60

West Virginia
Beckley MC/NH   OP 163.375 168.525
Clarksburg MC   AM 155.265 155.34   OP 168.00 168.525
Huntington MC   OP 164.20 164.70
Martinsburg MC/DO   PD 409.325   FD 33.90   OP 164.9875 168.525

Wisconsin
Madison MC   AM 155.325   PD 409.325   OP 163.00 168.00
Milwaukee   PD 409.325 414.325   PA 164.175   OP 168.525
Tomah MC/NH   OP 155.925 164.175 169.60
Wood MC/DO/NH/NC   AM 155.34   PD 409.325   PA 164.175   OP 168.525

Wyoming
Cheyenne MC/NH   OP 163.00 168.00
Sheridan MC   OP 36.16 164.9875 170.175

All Areas
164.675 164.70 166.20 168.00 168.525 406.325 409.325 409.40 414.325 414.40

VOA

USIA

Voice of America

CA	Delano		166.6125
CA	Dixon		166.6125
DC	Washington	KGA932	164.70 168.05 173.9625
NC	Blackjack		166.6125
NC	Greenville		166.6125
OH	Bethany		166.6125
US	all VOA sites		164.70 418.05 418.575

White House & U.S. Capitol

Helo Pad	46.70 46.75 46.80 375.0
Secret Service ("Oscar Base")	164.86 418.775
WHCA ("Boardwalk")	414.675 415.95

White House Police:

Channel 1	164.80/164.05	Primary Repeater
Channel 2	164.625/162.6125	Secondary Repeater
Channel 3	164.80	Primary Direct
Channel 4	164.625	Secondary Direct
Channel 5	164.60/164.325	Detective Repeater
Channel 6	164.60	Detective Direct
Channel 7	165.5375	Emergency Frequency
	453.55	Mutual Aid

Messengers	169.925
White House Comms Center	162.85 414.65 414.95
Mobile Telephones	172.365 172.3875 172.425
National Park Service	168.35 172.475 172.75
Pager	409.90
Capitol Police	164.60 165.5375/164.625 164.80/164.05 164.625
White House Staff & Misc	162.85 163.8125 164.40 165.37 165.78 165.925
166.395 166.70 166.925 167.025 167.825 168.7875 171.2875	
Architect of The Capitol	Operations 418.475
	Maintenance 414.875
	Pager 148.575 416.15
	Parking 409.15 414.875

Also see Secret Service listings

Miscellaneous

Frequencies used by miscellaneous small agencies not listed elsewhere in this Registry, also for all other agency low power, itinerant, and inter-agency purposes: 27.575 27.585 163.10 163.85 408.05 408.40 408.575 409.40 418.05 418.075 418.575 MHz.

During major fires at National Forests, National Forests, and for other large-scale disasters where there is fire or the threat of fire, various federal agencies may be monitored on frequencies of the Interagency National Emergency Fire Cache. These are: Tactical Ch #1 168.05;   Ch #2 168.20;   Ch #3 168.60
Command Ch #1 168.70;   Ch #2 168.10;   Ch #3 168.075
Air Dispatch 168.625/168.025
Air Tactics Ch #1 166.675;   Ch #2 169.15;   Ch #3 169.20;   Ch #4 170.00
Logistics Ch #1 414.65;   Ch #2 415.40;   Ch 3 415.50

Where's That Agency?

We covered a lot of federal agencies in this publication. In the Miscellaneous section (above), there are some additional catch-all frequencies used by various small federal agencies that aren't specifically listed by name in this Registry.

But what about agencies that aren't listed in this Registry and also don't use any of those "Miscellaneous" frequencies? They can fit into any of several categories:

1. Some federal agencies don't need or use their own special VHF or UHF comms systems. If they have sophisticated communications needs, perhaps they operate via private satellite network. Or, if their needs are unsophisticated, their needs might be adequately served by landline telephone and cellular phones.

2. There are federal activities that operate under such hush-hush conditions that even their very names almost never reach the public, and nobody is willing to go on record to confirm that they exist-- much less discuss their missions. The National Reconnaissance Office is one such agency whose existence was mentioned a few years ago, apparently being related to espionage via satellite. All communications connected with the activities of any agencies in such a category would be buried under so many dozens of layers of security measures that it is not realistic to expect that anything will ever surface in the way of signals, frequency data, or other information.

3. Undoubtedly there are agencies that fit into neither of these categories, but fall somewhere in the middle. There are smaller agencies that have their own modest VHF or UHF systems, and yet are still not listed in this Registry. That's because we don't have the information. We are always seeking information, so if you have something to add, please send it along. The 7th Edition was 240 pages in length, and we had room left for decorative pages between each section. This 8th Edition runs 269 pages, and it's got so much more information that we had to do away with all of those pages separating each section! This is because we required the page space to accommodate frequency information. Even though this is the largest amount of communications information relating to federal frequencies ever published, we know that more information is still out there. We hope you will find discover some of it and pass it along to us for the next edition. Thanks!

Additional Canadian Government Frequencies

In addition to ARTCC and other Canadian facility listings shown elsewhere in this Registry, we believe that Canadian Government communications, as indicated, may be taking place on the frequencies listed. Additional information is wanted.

Agriculture Canada: 464.1875

Bank of Canada: 151.085

Buildings, Public: 141.885 158.43 162.18 168.12 171.99

Canfors One: 461.275 461.375 461.725 (HF 9010 11233 13257 kHz)

Conservation: 39.26 39.83 39.96 40.26 40.30 122.8 122.9 122.925 139.83 139.86 139.935 139.95 140.055 141.36 150.125 152.72 153.53 163.62 163.80 167.17 167.73 414.2875 414.4125 414.5625 414.6875 414.9875 419.425

Customs & Immigration: 141.27 151.055 406.025 406.225 406.5375 406.5875 411.1625 411.1825 452.075 453.0375 461.6625 462.35

Coast Guard: 143.535 156.30 156.60 156.65 156.80 156.95 157.05 157.075 157.10 157.125 157.15 157.175 381.8 414.4375; Broadcasts 161.65 161.775; Search & Rescue 123.1 282.8

Communications, Dept. of: 34.06 142.395 149.08

Environment Canada: 34.16 39.64 142.695 149.05 155.85 158.34 173.22 407.0825 408.2875 413.925 418.05 418.075; Broadcasts 161.65 161.775

Film Board of Canada, National: 171.87

Fisheries & Oceans, Department of: 46.47 46.70 143.145 166.125 167.055 172.20 (Search 140.00 to 144.00 MHz band for operations.)

Forestry, Ministry of: Aircraft 131.275

Chan. #1 (Silver) 163.89	Chan. #5 (Blue) 163.215
Chan. #2 (Red) 163.065	Chan. #6 (Orange) 163.275
Chan. #3 (Gray) 163.095	Chan. #7 (Yellow) 163.335
Chan. #4 (Green) 163.125	Chan. #8 (Black) 163.395

Harbours Board, National: 155.94 158.46 159.63 159.99 167.61 168.99 172.26 418.0375 418.1125 418.2875 418.3375 418.3875 418.4875 418.6375 418.7325 465.1625

House of Commons: 411.0625 411.0875 411.1875

NATO: 30.15 30.20 30.60 30.80 34.60 34.80

NORAD: 34.05 34.51 34.60 34.85 34.94 36.05 123.55 126.7 228.9 251.0 256.6 263.6 270.4 274.4 364.2

Parks Canada: 38.42 49.04 49.42 143.145 149.04 149.05 149.56 152.12 152.48 166.65 166.635 166.92

Ports Canada: 410.24

Post Canada: 158.70   410.0375   410.1125   410.1375   410.6375   410.9625   411.7625   413.0375   413.4375   417.625   452.975   452.9875   464.0875   469.1375

Prisoner Transportation: 141.36   141.495   141.57   141.885   141.915   141.945   141.975   164.19

Prisons: 151.055

Public Works: 413.4375

Revenue Canada: 140.46

Royal Canadian Mounted Police: All areas: 155.64   155.70   155.80;   Other frequencies reported: 45.24   47.85   49.12   49.16   138.045   138.085   138.195   138.285   138.345   138.35   138.44   138.465   138.485   138.495   138.50   138.525   138.55   138.56   138.585   138.63   138.675   138.69   138.695   138.72   138.765   138.795   138.80   138.825   138.885   138.945   139.035   139.045   139.08   139.11   139.14   139.17   139.185   139.215   139.245   139.26   139.28   139.29   139.30   139.32   139.35   139.38   139.41   139.44   139.445   139.475   139.50   139.53   139.56   139.59   139.605   139.62   139.65   139.68   139.71   139.74   139.77   139.80   139.815   139.89   139.98   139.92   140.00   140.01   140.03   140.04   140.10   140.13   140.14   140.19   140.28   140.31   140.37   140.395   140.40   140.43   140.49   140.55   140.58   140.61   140.64   140.67   140.73   140.79   140.82   141.09   141.10   141.145   141.15   141.18   141.19   141.21   141.24   141.30   141.45   141.57   141.90   142.005   142.035   142.085   142.095   142.125   142.185   142.215   142.225   142.275   142.305   142.385   142.425   142.515   142.525   142.755   142.77   142.785   142.815   142.86   142.905   142.935   142.965   143.035   143.51   143.955   151.10   153.26   153.65   153.80   153.935   153.98   154.10   154.13   154.19   154.40   154.86   154.905   154.92   154.95   154.98   155.01   155.04   155.13   155.175   155.19   155.295   155.30   155.325   155.37   155.39   155.40   155.46   155.505   155.55   155.58   155.595   155.60   155.64   155.67   155.73   155.745   155.82   155.85   155.85   155.985   159.03   159.14   160.345   160.48   160.54   160.545   160.585   160.615   160.645   160.68   160.72   160.74   160.78   160.785   160.815   160.885   160.915   160.92   160.93   160.935   160.945   160.96   160.99   161.01   161.02   161.10   161.13   161.16   161.19   161.20   161.23   161.26   161.29   161.645   410.1875   410.2875   410.3125   410.4125   411.1625   411.7625   413.0375   413.0625   413.2875   413.8875   414.5875   451.0375   461.55

St. Lawrence Seaway Authority: 170.73   419.0875

Security Intelligence Service: 139.17/139.98

Snowbirds Team: 141.85   227.6   236.6   236.8   239.8   239.9   240.5   243.4   245.0   245.5   245.7   266.3   275.8   277.65   278.8   283.9   289.4   294.5   294.7   295.6   299.9   310.8   316.5   321.7   322.8   344.5   344.7   356.6   363.8   378.5   381.8   Ground Crew 413.025

Transportation Canada: 123.45   135.85   135.95   143.535   149.71   410.50   453.1125   453.4875   460.20   460.2125   461.075   463.1625   463.425   463.45   464.325   464.675

Scanner Programming Ideas:
By-Frequency Guide

This section is provided in order to offer some ideas on frequencies to program into your scanner. It covers selected national frequencies of certain high-interest agencies.

It does not seek to be a comprehensive listing of all possible frequencies, nor all possible agencies.

You may not find activity on all of these frequencies in your monitoring area. Or, you may find them in use by agencies other than those indicated here.

It's really intended only as a loose guideline, or starting point for you to build your own customized listing around. If you have thoughts on other frequencies that should be added, why not let us know them?

30.10	Army Avn FD/Crash
30.15	USN Special Warfare
30.36	USCG Reserve
30.38	USCG Reserve
30.41	USCG Reserve
30.45	Army Nuclear Accident
	Canada Marit Command
30.54	USN MARS
32.06	USN MARS
32.10	Canada Marit Command
32.23	USSS "Alpha" Chan
32.25	Canada Marit Command
34.25	Fish & Wildlife
34.30	USCG
34.41	Fish & Wildlife

34.45	USCG
34.81	Fish & Wildlife
34.83	Fish & Wildlife
34.85	USCG / Fish & Wildlife
	Canada Marit Command
34.90	Army Emergency
36.14	USN MARS
36.25	Oil Spill Cleanup
36.30	Army Nuclear Accid
36.50	USN Spec Warfare
36.85	USN MARS
37.50–38.25	Radio Astronomy
38.27	USCG
38.30	Army Nuclear Accid
38.50	Army Nuclear Accid
38.54	USN MARS
38.70	USN MARS
38.90	Army Control Towers
40.10	USN MARS
40.14	USN MARS
40.39	Fish & Wildlife
40.50	Mil Search/Rescue
40.68	Scientific Devices &
	Wildlife Tracking
40.77	USN MARS
40.95	USN MARS
41.00	Army/NG Aviation
41.50	Army Control Towers
41.59	Army MARS
41.71	Oil Spill Cleanup
41.80	USCG
46.60	USN Reserve
46.70	Army Control Towers
46.79	Army Mars
48.60	Bugs
49.70	Army EOD
49.79	Army MARS
49.80	Army EOD
49.93	Army MARS
49.98	USAF MARS
51.15	USCG
65.60	USCG

73.00–74.60	Radio Astronomy		141.375	Army Medevac
118.825	Dept Agri Cntrl Twrs		141.465	NG
118.95	Dept Agri Cntrl Twrs		142.125	USAF MARS
118.975	Dept Agri Cntrl Twrs		142.155	MARS
119.95	Dept Agri Cntrl Twrs		142.325	Army CID
119.975	Dept Agri Cntrl Twrs		142.417	MIR Spacelab (WFM)
120.375	DEA aero		142.455	USAF MARS
120.775	DEA aero		143.10	Army Aviation
121.5	Aero emergency		143.125	NG
121.6	Mil Search/Rescue		143.15	NG
121.75	MIR Spacecraft (WFM)		143.175	NG
122.2	FAA Weather		143.20	NG
122.925	Environmental		143.225	NG
123.075	Customs Aero		143.275	NG
123.1	Search/Rescue		143.28	USCG Auxiliary
123.55	Canadian NORAD		143.30	NG
126.2	Mil ATC Common		143.305	NG
129.525	Presidental Press A/C		143.335	NG
130.65	USAF Air Combat Cmd		143.35	NG
134.1	Mil ATC Common		143.40	NG
135.85	FAA Flight Check A/C		143.415	Army MARS
135.95	FAA Flight Check A/C		143.45	USAF MARS
136.11	Kiku-1 Satellite		143.46	MARS
136.37	ATS-3 Satellite		143.625	MIR Spacelab (WFM)
136.38	Goes-1/2/3 Satellites		143.64	USAF MARS
136.86	Iue Satellite		143.80	USCG Auxiliary
137.076	Meteosat Satellite		143.875	USCG Auxiliary
137.08	Meteosat Satellite		143.90	CAP
137.62	NOAA-9 Satellite		143.925	USAF MARS
138.075	USAF OSI		143.95	USAF MARS
138.165	USAF OSI		143.99	Army MARS
138.175	USAF OSI		148.075	USN MARS
138.185	USAF OSI		148.125	CAP
138.45	USAF Rescue		148.15	CAP
138.65	USN Investig Svc		148.25	Satellite Telecommand
138.78	Mil Rescue		148.305	USCG Auxiliary
138.90	USN MARS		148.375	USN MARS
138.975	Army Post Opns		148.40	USN Recruiting
139.00	Army Aviation		148.41	USN MARS
139.075	Army Aviation		148.565	Satellite Telecommand
139.10	NG		148.65	Army MARS
139.175	Army EOD		148.83	USN Base Security
139.20	Army Reserve		148.825	USCG Auxiliary
139.40	Army Post Opns		148.95	USN MARS
139.525	USN Investig Svc		148.975	USN MARS
140.025	USN Investig Svc		148.98	Satellite Telecommand
140.075	USN Investig Svc		149.00	Bugs
140.10	USN Crash Trucks		149.05	USN MARS
140.22	USN Crash Trucks		149.15	Canadian Marit Cmd
140.575	USN Base Security		149.175	Army Security
140.65	USN Investig Svc		149.205	Army Security
140.775	USN Investig Svc		149.282	Satellite Telecommand
140.82	USN Base Security		149.35	Bugs
141.325	Army CID		149.48	Satellite Telecommand

149.52	Satellite Telecommand
149.65	Canadian MP's
149.91	Army Civil Emergency
149.978	Navigation Satellites
149.982	Navigation Satellites
149.988	Navigation Satellites
150.00	Navigation Satellites
150.09	USN MARS
150.125	USN MARS
150.25	Canadian MP's
150.375	USN MARS
150.39	USN MARS
150.40	USN MARS
150.435	Army Security
150,55	Army CID
150.555	Army Security
150.625	Army MARS
154.20	Satellite Telecommand
156.25	USCG Ports/Harbors
156.30	USCG Search/Rescue
156.55	USCG Ports/Harbors
156.60	USCG Ports/Harbors
156.70	USCG Ports/Harbors
156.75	Environmental
156.80	USCG Distress
157.075	USCG Working Freq
157.05	USCG Working Freq
157.10	USCG Liason Freq
157.125	Misc Federal Vessels
157.15	USCG Working Freq
157.175	USCG Auxiliary
162.05	US Customs
162.375	USN Investig Svc
162.625	BP
162.6375	FBI
162.65	FBI
162.675	FBI
162.6875	USSS "Yankee" Chan
162.70	FBI
162.7125	FBI / Fed Courts
162.725	FBI
162.775	FBI
162.7875	FBI / US Marshal
162.85	INS
162.90	BP/INS
163.05	BP/INS
163.125	US Customs
163.175	USCG
163.20	US Marshal
163.375	BP
163.4125	Army Engineers
163.5375	FBI Nationwide
163.625	BP/INS

163.65	INS
163.675	INS
163.70	BP/INS
163.725	BP
163.75	INS
163.775	BP
163.8375	FBI
163.85	FBI
163.8625	FBI Nationwide
163.875	FBI
163.8875	FBI
163.90	FBI
163.9125	FBI
163.925	FBI
163.9375	FBI
163.95	FBI
163.9625	FBI/BP/INS
163.975	FBI
163.9875	FBI
164.025	FBI
164.05	FBI
164.10	US Customs
	USSS "Victor" Ch
164.1625	FBI
164.25	FBI
164.30	USCG Aero
164.35	FBI
164.40	USSS "Papa" Ch
164.4125	USCG
164.425	FBI
164.45	EPA
164.50	HUD
164.525	FBI
164.55	USCG
164.60	US Marshal
164.65	USSS "Tango" Ch
164.70	Depts State / Labor
164.775	US Customs
164.8625	FEMA / HUD / BIA
164.8875	WHCA
164.9375	BP/INS
165.0125	USCG Intelligence
165.2125	USSS "Mike" Ch
165.2375	US Customs
165.2875	ATF
165.3125	USCG
165.3375	FAA / USCG
165.375	USSS "Charlie" Ch
165.4375	US Customs
165.4625	US Customs
165.5125	US Customs
165.5625	USCG
165.65	FBI
165.6625	FEMA / HUD

165.7375	US Customs aero		167.5125	FBI
165.75	FAA Accid Investig		167.525	FBI
165.7625	US Customs / NTSB		167.5375	FBI
	USSS "Golf" Ch		167.55	FBI
165.7875	USSS "Baker" Ch		167.5625	FBI car/car
165.825	INS		167.575	FBI
165.8625	US Customs/BP/INS		167.5875	FBI
165.875	BP Anti-Smuggler		167.60	FBI
165.9125	ATF		167.6125	FBI
165.925	Org Crime Task Force		167.625	FBI
165.95	IRS		167.6375	FBI Org Crime
166.00	Soyuz telemetry/IRS		167.65	FBI
166.0625	NTSB		167.6625	FBI
166.2125	USSS "Hotel" Ch		167.675	FBI
166.2875	ATF		167.875	FBI
166.3375	Bugs		167.70	FBI
166.40	USSS "Romeo" Ch		167.7125	FBI
166.4625	Treasury Common Chan		167.725	FBI
166.5125	WHCA		167.7375	FBI
166.5375	ATF		167.75	FBI
166.5875	US Customs		167.7625	FBI
166.6125	BIA-FD's		167.775	FBI
166.70	WHCA		167.7875	FBI
166.75	FAA Accid Investig		167.825	WHCA
166.8625	US Customs		167.975	FEMA
167.00	IRS		168.00	ATF / CPSC / HUD
167.025	WHCA Pager		168.0115	Bugs
167.05	FCC		168.05	Interagency Fire Cache
167.10	IRS		168.075	Interagency Fire Cache
167.2125	FBI		168.10	Interagency Fire Cache
167.225	FBI		168.125	Interagency Fire Cache
167.2375	FBI		168.20	Interagency Fire Cache
167.25	FBI		168.25	FWS Undercover
167.2625	FBI		168.35	BP/INS
167.275	FBI		168.40	FWS Undercover / BIA
167.2875	FBI		168.50	USCG Environmental
167.30	FBI		168.60	Interagency Fire Cache
167.3125	FBI		168.70	Interagency Fire Cache
167.325	FBI		168.7875	WHCA
167.3375	FBI / Bugs		168.8625	BP
167.3475	Bugs		168.975	BP Anti-Smuggling
167.35	FBI		169.00	USPS
167.3625	FBI		169.05	Dept State
167.375	FBI		169.10	Dept State / HUD
167.3875	FBI		169.15	Interagency Fire Cache
167.40	FBI		169.20	Interagency Fire Cache
167.4125	FBI		169.225	Bugs
167.425	FBI		169.375	USPS
167.4375	FBI		169.445	Bugs
167.45	FBI		169.45	US Customs
167.4625	FBI		169.505	Bugs
167.475	FBI		169.60	USPS
167.4875	FBI / Bugs		169.6125	Dept State
167.50	FBI		169.65	USPS

169.7125	Dept State
169.85	USPS
169.925	USSS "Delta" Ch
170.00	Interagency Fire Cache
	FBI / USSS "Juliet"
170.245	Bugs
170.305	Bugs
170.4125	ATF
170.625	BP/INS
170.65	Bureau Prisons
170.675	BP/INS
170.70	FBI
170.725	BP/INS
170.75	BP/INS
170.80	FBI
170.825	BP/INS / FBI
	Bur Prisons
170.85	FBI / Fed Courts
170.875	Bur Prisons
170.90	FBI / Fed Courts
	Bur Prisons
170.925	Bur Prisons
171.045	Bugs
171.105	Bugs
171.2375	USCG
171.2875	USSS "Zulu" Ch
171.3125	USCG
171.3375	USCG
171.35	FBI
171.3625	USCG
171.3875	US Mint
171.45	Bugs
171.525	Dept Agriculture
171.575	Dept Agriculture
171.845	Bugs
171.85	Bugs
171.90	Bugs
171.905	Bugs
172.00	Bugs
172.20	Bugs
171.275	US Mint
172.30	Dept Labor
172.3375	Bugs
172.375	Bugs
172.60	Bugs
173.00	DEA
173.075	Stolen Auto Tracking
173.5875	USAF Crash Trucks
173.8875	ATF
174.60	Bugs
177.60	Bugs
181.60	Bugs
183.60	Bugs
186.60	Bugs

190.60	Bugs
192.60	Bugs
195.60	Bugs
196.60	Bugs
216.00–216.10	Bird Tracking
216.00–220.00	Animal Tracking
216.88–217–08	USN Spasur Syst
220.5525	Watch these new
220.5575	freqs for signs of
220.5625	activity. They are
220.5675	authorized for
220.5725	nationwide gov't
220.5775	systems. Mobiles use
220.5825	channels 1 MHz
220.5875	higher (221 MHz).
220.5925	Twenty channel
220.5975	pairs in all.
220.8525	
220.8575	
220.8625	
220.8675	
220.8725	
220.8775	
220.8825	
220.8875	
220.9925	
220.7795	
225.0	USN
228.9	NORAD Canada
229.6	Army & NG
234.5	NG Air/Air
234.55	NG Air/Air
234.8	USAF
235.0	USN
235.1	USAF Air Refuel
235.3	US Customs
236.6	Control Towers
237.9	USCG
238.2	USAF
238.9	USAF Air Refuel
239.8	Mil Weather
	Canadian Mil
240.2	US Customs
240.6	USN / USCG / NASA
241.0	Army & NG
242.2	USAF
242.4	NG
243.0	Emergency
245.0	Canadian MIL
	Radio Astronomy
250.6	USMC Weather
251.0	NORAD Canada
251.6	USN
252.1	USAF Reserve

254.2	USCG/US Customs		303.0	ANG Air/Air
255.4	FAA Flight Service		304.4	Army Weather
256.6	NORAD Canada		304.8	Hurricane Hunters
257.8	USAF Control Towers		305.4	USAF Direction Finding
258.2	USAF		305.55	Air Force 1 & 2 (WFM)
259.0	Air/Sea Rescue		305.6	USAF
259.7	Space Shuttle		305.7	USAF
260.2	USAF Air Refuel		306.35	USN
263.5	USN Weather		306.6	USAF
263.6	NORAD Canada		307.85	USN
264.2	USN		308.3	USMC Weather
264.5	USN Weather		308.8	Canadian Weather
265.8	Air Force 1 & 2		309.25	USN
266.5	USAF Air/Air		309.35	USN
270.6	USN		310.75	USN
271.9	USAF		310.85	USN
272.7	FAA Flight Service		311.0	USSTRATCOM
274.4	NORAD Canada			Canadian Air Cmd
274.5	USN Weather		313.6	USAF
275.1	USN/USCG		317.0	USN Weather
275.35	USN		319.0	USAF
275.8	Mil Control Towers		319.5	USAF Air Refuel
276.1	USAF Air Refuel		319.7	USAF Air Refuel
276.5	USAF Air Refuel		320.2	USN
277.0	USN		321.0	USSTRATCOM
277.7	Canadian Mil		321.1	USAF
277.8	USN Fleet Common		322.0-328.6	Radio Astronomy
	USCG		322.75	Air Force 1 & 2 (WFM)
280.5	USAF		322.8	Canadian Air Cmd
281.4	DEA/US Customs		333.3	Canadian Air Cmd
282.425	USCG/US Customs		336.8	Air Force 1 & 2 (WFM)
282.5	USAF		340.2	USN Control Towers
282.7	USAF Air Refuel		340.8	USAF
282.8	Search/Rescue		341.3	USN Weather
283.7	USAF		342.2	USAF
285.0	USN/USCG		342.5	Mil Weather
285.4	USAF Control Towers		343.0	USAF
288.4	DEW Line		343.5	USAF Air Refuel
288.6	USAF		344.6	Mil Weather
289.4	Canadian Mil		345.8	USN
289.7	USAF Air Refuel		348.6	Mil Control Towers
289.8	USN		349.4	USAF
292.1	USAF		349.9	Hurricane Hunters
292.2	USAF Global HF CP's			USMC Weather
293.0	USAF Air Refuel		353.0	USN Weather
295.4	USAF Air Refuel		353.9	USCG/US Customs
295.6	Canadian Mil		354.3	USAF
295.8	USAF Air Refuel		355.0	USN
296.8	USAF Air Refuel		355.3	USN/USMC Weather
297.0	USAF		356.2	USN Weather
297.4	Canadian Weather		356.8	USAF Air/Air
300.6	Mil Air/Air		357.9	USN
301.0	USN		358.9	USN
301.3	USN Weather		359.4	USN

359.6	USN Weather		408.30	BP/INS
359.9	DEW Line		408.35	BP/INS
360.2	USN Control Towers		408.375	BP/INS
361.6	Air Force 1 & 2		408.40	BP/INS
362.1	USMC Weather		408.425	Army CID
363.8	USAF Control Towers		408.925	USCG Base Security
	Canadian Air Cmd		409.00	USCG
363.9	USAF		409.025	Dept Labor
364.2	NORAD US/Canada		409.125	Army MP's
369.05	Satellite Telecommand		409.15	ATF
372.2	USAF Pilot/Dispatcher		409.20	ICC
372.8	USAF		409.25	Bur Prisons
373.1	USAF Weather		409.625	Dept State
375.0	White House heliport		409.75	Army MP's
375.2	Mil Weather		410.85	US Attorney
375.7	USAF		410.875	US Attorney
376.2	USAF		411.675	US Mint
378.5	Canadian Air Cmd		412.35	FBI
378.9	USAF		412.40	GSA Enforcement
380.55	USN		412.425	FBI
381.0	Air/Sea Rescue		412.45	FBI
381.1	USAF		412.475	FBI
381.3	USAF/ACC		412.50	FBI
	Canadian Air Command		412.55	FBI
381.7	USCG		412.575	FBI
381.8	USCG		412.675	FBI
382.35	Air Force 1 & 2 (WFM)		412.825	Army CID
382.5	USAF		412.90	Army CID
384.6	USAF Air Refuel		413.025	Army CID
385.0	USN Ports/Harbors		413.225	Army CID
385.25	USN Air/Air		413.2375	Army CID
387.4	USN Weather		413.425	Army CID
387.9	USAF		413.45	USAF Crew Alerts
397.05	Air Force 1 & 2 (WFM)		413.525	Army CID
400.00	Navigation Satellites		413.55	BP/INS
400.10	Std Freq Satellite		413.60	BP/INS/USPS
406.025	Emergency Beacons		413.625	BP/INS
406.10-410.00	Radio Astronomy		413.675	BP/INS
406.20	Dept Labor		413.70	BP/INS
406.675	FWS Enforcement		413.725	BP/INS
406.9375	Army CID		413.775	BP/INS
407.15	ATF		413.875	Federal Reserve
407.25	Army MP's		413.925	Federal Reserve
407.475	Army CID		414.00	FBI
407.625	USCG		414.025	FBI
407.7875	Treasury Dept		414.05	FBI
407.85	USSS "Echo" Ch		414.075	FBI
407.875	ATF		414.0875	FBI
407.925	USSS "India" Ch		414.10	FBI
407.975	USCG		414.125	FBI
408.025	Dept Labor		414.15	FBI
408.20	BP/INS		414.175	FBI
408.225	BP/INS		414.20	FBI
408.25	BP/INS		414.225	FBI

414.25	FBI
414.275	FBI
414.30	FBI
414.325	FBI
414.35	FBI
414.375	FBI
414.40	FBI
414.425	FBI
414.475	FBI
414.50	FBI
414.525	DEA
414.55	FBI
414.575	FBI
414.625	BP/INS
414.65	Interagency Fire Cache
414.75	FBI / USPS
414.80	Treasury
414.90	Treasury
415.00	US Mint
415.05	USPS
415.10	Federal Reserve
415.20	GSA
415.40	Interagency Fire Cache
415.50	Interagency Fire Cache
415.70	USSS "Foxtrot" Ch Air Force 1 & 2
416.05	DEA
416.075	USPS
416.225	USPS
416.875	USCG Base Security
417.025	DEA
417.05	BP/INS
417.125	USCG Base Security BP/INS
417.15	BP/INS
417.175	DEA
417.20	GSA Enforcement
417.40	DEA
417.425	GSA Enforcement
417.45	DEA
417.50	DEA
417.55	DEA
417.725	IRS
417.85	BP/INS
417.95	BP/INS
417.975	BP/INS
418.05	DEA Interagency
418.125	WHCA
418.175	WHCA / DEA / IRS

418.20	NTSB / IRS
418.225	IRS
418.30	USPS
418.50	DEA aero
418.575	DEA
418.625	DEA
418.65	WHCA
418.675	DEA
418.70	DEA
418.725	DEA
418.75	DEA
418.775	DEA
418.80	DEA
418.825	DEA
418.875	DEA
418.90	DEA
418.975	DEA
419.00	DEA
419.075	FBI
419.125	USCG Base Security
419.175	FBI
419.20	FBI
419.225	FBI
419.25	DEA
419.275	FBI
419.30	FBI
419.325	FBI
419.35	FBI
419.375	DEA
419.40	FBI
419.425	FBI
419.45	FBI
419.475	FBI
419.50	FBI
419.525	FBI
419.55	FBI
419.575	FBI
419.60	FBI
419.65	US Mint / BIA
419.925	USCG Base Security
419.95	DEA
450.00	Satellite telecommand
457.5625	Bugs
467.7875	Bugs
467.95	FBI aero surveillance
468.825	WWV/Satellite 135°W
468.8375	WWV/Satellite 75°W
608.00–614.00	Radio Astronomy

Frequency Hopping

When communications users want privacy, they sometimes turn to voice scrambling. Simple analog-type voice scramblers are inexpensive and unsophisticated, and are in wide use by civil agencies. Before the Electronic Communications Privacy Act made them illegal to use (or sell), there were several analog de-scramblers on the scanner market. Digital scrambling (which sounds like a hiss or "white noise" on a scanner) is far more sophisticated (and expensive to purchase) than analog scrambling systems. Digital scrambling is used by some federal agencies, and it is not easily descrambled by persons to whom the communications are not addressed.

A system commonly called Frequency Hopping is yet another method of communications privacy that is turning up on the federal bands. I have heard it in use at times on 163.625, 169.375, as well as other frequencies. To try and explain it in very basic terms, with this system, although the voice itself isn't modified, the transmission is broken up into brief pieces, with each of those pieces sent out over a rapidly changing assortment of several different preselected frequencies. At the receiving end, the transmissions on the several frequencies used are reassembled and the voice is made whole again.

If you monitor a frequency where there is a system using Frequency Hopping, if it doesn't use many hopping frequencies, you may be able to detect the transmissions as sounding like someone talking with their transmitter turning on and off two or three times per second. You can make out a word here and there. The more hopping frequencies used, however, the shorter the transmissions, and the better the privacy-- to the point where the transmissions are so brief they are either undetected, or are virtually unrecognizable as being components of a voice message. Even a scanner programmed to receive all frequencies used in a hopping system (if you knew them) could not scan quickly enough to keep up with the speed of the frequency hopping.

Perhaps a bank of different scanners, each set to one of the hopping frequencies would do the trick. You would need to know each of the frequencies. We don't know of anybody who has tried this yet.

To be sure, there are certainly other scrambling and privacy systems in use. The military frequencies can turn up several systems. The 225 to 400 MHz UHF aero band has some aircraft with capabilities for the Magnavox "Have Quick" anti-jamming communications system. This system requires that the equipment be precisely synchronized. Synchronization needs to be checked and adjusted regularly. This can be done over the radio via ground stations equipped for Have Quick timing facilities.

Agent 247 Urgent you call Ext 17 re Case #557F. Suspect may attempt to flee area

Radio Paging Frequencies

Some federal agency offices and facilities have established one-way radio paging to their own personnel. These systems operate on federal frequencies, primarily 162 to 174 MHz, and 406 to 420 MHz. Listed below are frequencies in the commercial bands most often used for one-way voice and non-voice radio paging by private and medical "beeper" users. Also shown are the frequencies used by companies providing radio paging services to public subscribers-- these channels are the ones shown with channel designators. The channel designators are unofficial, and are those used within the radio paging industry to refer to the industry's own channels. Note that in some areas, some commercial channels may also be used for subscriber two-way comms.

Frequencies 929.3625 through 929.4625 MHz, as well as 929.6375 through 929.9875 MHz are used by private carrier paging services to provide one-way radio paging to to police and fire officers, as well as others.

What with the popularity of beepers among drug dealers, all levels of law enforcement agencies have become interested in the contents of the messages sent out to certain suspects in criminal investigations. Law enforcement agencies have access to this information and can use it as evidence. Moreover, when pagers are found at crime scenes, or confiscated during raids, they are easily traced back to the person paying for the service. Based on the receiving frequency and access number of the pager, the law enforcement agency is able to check the office files of the paging company and look at the personal credit information supplied by the subscriber, as well as billing, message information, and other data.

Law enforcement agencies are also able to obtain court orders to get paging service suppliers to furnish cloned beepers that duplicate all non-voice messages sent to specific suspects. This can also be accomplished surreptitiously without bothering with court orders. Currently, investigative agencies have equipment available that can easily read all non-voice radio paging messages.

The Electronic Communications Privacy Act (ECPA) of 1986 does not allow monitoring voice radio paging, but allows monitoring of non-voice paging.

Radio Paging Channels

MHz	Designator		MHz	Designator
26.995	–		35.20	PA
27.045	–		35.22	P1
27.095	–		35.24	PB
27.145	–		35.26	PC
27.195	–		35.30	PD
35.02	–		35.34	PE
			35.38	PF
			35.42	PG
			35.46	PH

35.50	PI	158.70	P6
35.54	PJ	163.25	–
35.56	PK	453.025	–
35.58	P2	453.075	–
35.60	PL	453.125	–
35.62	PM	453.175	–
35.64	–	454.025	21
35.66	P7	454.050	22
35.68	–	454.075	23
43.20	PN	454.100	24
43.22	P3	454.125	25
43.24	PO	454.150	26
43.26	PP	454.175	27
43.30	PQ	454.200	28
43.34	PR	454.225	29
43.38	PS	454.250	30
43.42	PT	454.275	31
43.46	PU	454.300	32
43.50	PV	454.325	33
43.54	PW	454.350	34
43.56	PX	454.375	QC
43.58	P4	454.400	QJ
43.60	PY	454.425	QD
43.62	PZ	454.450	QA
43.64	–	454.475	QE
43.66	P8	454.500	QP
43.68	–	454.525	QK
152.005	–	454.550	QB
152.03	1	454.575	QO
152.06	3	454.600	QR
152.09	5	454.625	QY
152.12	7	454.650	QF
152.15	9	462.750	–
152.18	11	462.775	–
152.21	13	462.800	–
152.24	P5	462.825	–
152.48	–	462.850	–
152.51	JL	462.875	–
152.54	YL	462.900	–
152.57	JP	462.925	–
152.60	YP	465.000	–
152.63	YJ	929.0125	–
152.66	YK	929.0375	–
152.69	JS	929.0625	–
152.72	YS	929.0875	–
152.75	YR	929.1125	–
152.78	JK	929.1375	–
152.81	JR	929.1625	–
152.84	T1	929.1875	–
154.625	–	929.2125	–
157.45	–	929.2375	–
157.74	–	929.2625	–
158.10	T2	929.2875	–
158.46	–	929.3125	–

929.3375	-		931.2125	89
929.3625	-		931.2375	90
929.3875	-		931.2625	91
929.4125	-		931.2875	92
929.4375	-		931.3125	93
929.4625	-		931.3375	94
929.4875	-		931.3625	95
929.5125	-		931.3875	96
929.5375	-		931.4125	97
929.5625	-		931.4375	98
929.5875	-		931.4625	99
929.6125	-		931.4875	100
929.6375	-		931.5125	101
929.6625	-		931.5375	102
929.6875	-		931.5625	103
929.6875	-		931.5875	104
929.7125	-		931.6125	105
929.7375	-		931.6375	106
929.7625	-		931.6625	107
929.7875	-		931.6875	108
929.8125	-		931.7125	109
929.8375	-		931.7375	110
929.8625	-		931.7625	111
929.8875	-		931.7875	112
929.9125	-		931.8125	113
929.9375	-		931.8375	114
929.9625	-		931.8625	115
929.9875	-		931.8875*	116
931.0125	81		931.9125*	117
931.0375	82		931.9375*	118
931.0625	83		931.9625	119
931.0875	84		931.9875	120
931.1125	85			
931.1375	86			
931.1625	87			
931.1875	88			

*Nationwide Paging Chan.

Schedule of Selected Mil Facility Closing Dates
All Information Subject to Change.
Information courtesy of Joseph McCusker, NY.

Bergstrom AFB, 30 September 1993
Carswell AFB, 30 September 1993
Castle AFB, 30 September, 1995
Chanute AFB, 30 September, 1993
Eaker AFB, 15 December, 1992
England AFB, 15 December, 1992
Ft. Sheridan, 1 June 1993
Grissom AFB, 30 September, 1994
Loring AFB, 30 September, 1994
Lowry AFB, 30 September, 1994
MacDill AFB, 31 March, 1994
Mather AFB, 30 September, 1993
Myrtle Beach AFB, 31 March, 1993
Norton AFB, 31 March 1994
Richards-Gebaur Air Reserve Station, 30 September, 1994
Williams AFB, 30 September, 1993
Wurtsmith AFB, 30 June, 1993

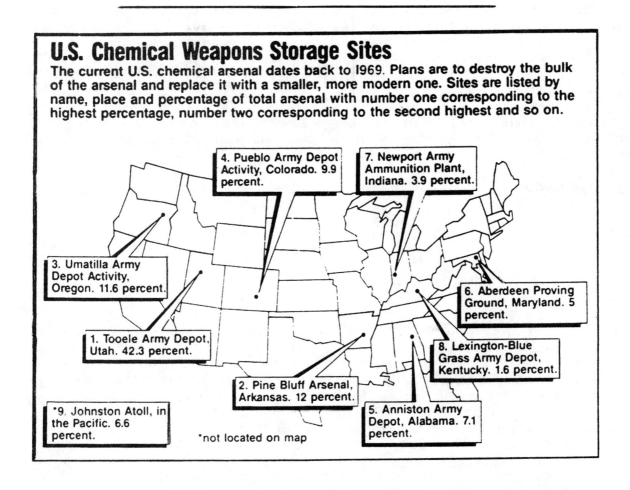

U.S. Chemical Weapons Storage Sites

The current U.S. chemical arsenal dates back to 1969. Plans are to destroy the bulk of the arsenal and replace it with a smaller, more modern one. Sites are listed by name, place and percentage of total arsenal with number one corresponding to the highest percentage, number two corresponding to the second highest and so on.

4. Pueblo Army Depot Activity, Colorado. 9.9 percent.

7. Newport Army Ammunition Plant, Indiana. 3.9 percent.

3. Umatilla Army Depot Activity, Oregon. 11.6 percent.

6. Aberdeen Proving Ground, Maryland. 5 percent.

1. Tooele Army Depot, Utah. 42.3 percent.

8. Lexington-Blue Grass Army Depot, Kentucky. 1.6 percent.

2. Pine Bluff Arsenal, Arkansas. 12 percent.

*9. Johnston Atoll, in the Pacific. 6.6 percent.

5. Anniston Army Depot, Alabama. 7.1 percent.

*not located on map

266

Some Monitoring Tips

1. When scanning or in search mode, set the scanner to operate at its fastest speed. This lets you check as many frequencies as possible within a given time period.

2. For searching out new active frequencies, consider concentrating or focussing your efforts rather than operating in a scattershot or disorganized manner. For instance, if you were going to search the 225 to 400 MHz UHF military aero band, you would start at 225 MHz and search no more than 2 MHz worth of spectrum at a time for activity. Conduct a concentrated search of that 2 MHz band segment for several days, or as much as a week. Note every active frequency you encounter so it may be entered in your scanner's memory. When you have completed your intensive survey of 225 to 227 MHz, then move your search to 227 to 229 MHz and start again. Of course, this technique is effective over any group of frequencies. You may find it of value to coordinate your search with monitors at other locations, and then periodically compare or combine the results.

3. Scanners do just fine with multi-band scanner antennas. If you are especially interested in monitoring a particular band, you should keep in mind that omnidirectional CB and ham antennas will serve you well on your favorite band. For instance, a base station CB antenna does quite a nice job on a scanner operating in the 30 to 50 MHz band. If you have no further use for it for CB purposes, you might even trim all of the elements down a foot or so in size for scanning purposes in this band. Ham antennas for the 50, 144, 222, 420, and 902 MHz ham bands are all tuned for operation very close to bands of interest to scanner users.

4. You can often locate an inexpensive VHF ground plane (GP) antenna, for instance one made only for VHF high band scanner use. A GP antenna consists of a single vertical element (which is connected to the center conductor of the coaxial antenna cable), and 4 horizontal elements (these are joined at the antenna base and connect to the braided shield of the coaxial antenna cable). With a bit of creative snipping, you can cut the elements down for peak scanner performance on various VHF/UHF federal bands. Use the following cutting chart as a guide:

Maximum Performance	Vert. Radiator	Horiz. Elements
118 to 137 MHz	21 in.	26.5 in.
137 to 144 NHz	18 in.	26.5 in.
148 to 151 MHz	16.5 in.	26.5 in.
162 to 174 MHz	14 in.	26.5 in.
225 to 300 MHz	9.5 in.	13 in.
300 to 400 MHz	6.5 in.	12 in.
400 to 420 MHz	5.5 in.	10 in.

5. For best distance, mount your antenna outside, as high as possible, and as far away as you can from other antennas, and from any metal objects such as chimneys, wires, water tanks, etc. Antenna systems should be properly protected from lightning strikes. Caution should always be exercised in installing an antenna system that no part of the antenna or supporting structure come into contact with electric wires-- or can topple into wires after installation. Electric wires contacting antennas create a dangerous and life threatening situation.

6. It's OK to use RG-58/U coaxial cable for runs 50 ft. and less. For longer runs, use RG-8/U type, or better. The longer the run, the larger the loss in signal between the antenna and your scanner. In any case, use 50 or 52 ohm coaxial, and do **not** use 72 ohm RG-59/U, which is intended for TV purposes.

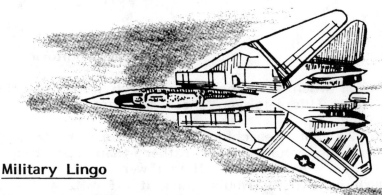

Military Lingo

Words & terms you may hear on the UHF aero band & elsewhere:

Angel	Unidentified aircraft assumed to be friendly.
Bandit	Enemy aircraft positively identified.
Bogey	Unidentified aircraft assumed to be an enemy.
Bone Dome	Kevlar helmet.
Buff	B-52 bomber.
Chocolate Chips	Desert camouflage uniforms.
Cold Smoked	A destroyed enemy aircraft.
Dog him out	To criticize someone.
Echelons beyond reality	A decision handed down from from high authority.
Face Shot	Air/air missile directed towards an enemy.
Fast Mover	Jet fighter.
Feet Dry	Flight over land.
Feet Wet	Flight over water.
Fur Ball	Dogfight.
Gomer	The enemy in a dogfight.
Good to go	A job well done.
Grease	Food.
Ground Pounder	A-6 Intruder, A-7 Corsair, A-10 Thunderbolt II attack aircraft.
High speed, low drag	State of the art, better than the enemy has.
Hummer or **Humvee**	High Mobility Multipurpose Wheeled Vehicle (HMMWV).
Iron Bomb	A bomb that is dropped without a guidance system.
Joe	Any Enlisted soldier.
MOPP	Mission Oriented Protected Suits. Protective outerwear for use in biological, chemical, or radiation hazmat areas.
Mud Mover	Same as **Ground Pounder**.
MRE	Meals Ready to Eat (usually Meals Rejected by Everyone).
No joy	Let's try Plan B.
Nuclear Coffee	Recipe: hot water, instant cocoa, instant coffee, cream & sugar from an MRE packet.
Quick Turn Burn	An F/A-18 refueled & reloaded in 5 min. with the engine running
Real time	Taking place right now.
Rumint	Intelligence developed completely from rumors.
Rumor Control	The unknown source from which all rumors are thought to flow.
Scud	To whip or pound.
Smart Bomb	A bomb that is guided to its target.
Snake	Cobra AF-1F Attack Helicopter.
Tree Heads	Special Forces personnel.
Tread Heads	Armored Forces personnel.
Weenies	Military personnel assigned to non-combat jobs.
Zoom Bag	Pressurized flight suit.